022

# Methods of Orbit Determination

# Methods
# of Orbit Determination

PEDRO RAMON ESCOBAL

*Head, Special Studies Section,*
*Mission Analysis and Simulation Laboratory*

*TRW* SPACE TECHNOLOGY LABORATORIES

*John Wiley & Sons, Inc., New York | London | Sydney*

Library of Congress Catalog Card Number: 65-19483
Printed in the United States of America

To PATRICIO PEDRO ESCOBAL
and MARIA TERESA ESCOBAL

# Preface

Orbit determination is a branch of celestial mechanics that has grown and matured since the spectacular entry of Gauss into dynamical astronomy over a century ago. Today there are many variations and techniques to the orbit determination problem. Some of these methods are new and some are rediscovered deviations of older classical orbit determination schemes. *Methods of Orbit Determination*, though by no means complete, attempts to collect some of the more popular methods employed in the computation of orbits. In essence, the purpose of this book is to provide an introduction and compendium of orbit determination schemes from an engineering point of view.

It is hoped that the presentation of each method can be treated as an entity, requiring minimum back reading in order to utilize a desired orbit computation technique. The notation used approximately follows the traditional astronomical notation with deviations and changes kept to a minimum.

Chapter 1 presents preliminary fundamentals, including a discussion of the system of units adopted throughout the book. For the novice entering into the realm of astrodynamics, the fundamental discussion of units may prove to be of considerable value.

Chapter 2 presents a development of the differential equations of motion for a system of $n$ bodies. It is perhaps out of place to introduce the equations of motion of a booster rocket in this chapter. However, this artifice prevents the new student in this area from being completely detached from practical problems of our rapidly developing space age.

Originally Chapter 3 was not included in my planning of the text. After a survey, however, and at the encouragement of several people, Chapter 3 was added in order to make the text internally self-sufficient. As the writing of the text progressed, it became evident that Chapter 3 was the link that held the book together, even though similar material has been covered by others much more proficient than I in the realm of Keplerian mechanics. It is hoped that the solution of the two-body problem contained in Chapter 3 will be of interest to the new student and serve as reference material to the more sophisticated engineer.

Chapter 4, which describes astrodynamic coordinate systems, was added as reference material and was purposely introduced after the complete solution of the two body problem in order not to confuse the reader. This chapter, along with Appendix I, attempts to tabulate in a consistent notation all the coordinate transformations that will ever be required—at least by a student of this text.

To acquaint the student with the manipulation of two-body formulas, and to introduce the philosophy of the closed or semiclosed solution, Chapter 5 was incorporated into the text. The problems treated within this chapter are, by the nature of this work, related to orbit determination techniques.

In Chapter 6, the preliminary orbit determination process is initiated, with a discussion of the determination of orbits from two-position vectors and the corresponding time interval between the respective position vectors. Complete derivations are presented first and then, for convenience, computational algorithms are included. I am very reluctant to claim that any of the algorithms presented are perfect; in fact, improvements can, and probably will, be made. In order to facilitate computational procedures and checkout of an ever-increasing amount of machine-computing programs, I also felt that a tabulation of certain sample orbits would be beneficial for consultation purposes. The methods presented in Chapter 6 can be applied to the solution of intercept, rendezvous, and interplanetary trajectory problems. It is unfortunate that lack of space prevented further development of this chapter.

The problem of orbit determination from angular observations only, that is, the classical orbit determination problem, is treated in Chapter 7. In this chapter I introduce what may be a new technique for the determination of an orbit from angular data spread over large arcs. Computational algorithms and sample orbits are also included.

Chapter 8 presents a tabulation of some of the more popular orbit methods used in modern analysis. This chapter presents various orbit determination schemes utilizing mixed data, that is, angles and distances. Range-rate and angle determinations are developed in order to handle modern orbit problems. It is again unfortunate that lack of space does not permit further extension of this material. Some of the techniques of Chapter 8 have not been tested to the limit of usefulness because of their newness.

Differential correction in regard to minimum data is discussed in

Chapter 9. The text does not enter into the realm of statistical filtering or data reduction. It was felt that this important problem can be handled outside the overall differential correction process. Furthermore, statistical filtering techniques require specialized background, and so this area was omitted from the text.

The last chapter, Chapter 10, provides an introduction to general perturbation techniques and was meant solely to do just this. Within this chapter, important secular rates of change, due to oblateness and drag are discussed. Specifically, from an engineering point of view, Chapter 10 provides the student and engineer with the concepts necessary to modify Keplerian analysis for the critical perturbations produced by oblateness and drag anomalies.

The reader who uses this book should have a firm understanding of the differential and integral calculus. Elementary vector and matrix methods are used throughout the text in order to preserve clarity and conciseness of presentation. An attempt was made to introduce vector and matrix analysis techniques at logical points, only when it was truly felt that their inclusion would be beneficial. The reader familiar with dot and cross products, along with the definition of the gradient of a function, should have little trouble with the analysis. The reader is assumed to have a working knowledge of matrix multiplication and inversion techniques.

The first five chapters could be used to teach an introductory course in two-body mechanics or astrodynamics. The remaining chapters would then be material for an advanced course on the determination of orbits.

Problems are included at the end of each chapter to further illustrate additional material. These problems stress the practical concepts and ideas of our space age. Some of the exercises are theoretical in nature, while others are numerical. Some of the numerical analyses, in order to be meaningful, are by their very nature complex and should be handled with modern calculating machine equipment. The availability of such machines, both in industry and at universities, prompted the inclusion of such problems or projects in this book.

I hope that this material will be of direct benefit to the engineer working in the field encompassed by this work, to which so many people have contributed. The engineer who utilizes this work should realize that *Methods of Orbit Determination* would certainly not have been possible without the assistance of many other helpful persons.

I am deeply indebted to Robert O. Chase, without whose unending efforts this book would not have been possible. It is also with deep gratitude that I wish to thank Taylor Gabbard, Bruce Douglas, Nancy Brandon, Jane Hunter, Paul Koskela, Roy DeBellis, Barry Knowles, Bernard Billik, and last but certainly not least, my father, for assistance and helpful suggestions in the assemblage of this text.   To Lona Case and Frances Rossiter belong my great thanks for a marvelous typing and illustrating effort which took great patience.   I wish to thank these and many other persons involved in this effort for their wonderful assistance. My very deep appreciation is extended to Operations Research Incorporated for its overall assistance.   To the unknown original reviewers of this work, I shall always remain indebted.

Pedro R. Escobal

*TRW Space Technology Laboratories*
*April, 1965*

# Contents

# 1 Fundamentals

*The infinite! No other question has ever moved so profoundly the spirit of man.*

DAVID HILBERT [14]

## 1.1 DEFINITION OF THE ORBIT DETERMINATION PROCESS

Preliminary orbit determination is the process of formulating a first approximation to the fundamental elements or parameters that define an orbit. Inherent in this approximation is rejection of all perturbative influences upon the motion of a body in space, such as drag or electromagnetic forces, which tend to deflect motion from two-body motion. The phenomenon of two-body motion is in turn defined as the motion of body A with respect to body B, with only the mutual attractions of A and B taken into consideration. Hence preliminary orbit determination is a two-body process. Characteristic of this analysis is the assumption that the mass of body A, where A denotes the central planet or focus about which motion occurs, and the mass of body B, where B denotes the body under consideration, can be accurately represented by point masses. That is to say that, in the physical domain, A and B are replaced by A' and B', with the understanding that A and B have the properties of length, width, and depth along with mass, whereas A' and B' are physical abstractions devoid of everything but mass. Therefore, in the two-body problem as considered here, when speaking of body A or B, body A' or B' is respectively implied. Furthermore, in order to achieve a closed-form solution to the equations of motion, it is assumed that an inverse square force field controls the motion of the respective bodies.

As shall be seen in the next chapter, these assumptions lead to the fundamental second-order differential vector equation,

$$\frac{d^2\mathbf{r}}{dt^2} = -k^2\mu\,\frac{\mathbf{r}}{r^3},$$
(1.1)

**1**

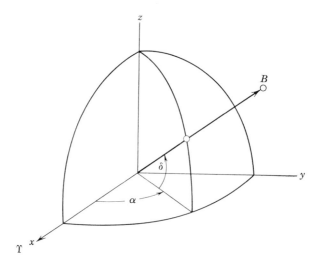

FIGURE 1.1    The right ascension-declination inertial coordinate system.

where $r$ is the distance between $A$ and $B$, and $k^2\mu$ is a constant.    This is the equation of motion of body $B$ with respect to body $A$ in a fixed or inertial coordinate system.

For the present, let a coordinate origin be taken at the center of the Earth, and let this origin also coincide with the center of a sphere of infinite radius called the *celestial sphere*.    The principal plane of reference can be taken as the infinite extension of the Earth's equatorial plane. Consider the plane traced upon the celestial sphere by the apparent annual motion of the Sun from south to north.    The intersection of this plane and the Earth's equatorial plane results in a line which is used to fix the principle or axis of $x$ of an orthogonal coordinate system.    This axis of $x$ points at the vernal equinox ($\Upsilon$), which for the present is assumed to be inertially fixed.[1]    Take the $y$ axis advanced to $x$ by a right angle in the equatorial plane of the Earth, and $z$ perpendicular to the plane defined by $x$ and $y$.    This coordinate frame is illustrated in Figure 1.1 and is called the *right ascension-declination* coordinate system because of the angles $\alpha$ and $\delta$, where $\alpha$ is the right ascension and $\delta$ is the declination. If it is understood that the origin of the coordinate system is placed at the

---

[1] For the present, the reader should think of $\Upsilon$ as pointing to some constellation in space.    At one time, this axis pointed towards the constellation of Aries or the Sign of the Ram's Horns, denoted by $\Upsilon$.

*dynamical center* of the planet Earth, that is, the point of mass concentration, then Eq. 1.1 represents the motion of body $B$ with respect to the planet Earth. It should be emphasized that Eq. 1.1 applies in any inertial coordinate system, the one just mentioned being a particular but very important system.

Obviously the solution of Eq. 1.1 implies that the three component equations which it defines yield three constants upon performing the first integration, and another three constants upon performing the second integration, six constants in total. These constants are the *elements* or fundamental quantities of the orbit. Therefore the problem of preliminary orbit determination deals with methods of computing these elements, subject to the aforementioned assumptions.

From the nature of Eq. 1.1, if it were possible to directly observe or measure the velocity of body $B$, at a known time, then the first three constants of the first integration of the fundamental equation (1.1) could be directly determined. By the same reasoning, if it were possible to directly observe or measure the position of body $B$, at a known time, then the second three constants of the second integration of the fundamental equation could also be determined without much trouble. Hence, in a reference frame, as shown in Figure 1.1, a fundamental set of six elements are

$$x_0, y_0, z_0, \dot{x}_0, \dot{y}_0, \dot{z}_0, \qquad\qquad (1.2)$$

that is, components of the position and velocity vectors evaluated at some epoch time $t_0$ as denoted by the subscript. These elements, however, are not usually directly observable. The aim of a preliminary orbit determination scheme is, therefore, the determination of the fundamental elements (1.2).

Usually, however, observations of body $B$ are made from a coordinate system that is rotating or is different from the preferred or actual system in which analysis is to be performed, that is, an inertial system. Thus a transformation of coordinates is required. For example, an observer standing on a particular meridian on the surface of the planet Earth sees an object in space and can perhaps only measure its angular elevation (angular distance above the observer's horizon denoted by $h$) and azimuth (angular distance from the north denoted by $A$) at a given time. If the observer repeats this operation another two times, then six constants will be available for determination of the orbit, that is,

$$[A, h]_{t_1}, \ [A, h]_{t_2}, \ [A, h]_{t_3}.$$

Thus this exemplary set of three angular observations, or six constants in a rotating coordinate system, must first be transformed to an inertial co-ordinate system such as that shown in Figure 1.1.   The result of this trans-formation will be a set of inertial angular observations.   Then the orbit determination scheme must be applied in order to transform observations at different times to a single epoch time, preferably the set of elements (1.2). Analysis of a preliminary orbit determination scheme is, therefore, one of transformation, both of coordinate systems and of observations.

Using the previous background material, a definition of the orbit determination process can be defined more rigorously as follows: *Pre-liminary orbit determination is a two-body analytical process, perhaps embodying certain coordinate transformations, which by virtue of other analytical transformations maps observations of an object, at the same or different times, into a common fundamental set of elements at some epoch time.*

The reader should not assume that this definition encompasses all the side benefits derivable from the particular orbit determination scheme. For example, the orbit schemes to be developed in Chapter 6 cannot be used to determine an orbit directly from observations, but from position vectors.   Hence, as will be seen, those methods yield solutions to the intercept, rendezvous, and interplanetary transfer problems of trajectory analysis.   As the reader progresses, it will become evident that the scope encompassed in the field of orbit determination is very broad and has a myriad of different applications.   At a much later point in the text, the reader will see how it is possible to nullify the two-body approximations and arrive at formulations which include critical perturbations.

Another definition the user of this text should bear in mind is that of *astrodynamics.*   Its importance rests in the fact that astrodynamics, that is, *the application of the techniques of celestial mechanics to the solution of space engineering problems,* contains orbit determination within its domain.

In the first part of this book, astrodynamics will be stressed and will play almost a solitary role.   Further on in the text, the orbit methods will be called forth and, at an even later stage, the processes of orbit correction and improvement will be presented.

## 1.2  PHYSICAL WORKING UNITS AND CONSTANTS

### 1.2.1  The heliocentric system of units

It suffices to say that in the fields of astronomy and astrodynamics a great deal of confusion and computational labor can be eliminated by proper choice of physical units, that is, length, mass, and time.

Obviously common sense would dictate adoption of a new yardstick or ruler if distances involved in an analytical problem were of the order of magnitude of the distance from the Sun to the Earth. Hence this distance would not be measured in feet, meters, or even kilometers, since these benchmarks would be too cumbersome to handle, but rather in some convenient unit of distance.

Let the mean distance between the centers of the Sun and Earth be the new benchmark, and let it be called the astronomical unit (a.u.).[2] From this point on, in order to solve a specific problem, all distances can be reckoned in astronomical units without any mention of miles, kilometers, etc. Later, perhaps after lengthy calculations, when an answer has been obtained in terms of astronomical units and a conversion is desired, say to miles, all that must be done is a multiplication of the a.u. distances by the conversion factor for the distance from the Earth to the Sun in terms of miles. Approximately

$$1 \text{ a.u.} \cong 93,000,000 \text{ miles.} \tag{1.3}$$

More exactly, the distances are tabulated in Table 1.1 for convenience and reference.

Once this convenient choice of distance units has been made, the question comes to mind as to whether it would be possible to choose the mass unit in a similar beneficial manner. Certainly, in most problems of two-body mechanics, the mass of the primary body $A$, about which motion occurs, is much greater than body $B$, the secondary body which moves about the primary. Furthermore, instead of computing masses in slugs, etc., it would be easier to use dimensionless ratios of masses. Thus it seems feasible to define the unit of mass in terms of the most ponderous body encountered in the analytical problem. This definition makes use of normalized units, so that

$$\mu \equiv \frac{1}{m_A}(m_A + m_B) = 1 + m_B', \tag{1.4}$$

and the dimensionless ratios, denoted by primes are

$$m_A' \equiv 1, \qquad m_B' \equiv \frac{m_B}{m_A}. \tag{1.5}$$

The mass of the primary[3] is therefore the unit mass, and the other mass is

[2] Today the definition of the a.u. is slightly different. The a.u. is actually the mean distance between the Sun and a fictitious planet, subjected to no perturbations, whose mass and sidereal period are the values adopted by Gauss for the Earth in his determination of $k_\odot$. The fundamental constant $k_\odot$ will be discussed in Section 1.2.3.

[3] If the masses are of equal magnitude, one mass can be arbitrarily chosen as the primary. The discussion of this section is by no means limited to two bodies; this is only used as a clarifying artifice in the presentation.

Table 1.1   Astronomical Unit in Kilometers and Miles

| DATE | LABORATORY OR AUTHOR | a.u. (km) | p.e. (km) | a.u. (mi) | p.e. (mi) | METHOD |
|---|---|---|---|---|---|---|
| 1904 | Hinks | 149,400,000 | ± 70,000 | 92,832,855 | ± 43,000 | Trigonometrically from Eros |
| 1921 | Noteboom | 149,520,000 | ± 20,000 | 92,907,420 | ± 12,000 | Dynamically from Eros |
| 1928 | Spencer Jones | 149,450,000 | ± 70,000 | 92,863,924 | ± 43,000 | Radial velocity of stars |
| 1935 | Witt | 149,520,000 | ± 20,000 | 92,907,420 | ± 12,000 | Dynamically from Eros |
| 1941 | Spencer Jones | 149,670,000 | ± 20,000 | 93,000,626 | ± 12,000 | Trigonometrically from Eros |
| 1941 | Adams | 149,410,000 | ± 120,000 | 92,839,069 | ± 75,000 | Radial velocity of stars |
| 1950 | Brouwer | 149,630,000 | ± 50,000 | 92,975,771 | ± 30,000 | Perturbations of Moon by Sun |
| 1950 | Rabe | 149,526,000 | ± 7,000 | 92,911,148 | ± 4,000 | Dynamically from Eros |
| 1960 | STL; McGuire, Morrison, Wong | 149,540,000 | ± 13,600 | 92,925,100 | ± 8,500 | Range-rate radio tracking of Pioneer V |
| 1961 | USSR, Kotelnikov | 149,599,500 | ± 800 | 92,956,819 | ± 500 | Radar range—Venus |
| 1961 | U. of Manchester, Jodrell Bank | 149,601,000 | ± 5,000 | 92,957,751 | ± 3,100 | Radar range—Venus |
| 1961 | MIT Millstone, Lincoln Lab. | 149,597,850 | ± 400 | 92,955,794 | ± 250 | Radar range—Venus $c = 299,729.5$ km/sec |
| 1961 | JPL Goldstone | 149,598,845 | ± 250 | 92,956,412 | ± 150 | Radar range and doppler— Venus $c = 299,730.0$ km/sec |

the ratio of the mass of the secondary body divided by the mass of the primary body.   In computing the mass ratio, both masses are, of course, taken in the same units.   As will be presently seen, this is indeed a convenient choice, for in most problems of the preliminary orbit,

$$m_A \gg m_B, \tag{1.6}$$

so that the sum of the masses of both bodies, $\mu$, which is the constant of the fundamental Eq. 1.1, is nearly equal to 1.   This can be readily seen if the orbit of the planet Jupiter, which is the second heaviest body in the solar system about the Sun, is under consideration, that is,

$$m_J \cong \frac{1}{1050.36}, \tag{1.7}$$

so that

$$\mu = 1.000952348. \tag{1.8}$$

Certainly then, for a small planetoid or spaceship, $\mu$ is for all intents and purposes unity, owing to the normalization adopted in Eq. 1.5.

For convenience, Table 1.2 is listed as reference.   An excellent compendium of planetary constants is available in references [10] and [11].

In continuing a convenient selection of units, the modified time variable $\tau$, can now be defined by the relation

$$\tau \equiv k_\odot (t - t_0), \tag{1.9}$$

where $k_\odot$ = the gravitational constant of the Sun,

$t_0$ = an arbitrary initial or epoch time,

$t$ = time.

It should be noted that $k_\odot = \sqrt{Gm_\odot}$ in which $G$ is the universal gravitational constant[4] and $m$ is the mass of the primary or central mass. The subscript $\odot$ refers to the fact that in the immediate discussion, the Sun is understood to be the body about which the motion is occurring; thus, $k_\odot$ is the Sun's gravitational constant.   If $t$ is measured in days, then by definition,[5]

$$k_\odot \equiv 0.01720209895 \text{ (a.u.)}^{3/2}/\text{day.} \tag{1.10}$$

As will be seen later, if $\tau$ is used in place of $t$, calculations are again simplified by a substantial amount.

An example using the modified time variable will perhaps aid in the mental replacement of $t$ by $\tau$.

---

[4] First successfully measured by Henry Cavendish (1798).
[5] See Section 1.2.3 for the reason that Eq. 1.10 is a definition.

Table 1.2   Reciprocal Masses of the Planets (*Sun's Mass* = 1)

| PLANET | $m^{-1}$ | | AUTHOR | METHOD |
|---|---|---|---|---|
| Mercury | 6,000,000 | | Newcomb, 1895 (Adopted by *Am. Ephm.* [1]) Clemence, 1953 | |
| | 7,500,000 ± | 1,500,000 | de Sitter, Brouwer, 1938 | Weighted mean |
| | 6,120,000 ± | 43,000 | Rabe, 1949 | Eros |
| | 5,970,000 ± | 460,000 | Duncombe, 1956 | Venus |
| | 6,100,000 ± | 50,000 | Adopted, 1961 | |
| Venus | 408,000 | | Newcomb, 1895 (Adopted by *Am. Ephm.* [1]) | |
| | 406,358 ± | 723 | Fotheringham, 1926 | Earth, Mars and Mercury |
| | 403,490 ± | 2,400 | Ross, 1916 | Mars |
| | 404,700 ± | 800 | Spencer Jones, 1926 | Sun |
| | 404,000 ± | 1,000 | de Sitter, 1938 | Weighted mean |
| | 407,000 ± | 500 | Morgan, Scott, 1939 | Sun |
| | 409,300 ± | 1,400 | Clemence, 1943 | Mercury |
| | 406,645 ± | 208 | Rabe, 1949 | Eros |
| | 407,000 ± | 1,000 | Adopted, 1961 | |
| Earth + Moon | 329,390 | | Newcomb, 1895 (Adopted by *Am. Ephm.* [1]) | |
| | 327,900 ± | 200 | de Sitter, 1938 | Weighted mean |
| | 328,390 ± | 103 | Witt, 1933 | Eros |
| | 328,452 ± | 43 | Rabe, 1949 | Eros |
| | 328,446 ± | 43 | E. Rabe, 1954 | Eros revised for precession |
| | 328,440 ± | 40 | de Vaucouleurs, 1961 | Average |
| | 328,450 ± | 50 | Adopted, 1961 | |
| Mars | 3,648,000 | | Leveau, 1890 | Vesta |
| | 3,093,500 | | Newcomb, 1895 (Adopted by *Am. Ephm.* [1]) | |
| | 3,601,280 | | Leveau, 1907 | Vesta |
| | 3,085,000 ± | 5,000 | de Sitter, 1938 | Weighted mean |
| | 3,110,000 ± | 7,700 | Rabe, 1949 | Eros |
| | 3,079,000 ± | 5,702 | Urey, 1952 | Deimos |
| | 3,090,000 ± | 10,000 | Adopted, 1961 | |

*Table 1.2 (cont'd)    Reciprocal Masses of the Planets (Sun's Mass = 1)*

| PLANET | $m^{-1}$ | | AUTHOR | METHOD |
|---|---|---|---|---|
| Jupiter | 1,050.36 | | Encke, 1938 | Vesta |
| | 1,051.42 | | Hansen, 1865 | Egeria |
| | 1,047.538 | | Kruger, 1865 | Themis |
| | 1,045.63 | | Leveau, 1890 | Vesta |
| | 1,047.355 ± | 0.065 | Newcomb, 1895 (Adopted by *Am. Ephm.* [1]) | Weighted mean |
| | 1,047.34 | | Newcomb, 1895 | Polyhymnia |
| | 1,046.04 | | Leveau, 1904 | Vesta |
| | 1,047.40 ± | 0.03 | de Sitter, 1938 | Weighted mean |
| | 1,047.4 ± | 0.1 | Adopted, 1961 | |
| Saturn | 3,501.9 | | Newcomb, 1895 | Weighted mean |
| | 3,490 ± | 5 | de Sitter, 1938 | Weighted mean |
| | 3,497.64 ± | 0.27 | Hertz, 1953 | |
| | 3,499.7 ± | 0.4 | Clemence, 1953, 1960 | Jupiter Perturbations |
| | 3,500 ± | 3 | Adopted, 1961 | |
| Uranus | 22,869 | | Newcomb, 1895 (Adopted by *Am. Ephm.* [1]) Clemence, 1953 | |
| | 22,750 ± | 200 | de Sitter, 1938 | |
| | 22,800 ± | 100 | Adopted, 1961 | |
| Neptune | 19,314 | | Clemence, 1953 (Adopted by *Am. Ephm.* [1]) | |
| | 19,700 | | Newcomb, 1895 | |
| | 19,500 ± | 200 | de Sitter, 1938 | |
| | 19,500 ± | 200 | Adopted, 1961 | |
| Pluto | 332,488 ± | 76,472 | Nicholson and Mayall, 1931 | |
| | 360,000 | | Clemence, 1953 | |
| | 307,000 | | Kuiper, 1950 | |
| | 350,000 ± | 50,000 | Adopted, 1961 | |

*Note:* This table has been reproduced from reference [4] by permission of the publisher.

*Illustrative Example*

If the distance of the planet Mars from the Sun is specified for the three dates,

$$t_1 = \text{June 10}$$

$$t_2 = \text{June 20}$$

$$t_3 = \text{June 30,}$$

what are the corresponding modified time variables?

SOLUTION. Since the arbitrary initial time, $t_0$, of definition (1.9) can be chosen as desired, let it be the central date. Then

$$\tau_1 = k_\odot(10 - 20) = -0.17202099$$

$$\tau_2 = k_\odot(20 - 20) = \quad 0.00000000$$

$$\tau_3 = k_\odot(30 - 20) = +0.17202099.$$

In the system of units so far described, in summary, it is to be realized that each physical quantity is related to its units, as indicated in the following table.

*Table 1.3*

| PHYSICAL QUANTITY | CANONICAL UNITS (DIMENSIONLESS) |
| --- | --- |
| Length | Astronomical units (a.u.) |
| Mass | Solar masses (s.m.) |
| Time | Modified time variable (m.t.v.) |

Hence preliminary orbit calculations should in most cases be performed in these special or characteristic units. It is well to note and will be presently shown (Chapter 3) that due to the above so-called characteristic units, velocities will have the units of circular satellite speed at the unit distance. That is, velocities are measured such that in characteristic units the unit of speed is

$$1 \text{ circular satellite unit} \cong 66584 \text{ mph} \tag{1.11}$$

or approximately the speed of the Earth around the Sun at 1 a.u.

### 1.2.2  The Geocentric system of units

Frequently, analysis of Earth satellites and space vehicles in close proximity to the Earth is desired.   Here again, common sense would dictate selection of a new system of units.

In this system a convenient benchmark or yardstick for measurement of distances would be the radius of the Earth.   Thus, in almost complete analogy to the heliocentric system of units, it is possible to adopt the unit distance as the Earth's equatorial radius,[6] which is abbreviated e.r. Approximately, then,

$$1 \text{ e.r.} \cong 3960 \text{ miles.} \qquad (1.12)$$

Distances are tabulated more exactly in Table 1.4 for convenience and reference.

*Table 1.4   Equatorial Radius of Earth* $(a_e)$

| $a_e$ (METERS) | AUTHOR |
| --- | --- |
| 6,378,301 | Clarke, 1880 |
| 6,378,298 ± 34 | Ledersteger, 1951 |
| 6,378,228 | Hayford Revision, 1953 |
| 6,377,879 ± 357 | Hirose, 1955 |
| 6,378,250 ± 95 | "Hough Ellipsoid," 1956 |
| 6,378,240 ± 100 | "Hough Ellipsoid," 1956 |
| 6,378,285 ± 100 | "Hough Ellipsoid," 1956 |
| 6,378,270 ± 100 | Herrick, Baker, Hilton, 1958 |
| 6,378,145 ± 50 | Herrick, Baker, Hilton, 1958 |
| 6,378,388 | Yaplee, Bruton, Craig, Roman, 1958 |
| 6,378,175 ± 20 | Yaplee, Bruton, Craig, Roman, 1958 |
| 6,378,200 | Fischer, 1959 |
| 6,378,200 ± 30 | de Vaucouleurs, 1961 |
| 6,378,163 ± 21 | Kaula, 1961 |
| 6,378,255 ± 35 | Yaplee, Bruton, Miller, 1960 |
| 6,378,150 ± 50 | Adopted, 1961 |

*Note:* This table has been reproduced from reference [4] by permission of the publisher.   Note 1 e.r. $\equiv a_e$.

[6] To be precise, a *g*-radii defined presently as 1 e.r. $= 0.999,99022$ *g*-radii or slightly scaled equatorial radius should be used; see the discussion of Eq. 1.20.

Masses are again treated as ratios, and, once more, it will be convenient to take all other masses as a fraction of the central mass. Thus the unit mass is again defined in terms of the most ponderous body encountered in the analytical problem. If the subscript $e$ denotes the Earth, then from the definition, it follows that by normalization,

$$\mu \equiv \frac{1}{m_e}(m_e + m_B) = 1 + m_B', \tag{1.13}$$

and the dimensionless ratios, denoted by primes are

$$m_e' \equiv 1, \qquad m_B' = \frac{m_B}{m_e}. \tag{1.14}$$

Here again, as in the heliocentric system of units $\mu$, the sum of the masses of both bodies will for all intents and purposes be equal to unity for most applications. This is due to the normalization adopted in Eq. 1.14.

If a convenient selection of units in the geocentric or Earth-centered system is continued, the modified time variable would be defined by

$$\tau \equiv k_e(t - t_0), \tag{1.15}$$

where $k_e = \sqrt{Gm_e}$ = gravitational constant of the Earth,
$t_0$ = an arbitrary initial or epoch time,
$t$ = time.

$G$ is, of course, the universal gravitational constant. If $t$ is measured in minutes, then by definition,[7]

$$k_e \equiv 0.07436574(\text{e.r.})^{3/2}/\text{min}. \tag{1.16}$$

Table 1.5 indicates the physical quantity and its related units in the geocentric unit system.

*Table 1.5*

| PHYSICAL QUANTITY | CANONICAL UNITS (*dimensionless*) |
|---|---|
| Length | Earth radii (e.r.) |
| Mass | Central Earth masses (e.m.) |
| Time | Modified time variable (m.t.v.) |

Preliminary orbit calculations should again, in most cases, be performed in these special or characteristic units. It is well to note and will be

[7] See Section 1.2.3.

presently shown (Chapter 3) that the above characteristic units cause velocities to have the units of a circular satellite at the unit distance. That is, velocities are measured such that in characteristic units, the unit of speed in the geocentric system is

$$1 \text{ circular satellite unit} \simeq 25936 \text{ ft/sec}, \tag{1.17}$$

or approximately the speed of a hypothetical Earth satellite moving in the equatorial plane of the Earth at 1 e.r.

### 1.2.3 Discussion of the two systems

A comparison of the heliocentric and geocentric system of units shows a fundamental difference. That is, in the former, the unit distance is taken as the distance between the centers of Sun and Earth; whereas, the latter takes the Earth's equatorial radius as the unity benchmark. It could have been just as feasible to adopt the radius of the Sun as the fundamental or unit benchmark and thus have a greater similarity between both systems; this, however, is not the case.

It should be kept in mind that if an observer were standing on the surface of the planet Saturn and wanted to conduct a study of the various moons of that planet, it might be beneficial and very convenient to devise a new system of characteristic units relating to Saturn.

If, for the present, it is accepted that the period ($P$) of a planet rotating about the Sun is given by the relation

$$P^2 = \frac{(2\pi)^2}{\mu k_\odot^2} a^3, \tag{1.18}$$

where $a$ is the semimajor axis[8] of the planet's orbit, then in a heliocentric system of characteristic units it is an easy matter to compute the numerical value of $k_\odot$, the Gaussian constant. For example, let Eq. 1.18 be written for the Earth. Now since the period of the Earth is 365.2563835 mean solar days, and if by definition the mean semi-major axis of the Earth's orbit about the Sun ($a_\oplus$) is taken to be exactly 1 a.u., then the only unknown in Eq. 1.18 is $\mu$, the sum of the masses. Furthermore, if the Moon and Earth are thought of as being one body with an approximate combined mass of 1/354710 solar masses,[9] then

$$k_\odot = \frac{2\pi a_\oplus^{3/2}}{P\sqrt{\mu}} = \frac{2\pi \cdot 1^{3/2}}{365.2563835\sqrt{1 + \dfrac{1}{354710}}} \tag{1.19}$$

$$k_\odot = 0.01720209895 \ (\text{a.u.})^{3/2}/\text{day}.$$

[8] Half the biggest axis of the ellipse of motion.
[9] Gauss adopted the Earth's mass as being $\frac{1}{354710}$ solar masses without any mention of the Moon's mass.

This, in effect, was the way that Gauss determined this rather important constant in the Theoria Motus,[10] Art 1.

As might be expected, when Gauss performed this determination of the heliocentric constant, his data on the masses of the planets were of limited accuracy.   Hence as new data on the period of the Earth and the masses of the planets came to light, the value of Gaussian constant would have to undergo change.   This would mean that all astronomical calculations functionally dependent upon $k_\odot$ performed with the old constant, would have to be repeated.   Astronomers, therefore, decided to accept the value determined by Gauss as a definition and let the value of $a_\oplus$ vary so as to make Eq. 1.18 hold true.   Therefore, the value of the mean semimajor axis of the Earth's orbit departs slightly from unity.   Today, for example,

$$a_\oplus \cong 1.000000230. \tag{1.20}$$

The result of this adjustment is, that whenever new and better data are found, all existing calculations only have to be scaled by a value of $a_\oplus$ defined by a slight variation of Eq. 1.20.

In an analogous manner, the same technique could be used in a geocentric system of characteristic units.   The point is emphasized that herein Eqs. 1.10 and 1.16 are definitions and not approximations.

The mathematically adopted value of $k_e$, or, as it is sometimes denoted, $k_\oplus$, can be determined from the Earth-centered form of the fundamental equation (1.1) written in the equatorial plane, i.e.,

$$\frac{d^2 a_e}{dt^2} \equiv g_e = \frac{k_e^2 \mu}{a_e^2}. \tag{1.21}$$

As indicated in reference [13], $\mu$ in this special case is actually an augmented or effective mass equal to

$$\mu = 1 - A - \tilde{\omega} + J + \tfrac{1}{2}K + \cdots. \tag{1.22}$$

In this expression, $A$ is the mass of an ellipsoidal shell of atmosphere taken to be $0.88 \times 10^{-6}$ e.m.   The auxiliary constant $\tilde{\omega} \equiv a_e^3 \omega^2 / k_e^2$ corrects for the component of acceleration due to centrifugal force and $\omega$ is the angular rotation of the Earth.   Finally, $J$ and $K$ are dimensionless numerical coefficients related to the second and fourth harmonics of the

[10] Published in 1809, the *Theoria motus corporum coelestium in sectionibus conicis solem ambientium* or, *Theory of the Motion of Heavenly Bodies Revolving Round the Sun in Conic Sections*, could be termed the second masterpiece of Gauss.   Truly, it is an exhaustive discussion of the determination of planetary and cometary orbits from observations of the motions of these bodies in space.

Earth (Chapter 2). Numerically, they may be taken as $J = 1623.41 \pm 4 \times 10^{-6}$ and $K = 6.37 \pm 0.23 \times 10^{-6}$. With the aid of expression (1.22) and rather extensive geodetic surveys to measure $a_e$ and $g_e$, the acceleration of gravity at the Earth's equator, Eq. 1.21 may be solved for $k_e$.

Actually, the acceleration of gravity, $g$, at any location throughout the Earth is obtained as a function of the geodetic latitude $\phi$ from

$$g = g_e(1 + \beta \sin^2 \phi + \gamma \sin^2 2\phi + \cdots), \qquad (1.23)$$

where

$$\beta = -f + \tfrac{5}{2}\tilde{\omega} - \tfrac{26}{7}f\tilde{\omega} + \tfrac{15}{4}\tilde{\omega}^2 + \cdots$$

$$\gamma = \tfrac{1}{8}f^2 - \tfrac{5}{8}f\tilde{\omega} + \cdots,$$

with $f \simeq 1/298.3$ taken to be the geometrical flattening of the Earth (see Section 1.4). Hence, $g$ may be measured throughout the world and by a least squares procedure the parameters $g_e$, $\beta$, and $\gamma$ determined. The immediate discussion may be concluded by stating that consistent data yield $g_e = 9.780320(1 \pm 3 \times 10^{-6})\text{m/sec}^2$. Interested readers are directed to reference [13] for a thorough discussion.

Table 1.6 Gravitational Constants of the Major Planets
(1 a.u. = 149,599,000 km)

$$(k_p = k_\odot \sqrt{m_p/m_\odot})$$

| PLANET | SEMIMAJOR AXIS (km) | GRAVITATIONAL CONSTANTS (a.u.$^{3/2}$/Mean Solar Day) | |
|---|---|---|---|
| Mercury | 2,424 | 6.960 | $\times 10^{-6}$ |
| Venus | 6,100 | 2.691 | $\times 10^{-5}$ |
| Earth | 6,378.15 | 2.99948 | $\times 10^{-5}$ |
| Mars | 3,412 | 9.786 | $\times 10^{-6}$ |
| Jupiter | 71,420 | 5.3153 | $\times 10^{-4}$ |
| Saturn | 60,440 | 2.908 | $\times 10^{-4}$ |
| Uranus | 24,860 | 1.136 | $\times 10^{-4}$ |
| Neptune | 26,500 | 1.240 | $\times 10^{-4}$ |
| Pluto | 4,000 | 2.700 | $\times 10^{-5}$ |

Apart from the convenience of small numbers, the characteristic system of units offers an easy branch point for obtaining values of the parameters of the preliminary orbit in any other system of units by simple multiplications. For comparison studies, it is also helpful to

have all numbers reduced to a common nondimensionalized base.    Internal to these units it is also possible to solve problems to a great number
of significant figures.    It is only later, in the transformation of these
units into laboratory units, that significance is lost.    It is for this reason
that great efforts have been made to obtain, for example, a better value
of the a.u. It will be found that adoption of such a system of units will be
of very great benefit, and to a point, an aid in the mental estimation
process involved in the solution of a given analytical problem.

    For the sake of convenience, a set of consistent gravitational constants
for the major planets are presented in Table 1.6.


### 1.3   THE MEASUREMENT OF TIME


### 1.3.1   Universal time

Without transcending into the rather lengthy and complicated question
of "what time is it?," the intent of this section is to relate only the necessary
definitions and equations needed in the preliminary orbit for the determination of time.

    An observer standing on Earth on a given meridian, that is, a north–
south line perpendicular to the equator, looks at a clock and observes a
specific number.    This number is nothing more than an index of the
distance the observer is from a magic arbitrarily set meridian, the Greenwich meridian.    For the sake of convenience, the planet Earth is divided
into twenty-four time zones.    Hence, each time zone is equivalent to
1 hour.    As shown in Figure 1.2, the Greenwich meridian is exactly in the
middle of time zone number 0.

    Actually, however, an observer measures local *mean solar time*[11] on
his clock.    If, therefore, an observer reads $x$ hours on his clock (which is
very accurate) and he knows that he is $z$ time zones to the west of the Greenwich meridian, then, of course, the time at the Greenwich Observatory is

$$t = x + z$$

    This time is called *universal time* and is denoted by the symbol U.T.,
that is,

$$\text{U.T.} \equiv x + z. \tag{1.24}$$

---

[11] Mean time at a particular meridian is defined as 12 hours plus the hour angle (the
angle measured west of the particular meridian) of a fictitious sun that has the same
period as the true Sun, but moves with constant speed along the equatorial plane.

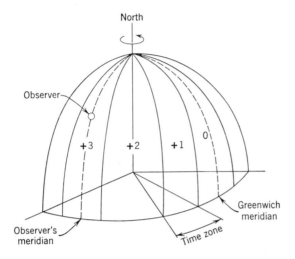

FIGURE 1.2    The division of the Earth into time zones.

It is well to note that angles can be measured in hours, minutes, and seconds, as well as degrees, minutes, and seconds.    Actually, then,

$$24 \text{ hours } = 360°$$
$$1 \text{ hour } = 15°. \tag{1.25}$$

This should not be confusing for it would be possible to define midnight as being zero degrees and, therefore, for example, 9 o'clock in the morning would be 135 degrees.

### 1.3.2    The Julian date

A concept of fundamental importance in the reckoning of time is that of the Julian Date, denoted by J.D.    This is nothing more than another arbitrary benchmark that is a continuing count of each day elapsed since some particular epoch.    This epoch was arbitrarily selected as January 1, 4713 B.C.    Each Julian date is measured from noon to noon, and hence, is an exact integer 12 hours after midnight.[12]

Julian dates for a given Gregorian date are obtainable from the *American Ephemeris and Nautical Almanac*.    They can also be calculated by adopting a known epoch Julian date with its associated Gregorian date and counting

---

[12] Astronomers preferred changing their day at noon so as not to have two separate dates on a given night of observation.

the number of days elapsed since the particular epoch.[13]   Table 1.7 might be useful as reference.

*Illustrative Example*

What is the Julian date corresponding to a U.T. of January 1, 1985, at 6:48 in the morning?

SOLUTION.   Since the Julian date is measured from noon to noon, then midnight, or exactly January 1, can be thought of as occurring 12 hours after the December 31 Julian date.   Hence, from Table 1.7, for December 31 (Jan. 0)

$$\text{J.D.}_{\text{(noon)}} = 2446066.0.$$

To this number is added 12 hours or 0.5 days so that

$$\text{J.D.}_{\text{(midnight)}} = 2446066.5,$$

and finally 6 hours and 48 minutes is converted into days as

$$\Delta = \frac{6}{24} + \frac{48}{60 \times 24} = 0.283333,$$

which added to the January 1, J.D. yields the Julian date at instant, that is,

$$\text{J.D.} = 2446066.783333 = 1985 \text{ January } 1^{\text{day}}6^{\text{hrs}}48^{\text{min}} \text{ U.T.}$$

### 1.3.3   Sidereal time

With the concept of the Julian date in mind, it is now possible to return to an observer standing on a given meridian.

So far, all the observer's time measurements have been relative to the prime or Greenwich meridian.   If, however, an inertial system such as that shown in Figure 1.1 comprises one of the basic astronomical systems, a relation is needed between the prime meridian and the adopted inertial coordinate system.   Let the Earth's axis of rotation coincide with the $z$ axis of Figure 1.1, then, as shown in Figure 1.3, there is a unique angle between the Greenwich prime meridian and the inertial $x$ axis.

---

[13] The advantages of having a continuing count of the days from some epoch are very great and avoid a great deal of confusion.   For example, in 1582, a decree was issued by Pope Gregory XIII that the day following October 4, 1582, should be called October 15, thus eliminating 10 days.   Again, in 1752, the British eliminated another 11 days, etc.   These actions were due to imperfections in the calendars, all in all, a very complicated business.

## Table 1.7  Julian Day Number†

### Days Elapsed at Greenwich Noon, A.D. 1950–2000

| YEAR | JAN. 0 | | FEB. 0 | MAR. 0 | APR. 0 | MAY 0 | JUNE 0 | JULY 0 | AUG. 0 | SEP. 0 | OCT. 0 | NOV. 0 | DEC. 0 |
|---|---|---|---|---|---|---|---|---|---|---|---|---|---|
| 1950 | 243 | 3282 | 3313 | 3341 | 3372 | 3402 | 3433 | 3463 | 3494 | 3525 | 3555 | 3586 | 3616 |
| 1951 | | 3647 | 3678 | 3706 | 3737 | 3767 | 3798 | 3828 | 3859 | 3890 | 3920 | 3951 | 3981 |
| 1952 | | 4012 | 4043 | 4072 | 4103 | 4133 | 4164 | 4194 | 4225 | 4256 | 4286 | 4317 | 4347 |
| 1953 | | 4378 | 4409 | 4437 | 4468 | 4498 | 4529 | 4559 | 4590 | 4621 | 4651 | 4682 | 4712 |
| 1954 | | 4743 | 4774 | 4802 | 4833 | 4863 | 4894 | 4924 | 4955 | 4986 | 5016 | 5047 | 5077 |
| 1955 | 243 | 5108 | 5139 | 5167 | 5198 | 5228 | 5259 | 5289 | 5320 | 5351 | 5381 | 5412 | 5442 |
| 1956 | | 5473 | 5504 | 5533 | 5564 | 5594 | 5625 | 5655 | 5686 | 5717 | 5747 | 5778 | 5808 |
| 1957 | | 5839 | 5870 | 5898 | 5929 | 5959 | 5990 | 6020 | 6051 | 6082 | 6112 | 6143 | 6173 |
| 1958 | | 6204 | 6235 | 6263 | 6294 | 6324 | 6355 | 6385 | 6416 | 6447 | 6477 | 6508 | 6538 |
| 1959 | | 6569 | 6600 | 6628 | 6659 | 6689 | 6720 | 6750 | 6781 | 6812 | 6842 | 6873 | 6903 |
| 1960 | 243 | 6934 | 6965 | 6994 | 7025 | 7055 | 7086 | 7116 | 7147 | 7178 | 7208 | 7239 | 7269 |
| 1961 | | 7300 | 7331 | 7359 | 7390 | 7420 | 7451 | 7481 | 7512 | 7543 | 7573 | 7604 | 7634 |
| 1962 | | 7665 | 7696 | 7724 | 7755 | 7785 | 7816 | 7846 | 7877 | 7908 | 7938 | 7969 | 7999 |
| 1963 | | 8030 | 8061 | 8089 | 8120 | 8150 | 8181 | 8211 | 8242 | 8273 | 8303 | 8334 | 8364 |
| 1964 | | 8395 | 8426 | 8455 | 8486 | 8516 | 8547 | 8577 | 8608 | 8639 | 8669 | 8700 | 8730 |
| 1965 | 243 | 8761 | 8792 | 8820 | 8851 | 8881 | 8912 | 8942 | 8973 | 9004 | 9034 | 9065 | 9095 |
| 1966 | | 9126 | 9157 | 9185 | 9216 | 9246 | 9277 | 9307 | 9338 | 9369 | 9399 | 9430 | 9460 |
| 1967 | | 9491 | 9522 | 9550 | 9581 | 9611 | 9642 | 9672 | 9703 | 9734 | 9764 | 9795 | 9825 |
| 1968 | | 9856 | 9887 | 9916 | 9947 | 9977 | *0008 | *0038 | *0069 | *0100 | *0130 | *0161 | *0191 |
| 1969 | 244 | 0222 | 0253 | 0281 | 0312 | 0342 | 0373 | 0403 | 0434 | 0465 | 0495 | 0526 | 0556 |
| 1970 | 244 | 0587 | 0618 | 0646 | 0677 | 0707 | 0738 | 0768 | 0799 | 0830 | 0860 | 0891 | 0921 |
| 1971 | | 0952 | 0983 | 1011 | 1042 | 1072 | 1103 | 1133 | 1164 | 1195 | 1225 | 1256 | 1286 |
| 1972 | | 1317 | 1348 | 1377 | 1408 | 1438 | 1469 | 1499 | 1530 | 1561 | 1591 | 1622 | 1652 |
| 1973 | | 1683 | 1714 | 1742 | 1773 | 1803 | 1834 | 1864 | 1895 | 1926 | 1956 | 1987 | 2017 |
| 1974 | | 2048 | 2079 | 2107 | 2138 | 2168 | 2199 | 2229 | 2260 | 2291 | 2321 | 2352 | 2382 |
| 1975 | 244 | 2413 | 2444 | 2472 | 2503 | 2533 | 2564 | 2594 | 2625 | 2656 | 2686 | 2717 | 2747 |
| 1976 | | 2778 | 2809 | 2838 | 2869 | 2899 | 2930 | 2960 | 2991 | 3022 | 3052 | 3083 | 3113 |
| 1977 | | 3144 | 3175 | 3203 | 3234 | 3264 | 3295 | 3325 | 3356 | 3387 | 3417 | 3448 | 3478 |
| 1978 | | 3509 | 3540 | 3568 | 3599 | 3629 | 3660 | 3690 | 3721 | 3752 | 3782 | 3813 | 3843 |
| 1979 | | 3874 | 3905 | 3933 | 3964 | 3994 | 4025 | 4055 | 4086 | 4117 | 4147 | 4178 | 4208 |
| 1980 | 244 | 4239 | 4270 | 4299 | 4330 | 4360 | 4391 | 4421 | 4452 | 4483 | 4513 | 4544 | 4574 |
| 1981 | | 4605 | 4636 | 4664 | 4695 | 4725 | 4756 | 4786 | 4817 | 4848 | 4878 | 4909 | 4939 |
| 1982 | | 4970 | 5001 | 5029 | 5060 | 5090 | 5121 | 5151 | 5182 | 5213 | 5243 | 5274 | 5304 |
| 1983 | | 5335 | 5366 | 5394 | 5425 | 5455 | 5486 | 5516 | 5547 | 5578 | 5608 | 5639 | 5669 |
| 1984 | | 5700 | 5731 | 5760 | 5791 | 5821 | 5852 | 5882 | 5913 | 5944 | 5974 | 6005 | 6035 |
| 1985 | 244 | 6066 | 6097 | 6125 | 6156 | 6186 | 6217 | 6247 | 6278 | 6309 | 6339 | 6370 | 6400 |
| 1986 | | 6431 | 6462 | 6490 | 6521 | 6551 | 6582 | 6612 | 6643 | 6674 | 6704 | 6735 | 6765 |
| 1987 | | 6796 | 6827 | 6855 | 6886 | 6916 | 6947 | 6977 | 7008 | 7039 | 7069 | 7100 | 7130 |
| 1988 | | 7161 | 7192 | 7221 | 7252 | 7282 | 7313 | 7343 | 7374 | 7405 | 7435 | 7466 | 7496 |
| 1989 | | 7527 | 7558 | 7586 | 7617 | 7647 | 7678 | 7708 | 7739 | 7770 | 7800 | 7831 | 7861 |
| 1990 | 244 | 7892 | 7923 | 7951 | 7982 | 8012 | 8043 | 8073 | 8104 | 8135 | 8165 | 8196 | 8226 |
| 1991 | | 8257 | 8288 | 8316 | 8347 | 8377 | 8408 | 8438 | 8469 | 8500 | 8530 | 8561 | 8591 |
| 1992 | | 8622 | 8653 | 8682 | 8713 | 8743 | 8774 | 8804 | 8835 | 8866 | 8896 | 8927 | 8957 |
| 1993 | | 8988 | 9019 | 9047 | 9078 | 9108 | 9139 | 9169 | 9200 | 9231 | 9261 | 9292 | 9322 |
| 1994 | | 9353 | 9384 | 9412 | 9443 | 9473 | 9504 | 9534 | 9565 | 9596 | 9626 | 9657 | 9687 |
| 1995 | 244 | 9718 | 9749 | 9777 | 9808 | 9838 | 9869 | 9899 | 9930 | 9961 | 9991 | *0022 | *0052 |
| 1996 | 245 | 0083 | 0114 | 0143 | 0174 | 0204 | 0235 | 0265 | 0296 | 0327 | 0357 | 0388 | 0418 |
| 1997 | | 0449 | 0480 | 0508 | 0539 | 0569 | 0600 | 0630 | 0661 | 0692 | 0722 | 0753 | 0783 |
| 1998 | | 0814 | 0845 | 0873 | 0904 | 0934 | 0965 | 0995 | 1026 | 1057 | 1087 | 1118 | 1148 |
| 1999 | | 1179 | 1210 | 1238 | 1269 | 1299 | 1330 | 1360 | 1391 | 1422 | 1452 | 1483 | 1513 |
| 2000 | 254 | 1544 | 1575 | 1604 | 1635 | 1665 | 1696 | 1726 | 1757 | 1788 | 1818 | 1849 | 1879 |

† A machine routine that works on the principle that "Thirty days hath September, April, June, and November, all the rest have thirty-one, save February that has twenty-eight," along with a specific epoch J.D. from this table, has found great use in modern-day calculation techniques as an internal machine method of generating the J.D.

*Note:* This table has been reproduced from reference [1] by permission of the publisher.

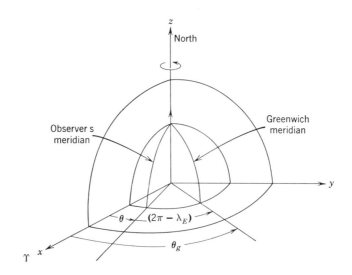

FIGURE 1.3   The rotating Earth in an inertial coordinate system.

This angle is denoted by $\theta_g$ and is defined as the *sidereal time*[14] of the Greenwich prime meridian. The observer's meridian, by the same reasoning, has a sidereal time which is denoted by $\theta$. This angle is called the *local sidereal time*. Obviously, if $\theta_g$ is known and $\lambda_E$ is the *east longitude*, that is, the angle measured eastward in the equatorial plane between the Greenwich meridian and the observer's meridian, then, from Figure 1.3, the local sidereal time is

$$\theta = \theta_g + \lambda_E, \qquad 0 \le \theta \le 2\pi. \tag{1.26}$$

Usually, the east longitude of a geographic location is known, and so a method of calculating $\theta$ is required. Once $\theta$ is calculated, a very important basic linkage between the rotating and nonrotating frames will be available.

The practical calculation of Greenwich sidereal time at 12 midnight or $0^{\mathrm{hr}}$ U.T., can be accomplished by means of the following formula [2]:

$$\theta_{g0} = 99\overset{\circ}{.}6909833 + 36000\overset{\circ}{.}7689T_u + 0\overset{\circ}{.}00038708T_u{}^2, \tag{1.27}$$

where the time is measured in centuries as

$$T_u = \frac{\mathrm{J.D.} - 2415020.0}{36525} \tag{1.28}$$

and $\theta_{g0}$ is in degrees.

---

[14] It is assumed that the $x$ axis points at a mean vernal equinox. Mean sidereal (equinoctial) time will always be implied herein.

In recapitulation, the Greenwich sidereal time at $0^{hr}$ U.T., that is, $\theta_{g0}$, is directly obtainable as a function of the Julian date at $0^{hr}$ U.T.

Sidereal time at any other time of day can be obtained if it is known that there is one extra sidereal day for every tropical year,[15] i.e.,

$$\frac{d\theta}{dt} = 1 + \frac{1}{365.24219879} \text{ revolutions/year}$$
$$= 4.3752695 \times 10^{-3} \text{ radians/minute}$$
$$= 2.5068447 \times 10^{-1} \text{ degrees/minute.} \qquad (1.29)$$

To a very high degree of approximation, Greenwich sidereal time is therefore calculable from

$$\theta_g = \theta_{g0} + (t - t_0)\frac{d\theta}{dt}. \qquad (1.30)$$

*Illustrative Example*

What was the local sidereal time at Wantig, West Antigua ($\lambda_E = 298°2213$) at a U.T. of 1962 October $12^{day}$ $10^{hr}$ $15^{min}$ $30^{sec}$?

SOLUTION. By means of Table 1.7, the J.D. at $0^{hr}$ U.T. is obtained as

2437938.0 (J.D. 12 hours previous to October 1)
     0.5 (Add 0.5 days to obtain the J.D. October 1, 1962)
+   11.0 (Add 11 days to October 12)
———————
2437949.5 (J.D. 0 hours U.T. October 12)

The time in centuries, since the epoch of Eq. 1.27 is obtained by Eq. 1.28, that is,

$$T_u = \frac{2437949.5 - 2415020.0}{36525} = 0.62777549.$$

Substituting this value into Eq. 1.27 yields the Greenwich sidereal time at $0^{hr}$ U.T. as

$$\theta_{g0} = 99°69098 + 280°40033 + 0°0001525 \cong 20°0915.$$

Now, since

$$10^{hr} \ 15^{min} \ 30^{sec} = 615.5 \text{ min,}$$

it is possible to apply Eq. 1.30 to obtain the Greenwich sidereal time, that is,

$$\theta_g = 20°0915 + (615.5 - 0)(0.25068447) = 174°3878.$$

---

[15] A year that has an approximate length of 365.24219879 mean solar days. See Section 7.2.2 for a further discussion of the tropical year.

Therefore, by virtue of Eq. 1.26, the local sidereal time at Wantig is

$$\theta = 174°\!.3878 + 298°\!.2213 \cong 112°\!.6091.$$

### 1.3.4    Ephemeris time

Unfortunately, for the sake of analysis, the rotation of the Earth about its axis is not truly constant.    It has been found that the Earth suffers from periodic and secular variations in its rotational rate.    In order to have a more uniform time, *Ephemeris time* was developed.    Thus, whenever the mean solar second is not considered to be accurate enough for the purposes of calculation, this new or truly more constant time can be used in the calculations.

Ephemeris time, denoted by E.T., is defined as

$$E.T. \equiv U.T. + \Delta T, \tag{1.31}$$

where $\Delta T$ is an annual increment tabulated in the *American Ephemeris and Nautical Almanac*.    A few of these values are given in Table 1.8.

*Table 1.8*

| YEAR | SEC |
|------|------|
| 1951.5 | +29.66 |
| 1952.5 | 30.29 |
| 1953.5 | 30.96 |
| 1954.5 | 31.09 |
| 1955.5 | 31.59 |
| 1956.5 | 32.06 |
| 1957.5 | 31.82 |
| 1958.5 | 32.80 |

Actually, the value of $\Delta T$ is small and in most cases, not of much consequence.    It is, however, a good procedure to calculate all new orbits with reference to E.T.[16]

The reason for not extending Table 1.8 is that Ephemeris time cannot be calculated in advance.    It is only after long reductions of the observed and predicted longitudes of the Moon that $\Delta T$ can be computed.    Hence, it is always an estimated quantity.

---

[16] One second is defined as 1/31556925.9747 of the tropical year for 1900 January 0 at 12 hours E.T.    A second of mean solar time may be in discrepancy from the ephemeris second by 1 part in $10^7$.

It may be noted that in the modified time variable $\tau$ (Sections 1.2.1, 1.2.2), that is

$$\tau = k(t - t_0), \tag{1.32}$$

or more explicitly,

$$\tau = k(\text{U.T.} + \Delta T - [\text{U.T.}]_0 - \Delta T), \tag{1.33}$$

the variation is inconsequential for short periods of time, since it cancels.

For an extended general outlook on the rather complicated subject of time, the interested reader would be wise to consult references [2], [3], and [7]. An excellent discussion is presented in [12].

## 1.4 STATION COORDINATES

### 1.4.1 The model of the Earth

*Station coordinates* is the term used to denote the position of an observer on the surface of the Earth or central planet.

It is known, for example, that the Earth is not a perfect geometric sphere. Therefore, in order to increase the accuracy of the calculations, a model for the geometric shape of the Earth must be adopted. In preliminary orbit determination, an oblate spheroid is taken as the model of the Earth. This, in effect, is an excellent representation.

In this adopted model (see Figure 1.4), sections parallel to the equator

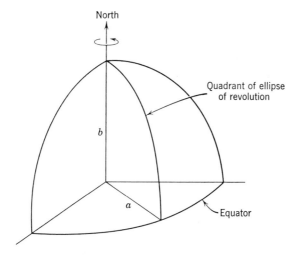

FIGURE 1.4   The geometric model of the Earth.

are perfect circles, and meridians are ellipses whose semimajor and semiminor diameters are denoted by $a$ and $b$, respectively. The semimajor axis is, of course, the equatorial radius of the Earth ($a_e$). A parameter related to the eccentricity of the ellipsoid of revolution is called the flattening, denoted by $f$ and defined as the difference of the largest and smallest semiaxis of the ellipse of revolution (Figure 1.4), divided by the semimajor axis. Thus $f$ is given by

$$f = \frac{a - b}{a}.\qquad(1.34)$$

This parameter has been measured for the Earth and found to be approximately equal to 1/298.3. Table 1.9 is included as reference.
Flattening is related to eccentricity by the relation:

$$e^2 = 2f - f^2.\qquad(1.35)$$

*Table 1.9    Flattening of the Earth*

| $1/f$ | AUTHOR |
|---|---|
| 298.38 ± 0.07 | O'Keefe, 1958 |
| 298.28 ± 0.11 | Jacchia, 1958 |
| 298.32 ± 0.05 | Lecar, Sorenson, Eckels, 1959 |
| 298.24 | O'Keefe, Eckels, Squires, 1959 |
| 298.20 ± 0.03 | King-Hele, Merson, 1959 |
| 298.24 ± 0.02 | King-Hele, 1960 |
| 298.30 ± 0.03 | Kozai, 1960 |
| 298.24 ± 0.01 | Kaula, 1961 |
| 298.2 ± 0.1 | de Vaucouleurs, 1961, weighted mean |
| 298.30 ± 0.05 | Adopted |

### 1.4.2 Geocentric latitude

Consider an ellipse comprising a section of the adopted model of the Earth. Then, as illustrated in Figure 1.5, it is possible to define two angles. The angle $\phi'$ is called the *geocentric latitude* and is verbally defined as follows.

$\phi'$ (*Geocentric Latitude*).  The acute angle measured perpendicular to the equatorial plane between the equator and a line connecting the geometric center of the coordinate system with a point on the surface of the reference ellipsoid.

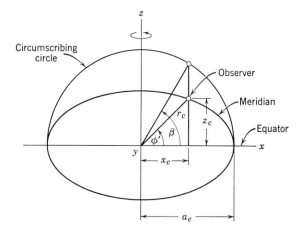

FIGURE 1.5 A cross section of the adopted Earth model.

A convenient angle to introduce is $\beta$, the *reduced latitude*, which is defined as follows.

$\beta \equiv$ The acute angle measured perpendicular to the equatorial plane between a line connecting the origin of the coordinates and a point defined by vertical projection of the observer on to a circle that circumscribes the reference ellipse.

These two angles play important roles in the determination of analytical expressions which define the position of the observer.

Let the rectangular components of the distance $r_c$, that is, distance between the surface observer and the origin of the coordinates, be denoted by $x_c$ and $z_c$. Then, by Figure 1.5,

$$x_c = r_c \cos \phi', \qquad z_c = r_c \sin \phi', \tag{1.36}$$

but,

$$x_c = a_e \cos \beta, \qquad z_c = a_e \sqrt{1 - e^2} \sin \beta, \tag{1.37}$$

and

$$r_c = \sqrt{x_c^2 + z_c^2} = a_e \sqrt{1 - e^2 \sin^2 \beta}. \tag{1.38}$$

It follows that the geocentric latitude can be directly obtained in terms of the reduced latitude by

$$\sin \phi' = \frac{z_c}{r_c} = \frac{\sqrt{1 - e^2} \sin \beta}{\sqrt{1 - e^2 \sin^2 \beta}}, \tag{1.39}$$

$$\cos \phi' = \frac{x_c}{r_c} = \frac{\cos \beta}{\sqrt{1 - e^2 \sin^2 \beta}}. \tag{1.40}$$

Multiplying Eq. 1.40 by $\sqrt{1 - e^2}$ and squaring the last two equations produces

$$\sin^2 \phi' = \frac{(1 - e^2) \sin^2 \beta}{1 - e^2 \sin^2 \beta} \tag{1.41}$$

$$(1 - e^2) \cos^2 \phi' = \frac{(1 - e^2) \cos^2 \beta}{1 - e^2 \sin^2 \beta}, \tag{1.42}$$

which upon addition and extraction of the square root of both sides, yields

$$\sqrt{1 - e^2 \sin^2 \beta} = \frac{\sqrt{1 - e^2}}{\sqrt{1 - e^2 \cos^2 \phi'}}. \tag{1.43}$$

If Eq. 1.39 is solved for the sine of the reduced latitude, then by virtue of Eq. 1.43,

$$\sin \beta = \frac{\sin \phi'}{\sqrt{1 - e^2}} \sqrt{1 - e^2 \sin^2 \beta} = \frac{\sin \phi'}{\sqrt{1 - e^2 \cos^2 \phi'}}. \tag{1.44}$$

In the same manner,

$$\cos \beta = \cos \phi' \sqrt{1 - e^2 \sin^2 \beta} = \frac{\sqrt{1 - e^2} \cos \phi'}{\sqrt{1 - e^2 \cos^2 \phi'}}. \tag{1.45}$$

Hence, returning to Eq. 1.37,

$$x_c = \frac{a_e \sqrt{1 - e^2} \cos \phi'}{\sqrt{1 - e^2 \cos^2 \phi'}} \tag{1.46}$$

$$z_c = \frac{a_e \sqrt{1 - e^2} \sin \phi'}{\sqrt{1 - e^2 \cos^2 \phi'}}. \tag{1.47}$$

These are the rectangular components of a station on the surface of the adopted elliptical cross section of the Earth.

### 1.4.3   Geodetic latitude

In this section the rectangular components of an observer will be derived as a function of geodetic latitude. *Geodetic latitude*, denoted by $\phi$, is defined as follows.

$\phi$ (*Geodetic Latitude*).  The acute angle measured perpendicular to the equatorial plane, between a line normal to a tangent plane touching the reference ellipsoid, and the equatorial plane.

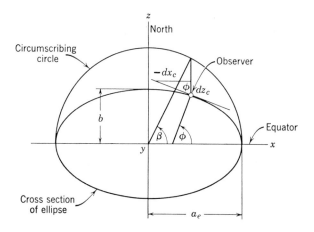

FIGURE 1.6    A cross section of the adopted Earth model with geodetic latitude as a variable.

Examination of Figure 1.6 immediately yields the two relations:

$$x_c = a_e \cos \beta, \qquad z_c = a_e \sqrt{1 - e^2} \sin \beta. \tag{1.48}$$

By differentiation, it is possible to write

$$-dx_c = a_e \sin \beta \, d\beta, \qquad dz_c = a_e \sqrt{1 - e^2} \cos \beta \, d\beta. \tag{1.49}$$

Therefore, it follows that

$$ds \equiv \sqrt{(-dx_c)^2 + (dz_c)^2} = a_e \sqrt{1 - e^2 \cos^2 \beta} \, d\beta \tag{1.50}$$

and

$$\sin \phi = -\frac{dx_c}{ds} = \frac{\sin \beta}{\sqrt{1 - e^2 \cos^2 \beta}} \tag{1.51}$$

$$\cos \phi = \frac{dz_c}{ds} = \frac{\sqrt{1 - e^2} \cos \beta}{\sqrt{1 - e^2 \cos^2 \beta}}. \tag{1.52}$$

Now, by multiplying Eq. 1.51 by $\sqrt{1 - e^2}$ and squaring the last two equations, it is possible to write

$$(1 - e^2) \sin^2 \phi = \frac{(1 - e^2) \sin^2 \beta}{1 - e^2 \cos^2 \beta} \tag{1.53}$$

$$\cos^2 \phi = \frac{(1 - e^2) \cos^2 \beta}{1 - e^2 \cos^2 \beta}. \tag{1.54}$$

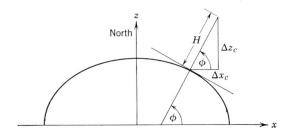

FIGURE 1.7    Deviations from the adopted ellipse.

Addition of these two forms and extraction of the square root of both sides of the resulting equation produces the relation

$$\sqrt{1 - e^2 \cos^2 \beta} = \frac{\sqrt{1 - e^2}}{\sqrt{1 - e^2 \sin^2 \phi}}. \tag{1.55}$$

But, by virtue of Eqs. 1.51 and 1.52,

$$\sin \beta = \sin \phi \sqrt{1 - e^2 \cos^2 \beta} = \frac{\sqrt{1 - e^2} \sin \phi}{\sqrt{1 - e^2 \sin^2 \phi}} \tag{1.56}$$

$$\cos \beta = \frac{\cos \phi \sqrt{1 - e^2 \cos^2 \beta}}{\sqrt{1 - e^2}} = \frac{\cos \phi}{\sqrt{1 - e^2 \sin^2 \phi}}. \tag{1.57}$$

Therefore, owing to Eqs. 1.48, the sought-for rectangular coordinates of the observing station are

$$x_c = \frac{a_e \cos \phi}{\sqrt{1 - e^2 \sin^2 \phi}} \tag{1.58}$$

$$z_c = \frac{a_e(1 - e^2) \sin \phi}{\sqrt{1 - e^2 \sin^2 \phi}}. \tag{1.59}$$

Up to this point, only the rectangular coordinates of a point or observer on the surface of the adopted ellipsoid are known. Since it happens that variations above and below the surface are quite prevalent, e.g., Denver, U.S.A., is about a mile above sea level, the method required to account for these deviations will now be developed.

It can readily be seen by means of Figure 1.7 that the components of the *elevation* or deviation $(H)$ normal to the adopted ellipsoid are

$$\Delta x_c = H \cos \phi \tag{1.60}$$

$$\Delta z_c = H \sin \phi. \tag{1.61}$$

Hence, upon adding these quantities to the relations for $x_c$ and $z_c$, the following station coordinate expressions are obtained as functions of the flattening, geodetic latitude and elevation

$$x_c = G_1 \cos \phi \tag{1.62}$$

$$z_c = G_2 \sin \phi, \tag{1.63}$$

where

$$G_1 \equiv \frac{a_e}{\sqrt{1 - (2f - f^2) \sin^2 \phi}} + H \tag{1.64}$$

$$G_2 \equiv \frac{a_e(1 - f)^2}{\sqrt{1 - (2f - f^2) \sin^2 \phi}} + H. \tag{1.65}$$

### 1.4.4    Astronomical latitude

Another type of latitude, called *astronomical latitude*, is defined as follows.

$\phi_a$ (*Astronomical Latitude*).   The acute angle measured perpendicular to the equatorial plane formed by the intersection of a gravity ray (plumb bob) with the equatorial plane.

Since this latitude is a function of the local gravitational field, it is affected by the presence of any anomalies such as mountains, seas, etc. Differences between geodetic and astronomical latitude are termed *station error*. When these station errors have not been removed from the astronomical latitude owing to lack of information of a particular site or observatory, then astronomical latitude is used as a first approximation to geodetic latitude. Discrepancies between geodetic and astronomical latitude are usually quite differential.

### 1.5  SUMMARY

In this chapter, a definition of preliminary orbit determination has been formulated. The heliocentric and geocentric systems of units have been introduced as a helpful and practical aid in calculations. Advantages of these characteristic systems of units have been indicated. The question of time is investigated from the point of view of relating an observer's mean solar time on a given Earth meridian to fundamental or basic time units, that is, universal and ephemeris time. Sidereal time has been introduced as a basic link between a rotating and nonrotating coordinate system. Certain equations are given that permit the calculation of sidereal time as a function of the Julian date or continuing count of each day since a particular epoch. An observer who measures time at a given location also requires that the coordinates of his position be known. It is for this reason that station coordinates are introduced. Concepts of geocentric, geodetic, and astronomical latitudes and their relation to an observer's rectangular coordinates, with respect to an adopted model for the Earth's shape, are also developed.

**EXERCISES**

1. If an observer measures six elevation angles of a geocentric satellite and their related times, is the fundamental set of elements theoretically determinate?

2. Can a fundamental set of elements be determined from two position vectors? Two velocity vectors?

3. Why is it convenient to transform observations in a rotating frame into an inertial frame?

4. In the heliocentric system of units a curve fit of the $X$ coordinate of the Earth as a function of time with respect to the Sun is desired. Hence, given $X_1$, $X_2$, $X_3$ and $t_1$, $t_2$, $t_3$, determine the coefficients of the corresponding quadratic fit. Use the modified time variable $\tau$, with $t_2$ as epoch. Compare the results and note the added complexity if $t$ is used as a variable.

5. The velocity of a spaceship is 35,000 miles per hour. What is its velocity in geocentric characteristic units? In heliocentric characteristic units?

6. Devise a characteristic system of units for the planet Mars.

7. The east longitude of New York, New York, is 286°. Determine the corresponding time zone.

8. If the date at Point Mugu, California ($\lambda_E = 240°$), is January 15, 1984 at 1:20 A.M., Pacific Standard Time, what is the U.T.?

9. What is the J.D. corresponding to a U.T. of December 23, 1975? The J.D. corresponding to a U.T. of August 24, 1978 at $5^{hr}$ $30^{min}$ $22.3^{sec}$?

10. A satellite passes over Nutley, New Jersey ($\lambda_E = 289°$) on July 15, 1962 at 10:10 A.M., Eastern Standard Time. What is the J.D.?

11. Calculate the sidereal time at the Palomar Mountain Observatory ($\lambda_E = 243°.1367$) on June 20, 1962 at 4:17.5 A.M., Pacific Standard Time.

12. If the U.T. is 1958, June 1, $0^{hr}$ $1^{min}$ $30^{sec}$, what is the E.T.?

13. Develop the relationship,

$$\phi = \tan^{-1}\left[\frac{1}{(1-f)^2}\tan\phi'\right], \quad -\frac{\pi}{2} \leq \phi \leq \frac{\pi}{2},$$

between geocentric and geodetic latitude. For $f = 1/298.3$, find the maximum difference between both latitudes.

**14.** What are the rectangular station coordinates of an observer at Boulder, Colorado? ($\phi = 40°$, $H = 5000$ ft.)

**15.** If the flattening of Mars is 1/150, what are the rectangular station coordinates of an observer at a geodetic latitude of 30 degrees and elevation of 500 meters? Assume the diameter of Mars is 6830 km.

**REFERENCES**

1. *American Ephemeris and Nautical Almanac*, U.S. Government Printing Office, Washington D.C., 1960, 1961, 1962, 1963.
2. *Explanatory Supplement to the Astronomical Ephemeris and the American Ephemeris and Nautical Almanac*, Her Majesty's Stationery Office, London, 1961.
3. S. Newcomb, *A Compendium of Spherical Astronomy*, Dover Publications, New York, 1960.
4. M. W. Makemson, R. M. L. Baker, Jr., and G. B. Westrom, "Analysis and Standardization of Astrodynamic Constants," *The Journal of the Astronautical Sciences*, Vol. VIII, No. 1, Spring 1961.
5. F. R. Moulton, *Celestial Mechanics*, Macmillan Company, New York, 1914.
6. R. M. L. Baker, Jr., and M. W. Makemson, *An Introduction to Astrodynamics*, Academic Press, New York, 1960.
7. *Encyclopaedia Britannica*, Vol. 22, 1961.
8. M. P. Francis, *Errors Associated with the Selection of a Numerical Value of the Astronomical Unit*, Lockheed California Company, LTM 50249, October, 1962.
9. M. P. Francis, *The Geocentric and Heliocentric Systems of Constants*, Lockheed California Company, LR 17055, July 1963.
10. M. P. Francis, *Planetary Constants Standardization*, Lockheed California Company, LR 17061, July 1963.
11. M. W. Makemson, *Selenocentric Constants*, Lockheed California Company, LR 17060, July 1963.
12. G. Veis, *Precise Aspects of Terrestrial and Celestial Reference Frames*, Smithsonian Institution Astrophysical Observatory, Special Report No. 123, April 1963.
13. S. Herrick, R. M. L. Baker, Jr., and C. G. Hilton, *Gravitational and Related Constants for Accurate Space Navigation*, U.C.L.A. Astronomical Paper No. 24, Vol. I, pp. 297–338, 1957.
14. E. T. Bell, *Men of Mathematics*, Simon Schuster, New York, 1937.

# 2 Equations of motion

## 2.1 COMPLETE EQUATIONS OF MOTION

Motion of a body or object in space is an integral part of the preliminary orbit determination process. It is for this reason that a fully rigorous derivation of the equations of motion for a particle in space will be presented in this chapter.

Owing to the rather important nature of these equations, the derivations are presented from the point of view of $n$ bodies subjected to their mutual attractions. Even perturbative effects due to thrust, drag, etc., are briefly included. Intuitively, of course, it might appear easier to derive only the two-body equations of motion. The ideology of preliminary orbit determination is, however, not separable from the equations of motion of more than two bodies. This may indeed seem like a contradiction of the definition which was stated in Section 1.1.1. Actually, this is fallacious, for the concept of *differential correction* in which the complete equations of motion become manifest, has not yet been introduced. The process of differential correction, which is a branch of the fundamental process of determining the basic two-body elements of an orbit, will be introduced in a later chapter. Conceptually, this process is of negligible importance at the present stage of development. In order to circumvent redundancy of presentation, and since the two-body equations are a special case of the general equations, it is felt that complete presentation will be beneficial at the present time. Reduction to the fundamental equation (1.1) will become evident in Section 2.6.1.

32

## 2.2   INERTIAL FORM

### 2.2.1   Equations of motion referred to an inertial coordinate system

Newton's law of universal gravitation states that

$$F_{12} = \frac{k^2 m_1 m_2}{r_{12}^2}. \tag{2.1}$$

That is, two bodies attract each other with a force ($F_{12}$) directly proportional to their masses ($m_1$, $m_2$) and inversely proportional to the square of the distance between them ($r_{12}$).   The constant of gravitation is defined as $k^2$.[1]

Consider a number of bodies in the equatorial plane of the right ascension-declination inertial coordinate system defined in Section 1.1. It is possible to illustrate this as shown in Figure 2.1.

From Figure 2.1, it is easy to see that the force in the $x$ direction between bodies one and two is given by

$$F_{12x} = F_{12} \cos \psi = F_{12} \frac{x_2 - x_1}{r_{12}}, \tag{2.2}$$

where

$$r_{12} = \sqrt{(x_2 - x_1)^2 + (y_2 - y_1)^2}. \tag{2.3}$$

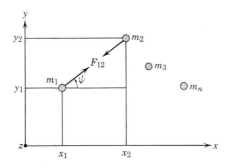

FIGURE 2.1   A system of bodies in an inertial coordinate frame.

[1] $k^2$ is defined as being equal to $Gm$, which is the product of the universal gravitational constant and the first mass.   This is done because $k$ can be determined to much greater accuracy than $G$.   (See Sections 1.2.1 and 1.2.2).   Note that $m_2$ is actually, even though denoted by $m_2$, the mass ratio of $m_2/m_1$, that is, $m_2$ is normalized with respect to $m_1$.

Hence, utilizing Eq. 2.1, it is possible to write

$$F_{12x} = \frac{k^2 m_1 m_2}{r_{12}^2} \cdot \frac{x_2 - x_1}{r_{12}}, \tag{2.4}$$

or

$$F_{12x} = \frac{k^2 m_1 m_2}{r_{12}^3} \cdot (x_2 - x_1). \tag{2.5}$$

In exactly the same manner, the component of attraction between body one and three in the $x$ direction is given by

$$F_{13x} = \frac{k^2 m_1 m_3}{r_{13}^3} \cdot (x_3 - x_1). \tag{2.6}$$

The analogy is carried on and, in brief, for the last body $m_n$,

$$F_{1nx} = \frac{k^2 m_1 m_n}{r_{1n}^3} \cdot (x_n - x_1), \tag{2.7}$$

so that the total force on body one in the $x$ direction, due to $n$ bodies, is

$$F_{1x} = F_{12x} + F_{13x} + \cdots + F_{1nx} \tag{2.8}$$

or

$$F_{1x} = k^2 \sum_{j=2}^{n} m_1 m_j \frac{(x_j - x_1)}{r_{1j}^3}, \tag{2.9}$$

where the summation must exclude the attraction of body one upon itself. It follows, therefore, that the force in the $x$ direction upon any arbitrary body denoted by $m_i$ is

$$F_{ix} = k^2 \sum_{\substack{j=1 \\ i \neq j}}^{n} m_i m_j \frac{(x_j - x_i)}{r_{ij}^3}. \tag{2.10}$$

Newton's second law states that the unbalanced force on a body in the $x$ direction is given by

$$F_{ix} = m_i \frac{d^2 x_i}{dt^2}. \tag{2.11}$$

Substituting Eq. 2.11 into Eq. 2.10 results in

$$m_i \frac{d^2 x_i}{dt^2} = k^2 m_i \sum_{\substack{j=1 \\ i \neq j}}^{n} \frac{m_j (x_j - x_i)}{r_{ij}^3}. \tag{2.12}$$

By repeating this analysis for the $y$ and $z$ components, it is possible to verify the vector equation

$$m_i \frac{d^2 \mathbf{r}_i}{dt^2} = k^2 m_i \sum_{\substack{j=1 \\ i \neq j}}^{n} m_j \frac{(\mathbf{r}_j - \mathbf{r}_i)}{r_{ij}^3}, \tag{2.13}$$

which is the inertial equation of motion of a particular body $m_i$ subject to the attractions of $n - 1$ other bodies.  To be perfectly general, it is possible to write

$$m_i \frac{d^2 \mathbf{r}_i}{dt^2} = k^2 m_i \sum_{\substack{j=1 \\ i \neq j}}^{n} m_j \frac{(\mathbf{r}_j - \mathbf{r}_i)}{r_{ij}^3} + m_i \sum_{ri},  \tag{2.14}$$

where $\sum_{ri}$ is the sum of accelerations of all other pertinent forces, e.g., drag, thrust, magnetic, electric, etc.  It should be noted that the $m_i$ may be cancelled from both sides of the equation.

## 2.3   RELATIVE FORM

### 2.3.1   Equations of motion referred to a relative coordinate system

In the last section it was shown that the equations of motion of a body $m_i$, with respect to an inertial origin, are given by

$$m_i \frac{d^2 \mathbf{r}_i}{dt^2} = k^2 \sum_{\substack{j=1 \\ i \neq j}}^{n} m_i m_j \frac{\mathbf{r}_{ij}}{r_{ij}^3} + m_i \sum_{ri},  \tag{2.15}$$

where

$$\mathbf{r}_{ij} = \mathbf{r}_j - \mathbf{r}_i.$$

However, the utility of Eq. 2.15 is not very great for practical applications.  This is said in light of the fact that the equations of motion are usually written with respect to a particular body, e.g., the equations of motion of the Moon about the Earth or the equations of motion of the Earth about the Sun.  Hence in practical applications the concept of an inertial origin is not explicitly utilized.

Suppose that the equations of motion of body 2, with mass $m_2$, are to be written with respect to body 1, with mass $m_1$.  Therefore, a translation of origins from $A$ to $B$ (as shown in Figure 2.2) is desired.

Thus the primary reference is shifted from the unknown inertial origin $A$ to the center of one of the bodies of the system $B$, here denoted by $m_1$.  Certainly $x_2' = x_{12}$, $y_2' = y_{12}$ and $z_2' = z_{12}$ with the understanding that the primed axis will be denoted by a double subscript, that is,

$$\mathbf{r}_{12} = \mathbf{r}_2' = \mathbf{r}_2 - \mathbf{r}_1.  \tag{2.16}$$

In order to make the analysis clear, let only the $x$ component equation

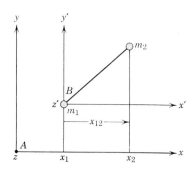

FIGURE 2.2    A translation in space.

be considered.   It is therefore desirable to obtain an expression for the acceleration of body 2 with respect to body 1, that is,

$$\frac{d^2 x_{12}}{dt^2}.$$

From Eq. 2.16,

$$x_{12} = x_2 - x_1,\tag{2.17}$$

or differentiating twice with respect to time,

$$\frac{d^2 x_{12}}{dt^2} = \frac{d^2 x_2}{dt^2} - \frac{d^2 x_1}{dt^2},\tag{2.18}$$

which is the desired expression for the acceleration of body 2 with respect to body 1.   It only remains to write the expression for $d^2 x_2/dt^2$ from Eq. 2.15, that is,

$$m_2 \frac{d^2 x_2}{dt^2} = k^2 \sum_{\substack{j=1 \\ j \neq 2}}^{n} m_2 m_j \frac{x_{2j}}{r_{2j}{}^3} + m_2 \Sigma_{x2}.\tag{2.19}$$

Again, from Eq. 2.15 the acceleration $d^2 x_1/dt^2$ is given by

$$m_1 \frac{d^2 x_1}{dt^2} = k^2 \sum_{\substack{j=2 \\ j \neq 1}}^{n} m_1 m_j \frac{x_{1j}}{r_{1j}{}^3} + m_1 \Sigma_{x1}.\tag{2.20}$$

Both Eqs. 2.19 and 2.20 can be given the same lower summation index by extracting one term from each summation.   Therefore, these equations can be rewritten, after cancelling $m_2$ and $m_1$ from each equation, as

$$\frac{d^2 x_2}{dt^2} = k^2 m_1 \frac{x_{21}}{r_{21}{}^3} + k^2 \sum_{j=3}^{n} m_j \frac{x_{2j}}{r_{2j}{}^3} + \Sigma_{x2}\tag{2.21}$$

and

$$\frac{d^2x_1}{dt^2} = k^2 m_2 \frac{x_{12}}{r_{12}^3} + k^2 \sum_{j=3}^{n} m_j \frac{x_{1j}}{r_{1j}^3} + \Sigma_{x1}. \tag{2.22}$$

Evidently then, by virtue of Eq. 2.18 after subtracting Eq. 2.22 from Eq. 2.21, there results

$$\frac{d^2x_{12}}{dt^2} = k^2 m_1 \frac{x_{21}}{r_{21}^3} - k^2 m_2 \frac{x_{12}}{r_{12}^3}$$

$$+ k^2 \sum_{j=3}^{n} m_j \left( \frac{x_{2j}}{r_{2j}^3} - \frac{x_{1j}}{r_{1j}^3} \right) + \Sigma_{x2} - \Sigma_{x1}, \tag{2.23}$$

or since $x_{12} = -x_{21}$ and $r_{12} = r_{21}$,

$$\frac{d^2x_{12}}{dt^2} = -k^2(m_1 + m_2) \frac{x_{12}}{r_{12}^3}$$

$$+ k^2 \sum_{j=3}^{n} m_j \left( \frac{x_{2j}}{r_{2j}^3} - \frac{x_{1j}}{r_{1j}^3} \right) + \Sigma_{x2} - \Sigma_{x1}. \tag{2.24}$$

The other two components of acceleration are handled in the same way. Therefore, the vector equation for the motion of body 2 with respect to body 1 is

$$\frac{d^2\mathbf{r}_{12}}{dt^2} = -k^2(m_1 + m_2) \frac{\mathbf{r}_{12}}{r_{12}^3}$$

$$+ k^2 \sum_{j=3}^{n} m_j \left( \frac{\mathbf{r}_{2j}}{r_{2j}^3} - \frac{\mathbf{r}_{1j}}{r_{1j}^3} \right) + \Sigma_{r2} - \Sigma_{r1}. \tag{2.25}$$

It is perhaps beneficial to state again the meaning of all the variables and constants used in this equation. Hence, with respect to Eq. 2.25, the following associations can be made.

$k$   The gravitational constant. In this case a natural choice of $k$ would be the $k$ of the body to which motion is referred. Then it should be remembered that masses are measured as the ratio of each mass to the mass of the body to which motion is referred.

$m_j$   With $k$ chosen as above, this is the mass ratio of any mass to the mass of the body to which motion is referred, that is, normalized masses denoted by $m_j \doteq m_j/m_1$.

$n$   Number of bodies in the system.

1   Refers to the central body (origin).

2   Refers to the body under consideration.

$j$   Refers to the existing $j$th body in the system not counting body 1 or 2.

$\mathbf{r}_{2j}$   The distances between the $j$th body and the body under consideration.

$\mathbf{r}_{1j}$   The distances between the $j$th body and the central body (origin).

The distance $\mathbf{r}_{2j}$ may readily be obtained if it is realized that

$$\mathbf{r}_{2j} = \mathbf{r}_j - \mathbf{r}_2 = \mathbf{r}_{1j} - \mathbf{r}_{12}. \qquad (2.26)$$

*Illustrative Example*

As an illustration of the use of Eq. 2.25, the equations of motion of a spaceship moving about the Earth, including the perturbations of the Moon, Sun, and Jupiter will be developed.

Let the following be defined:

$m_1$ = mass of the Earth,

$m_2$ = mass of the spaceship,

$m_3$ = mass of the Moon,

$m_4$ = mass of the planet Jupiter,

$m_5$ = be the mass of the Sun.

Then, by means of Eq. 2.25 where the variables with subscripts 12, that is, $(\mathbf{r}_{12}, r_{12})$ are now simply replaced by $\mathbf{r}$ and $r$,

$$\frac{d^2\mathbf{r}}{dt^2} = -k^2(m_1 + m_2)\frac{\mathbf{r}}{r^3} + k^2 m_3\left(\frac{\mathbf{r}_{23}}{r_{23}{}^3} - \frac{\mathbf{r}_{13}}{r_{13}{}^3}\right)$$

$$+ k^2 m_4\left(\frac{\mathbf{r}_{24}}{r_{24}{}^3} - \frac{\mathbf{r}_{14}}{r_{14}{}^3}\right) + k^2 m_5\left(\frac{\mathbf{r}_{25}}{r_{25}{}^3} - \frac{\mathbf{r}_{15}}{r_{15}{}^3}\right). \qquad (2.27)$$

This embodies the three component equations of motion of the space vehicle. Note that $\sum_{ri}$ have been neglected in the illustration. A brief examination of Eq. 2.27 shows that the first term is the "two-body" term. The second term accounts for the effect of the Moon, the third for the effect of the planet Jupiter, and the last for the Sun. Inherent in the omission of the subscripts 12 is the assumption that it is understood that motion of the vehicle occurs in a coordinate system whose origin is the center of the Earth. The distances $\mathbf{r}_{23}$, $\mathbf{r}_{24}$, and $\mathbf{r}_{25}$, as noted by Eq. 2.26, can be obtained from the tables of the motion of the Moon, Jupiter, and the Sun about the Earth. From a computational standpoint, one can easily form

$$\mathbf{r}_{23} = \mathbf{r}_{13} - \mathbf{r}$$

$$\mathbf{r}_{24} = \mathbf{r}_{14} - \mathbf{r} \qquad (2.28)$$

$$\mathbf{r}_{25} = \mathbf{r}_{15} - \mathbf{r},$$

since the coordinates of the other bodies of the solar system usually are tabulated with respect to a specific body.

Numerically, therefore, if the position and velocity of the space vehicle $(\mathbf{r}, \dot{\mathbf{r}})$ are known at a specific time, an interpolation either on tapes or tables is performed, and the vectors

$$\mathbf{r}_{13}, \quad \mathbf{r}_{14}, \quad \mathbf{r}_{15},$$

that is, the distances between the Earth and Moon, the Earth and Jupiter, and the Earth and Sun, are obtained.    This in turn allows computation of

$$\mathbf{r}_{23}, \quad \mathbf{r}_{24}, \quad \mathbf{r}_{25}$$

by means of Eqs. 2.28.    These quantities along with the interpolated values are used to compute

$$r_{23}, \quad r_{13}, \quad r_{24}, \quad r_{14}, \quad r_{25}, \quad r_{15},$$

that is, the magnitudes of the radius vectors.    Finally, these variables, along with the masses of the respective bodies, are substituted into Eq. 2.27, and the three accelerations

$$\frac{d^2x}{dt^2}, \quad \frac{d^2y}{dt^2}, \quad \frac{d^2z}{dt^2}$$

are obtained.    Now a numerical integration yields the next point of the trajectory.

### 2.4   BARYCENTRIC FORM

### 2.4.1   Equations of motion referred to a barycentric coordinate system

In this form the equations of motion are referred to an origin that is defined as the barycenter (mass center) of the $n$-body system.    To be repetitive, motion is relative to the barycenter, not the central body. The utility of these equations is found in the fact that the trajectory of a particular space vehicle is, at certain positions, disturbed less if motion is referred to the barycenter.

A translation of coordinate frames from $A$ to $B$, as shown in Figure 2.3, is desired.

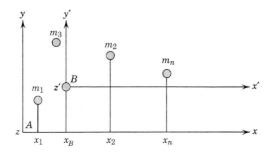

FIGURE 2.3   A translation to the barycenter of a number of bodies.

It should be noted that $B$ is the barycenter of the system of $m_n$ masses. The center of such a system is

$$\sum_{j=1}^{n} m_j \mathbf{r}_j = \sum_{j=1}^{n} m_j \mathbf{r}_B, \tag{2.29}$$

or writing each component of Eq. 2.29 and dividing, the coordinates of the barycenter become

$$x_B = \frac{\sum_{j=1}^{n} m_j x_j}{\sum_{j=1}^{n} m_j} \tag{2.30}$$

$$y_B = \frac{\sum_{j=1}^{n} m_j y_j}{\sum_{j=1}^{n} m_j} \tag{2.31}$$

$$z_B = \frac{\sum_{j=1}^{n} m_j z_j}{\sum_{j=1}^{n} m_j}. \tag{2.32}$$

Naturally, the radius to the barycenter is given by

$$r_B^2 = x_B^2 + y_B^2 + z_B^2. \tag{2.33}$$

In order to be consistent with the previous section, let the subscript 2 represent the body under study, that is, the space vehicle. Therefore, from the Figure 2.3, the $x$ component of distance from the space vehicle to the center of mass is given by

$$x_2' = x_{B2} = x_2 - x_B. \tag{2.34}$$

Thus, by differentiating Eq. 2.34 twice with respect to time, it is possible to write

$$\frac{d^2 x_{B2}}{dt^2} = \frac{d^2 x_2}{dt^2} - \frac{d^2 x_B}{dt^2}. \tag{2.35}$$

But the inertial equations of motion (2.15) yield for the $x$ component

$$m_2 \frac{d^2 x_2}{dt^2} = k^2 \sum_{\substack{j=1 \\ j \neq 2}}^{n} m_2 m_j \frac{x_{2j}}{r_{2j}^3} + m_2 \Sigma_{x2} \tag{2.36}$$

and

$$m_B \frac{d^2 x_B}{dt^2} = m_B \Sigma_{xB}. \tag{2.37}$$

Equation 2.37 is true by virtue of the fact that the barycenter experiences no accelerations from the other bodies. Only $\Sigma_{rB}$ terms cause motion.

By cancelling $m_2$ and $m_B$ and subtracting Eq. 2.37 from Eq. 2.36, the acceleration of the space vehicle with respect to the barycenter is obtained as

$$\frac{d^2 x_{B2}}{dt^2} = k^2 \sum_{\substack{j=1 \\ j \neq 2}}^{n} m_j \frac{x_{2j}}{r_{2j}^3} + \Sigma_{x2} - \Sigma_{xB} \tag{2.38}$$

or

$$\frac{d^2 x_{B2}}{dt^2} = -k^2 \sum_{\substack{j=1 \\ j \neq 2}}^{n} m_j \frac{x_{j2}}{r_{j2}^3} + \Sigma_{x2} - \Sigma_{xB}. \tag{2.39}$$

Furthermore, the distance between the space vehicle and the $j$th body is

$$x_{j2} = x_2 - x_j = x_{B2} - x_{Bj}, \tag{2.40}$$

which, upon multiplying by $m_j$, results in

$$m_j x_{j2} = m_j x_{B2} - m_j x_{Bj}, \tag{2.41}$$

so that upon summing both sides from 1 to $n$, the following relation is evident.

$$\sum_{\substack{j=1 \\ j \neq 2}}^{n} m_j x_{j2} = \sum_{j=1}^{n} m_j x_{j2} = \sum_{j=1}^{n} m_j x_{B2} - \sum_{j=1}^{n} m_j x_{Bj}, \tag{2.42}$$

where the left equality holds by virtue of the fact that $x_{22} = 0$. Now if it is noticed that

$$x_{Bj} = x_j - x_B, \tag{2.43}$$

upon substitution of this relation into the right side of Eq. 2.42,

$$\sum_{\substack{j=1 \\ j \neq 2}}^{n} m_j x_{j2} = \sum_{j=1}^{n} m_j x_{B2} - \sum_{j=1}^{n} m_j x_j + \sum_{j=1}^{n} m_j x_B, \tag{2.44}$$

where the last two summations on the right side cancel due to Eq. 2.30. Hence, it is seen that

$$\sum_{\substack{j=1 \\ j \neq 2}}^{n} m_j x_{j2} = \sum_{j=1}^{n} m_j x_{B2}. \tag{2.45}$$

It is now certainly possible to write the identity

$$k^2 \sum_{\substack{j=1 \\ j \neq 2}}^{n} m_j \frac{x_{j2}}{r_{B2}^3} - k^2 \sum_{j=1}^{n} m_j \frac{x_{B2}}{r_{B2}^3} = 0, \tag{2.46}$$

by transposing Eq. 2.45 and multiplying by $k^2/r_{B2}{}^3$. Therefore, by adding this identity to Eq. 2.39 and collecting terms, the equation of motion of the space vehicle with respect to the barycenter of the $n$-body system becomes

$$\frac{d^2 x_{B2}}{dt^2} = -k^2 \left[ \sum_{j=1}^{n} m_j \right] \frac{x_{B2}}{r_{B2}{}^3} + k^2 \sum_{\substack{j=1 \\ j \neq 2}}^{n} m_j x_{j2} \left( \frac{1}{r_{B2}{}^3} - \frac{1}{r_{j2}{}^3} \right)$$

$$+ \Sigma_{x2} - \Sigma_{xB}. \quad (2.47)$$

By repeating the analysis for the $y$ and $z$ variables, it is possible to verify that

$$\frac{d^2 \mathbf{r}_{B2}}{dt^2} = -k^2 \left[ \sum_{j=1}^{n} m_j \right] \frac{\mathbf{r}_{B2}}{r_{B2}{}^3} + k^2 \sum_{\substack{j=1 \\ j \neq 2}}^{n} m_j \mathbf{r}_{j2} \left( \frac{1}{r_{B2}{}^3} - \frac{1}{r_{j2}{}^3} \right)$$

$$+ \Sigma_{r2} - \Sigma_{rB}, \quad (2.48)$$

which is the complete vector equation of motion with the first term on the right side being in two-body form. Summarizing notation, the following associations may be made.

$k$    The gravitational constant. In this case it is perhaps convenient to use the value of $k$ for the Earth. Then, it should be remembered that masses are the ratios of the masses of all bodies to the mass of the Earth, e.g., $m_j \doteq m_j/m_e$.

$m_j$    With $k$ chosen as above, this is the mass ratio of any mass to the mass of the Earth, i.e., normalized masses denoted by $m_j \doteq m_j/m_e$.

$n$    Number of bodies in the system.

$2$    Refers to the body under consideration (space vehicle).

$j$    Refers to the existing $j$th body in the system not counting body 2.

$\mathbf{r}_{2j}$    The distances between the $j$th body and the body under consideration.

$\mathbf{r}_{B2}$    The distance between the barycenter and the body under consideration.

*Illustrative Example*

As an illustration of the use of Eq. 2.48 the equations of motion of a spaceship with respect to the barycenter of the Earth-Moon center will be developed.

Let the following be defined:

$m_2 = $ mass of the spaceship,

$m_1 = $ mass of the Earth,

$m_3 = $ mass of the Moon.

Then, by means of Eq. 2.48 where the variable with subscripts $B2$, that is, $(\mathbf{r}_{B2}, r_{B2})$ are now simply replaced by $\mathbf{r}$ and $r$

$$\frac{d^2\mathbf{r}}{dt^2} = -k^2[m_1 + m_2 + m_3]\frac{\mathbf{r}}{r^3} + k^2 m_1 \mathbf{r}_{12}\left(\frac{1}{r^3} - \frac{1}{r_{12}{}^3}\right)$$

$$+ k^2 m_3 \mathbf{r}_{32}\left(\frac{1}{r^3} - \frac{1}{r_{32}{}^3}\right). \quad (2.49)$$

Note that due to the omission of the perturbative $\sum$'s, that is, the last term of Eq. 2.48, there is no thrust, drag, etc.   Also, note that by dropping subscript $B2$, the fact is assumed that the coordinate frame has its origin at the barycenter.   Equation 2.49 embodies the three component equations of the motion of a spaceship relative to the barycenter of the Earth-Moon system.

The choice between which form, that is, relative or barycentric equations of motion, is used in a particular numerical situation depends upon the ratio of the perturbative accelerations.   Thus, if this ratio is denoted by $R_p$, where

$$R_p = \frac{k^2 \sum_{j=3}^{n} m_j \left(\dfrac{\mathbf{r}_{2j}}{r_{2j}{}^3} - \dfrac{\mathbf{r}_{1j}}{r_{1j}{}^3}\right) + \sum_{r2} - \sum_{r1}}{k^2 \sum_{\substack{j=1 \\ j \neq 2}}^{n} m_j \mathbf{r}_{j2}\left(\dfrac{1}{r_{B2}{}^3} - \dfrac{1}{r_{j2}{}^3}\right) + \sum_{r2} - \sum_{rB}}, \quad (2.50)$$

it suffices to say that $|R_p| > 1$ implies that the barycentric form should be used.

## 2.5  COMPENDIUM OF THE THREE BASIC EQUATIONS

### 2.5.1  The inertial, relative, and barycentric forms

For purposes of comparison and for future reference, the three previously developed forms of the equations of motion are listed as

*Inertial (coordinate frame fixed to an inertial origin)*

$$\frac{d^2\mathbf{r}_i}{dt^2} = k^2 \sum_{\substack{j=1 \\ i \neq j}}^{n} m_j \frac{\mathbf{r}_{ij}}{r_{ij}{}^3} + \sum_{ri} \quad (2.51)$$

It should be noticed that:

$$\mathbf{r}_{ij} = \mathbf{r}_j - \mathbf{r}_i.$$

*Relative (coordinate frame fixed to body 1)*

$$\frac{d^2\mathbf{r}}{dt^2} = -k^2(m_1 + m_2)\frac{\mathbf{r}}{r^3} + k^2 \sum_{j=3}^{n} m_j\left(\frac{\mathbf{r}_{2j}}{r_{2j}^3} - \frac{\mathbf{r}_{1j}}{r_{1j}^3}\right)$$
$$+ \Sigma_{r2} - \Sigma_{r1} \quad (2.52)$$

It should be noticed that

$$\mathbf{r}_{2j} = \mathbf{r}_j - \mathbf{r}_2$$
$$\mathbf{r}_{1j} = \mathbf{r}_j - \mathbf{r}_1$$
$$\mathbf{r} = \mathbf{r}_2 - \mathbf{r}_1,$$

where the subscript 2 refers to the body under consideration.

*Barycentric (coordinate frame fixed to the mass center of the system)*

$$\frac{d^2\mathbf{r}}{dt^2} = -k^2\left[\sum_{j=1}^{n} m_j\right]\frac{\mathbf{r}}{r^3} + k^2 \sum_{\substack{j=1 \\ j \neq 2}}^{n} m_j \mathbf{r}_{j2}\left(\frac{1}{r^3} - \frac{1}{r_{j2}^3}\right)$$
$$+ \Sigma_{r2} - \Sigma_{rB} \quad (2.53)$$

It should be noticed that

$$\mathbf{r}_{j2} = \mathbf{r}_2 - \mathbf{r}_j$$
$$\mathbf{r} = \mathbf{r}_2 - \mathbf{r}_B,$$

where the subscript $B$ denotes the barycenter of the system and 2 denotes the body under consideration.

## 2.6   REDUCTION OF THE EQUATIONS INTO THE TWO-BODY FORMS

### 2.6.1   The reduced relative and barycentric forms

Of paramount importance are the basic differential equations where only two bodies are considered in the analysis.   Thus, by neglecting all bodies where $j \geq 3$ and all other external perturbations, Eqs. 2.52 and 2.53 take the following forms.

*Relative form*

$$\frac{d^2\mathbf{r}}{dt^2} = -\mu k^2 \frac{\mathbf{r}}{r^3} \tag{2.54}$$

*Barycentric form*

$$\frac{d^2\mathbf{r}}{dt^2} = -\mu k^2 \frac{\mathbf{r}}{r^3} + m_1 k^2 \mathbf{r}_{12}\left(\frac{1}{r^3} - \frac{1}{r_{12}^3}\right) \tag{2.55}$$

It should be noticed that

$$\mu = (m_1 + m_2).$$

## 2.7   THE POTENTIAL OF A CENTRAL PLANET

### 2.7.1   Restatement of the reduced relative equations of motion

In this section, the reduced relative equations of motion, Eq. 2.54, will be slightly recast and written in terms of an auxiliary function.
   Consider the function defined by

$$V \equiv \frac{\mu k^2}{r} \tag{2.56}$$

with $r^2 = x^2 + y^2 + z^2$.   Partial differentiation of $V$, with respect to $\mathbf{r}$, results in

$$\frac{\partial V}{\partial x} = -\frac{\mu k^2}{r^2} \frac{\partial r}{\partial x}, \qquad \frac{\partial V}{\partial y} = -\frac{\mu k^2}{r^2} \frac{\partial r}{\partial y}, \qquad \frac{\partial V}{\partial z} = -\frac{\mu k^2}{r^2} \frac{\partial r}{\partial z}, \tag{2.57}$$

and since $\partial r/\partial x = x/r$, $\partial r/\partial y = y/r$, $\partial r/\partial z = z/r$, it is evident that

$$\frac{d^2 x}{dt^2} = \frac{\partial V}{\partial x}, \qquad \frac{d^2 y}{dt^2} = \frac{\partial V}{\partial y}, \qquad \frac{d^2 z}{dt^2} = \frac{\partial V}{\partial z}. \tag{2.58}$$

Apparently a knowledge of the function $V$ enables the two-body equations of motion[2] to be immediately written as

$$\frac{d^2 \mathbf{r}}{dt^2} = \nabla V. \tag{2.59}$$

The question which naturally arises involves an explanation of the physical significance of $V$.   To answer this question, it is necessary to introduce the concept of the *potential*.   From the statement of Newton's universal gravitational law, Eq. 2.1, the attraction of point mass $p_1$ on point mass $p$, Figure 2.4 is

$$F_1 = \frac{k^2 m_1 m}{r_{1p}{}^2},$$

[2] The function $V$, since it is explicitly free of velocity terms, that is, is only position dependent, is indicative of a conservative system.   Hence the work done in such a conservative system is independent of the path taken by the associated force.

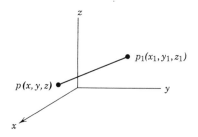

FIGURE 2.4    Attraction of two point masses.

with $r_{1p}^2 = (x_p - x_1)^2 + (y_p - y_1)^2 + (z_p - z_1)^2$. The force in the $x$ direction is given by Eq. 2.4.

$$F_{1x} = -\frac{k^2 m_1 m}{r_{1p}^2} \frac{\partial r_{1p}}{\partial x}, \tag{2.60}$$

or equivalently, the acceleration can be expressed as

$$\frac{F_{1x}}{m} = \frac{\partial}{\partial x}\left(\frac{k^2 m_1}{r_{1p}}\right). \tag{2.61}$$

If there are masses positioned at $p_1, p_2, \ldots p_n$, in a similar fashion, the total force in the $x$ direction is given by

$$F_x = m \frac{\partial}{\partial x}\left(\sum_1^n \frac{k^2 m_i}{r_{ip}}\right), \tag{2.62}$$

or in vector notation,

$$\frac{d^2 \mathbf{r}}{dt^2} = \frac{\mathbf{F}}{m} = \nabla U, \tag{2.63}$$

where

$$U \equiv \sum_1^n \frac{k^2 m_i}{r_{ip}}. \tag{2.64}$$

Equation 2.64 is defined as the *potential U* at $p$, arising from a system of point masses $m_1, m_2, \ldots m_n$. The potential at any point, $p(x, y, z)$, is therefore the scalar function whose partial derivatives, with respect to $x$, $y$, $z$, yield the components of acceleration on a particle of unit mass at $p$, by a system of $m_n$ masses located at $p_n$ points.

The system of $m_n$ point masses can be considered additively, and, in an infinite summation process, these points will form such objects as spheres and ellipsoids. It is now possible to recast the problem at

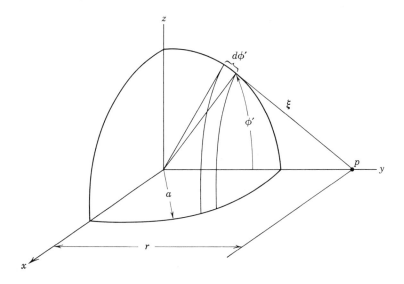

FIGURE 2.5 A quadrant of the Earth assuming a spherical model.

hand and ask for the potential function of a given solid body upon a particle exterior to the body.

Assume that the Earth, taken to be a sphere of radius $a$, is composed of a great number of uniform, thin, concentric shells of mass $\sigma$ per unit area. The thin annulus depicted in Figure 2.5 has a mass

$$m_1 = 2\pi a^2 \sigma \sin \phi' \, d\phi'. \tag{2.65}$$

The potential due to this mass at $p$ is given by definition (2.64) as [3]

$$dU_1 = \frac{2\pi k^2 a^2 \sigma \sin \phi' \, d\phi'}{\xi}$$

or

$$U_1 = 2\pi k^2 a^2 \sigma \int_0^\pi \frac{\sin \phi'}{\xi} \, d\phi'. \tag{2.66}$$

To evaluate the integral in Eq. 2.66, notice that

$$\xi^2 = a^2 + r^2 - 2ar \cos \phi', \tag{2.67}$$

[3] Because of symmetry, the analysis is not restricted by taking $p$ along the $y$ axis.

where $a$ and $r$ are constants. By differentiation, $\xi \, d\xi = ar \sin \phi' \, d\phi'$, so that

$$U_1 = 2\pi k^2 \sigma \frac{a}{r} \int_{\xi_1}^{\xi_2} d\xi = 2\pi k^2 \sigma \frac{a}{r} (\xi_2 - \xi_1). \tag{2.68}$$

To evaluate $\xi_2$ and $\xi_1$, notice that when $\phi' = 0$, $\xi_1 = r - a$, and when $\phi' = \pi$, $\xi_2 = r + a$, so that

$$U_1 = 2\pi k^2 \sigma \frac{a}{r} (2a). \tag{2.69}$$

Now, since the mass of this shell, call it $m_1$, is $4\pi a^2 \sigma$,

$$U_1 = \frac{k^2 m_1}{r}. \tag{2.70}$$

Adding up all the shells and utilizing definition (2.64),

$$U = \frac{k^2 m}{r}, \tag{2.71}$$

with $m$ defined as the total mass of the sphere. The original question, asking the physical significance of $V$, can now be answered in the following manner. $V$ is the potential function of a sphere whose mass $m$ has been augmented by the mass of the satellite $m_s$, that is,

$$V \equiv \frac{k^2 (m + m_s)}{r}. \tag{2.72}$$

Usually, in limiting cases, $m_s$ is assumed to be zero, with very little error.

To recapitulate, if the potential of a given solid body is known, the equations of motion are obtained by taking the partial derivatives of $V$, with respect to $x$, $y$, $z$. In short, the fundamental relative form is given directly from the scalar function $V$ as

$$\frac{d^2 \mathbf{r}}{dt^2} = \nabla \left( \frac{k^2 \mu}{r} \right) = \nabla(V). \tag{2.73}$$

Therefore, in the language of vector notation, the acceleration vector of a body moving about a central planet is equal to the gradient of the potential $V$.

### 2.7.2  The potential of an aspherical Earth

In the previous section, the equations of motion of a body were written in terms of a spherical or *central force field*. Frequently, it suffices to know the position of particle in order to determine the acting force, or forces. The force **F** is then a vector point function **F(r)**, which is associated with a field of force. Owing to the fact that the Earth is *aspherical* or nonsymmetric, it has a tendency to produce a noncentral force field. If it is desired to write the equations of motion of a body in a noncentral force field, the potential of the aspherical body, or in brief, an aspherical potential, must be determined.

Proceeding along the same lines of reasoning that enabled the determination of a spherical potential in Section 2.7.1, it is possible to develop the aspherical potential $\Phi$ as

$$
\begin{aligned}
\Phi = \frac{k^2 m}{r} \Bigg[ &1 + \frac{J_2}{2r^2}\,(1 - 3\sin^2 \delta) \\
&+ \frac{J_3}{2r^3}\,(3 - 5\sin^2 \delta)\sin \delta \\
&- \frac{J_4}{8r^4}\,(3 - 30\sin^2 \delta + 35\sin^4 \delta) \\
&- \frac{J_5}{8r^5}\,(15 - 70\sin^2 \delta + 63\sin^4 \delta)\sin \delta \\
&+ \frac{J_6}{16r^6}\,(5 - 105\sin^2 \delta + 315\sin^4 \delta - 231\sin^6 \delta) \\
&+ \epsilon \Bigg],
\end{aligned}
\tag{2.74}
$$

where the following associations are made.

$m$   The mass of the Earth (in Earth masses) $= 1$.

$k$   The gravitational constant.

$J_i$   Coefficient of the $i$th harmonic.

$\epsilon$   Terms of higher order.

The distance from the center of Earth to the vehicle is $r$, measured in e.r.,[4] and $\sin \delta \equiv z/r$. For explicit development of Eq. 2.74, the interested reader is directed to reference [2].

The $J$ coefficients are referred to as the first, second, etc., harmonics of the Earth's gravitational potential. The first harmonic has been eliminated from Eq. 2.74 by proper choice of coordinate origin. Values for the remaining harmonics are collected in Table 2.1. Coefficients adopted in Table 2.1 are extracted from reference [3]. As more accurate

---

[4] If canonical units are not used, care must be exercised to introduce $r/a_e$ for $r$, where $a_e$ is the Earth's equatorial radius.

data are collected, improved values for these coefficients will be determined. However, for most engineering applications, the values tabulated herein will suffice.

*Table 2.1   Coefficients of Earth's Gravitational Harmonics*

|       |                                    |
| ----- | ---------------------------------- |
| $J_2$ | $+ 1082.28 \pm 0.3 \times 10^{-6}$ |
| $J_3$ | $- \quad 2.3 \pm 0.2 \times 10^{-6}$ |
| $J_4$ | $- \quad 2.12 \pm 0.5 \times 10^{-6}$ |
| $J_5$ | $- \quad 0.2 \pm 0.1 \times 10^{-6}$ |
| $J_6$ | $+ \quad 1.0 \pm 0.8 \times 10^{-6}$ |

Equation 2.74 is actually a simplified model of the potential of the Earth.[5]   The departures, due to asymmetry from a concentrically homogeneous sphere, are of two kinds, *zonal departures* and *tesseral departures*. Zonal harmonics are due to meridian ellipticity, while tesseral harmonics are due to longitudinal variations in the shape of the Earth. Only zonal harmonics are present in the mathematical model proposed by Eq. 2.74. This model is frequently adopted and forms a very useful analytical reference model. It is the model usually adopted in *general perturbation techniques* (Chapter 10).

Evidently, from Section 2.7.1, since   $d^2\mathbf{r}/dt^2 = \nabla\Phi$, and by direct differentiation of Eq. 2.74, that is,

$$
\begin{aligned}
\frac{\partial \Phi}{\partial x} = -\frac{k^2 mx}{r^3} \Bigg[ & 1 + \frac{3}{2}\frac{J_2}{r^2}(1 - 5\sin^2\delta) \\
& + \frac{5}{2}\frac{J_3}{r^3}(3 - 7\sin^2\delta)\sin\delta \\
& - \frac{5}{8}\frac{J_4}{r^4}(3 - 42\sin^2\delta + 63\sin^4\delta) \\
& - \frac{3}{8}\frac{J_5}{r^5}(35 - 210\sin^2\delta + 231\sin^4\delta)\sin\delta \\
& + \frac{1}{16}\frac{J_6}{r^6}(35 - 945\sin^2\delta \\
& \qquad\qquad + 3465\sin^4\delta - 3003\sin^6\delta)\Bigg] \quad (2.75)
\end{aligned}
$$

[5] The same potential function applies to any oblate planet with different $J$ coefficients.

$$\frac{\partial \Phi}{\partial y} = y\left(\frac{1}{x}\frac{\partial \Phi}{\partial x}\right) \tag{2.76}$$

$$\frac{\partial \Phi}{\partial z} = -\frac{k^2 mz}{r^3}\left[1 + \frac{3}{2}\frac{J_2}{r^2}(3 - 5\sin^2 \delta)\right.$$

$$+ \frac{5}{2}\frac{J_3}{r^3}(6 - 7\sin^2 \delta)\sin \delta$$

$$- \frac{5}{8}\frac{J_4}{r^4}(15 - 70\sin^2 \delta + 63\sin^4 \delta)$$

$$- \frac{3}{8}\frac{J_5}{r^5}(105 - 315\sin^2 \delta + 231\sin^4 \delta)\sin \delta$$

$$+ \frac{1}{16}\frac{J_6}{r^6}(245 - 2205\sin^2 \delta$$

$$\left. + 4851\sin^4 \delta - 3003\sin^6 \delta)\right]$$

$$+ \frac{k^2 m}{r^2}\left[\frac{3}{2}\frac{J_3}{r^3} - \frac{15}{8}\frac{J_5}{r^5}\right], \tag{2.77}$$

the equations of motion for a satellite about an oblate planet become

$$\frac{d^2\mathbf{r}}{dt^2} \equiv \begin{bmatrix} \dfrac{d^2x}{dt^2} \\[2mm] \dfrac{d^2y}{dt^2} \\[2mm] \dfrac{d^2z}{dt^2} \end{bmatrix} = \begin{bmatrix} \dfrac{\partial \Phi}{\partial x} \\[2mm] \dfrac{\partial \Phi}{\partial y} \\[2mm] \dfrac{\partial \Phi}{\partial z} \end{bmatrix} \equiv \nabla \Phi. \tag{2.78}$$

It should be clear that Eqs. 2.78 assume that the mass of the satellite is negligible compared to the mass of the primary.

*Illustrative Example*
Write the equations of motion of a satellite moving about an aspherical Earth with the Moon's influence (as a point mass) taken into account.
    Let the following definitions be made:
$\mu = m_1 + m_2 = $ sum of masses of Earth and satellite,
$m_3 = $ mass of the Moon.
Equation 2.52 can then be conveniently rewritten as

$$\frac{d^2\mathbf{r}}{dt^2} = -k^2\mu\frac{\mathbf{r}}{r^3} + k^2 m_3\left(\frac{\mathbf{r}_{23}}{r_{23}{}^3} - \frac{\mathbf{r}_{13}}{r_{13}{}^3}\right),$$

or in terms of the two-body potential $V$,

$$\frac{d^2\mathbf{r}}{dt^2} = \nabla V + k^2 m_3\left(\frac{\mathbf{r}_{23}}{r_{23}{}^3} - \frac{\mathbf{r}_{13}}{r_{13}{}^3}\right).$$

Hence, to include the effects of an aspherical Earth, $V$ is replaced by $\Phi$, that is, the aspherical potential, so that

$$\frac{d^2\mathbf{r}}{dt^2} = \nabla\Phi + k^2 m_3 \left( \frac{\mathbf{r}_{23}}{r_{23}{}^3} - \frac{\mathbf{r}_{13}}{r_{13}{}^3} \right).$$

It should be noticed that if the mass of the Earth $m_1$ is taken as unity, then $m_3$ is the ratio of the mass of the Moon to the mass of the Earth $\approx 1/81.3$. Note also that the mass of the satellite, or $m_2/m_1$, is neglected in the above equation.

### 2.8  THRUST AND DRAG EFFECTS

### 2.8.1  The effect of thrust

So far, in the analysis of the trajectory equations only effects of distant bodies, and spherical or aspherical primary bodies, have played a dominant role. The effects of thrust, when a space craft is undergoing a powered flight arc, are extremely important. In fact, depending on the power generated by the propulsive system, it may well be the case that thrusting force is the dominant perturbation acting on the vehicle. Thrusting forces can be conveniently included in the last term of Eq. 2.14, that is, the additional perturbative effects, denoted by $\sum_{ri}$. Thrust perturbations will be denoted by the symbol $\sum_{T}$. For the purposes of discussion herein, the variation of thrust as a function of time, if any, is assumed to be known. Thrust variations are caused by vehicle staging, in-flight power up rating, or internal effects on the propulsion system caused by external accelerations. If there are existing thrust variations, usually accompanying in-flight propellant flow-rate variations will also be present. Hence it will also be assumed herein that the mass flow rate $dm/dt$ of a given rocket configuration or stage is known as a function of time. In functional notation,

$$T = T(t)$$

$$\frac{dm}{dt} = \frac{dm}{dt}(t),$$

(2.79)

where $T$ is the thrust and $dm/dt$ is the vehicle flow rate.

From the statement of Newton's second law, it is possible to write

$$\frac{d^2\mathbf{r}_T}{dt^2} = \frac{\mathbf{T}(t)}{m_v},$$

(2.80)

where $m_v$ is the vehicle mass computed from

$$m_v = m_0 - \int_{t_0}^{t_v} \frac{dm}{dt}(t)\, dt \tag{2.81}$$

with

$m_0$ = the vehicle gross or total mass before thrusting,
$t_0$ = the initial thrusting time.

The magnitude of the thrust vector $T$ is obtained by solution of propulsion system equations [9]. The conversion of the scalar ratio $T/m$ into canonical units can be effected easily by the relationship

$$\frac{T}{m}\left(\frac{\text{e.r.}}{\text{min}^2}\right) = \frac{T(\text{lbs})}{m(\text{slugs})} \times \frac{60^2}{a_e(\text{ft})}. \tag{2.82}$$

As should be evident, the thrust vector direction is usually defined by a set of angles relative to a coordinate system fixed to the vehicle, and therefore several coordinate rotations must be performed to resolve **T** along the $x$, $y$, and $z$ directions. Examination of Figure 2.6 will be beneficial in the analysis to be developed herein.

The coordinate rotations will be developed in this section by projective principles. At a later point (Chapters 3 and 4), the reader will see how these rotations can be effected easily with the aid of matrix analysis. However, for the present, a direct explicit development utilizing projective principles, will be undertaken.

Consider first the orthogonal coordinate system defined by $c_1$, $c_2$, $c_3$, with origin at the exhaust exit plane of the space vehicle. The unit vector $c_2$ is taken as pointing in a positive direction, forward along the vehicle centerline. To fix this coordinate system relative to the space vehicle, imagine that $c_1$ passes through some arbitrary reference point on the vehicle's surface, perpendicular to the centerline. The last unit vector $c_3$ is taken so that $c_1$, $c_2$, $c_3$ form a right-handed system. The direction of the thrust vector can now be defined by the gimbal or thrust vector alignment angles $\psi_1$ and $\psi_2$ (Figure 2.6). Hence $\psi_1$ is the angle measured from the vehicle centerline to the thrust vector, with range $0 \le \psi_1 \le \pi$, while $\psi_2$ is the angle measured from $c_1$ between $c_1$ and the projection of **T** in the $c_1 c_3$ plane, with range $0 \le \psi_2 \le 2\pi$. Immediately, the components of **T** along $c_1$, $c_2$, and $c_3$ are given by

$$\begin{aligned}
T_{c1} &= T \sin \psi_1 \cos \psi_2, \\
T_{c2} &= T \cos \psi_1, \\
T_{c3} &= T \sin \psi_1 \sin \psi_2.
\end{aligned} \tag{2.83}$$

It should be noticed that if $\psi_1 = 0$, thrusting is along the vehicle centerline.

Usually as a vehicle moves through space, it has a tendency to roll

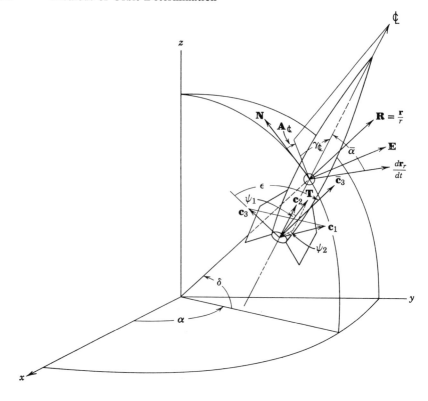

FIGURE 2.6   Space vehicle executing a thrusting arc.

along its longitudinal axis of symmetry. Consider that the missile has rolled over through an angle $\epsilon$, measured clockwise as seen from the thrust chamber, from the original reference point defined by $c_3$ (Figure 2.6), that is, $\epsilon$ is the angle of rotation of $c_3$ out of the northeast plane, measured in a plane perpendicular to the vehicle centerline. More explicitly, looking into the vehicle thrust chamber as depicted in Figure 2.7, it is evident that a rotation perpendicular to the missile axis must be performed. The following transformation from the $c_1$, $c_2$, $c_3$ to the $\bar{c}_1$, $\bar{c}_2$, $\bar{c}_3$ system is directly written as

$$\bar{T}_{c1} = T_{c1} \cos \epsilon - T_{c3} \sin \epsilon,$$
$$\bar{T}_{c2} = T_{c2},$$
$$\bar{T}_{c3} = T_{c3} \cos \epsilon + T_{c1} \sin \epsilon.$$

(2.84)

Evidently, if $\epsilon$ and $d\epsilon/dt$ are zero, the missile experiences no roll.

The orientation of the missile centerline can be conveniently defined herein by the angles $A_{\text{¢}}$ and $\gamma_{\text{¢}}$, that is, the *azimuth* and *elevation* angles

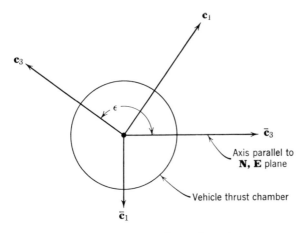

FIGURE 2.7   Roll transformation.

of the vehicle centerline.   If desired, these angles can be translated to the standard *yaw* and *pitch* angles of guidance analysis.   Since $A_{\mathbb{C}}$ and $\gamma_{\mathbb{C}}$ are more intuitively appealing than yaw and pitch, the analysis will develop the thrust transformation using these angles.   In essence, as will be discussed further in Chapter 4, azimuth is the instantaneous angle of (in this case) the vehicle centerline measured from the north, while elevation is the instantaneous angle of the centerline above or below a plane perpendicular to $\mathbf{r}$, the radius vector.   The ranges are usually taken as $0 \leq A_{\mathbb{C}} \leq 2\pi$, $-\pi/2 < \gamma_{\mathbb{C}} < \pi/2$.

With the assistance of Figure 2.8, the components of thrust in the

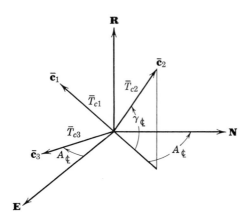

FIGURE 2.8   Superposition of the **E, N, R** and $\bar{\mathbf{c}}_1$, $\bar{\mathbf{c}}_2$, $\bar{\mathbf{c}}_3$ coordinate systems.

$\bar{c}_1, \bar{c}_2, \bar{c}_3$ system can be resolved into the north, east, and radial directions. Hence a first rotation about $\mathbf{R}$, assuming $\mathbf{R}$ and $\bar{c}_2$ as coincident, through the angle $A_{\mathbb{C}}$ and then a second rotation about $\bar{c}_3$, contained in the $\mathbf{E}$, $\mathbf{N}$ plane up through an angle $\gamma_{\mathbb{C}}$ will yield

$$T_E = -\bar{T}_{c1} \sin \gamma_{\mathbb{C}} \sin A_{\mathbb{C}} + \bar{T}_{c2} \cos \gamma_{\mathbb{C}} \sin A_{\mathbb{C}} + \bar{T}_{c3} \cos A_{\mathbb{C}}$$

$$T_N = -\bar{T}_{c1} \sin \gamma_{\mathbb{C}} \cos A_{\mathbb{C}} + \bar{T}_{c2} \cos \gamma_{\mathbb{C}} \cos A_{\mathbb{C}} - \bar{T}_{c3} \sin A_{\mathbb{C}} \qquad (2.85)$$

$$T_R = +\bar{T}_{c1} \cos \gamma_{\mathbb{C}} \qquad\qquad + \bar{T}_{c2} \sin \gamma_{\mathbb{C}}.$$

The $\mathbf{E}$, $\mathbf{N}$, $\mathbf{R}$ coordinate system can be finally rotated into the $x$, $y$, $z$ system by

$$T_x = -T_E \sin \alpha - T_N \sin \delta \cos \alpha + T_R \cos \delta \cos \alpha,$$

$$T_y = \quad T_E \cos \alpha - T_N \sin \delta \sin \alpha + T_R \cos \delta \sin \alpha, \qquad (2.86)$$

$$T_z = \qquad\qquad\qquad T_N \cos \delta \quad + T_R \sin \delta,$$

where $\alpha$ is the *right ascension* with range $0 \le \alpha \le 2\pi$, and $\delta$ is the *declination* with range $-\pi/2 \le \delta \le \pi/2$. Note that $\sum_{\mathbf{T}} = \mathbf{T}/m_v$.

*Illustrative Example*
Obtain the final rotation equations of the thrust transformation.

The first step is drawing a good illustration, for example, the following figure.

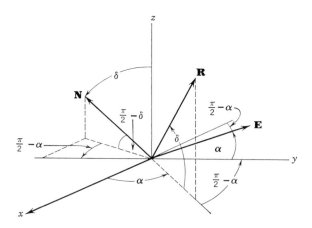

Next, consider the summation of all the projections in the positive sense along the $x$ axis. Therefore, components along $\mathbf{E}$ contribute $-T_E \cos$

$(\pi/2 - \alpha)$, or $-T_E \sin \alpha$, components along $N$ contribute $-T_N \sin \delta \cos \alpha$. Finally, the radial contribution is $T_R \cos \delta \cos \alpha$ so that

$$T_x = -T_E \sin \alpha - T_N \sin \delta \cos \alpha + T_R \cos \delta \cos \alpha,$$

the other components are obtained in a similar manner.

The reader may be puzzled by the barrage of angles required to determine completely the attitude and position of a missile in space. To be concise, the functional equation for thrust components along the axes of the $x$, $y$, $z$ coordinate system is

$$\mathbf{T}_i = \mathbf{T}_i\left(T, \frac{dm}{dt}, \psi_1, \psi_2, \epsilon, A_{\mathcal{C}}, \gamma_{\mathcal{C}}, \alpha, \delta\right). \tag{2.87}$$

The gimbal angles $\psi_1$ and $\psi_2$ are the thrust vector control-driving functions, and are preprogrammed or input by the spacecraft pilot for purposes of maneuvering. Vehicle roll and attitude are determined by $\epsilon$, $A_{\mathcal{C}}$, $\gamma_{\mathcal{C}}$. In general, these angles are uniquely determined as functions of time by solution of the rotational differential equations of motion, that is, differential equations for $d\epsilon/dt$, $dA_{\mathcal{C}}/dt$, $d\gamma_{\mathcal{C}}/dt$ derivable in essence from the angular form of Newton's second law.

For purposes of simplification, the analysis developed herein will not consider the effects of rotation upon the given space vehicle. By suitable choice of angles $\epsilon$, $A_{\mathcal{C}}$, and $\gamma_{\mathcal{C}}$, the equations of motion will be reduced to the usual three-dimensional equations of trajectory analysis. In these equations, the azimuth of the missile centerline $A_{\mathcal{C}}$ is taken to be the azimuth of the relative velocity vector $d\mathbf{r}_r/dt$. The *relative velocity vector* is the velocity vector that is observed when the rotation of the planet is subtracted from the inertial velocity vector. For an explicit formula, see Eq. 2.98. Furthermore, the elevation angle of the centerline $\gamma_{\mathcal{C}}$ is taken to be the elevation angle of the relative velocity vector plus the *angle of attack*, $\bar{\alpha}$, Figure 2.9. Vehicle angle of attack is the angle between the relative velocity vector and the missile centerline. The roll angle $\epsilon$ is taken to be zero. Symbolically, motion is constrained by the equations

$$\epsilon = 0, \qquad A_{\mathcal{C}} = A_r, \qquad \gamma_{\mathcal{C}} = \bar{\alpha} + \gamma_r, \tag{2.88}$$

where, by projection of $d\mathbf{r}/dt$ on the plane defined by $N$, $E$ of Figure 2.6,

$$A = \tan^{-1}\left[\frac{r\left(x\dfrac{dy}{dt} - \dfrac{dx}{dt}y\right)}{y\left(\dfrac{dz}{dt}y - z\dfrac{dy}{dt}\right) - x\left(\dfrac{dx}{dt}z - x\dfrac{dz}{dt}\right)}\right], \quad 0 \leq A \leq 2\pi \tag{2.89}$$

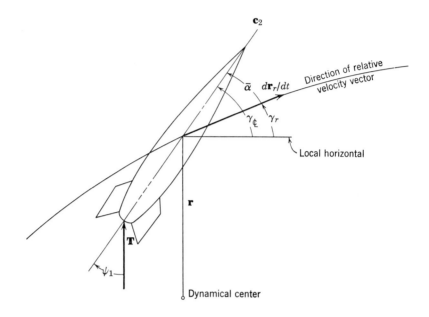

FIGURE 2.9    Planor vehicle dynamics.

with the quadrant of $A$ uniquely defined by examination of the numerator and denominator of the arc tangent. Also, from the dot product of $\mathbf{r}$ and $d\mathbf{r}/dt$, the inclination of the velocity vector is given by

$$
\gamma = \sin^{-1}\left[ \frac{x\dfrac{dx}{dt} + y\dfrac{dy}{dt} + z\dfrac{dz}{dt}}{r\left\{ \left(\dfrac{dx}{dt}\right)^2 + \left(\dfrac{dy}{dt}\right)^2 + \left(\dfrac{dz}{dt}\right)^2 \right\}^{\frac12}} \right], \qquad -\frac{\pi}{2} \le \gamma \le \frac{\pi}{2}. \quad (2.90)
$$

It should be noticed that $A_r$ and $\gamma_r$, as used in Eqs. 2.88 are obtained from Eqs. 2.89 and 2.90 with $dx_r/dt$, $dy_r/dt$, $dz_r/dt$ replacing $dx/dt$, $dy/dt$, $dz/dt$.

The angle of attack $\bar{\alpha}$ as a function of time, or angle of attack history, is always an input which has been preprogrammed for a given mission. Hence, the control or driving functions in the constrained three-dimensional case are $\psi_1$ and $\bar{\alpha}$. If these angles are not chosen randomly, they are at times mathematically determined from variational principles (references [5] and [6]) in order to maximize or minimize a certain objective, such as range or payload, etc. A trajectory satisfying $\bar{\alpha} = 0$ over the given coasting or thrusting arc is referred to as a "zero-g" trajectory.

The reader should notice that, with the above restrictions,

$$\mathbf{T}_i = \mathbf{T}_i\!\left(T, \frac{dm}{dt}, \mathbf{r}, \frac{d\mathbf{r}}{dt}, \bar{\alpha}, \psi_1\right), \tag{2.91}$$

since $\alpha$ and $\delta$ are always directly obtained in terms of the rectangular geocentric coordinates as

$$\sin \alpha = \frac{y}{\sqrt{x^2 + y^2}}, \qquad \cos \alpha = \frac{x}{\sqrt{x^2 + y^2}}, \quad 0 \le \alpha \le 2\pi,$$

$$\sin \delta = \frac{z}{\sqrt{x^2 + y^2 + z^2}} = \frac{z}{r}, \quad -\frac{\pi}{2} \le \delta \le \frac{\pi}{2}. \tag{2.92}$$

### 2.8.2   The effects of drag and lift

As a body moves through a viscous medium, it experiences a *drag* force. By the methods of dimensional analysis [7], it can be shown that

$$D = \tfrac{1}{2}C_D \rho A V_r^2, \tag{2.93}$$

where $D$ = drag force magnitude,
$\quad C_D$ = dimensionless empirical drag coefficient,
$\quad \rho$ = density of the resisting medium,
$\quad A$ = cross-sectional area exposed to the resisting medium,
$\quad V_r$ = relative velocity magnitude between the moving body and resisting medium.

Usually,

$$D(\text{lbs}) = \tfrac{1}{2}\rho(\text{slugs/ft}^3)A(\text{ft}^2)C_D[V_r(\text{ft/sec})]^2 \tag{2.94}$$

with the resisting medium density, that is, atmospheric density, obtained directly as a function of height from standard atmospheric density tables or exponential models given in reference [5]. By Newton's second law, the drag acceleration is given by:

$$\frac{d^2\mathbf{r}_D}{dt^2} = \frac{\mathbf{D}}{m_v}, \tag{2.95}$$

with $m_v$ defined by Eq. 2.81. Equation 2.82, with $T$ replaced by $D$, yields the conversion to canonical units. The orientation of $\mathbf{D}$ will be taken up presently.

The difference in pressure on both sides of a body moving through a viscous medium also has a tendency to produce *lift* forces defined by

$$L = \tfrac{1}{2}C_L \rho A V_r^2, \tag{2.96}$$

where, along with the drag force definitions,

$L$ = lift force magnitude,

$C_L$ = dimensionless empirical lift coefficient.

Lift and drag forces are defined to be perpendicular to each other. Furthermore, if the planetary atmosphere is assumed to rotate with the parent planet, the relative velocity vector $d\mathbf{r}_r/dt$ is given by

$$\frac{d\mathbf{r}_r}{dt} = \frac{d\mathbf{r}}{dt} + \mathbf{r} \times \boldsymbol{\omega} = \begin{bmatrix} \dfrac{dx}{dt} + \omega y \\[2mm] \dfrac{dy}{dt} - \omega x \\[2mm] \dfrac{dz}{dt} \end{bmatrix}, \tag{2.97}$$

where $\boldsymbol{\omega}$ is the angular rotation vector of the Earth with magnitude $\omega$. To be perfectly general, if wind variations are to be included, the components of the relative velocity vector are to be augmented such that

$$\frac{dx_r}{dt} = \frac{dx}{dt} + \omega y + q(\cos \alpha \sin \delta \cos A_w + \sin \alpha \sin A_w)$$

$$\frac{dy_r}{dt} = \frac{dy}{dt} - \omega x + q(\sin \alpha \sin \delta \cos A_w + \cos \alpha \sin A_w) \tag{2.98}$$

$$\frac{dz_r}{dt} = \frac{dz}{dt} - q(\cos \delta \cos A_w),$$

where

$A_w$ = the azimuth angle of the wind,

$q$   = wind speed.

The wind parameters, $A_w$ and $q$, are obtained as tabulated quantities from "Sissenwine" wind tables [8], with argument $H$ defined as equal to $r - r_c$ (Eq. 1.38).

Knowing the relative velocity vector, a unit vector directly along $d\mathbf{r}_r/dt$ can be defined as

$$\mathbf{D}_r \equiv \frac{d\mathbf{r}_r}{dt} \bigg/ \sqrt{\left(\frac{dx_r}{dt}\right)^2 + \left(\frac{dy_r}{dt}\right)^2 + \left(\frac{dz_r}{dt}\right)^2} = \frac{1}{V_r}\frac{d\mathbf{r}_r}{dt}, \tag{2.99}$$

and the drag force, which is opposed to $d\mathbf{r}_r/dt$, can be resolved along the $x, y, z$ directions by

$$\mathbf{D} = -D\mathbf{D}_r \tag{2.100}$$

so that

$$\Sigma_{\mathbf{D}} = \frac{\mathbf{D}}{m_v},$$

(2.101)

where the magnitude of $D$ is evaluated with $\dfrac{d\mathbf{r}_r}{dt} \cdot \dfrac{d\mathbf{r}_r}{dt} = V_r^2$.

Resolution of the lift vector is a little more detailed. Consider a plane perpendicular to the relative velocity unit vector $\mathbf{D}_r$, defined by Eq. 2.99. A unit vector in this plane, wherein the lift force is acting, can be written as

$$\mathbf{L}_1 = \frac{\mathbf{D}_r \times (\mathbf{r} \times \mathbf{D}_r)}{r},$$

(2.102)

Since this unit vector is well defined as a function of the trajectory parameters, it is a convenient direction from which to reference the lift vector. The angle between $L_1$ and $L$ is called the angle of *bank*, denoted by $\beta$ (Figure 2.10).

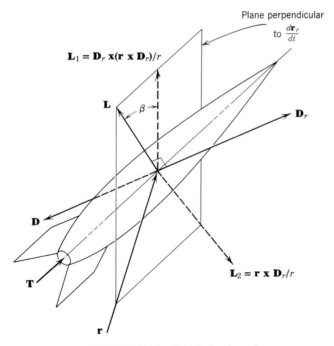

FIGURE 2.10   Vehicle bank angle.

A second unit vector can be taken in the $\mathbf{r} \times \mathbf{D}_r/r$ direction, call it $\mathbf{L}_2$, so that by resolving the lift vector along $\mathbf{L}_1$ and $\mathbf{L}_2$ directions, it is possible to write

$$\mathbf{L} = L(\mathbf{L}_1 \cos \beta + \mathbf{L}_2 \sin \beta), \tag{2.103}$$

so that

$$\Sigma_{\mathbf{L}} = \frac{\mathbf{L}}{m_v}, \tag{2.104}$$

where the magnitude of $\mathbf{L}$ is evaluated with $\dfrac{d\mathbf{r}_r}{dt} \cdot \dfrac{d\mathbf{r}_r}{dt} = V_r^2$. Assuming that the bank angle is zero will yield the lift perturbation $\Sigma_{\mathbf{L}}$ in the plane defined by $\mathbf{r}$ and $d\mathbf{r}/dt$.

### 2.8.3  Symbolic representation of the trajectory process

It may be helpful to quickly describe how the initial total acceleration vector $d^2\mathbf{r}/dt^2$ is computed. The reader should realize that for a given launch time, the initial conditions, that is, $\mathbf{r}_L$, $d\mathbf{r}_L/dt$ of a given vehicle are known. To be specific, the position vector of a vehicle is nothing more than the corresponding station coordinates (Section 3.11), resolved through the angle $\theta$, functionally dependent upon the universal time of launch and east longitude $\lambda_E$, into the inertial geocentric right ascension-declination coordinate frame. In other words, the vehicle is standing on a given launch pad with coordinates $\phi$ and $\lambda_E$ so that

$$\begin{aligned}
x_L &= G_1 \cos \phi \cos \theta \\
y_L &= G_1 \cos \phi \sin \theta \\
z_L &= G_2 \sin \phi,
\end{aligned} \tag{2.105}$$

and by direct differentiation,

$$\begin{aligned}
\frac{dx_L}{dt} &= -G_1 \cos \phi \sin \theta \frac{d\theta}{dt} \\
\frac{dy_L}{dt} &= +G_1 \cos \phi \cos \theta \frac{d\theta}{dt} \\
\frac{dz_L}{dt} &= 0,
\end{aligned} \tag{2.106}$$

where the subscript $L$ denotes initial launch conditions. Furthermore, since the launch time is known, an interpolation into magnetic tapes containing the positions of the neighboring planets will yield the planetary perturbations, that is, determination of the second term of Eq. 2.52.

The next step is the computation of $\sum_T$, $\sum_D$, and $\sum_L$.  First, the relative velocity vector $d\mathbf{r}_r/dt$ is computed through Eqs. 2.98, where $\mathbf{r}$, $d\mathbf{r}/dt$ are replaced by $\mathbf{r}_L$, $d\mathbf{r}_L/dt$ and $D$, $L$ (the drag and lift magnitudes) evaluated through Eqs. 2.93 and 2.96.  Equations 2.101 and 2.104 immediately yield the drag and lift perturbations in the $x$, $y$, $z$ coordinate system. The thrust vector is computed by Eqs. 2.86, where $\alpha$ and $\delta$ are known in terms of the rectangular coordinates, Eqs. 2.92.  Essentially then, restricting perturbative effects to the primary body, planetary influences, thrust, drag and lift, the total acceleration is given by

$$\frac{d^2\mathbf{r}}{dt^2} = \nabla\Phi + \sum_P + \sum_T + \sum_D + \sum_L, \tag{2.107}$$

where $\nabla\Phi$ can be directly determined from the initial position of the vehicle, $\mathbf{r}_L$, and $\sum_P$ denotes the planetary perturbations.  The reader should grasp the fact that $d^2\mathbf{r}/dt^2$ is numerically known.  This acceleration vector is numerically integrated to yield the next trajectory point.

It is not within the domain of this text to enter into the vast field of numerical integration.  There are many methods available for proceeding from acceleration to velocity and finally position.  The following method, though not very sophisticated, will serve to demonstrate the numerical integration process.

Imagine that the initial position and launch velocity are known, for example, in an inertial frame.  In other words, the ground position along with the direction and magnitude of the Earth's velocity, $(\mathbf{r})_L$, $(d\mathbf{r}/dt)_L$ are numerically known.  Hence, over a small interval of time $\Delta t$, where $(d^2\mathbf{r}/dt^2)$ does not vary appreciably, the velocity at the $i$th $+ 1$ integration interval is given by

$$\left(\frac{d\mathbf{r}}{dt}\right)_{i+1} = \left(\frac{d\mathbf{r}}{dt}\right)_i + \left(\frac{d^2\mathbf{r}}{dt^2}\right)_i \Delta t, \qquad i = L, 1, 2, \ldots N. \tag{2.108}$$

Since $(d\mathbf{r}/dt)_i$, $(d^2\mathbf{r}/dt^2)_i$ are known, and $\Delta t$ is small, say a second or two, the velocity at the next step is approximated numerically by $(d\mathbf{r}/dt)_{i+1}$. Notice that

$$(\mathbf{r})_{i+1} = (\mathbf{r})_i + \left(\frac{d\mathbf{r}}{dt}\right)_i \Delta t \tag{2.109}$$

approximates the position $\Delta t$ time units later.

Now with the estimates $(\mathbf{r})_{i+1}$, $(d\mathbf{r}/dt)_{i+1}$, return to Eq. 2.107 and numerically calculate $(d^2\mathbf{r}/dt^2)_{i+1}$ and compute

$$\left(\frac{d^2\mathbf{r}}{dt^2}\right)_m = \frac{1}{2}\left[\left(\frac{d^2\mathbf{r}}{dt^2}\right)_{i+1} + \left(\frac{d^2\mathbf{r}}{dt^2}\right)_i\right]. \tag{2.110}$$

Equation 2.110 provides for an approximate mean value of the acceleration over the interval $\Delta t$. To greater precision, it is possible to re-estimate $(d\mathbf{r}/dt)_{i+1}$ from

$$\left(\overline{\frac{d\mathbf{r}}{dt}}\right)_{i+1} = \left(\frac{d\mathbf{r}}{dt}\right)_i + \left(\frac{d^2\mathbf{r}}{dt^2}\right)_m \Delta t. \tag{2.111}$$

Next, the mean velocity over $\Delta t$ can be computed with the aid of

$$\left(\frac{d\mathbf{r}}{dt}\right)_m = \frac{1}{2}\left[\left(\overline{\frac{d\mathbf{r}}{dt}}\right)_{i+1} + \left(\frac{d\mathbf{r}}{dt}\right)_i\right], \tag{2.112}$$

and a re-estimate of the position obtained from

$$(\bar{\mathbf{r}})_{i+1} = (\mathbf{r})_i + \left(\frac{d\mathbf{r}}{dt}\right)_m \Delta t. \tag{2.113}$$

Finally, evaluate $(d^2\mathbf{r}/dt^2)_{i+1}$, that is, Eq. 2.107 with the latest values of $(\bar{\mathbf{r}})_{i+1}$ and $(\overline{d\mathbf{r}/dt})_{i+1}$. Return to Eq. 2.110 and repeat the above loop until the mean values of velocity and acceleration no longer vary. The integration has been carried forward one time step. Naturally, the newly obtained position and velocity at $t_{i+1} = t_i + \Delta t$ are the initial conditions for integrating forward the next step, etc.

The above method is due to Euler and is a direct application of the mean value theorem from the integral calculus. Hence

$$x_{i+1} = x_i + \int_{t_i}^{t_i+\Delta t} \left(\frac{dx}{dt}\right) dt$$

$$= x_i + \left(\frac{dx}{dt}\right)_m \Delta t,$$

where the $m$ subscript denotes some value of $(dx/dt)$ in the interval $t_i \leq t \leq t_i + \Delta t$. The above technique, even though simple, possesses the advantages of self-start, variable step size, and rapidity. However, other methods [11] are more accurate.

### 2.9  SUMMARY

A complete development of the inertial, relative, and barycentric equations of motion has been presented. Reduction of the equations to the fundamental forms has also been shown. The reduced equations are basic to the preliminary orbit determination process; the complete equations are fundamental to the differential correction process which will be introduced in a later chapter.

It was also shown how the concept of the potential of a primary body can be utilized to obtain the equations of motion about spherical and aspherical planets. With aid of a potential function, the analyst has the choice of introducing an aspherical model when a satellite is near the primary body, while distant disturbing planets are considered as point masses. Furthermore, simultaneous potentials of two disturbing aspherical planets can also be used to describe more accurately the trajectory process. In essence, any combination of aspherical potential functions and auxiliary point masses can be used in the determination of a highly accurate space trajectory.

The last part of this chapter developed the perturbations on a moving space vehicle, due to thrust, drag, and lift. In the equations developed herein, only effects of translation were fully developed. It has further been shown how an amalgamation of all the perturbative influences result in the general equations of motion with the effects of planetary influences, oblateness effects, thrust, drag, and lift, all contributing to the total acceleration vector. It is this acceleration vector that is numerically integrated to yield the next point of the trajectory.

**EXERCISES**

1. Why must $j \neq 1$ in Eq. 2.9?
2. Why is it convenient to segregate the two-body term in the general equations of motion?
3. Develop by means of the relative equations a mathematical solar system for the nine basic planets. Use a heliocentric system (origin at the center of the Sun) and vary the equations such that an ephemeris of the distances from the Sun to the planets is a direct input to the vector equation. Insert the appropriate masses and constants.
4. Consider a potential $\Phi$ defined by Eq. 2.74. Analytically verify the given expressions for $\partial\Phi/\partial x$, $\partial\Phi/\partial y$, $\partial\Phi/\partial z$.
5. What are the relative equations of motion of a spaceship moving about a nonspherical Moon with the Earth's influence taken into account? Assume the potential of the Moon $\Phi_m$ is known.
6. Given that the gravitational constant $G$ has been determined by experiments as $G = 6.673 \times 10^{-8}$ dyne-cm$^2$/gm$^2$, and that the mass of the Earth is $5.977 \times 10^{24}$ kg, what is an approximate value for $k_e^2$ in (e.r.)$^{3/2}$/min? Assume that 1 e.r. $= 6,378,175$ m.
7. If a 50,000-lb. rocket rises vertically and ejects 30,000 lb of propellant gas for 150 sec, with a relative velocity of 8,000 ft/sec, ignoring the effects of drag, lift, and gravitational variations, what is the burnout velocity in ft/sec? Assume that the gravitational acceleration $g$ is equal to 32.2 ft/sec$^2$.

**8.** Derive an expression for the azimuth $A$, of the velocity vector $d\mathbf{r}/dt$, as a function of $\mathbf{r}$ and $d\mathbf{r}/dt$. See Eq. 2.89.

**9.** Derive an expression for the flight path angle $\gamma$ of the velocity vector $d\mathbf{r}/dt$, as a function of $\mathbf{r}$ and $d\mathbf{r}/dt$. See Eq. 2.90.

## REFERENCES

1. F. R. Moulton, *An Introduction to Celestial Mechanics*, The Macmillan Company, New York, 1914.
2. D. Brouwer and G. M. Clemence, *Methods of Celestial Mechanics*, Academic Press, New York, 1961.
3. M. W. Makemson, R. L. M. Baker, Jr., and G. B. Westrom, "Analysis and Standardization of the Astrodynamic Constants," *Journal of the Astronautical Sciences*, Vol. III, No. 1, Spring 1961.
4. J. M. A. Danby, *Fundamentals of Celestial Mechanics*, The Macmillan Company, New York, 1962.
5. F. J. White, *Flight Performance Handbook for Powered Flight Operations*, John Wiley and Sons, New York, 1963.
6. J. V. Breakwell, "The Optimization of Trajectories," *Journal of the Society for Industrial and Applied Mathematics*, Vol. 7, No. 2, June 1959.
7. J. H. Dwinnel, *Principles of Aerodynamics*, McGraw-Hill Book Company, New York, 1949.
8. N. Sissenwine, "Wind Speed Profiles...for Vertically Rising Vehicles," *Air Force Surveys in Geophysics*, No. 57, 1954.
9. R. O. Chase and E. Wendorf, *Generalized Steady-State Rocket Engine Performance Equations and Algorithms of Solution*, Operations Research Inc. Technical Report No. 225, December 1963.
10. W. T. Thomson, *Introduction to Space Dynamics*, John Wiley and Sons, New York, 1961.
11. F. B. Hildebrand, *Introduction to Numerical Analysis*, McGraw-Hill Book Company, 1956.
12. A. Berry, *A Short History of Astronomy*, Dover Publications, New York, 1961.

# 3 The two-body problem

## 3.1 THE KEPLERIAN CONCEPT

### 3.1.1 Kepler's laws

Law    I. Within the domain of the solar system all planets describe elliptical paths with the Sun at one focus.

Law   II. The radius vector from the Sun to a planet generates equal areas in equal times.

Law  III. The squares of the periods of revolution of the planets about the Sun are proportional to the cubes of their mean distances from the Sun.

Apart from some nonsensical ideas about finding a relation between planetary bodies and music as proposed in *Harmony of the World*,[1] one is led to great admiration of the man Kepler who early in the seventeenth century empirically obtained his now famous three laws. One must remember Kepler's great difficulty in arriving at these laws without the overpowering help of Newton, who was still fifty years short of making his mark on the astronomical world. It was tedious work on Kepler's behalf, enhanced by the excellent astronomical observations of Tycho

---

[1] "The Earth sings the notes MI, FA, MI so that you may guess from them that in this abode of ours MIsery (miseria) and FAmine (fames) prevail" [10].

**67**

Brahe, that led to the formulation of the above three laws and it was Newton, by the introduction of law of gravitation, who demonstrated their amalgamation in his more general theory.

## 3.2 DIFFERENTIATION WITH RESPECT TO THE MODIFIED TIME VARIABLE

### 3.2.1   Modified time differentiation

Examination of the fundamental equation, Eq. 2.54, shows that it possesses the constant $k^2$, that is, the gravitational constant.   Simplification or elimination of this constant in most equations would be a desirable objective.   Consider the definition, Eq. 1.9,

$$\tau \equiv k(t - t_0),$$  (3.1)

along with the fundamental equation,

$$\frac{d^2\mathbf{r}}{dt^2} = -k^2\mu\,\frac{\mathbf{r}}{r^3},$$  (3.2)

and introduce the additional definition

$$\ddot{\mathbf{r}} \equiv \frac{d^2\mathbf{r}}{d\tau^2} = \frac{1}{k^2}\frac{d^2\mathbf{r}}{dt^2}.$$  (3.3)

It follows that the fundamental equation can be written as

$$\ddot{\mathbf{r}} = -\mu\,\frac{\mathbf{r}}{r^3},$$  (3.4)

in which $k^2$ is lacking.   Hence, in future analysis, the overhead dot will be used as a symbol for differentiation with respect to $\tau$, the modified time variable.   The symbol $d/dt$ will symbolize differentiation with respect to time, that is, ephemeris time (Section 1.3.4).   This will prove to be of great benefit in future analytic processes.

## 3.3   A NEWTONIAN ANALYSIS OF KEPLER'S LAWS

### 3.3.1   Dynamics and geometry

If the fundamental equation of motion of a body in space is given as

$$\ddot{\mathbf{r}} = -\mu\,\frac{\mathbf{r}}{r^3},$$  (3.5)

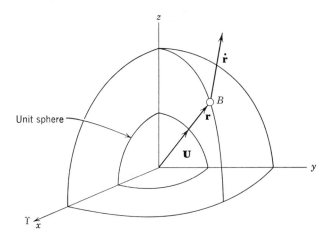

FIGURE 3.1    A body in space.

then by defining a unit vector pointing at the body under consideration
(*B*) of Figure 3.1, Eq. 3.5 becomes

$$\ddot{\mathbf{r}} = -\frac{\mu}{r^2}\,\mathbf{U}, \tag{3.6}$$

where

$$\mathbf{U} \equiv \frac{\mathbf{r}}{r}. \tag{3.7}$$

It is evident that taking the cross product of Eq. 3.6 with **r** results in

$$\mathbf{r} \times \ddot{\mathbf{r}} = -\frac{\mu}{r^2}\,\mathbf{r} \times \mathbf{U} \tag{3.8}$$

or

$$\mathbf{r} \times \ddot{\mathbf{r}} = 0, \tag{3.9}$$

by virtue of the fact that **r** and **U** are collinear.    Now, since

$$\frac{d}{d\tau}(\mathbf{r} \times \dot{\mathbf{r}}) = \mathbf{r} \times \ddot{\mathbf{r}} + \dot{\mathbf{r}} \times \dot{\mathbf{r}}, \tag{3.10}$$

it follows from Eq. 3.9 that

$$\frac{d}{d\tau}(\mathbf{r} \times \dot{\mathbf{r}}) = 0 \tag{3.11}$$

or

$$\mathbf{r} \times \dot{\mathbf{r}} \equiv \mathbf{h} = \mathbf{constant}. \tag{3.12}$$

Equation 3.12 by itself lends a great deal of insight into the general problem of two bodies. Obviously, from the definition of a cross product, if $\mathbf{h}$ is not the null vector, that is, $\mathbf{h} \neq \mathbf{0}$, then $\mathbf{r}$ and $\dot{\mathbf{r}}$ must be perpendicular to $\mathbf{h}$. Furthermore, since $\mathbf{r}$ emanates from the origin, it follows that the orbit of body $B$ lies in a plane which passes through the origin. As a sidelight, another segment of information can be extracted by considering the case when $\mathbf{h} = \mathbf{0}$. Obviously then, $\mathbf{r}$ and $\dot{\mathbf{r}}$ are collinear and the motion is therefore rectilinear. Let Eq. 3.6 be crossed with $\mathbf{h}$,

$$\ddot{\mathbf{r}} \times \mathbf{h} = -\frac{\mu}{r^2} \mathbf{U} \times \mathbf{h}. \tag{3.13}$$

But, by Eq. 3.12 upon substituting for $\mathbf{h}$,

$$\ddot{\mathbf{r}} \times \mathbf{h} = -\frac{\mu}{r^2} \mathbf{U} \times (\mathbf{r} \times \dot{\mathbf{r}}) \tag{3.14}$$

$$= -\frac{\mu}{r^2} [(\mathbf{U} \cdot \dot{\mathbf{r}})\mathbf{r} - (\mathbf{U} \cdot \mathbf{r})\dot{\mathbf{r}}]. \tag{3.15}$$

Hence, by definition (3.7),[2]

$$\ddot{\mathbf{r}} \times \mathbf{h} = \mu \frac{(r\dot{\mathbf{r}} - \dot{r}\mathbf{r})}{r^2} \tag{3.16}$$

$$= \mu \frac{d}{d\tau}\left(\frac{\mathbf{r}}{r}\right) \tag{3.17}$$

or in terms of $\mathbf{U}$,

$$\ddot{\mathbf{r}} \times \mathbf{h} = \mu\dot{\mathbf{U}}, \tag{3.18}$$

which can be integrated at once as

$$\dot{\mathbf{r}} \times \mathbf{h} = \mu[\mathbf{U} + \mathbf{e}], \tag{3.19}$$

where $\mathbf{e}$ is a vector constant of integration. Upon dotting with $\mathbf{r}$ it is possible to write

$$(\dot{\mathbf{r}} \times \mathbf{h}) \cdot \mathbf{r} = \mu[\mathbf{U} \cdot \mathbf{r} + \mathbf{e} \cdot \mathbf{r}]. \tag{3.20}$$

Remembering Eq. 3.20, let Eq. 3.12 be dotted with $\mathbf{h}$,

$$(\mathbf{r} \times \dot{\mathbf{r}}) \cdot \mathbf{h} = h^2. \tag{3.21}$$

However, since

$$(\mathbf{r} \times \dot{\mathbf{r}}) \cdot \mathbf{h} \equiv (\dot{\mathbf{r}} \times \mathbf{h}) \cdot \mathbf{r}, \tag{3.22}$$

[2] It should be understood that $\dot{r}$ is the component of $\dot{\mathbf{r}}$ in the $\mathbf{U}$ direction, that is, $\dot{r} \neq |\dot{\mathbf{r}}|$. The magnitude of $\dot{\mathbf{r}}$ is denoted by $V$, the speed.

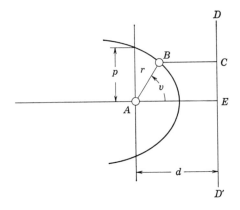

FIGURE 3.2    A conic section.

it is evident that a direct comparison of Eqs. 3.20 and 3.22 reveals that

$$h^2 = \mu[\mathbf{U} \cdot \mathbf{r} + \mathbf{e} \cdot \mathbf{r}].$$  (3.23)

But,

$$\mathbf{U} \cdot \mathbf{r} = r, \qquad \mathbf{e} \cdot \mathbf{r} = er \cos (\angle \mathbf{e}, \mathbf{r}),$$  (3.24)

so that upon resolving the dot products and solving Eq. 3.23 for the magnitude of the radius vector to body $B$, one has

$$r = \frac{h^2/\mu}{1 + e \cos (\angle \mathbf{e}, \mathbf{r})}.$$  (3.25)

Equation (3.25), derived from dynamical concepts, can be interpreted geometrically by considering Figure 3.2. Furthermore, since a conic is the locus of a point $(B)$ whose distance $(r)$ from a given fixed point called the focus $(A)$ is in a constant ratio $(e)$ from a fixed line called the *directrix* $(DD')$, it is possible to write

$$r = e\overline{BC} = e(\overline{AE} - r \cos v)$$  (3.26)

or

$$r = e(d - r \cos v),$$

which can be put in standard form by solving for $r$ as

$$r = \frac{p}{1 + e \cos v}$$  (3.27)

with

$$p \equiv ed.$$  (3.28)

A direct comparison of Eqs. 3.25 and 3.27, or the identification of

$$\frac{h^2}{\mu} = p, \qquad \angle\,\mathbf{e, r} = v, \tag{3.29}$$

constitutes a proof of Kepler's first law (I). The angle $v$ is called the *true anomaly*, and $p$ is known as the *semiparameter* of the conic. From Eq. 3.27, it is possible to see that $v = \pi/2$ corresponds to $r = p$; hence the name semiparameter or half-width of the conic on a traverse line intersecting the focus. The constant $e$ is called the *eccentricity* of the conic section.

It follows from the theory of conic sections that, if $p \neq 0$,

$e = 0$,    the conic is a circle,
$0 < e < 1$,    the conic is an ellipse,
$e = 1$,    the conic is a parabola,
$1 < e < \infty$,    the conic is a hyperbola.

In these illustrations the parameter $a$, or half the maximum diameter, is called the *semimajor axis* of the orbit. It should be noted that

$a = \infty$        for parabolic motion,
$0 < a < \infty$        for elliptic motion,
$-\infty < a < 0$    for hyperbolic motion.

For future convenience, a set of axes, $x_\omega$ and $y_\omega$ is introduced with origin at the focus; the positive $x_\omega$ axis pointing along the minimum radius and the positive $y_\omega$ axis advanced by a right angle to $x_\omega$ in the orbit plane.

Pertinent parameters of these types of orbits in the orbit plane coordinate system are illustrated in Figures 3.3, 3.4, 3.5.

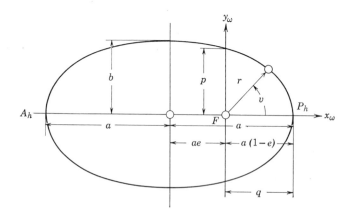

FIGURE 3.3   An elliptic orbit.

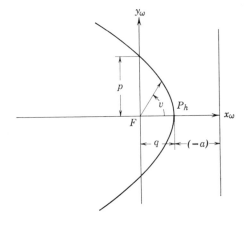

FIGURE 3.4    A hyperbolic orbit.

Furthermore, if $p = 0$ and $e = 1$,

$a = \infty$    corresponds to a rectilinear parabola,
$a > 0$    corresponds to a rectilinear ellipse,
$a < 0$    corresponds to a rectilinear hyperbola.

Therefore, orbits of bodies in space fall into one of the above seven categories corresponding to *circular, elliptic, parabolic, hyperbolic, rectilinear elliptic, rectilinear parabolic,* and *rectilinear hyperbolic* two-body motion.

An important relation between the semiparameter, semimajor axis,

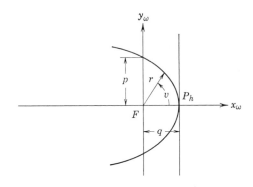

FIGURE 3.5    A parabolic orbit.

and eccentricity may be derived by evaluating Eq. 3.27 at $v = 0$, and $\pi$ for $r_{min}$ and $r_{max}$, and adding.   Therefore,

$$(r_{min} + r_{max}) = 2a = \frac{2p}{1 - e^2} \quad \text{or} \quad p = a(1 - e^2). \tag{3.30}$$

The point on a conic, where

$$\frac{dr}{d\tau} = 0, \tag{3.31}$$

is a special point called an *apse*.   Elliptical or noncircular closed orbits are possessed of two points where Eq. 3.31 is satisfied.   Hence the minimum radius of a conic occurs at *perifocus*, denoted by $P_h$ in Figures 3.3, 3.4, and 3.5.   The point where the radius is a maximum is called *apofocus*, denoted by $A_h$.

Kepler's second law (II) can be readily proved if the area generated or swept out by a given radius vector is formulated by means of a special case of Stokes' theorem,

$$A\mathbf{W} = \tfrac{1}{2} \oint \mathbf{r} \times d\mathbf{r}. \tag{3.32}$$

This important theorem provides a rapid method of computing any vector area (area times a unit vector $\mathbf{W}$ normal to surface) of a surface as a circuit integral around its boundary.   By a standard change of variable that is, introduction of $\tau$, it is evident that

$$A\mathbf{W} = \tfrac{1}{2} \int_0^\tau \mathbf{r} \times \dot{\mathbf{r}} \, d\bar{\tau}. \tag{3.33}$$

However, Eq. 3.12 permits

$$A\mathbf{W} = \tfrac{1}{2} \int_0^\tau \mathbf{h} \, d\bar{\tau} \tag{3.34}$$

to be written, so that

$$\frac{dA}{d\tau} \mathbf{W} = \tfrac{1}{2}\mathbf{h}, \tag{3.35}$$

which, upon taking the dot product with $\mathbf{W}$, yields

$$\frac{dA}{d\tau} = \frac{1}{2} h = \text{constant}. \tag{3.36}$$

The third law (III) can be obtained as a consequence of the second, by means of Eqs. 3.29 and 3.30 modified to read

$$\sqrt{\mu p} = h = \sqrt{\mu a(1 - e^2)}. \tag{3.37}$$

Furthermore, since the area of an ellipse [9] is given by

$$A = \pi ab = \pi a^2 \sqrt{1 - e^2},$$ (3.38)

then integration of Eq. 3.36, that is,

$$\int_0^A d\bar{A} = \tfrac{1}{2}h \int_0^P d\tau = \tfrac{1}{2}hk \int_0^P dt,$$ (3.39)

where the upper limit $(P)$ is the *period of revolution* of a body about the central body, yields

$$A = \pi a^2 \sqrt{1 - e^2} = \tfrac{1}{2}hkP.$$ (3.40)

Hence, by Eq. 3.37 substituting for $h$,

$$P = \frac{2\pi}{k\sqrt{\mu}} a^{3/2}$$ (3.41)

or in the words of the third law (III)

$$P^2 = \frac{(2\pi)^2}{k^2\mu} a^3.$$ (3.42)

Note the factor $\mu$ in Eq. 3.42 is absent from the statement of the third law.[3]

### 3.4  INTRODUCTION OF PERTINENT UNIT VECTORS

#### 3.4.1  The orthogonal set P, Q, W

In the right ascension-declination coordinate system, the unit vectors **I**, **J**, **K** (Figure 3.6), are usually introduced, with **I** taken along the principal or $x$ axis and **J**, **K** associated with $y$ and $z$ axes, respectively.

Consider again Figure 3.6 and note the orbit plane which is inclined to the equatorial plane by an angle $i$.  This angle, called the inclination of the orbit or *orbital inclination*, is defined as follows.

$i$ (*Orbital Inclination*).  The angle between the orbit and equatorial planes measured in a plane perpendicular to a line defining their respective intersection.

Another angle of interest, $\Omega$, is called the *longitude of the ascending node*. It is defined as follows.

---

[3] As stated previously, Kepler derived this equation empirically and therefore, due to lack of precise data, was not able to detect the mass of the secondary body.

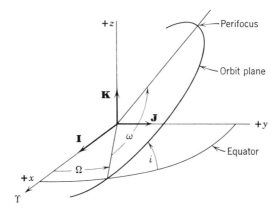

FIGURE 3.6    Unit vectors in the right ascension-declination coordinate systems.

$\Omega$ (*Longitude of the Ascending Node*).   The angle measured in the equatorial plane between the principal axis (vernal equinox) and the line defining the intersection of the equatorial and orbit planes, as a point in the orbit plane passes through the equator in the sense negative to positive with respect to the $z$ axis.

It should be noted that another angle exists called the *longitude of the descending node*, $\mho$, which is similar to the above-mentioned angle except that a point in the orbit plane passes through the equator in a positive to negative sense.

A third angle $\omega$, *the argument of perigee*, is defined as follows.

$\omega$ (*Argument of Perigee*).   The angle measured in the orbit plane from the line defined by the longitude of the ascending node to another line in the orbit plane, which contains the focus and passes through perifocus.

The angles $i$, $\Omega$, and $\omega$ are the *classical orientation angles* used to define the position of the orbit plane in space.   Their range is defined in Table 3.1.

The range of $i$ might seem restrictive; however, the concept of *direct* and *retrograde* orbits must be kept in mind.   Hence all orbits whose motion is in the sense from $x$ to $y$ as seen from $+z$ are termed direct. All orbits whose motion is from $y$ to $x$ as seen from $+z$ are termed retrograde.   Actually, then, $i$ is measured from the appropriate node.

At times, the use of these angles is cumbersome and, therefore, a means

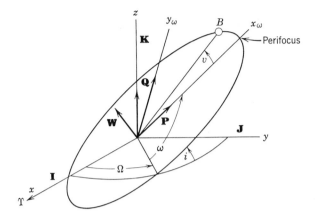

FIGURE 3.7    Introduction of the orthogonal set **P**, **Q**, **W** into the orbit plane coordinate system.

*Table 3.1*

| VARIABLE | RANGE |
|----------|-------|
| $i$ | $0 \leq i \leq \pi$ |
| $\Omega$ | $0 \leq \Omega \leq 2\pi$ |
| $\omega$ | $0 \leq \omega \leq 2\pi$ |

of bypassing them should be sought.    Assignment of an orthogonal set of unit vectors, **P**, **Q**, **W**, as shown in Figure 3.7, can be of great assistance in calculations and, as will be presently seen, permit direct orientation without the use of $i$, $\Omega$, $\omega$.    **P** is taken as pointing towards perifocus; **Q** is in the orbit plane advanced to **P** by a right angle in the direction of increasing true anomaly; and **W** completes the right-handed system.

The orthogonal right-handed set, **P**, **Q**, **W** finds considerable use in two-body mechanics.    By aligning both fundamental triads and performing the rotations through $\Omega$, $i$, $\omega$, it follows that the direction cosines of **P**, **Q**, and **W** are given by:

$$P_x = \cos \omega \cos \Omega - \sin \omega \sin \Omega \cos i$$

$$P_y = \cos \omega \sin \Omega + \sin \omega \cos \Omega \cos i \qquad (3.43)$$

$$P_z = \sin \omega \sin i$$

$$Q_x = -\sin \omega \cos \Omega - \cos \omega \sin \Omega \cos i$$
$$Q_y = -\sin \omega \sin \Omega + \cos \omega \cos \Omega \cos i \qquad (3.44)$$
$$Q_z = \cos \omega \sin i$$

$$W_x = \sin \Omega \sin i$$
$$W_y = -\cos \Omega \sin i \qquad (3.45)$$
$$W_z = \cos i.$$

*Illustrative Example*
Derive the expressions for the direction cosines of the **P**, **Q**, and **W** vectors.

By aligning both fundamental sets, that is, **I**, **J**, **K** and **P**, **Q**, **W**, so that **P**, **Q**, **W** are coincident with **I**, **J**, **K**, it is possible to proceed as follows. Rotate through the angle $\Omega$ about $z$ as follows:

$$\mathbf{I}' = \cos \Omega \mathbf{I} + \sin \Omega \mathbf{J}$$
$$\mathbf{J}' = -\sin \Omega \mathbf{I} + \cos \Omega \mathbf{J}$$
$$\mathbf{K}' = \mathbf{K},$$

or more compactly,

$$\begin{bmatrix} \mathbf{I}' \\ \mathbf{J}' \\ \mathbf{K}' \end{bmatrix} = \begin{bmatrix} \cos \Omega & \sin \Omega & 0 \\ -\sin \Omega & \cos \Omega & 0 \\ 0 & 0 & 1 \end{bmatrix} \begin{bmatrix} \mathbf{I} \\ \mathbf{J} \\ \mathbf{K} \end{bmatrix},$$

the primed variables denoting a first rotation.

Rotate the primed axes through the angle $i$ about $\mathbf{I}'$ as follows:

$$\begin{bmatrix} \mathbf{I}'' \\ \mathbf{J}'' \\ \mathbf{K}'' \end{bmatrix} = \begin{bmatrix} 1 & 0 & 0 \\ 0 & \cos i & \sin i \\ 0 & -\sin i & \cos i \end{bmatrix} \begin{bmatrix} \mathbf{I}' \\ \mathbf{J}' \\ \mathbf{K}' \end{bmatrix},$$

the double primes denoting a second rotation.

Finally, rotate the double primed axes through the angle $\omega$ about $\mathbf{K}''$ to obtain

$$\begin{bmatrix} \mathbf{P} \\ \mathbf{Q} \\ \mathbf{W} \end{bmatrix} = \begin{bmatrix} \cos \omega & \sin \omega & 0 \\ -\sin \omega & \cos \omega & 0 \\ 0 & 0 & 1 \end{bmatrix} \begin{bmatrix} \mathbf{I}'' \\ \mathbf{J}'' \\ \mathbf{K}'' \end{bmatrix}.$$

A compound transformation can be written by substituting for

$$\begin{bmatrix} \mathbf{I}'' \\ \mathbf{J}'' \\ \mathbf{K}'' \end{bmatrix},$$

its mapping in the previous equations as

$$\begin{bmatrix} \mathbf{P} \\ \mathbf{Q} \\ \mathbf{W} \end{bmatrix} = \begin{bmatrix} \cos\omega & \sin\omega & 0 \\ -\sin\omega & \cos\omega & 0 \\ 0 & 0 & 1 \end{bmatrix} \begin{bmatrix} 1 & 0 & 0 \\ 0 & \cos i & \sin i \\ 0 & -\sin i & \cos i \end{bmatrix}$$
$$\times \begin{bmatrix} \cos\Omega & \sin\Omega & 0 \\ -\sin\Omega & \cos\Omega & 0 \\ 0 & 0 & 1 \end{bmatrix} \begin{bmatrix} \mathbf{I} \\ \mathbf{J} \\ \mathbf{K} \end{bmatrix},$$

which, upon multiplying, yields

$$\begin{bmatrix} \mathbf{P} \\ \mathbf{Q} \\ \mathbf{W} \end{bmatrix} = \begin{bmatrix} (\cos\omega\cos\Omega & (\cos\omega\sin\Omega & (\sin\omega\sin i) \\ -\sin\omega\cos i\sin\Omega) & +\sin\omega\cos i\cos\Omega) & \\ (-\sin\omega\cos\Omega & (-\sin\omega\sin\Omega & (\cos\omega\sin i) \\ -\cos\omega\cos i\sin\Omega) & +\cos\Omega\cos\omega\cos i) & \\ (\sin\Omega\sin i) & (-\sin i\cos\Omega) & (\cos i) \end{bmatrix} \begin{bmatrix} \mathbf{I} \\ \mathbf{J} \\ \mathbf{K} \end{bmatrix}.$$

It follows upon matrix multiplication of the right side of this equation that

$$\mathbf{P} = a_{11}\mathbf{I} + a_{12}\mathbf{J} + a_{13}\mathbf{K}$$
$$\mathbf{Q} = a_{21}\mathbf{I} + a_{22}\mathbf{J} + a_{23}\mathbf{K}$$
$$\mathbf{W} = a_{31}\mathbf{I} + a_{32}\mathbf{J} + a_{33}\mathbf{K},$$

the $a$ coefficients being associated with each element of the transformation matrix $a_{ij}$. Hence, upon dotting each of these equations with $\mathbf{I}$, $\mathbf{J}$, and $\mathbf{K}$,

$$\mathbf{P}\cdot\mathbf{I} = a_{11} = P_x \quad \mathbf{Q}\cdot\mathbf{I} = a_{21} = Q_x \quad \mathbf{W}\cdot\mathbf{I} = a_{31} = W_x$$
$$\mathbf{P}\cdot\mathbf{J} = a_{12} = P_y \quad \mathbf{Q}\cdot\mathbf{J} = a_{22} = Q_y \quad \mathbf{W}\cdot\mathbf{J} = a_{32} = W_y$$
$$\mathbf{P}\cdot\mathbf{K} = a_{13} = P_z \quad \mathbf{Q}\cdot\mathbf{K} = a_{23} = Q_z \quad \mathbf{W}\cdot\mathbf{K} = a_{33} = W_z.$$

Naturally, since $\mathbf{P}\cdot\mathbf{I} = (1)(1)\cos(\angle\mathbf{P},\mathbf{I})$, etc., it is evident that the components of $\mathbf{P}$, $\mathbf{Q}$, $\mathbf{W}$ are the direction cosines of $\mathbf{P}$, $\mathbf{Q}$, $\mathbf{W}$ axes.

### 3.4.2   The orthogonal set U, V, W

Another valuable set of unit vectors is the $\mathbf{U}$, $\mathbf{V}$, $\mathbf{W}$ orthogonal triad. The unit vector $\mathbf{U}$ has been partially introduced in Section 3.3 and, as then, is defined as a vector which always points at the body under consideration. $\mathbf{V}$ is advanced to $\mathbf{U}$ in the sense of increasing true anomaly

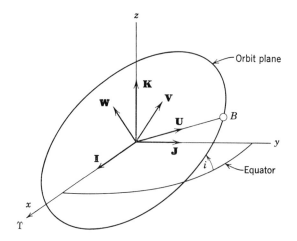

FIGURE 3.8   Introduction of the orthogonal set **U**, **V**, **W** into the orbit plane
coordinate system.

by a right angle in the plane of instantaneous motion. **W** completes
the orthogonal set. Crystalization of the location of these unit vectors
with respect to the **I**, **J**, **K** axes may be gleaned from an examination of
Figure 3.8.

It becomes evident that if a space vehicle or body (*B*) is at perifocus,
the triads **U**, **V**, **W** and **P**, **Q**, **W** are coincident. Since at this point the
true anomaly is zero, the direction cosines are identical to those calculated
in Section 3.4.1.

Actually, since $v$, the true anomaly, is measured in the orbital plane
from a line containing the near and far apsis or *line of apsides*, it follows
that the *argument of latitude u*, defined by

$$u = v + \omega, \tag{3.46}$$

could be substituted for $\omega$ into Eqs. 3.43, 3.44, and 3.45, in order to
obtain the direction cosines of the set **U**, **V**, **W**, that is, $\mathbf{U} = \mathbf{P}(i, \Omega, u)$ and
$\mathbf{V} = \mathbf{Q}(i, \Omega, u)$. See Figure 3.7.

### 3.4.3   Orthogonal transformations

Transformations to and from the orbit plane are very frequently used in
the preliminary orbit determination process. In practice, a body located
in the right ascension-declination coordinate system is mapped from this
system to the orbit plane system. Analysis is then performed in the orbit

plane system and later the body is mapped back to the right ascension-declination system. This is done for the simple reason that in two-body mechanics, as has been shown, the orbit of a vehicle is contained in a plane. Therefore, by mapping into the orbit plane, an analytical problem is reduced to a problem in two, instead of three dimensions. Obviously, it will be easier to work in a system of two rather than three dimensions. Velocity and acceleration transformations will be discussed in Chapter 4.

Suppose then, that a body is located by the vector **r** in the three-dimensional **P, Q, W** system of Figure 3.7. If the direction cosines of the **P, Q, W** system are known, Eqs. 3.43, 3.44, and 3.45, it has been shown that

$$
\begin{bmatrix} \mathbf{P} \\ \mathbf{Q} \\ \mathbf{W} \end{bmatrix} = \begin{bmatrix} P_x & P_y & P_z \\ Q_x & Q_y & Q_z \\ W_x & W_y & W_z \end{bmatrix} \begin{bmatrix} \mathbf{I} \\ \mathbf{J} \\ \mathbf{K} \end{bmatrix},
\tag{3.47}
$$

or since **I, J, K** correspond to $x$, $y$, $z$ coordinates, and **P, Q, W** correspond to the $x_\omega$, $y_\omega$, $z_\omega$ coordinates of Section 3.3,

$$
\begin{bmatrix} x_\omega \\ y_\omega \\ z_\omega \end{bmatrix} = \begin{bmatrix} P_x & P_y & P_z \\ Q_x & Q_y & Q_z \\ W_x & W_y & W_z \end{bmatrix} \begin{bmatrix} x \\ y \\ z \end{bmatrix}.
\tag{3.48}
$$

This is the mapping from the **I, J, K** system to the **P, Q, W** system. The matrix

$$
[M] = \begin{bmatrix} P_x & P_y & P_z \\ Q_x & Q_y & Q_z \\ W_x & W_y & W_z \end{bmatrix}
\tag{3.49}
$$

is called the transformation matrix of the system. Hence, Eq. 3.48 can be written as

$$
\begin{bmatrix} x_\omega \\ y_\omega \\ z_\omega \end{bmatrix} = [M] \begin{bmatrix} x \\ y \\ z \end{bmatrix}.
\tag{3.50}
$$

Upon premultiplication by $[M]^{-1}$, that is, the inverse of $[M]$, it follows that

$$
[M]^{-1} \begin{bmatrix} x_\omega \\ y_\omega \\ z_\omega \end{bmatrix} = [M]^{-1} [M] \begin{bmatrix} x \\ y \\ z \end{bmatrix}
\tag{3.51}
$$

or

$$\begin{bmatrix} x \\ y \\ z \end{bmatrix} = [M]^{-1} \begin{bmatrix} x_\omega \\ y_\omega \\ z_\omega \end{bmatrix}.$$  (3.52)

Since an orthogonal transformation is a rigid rotation about the origin in a Cartesian frame, the transpose $[M]^T$ is equal to the inverse $[M]^{-1}$, and so

$$\begin{bmatrix} x \\ y \\ z \end{bmatrix} = [M]^T \begin{bmatrix} x_\omega \\ y_\omega \\ z_\omega \end{bmatrix}.$$  (3.53)

Hence, by transposing the rows and columns of $[M]$,

$$[M]^T = \begin{bmatrix} P_x & Q_x & W_x \\ P_y & Q_y & W_y \\ P_z & Q_z & W_z \end{bmatrix}$$  (3.54)

is the inverse transformation matrix, which defines a mapping from $\mathbf{r}$ in the $\mathbf{P}$, $\mathbf{Q}$, $\mathbf{W}$ system to $\mathbf{r}$ in the $\mathbf{I}$, $\mathbf{J}$, $\mathbf{K}$ system.[4]    Carrying out the matrix multiplication on the right side of Eq. 3.53, yields the three equations

$$x = x_\omega P_x + y_\omega Q_x + z_\omega W_x$$
$$y = x_\omega P_y + y_\omega Q_y + z_\omega W_y$$  (3.55)
$$z = x_\omega P_z + y_\omega Q_z + z_\omega W_z,$$

or the single vector equation

$$\mathbf{r} = x_\omega \mathbf{P} + y_\omega \mathbf{Q} + z_\omega \mathbf{W}.$$  (3.56)

However, since $z_\omega$ is zero (because the motion is always in the $x_\omega y_\omega$ plane under Keplerian or two-body assumptions), it follows that

$$\mathbf{r} = x_\omega \mathbf{P} + y_\omega \mathbf{Q}.$$  (3.57)

In a similar manner, consideration of Eq. 3.48 will result in

$$x_\omega = x P_x + y P_y + z P_z$$
$$y_\omega = x Q_x + y Q_y + z Q_z$$  (3.58)
$$z_\omega = x W_x + y W_y + z W_z$$

as the inverse mapping. It should be noticed that the unit vectors $\mathbf{P}$, $\mathbf{Q}$, and $\mathbf{W}$ are constants.

[4] The interested reader is directed to reference [8].

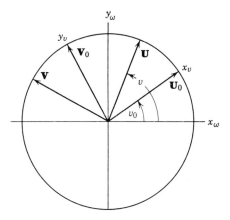

FIGURE 3.9    Relation between **U**, **V** at an instant and $U_0$, $V_0$ at some epoch.

The set **U**, **V**, **W** is constantly moving, with **U** pointing towards the vehicle or body under consideration.   Suppose that the set is considered at some specific time $t_0$, then of course $U_0$, $V_0$, $W_0$ are constant.   Note that **W** is actually always constant; it is only **U** and **V** that move.   However, for consistency, the subscript zero is attached to all three unit vectors.

Suppose further that an instantaneous set of axes coincident with **U**, **V** is chosen at time $t_0$; let them be denoted by $x_v$, $y_v$ in analogous fashion to $x_\omega$ and $y_\omega$.   Then, from Figure 3.9,

$$x_v = r \cos (v - v_0)$$
$$y_v = r \sin (v - v_0) \tag{3.59}$$
$$z_v = 0.$$

Assuming that $U_0$, $V_0$, and $W_0$ are known, that is, the components are the direction cosines of **U**, **V**, and **W** at some time $t_0$, then, by exactly the same procedure as before, a mapping to the right ascension-declination system, or **I**, **J**, **K** frame, is obtained through

$$\mathbf{r} = x_v \mathbf{U}_0 + y_v \mathbf{V}_0. \tag{3.60}$$

The inverse transformation is

$$x_v = xU_x + yU_y + zU_z$$
$$y_v = xV_x + yV_y + zV_z \tag{3.61}$$
$$z_v = xW_x + yW_y + zW_z,$$

where, in two-body motion, $z_v$ will be zero.

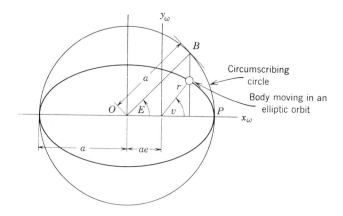

FIGURE 3.10    Introduction of the auxiliary angle **E**.

### 3.5  RELATION BETWEEN GEOMETRY
### AND TIME—KEPLER'S EQUATION

### 3.5.1  Elliptic formulation

An equation of great importance, *Kepler's equation*, relates geometry or position in the orbit plane to time.  The equation to be derived is not directly related to Kepler's three famous laws, but is a separate and independent equation.

However, before proceeding with the development of this important form, a slight digression will be made in order to relate the $x_\omega$ and $y_\omega$ parameters of Section 3.3 to the angles $E$ and $v$.  The angle $E$ is called the *eccentric anomaly* (Figure 3.10), whereas, $v$ is, as usual, the true anomaly.  Hence, for elliptical or circular motion, it is possible to parametrically represent $x_\omega$ and $y_\omega$ by utilization of Figure 3.10, that is,

$$x_\omega = r \cos v$$
$$y_\omega = r \sin v. \tag{3.62}$$

The eccentric anomaly is defined as follows.

$E$ (*Eccentric Anomaly*).  The angle measured in the orbital plane from the $x_\omega$ axis to a line containing the center and another point defined by the projection of the moving vehicle in the $y_\omega$ direction upon an auxiliary circle that circumscribes the actual ellipse of motion.

This angle can also be used to compute $x_\omega$.  Again, from Figure 3.10,

$$x_\omega = a \cos E - ae, \tag{3.63}$$

or

$$x_\omega = a(\cos E - e).$$ (3.64)

Then from Eq. 3.62,

$$\cos v = \frac{x_\omega}{r},$$ (3.65)

which, when substituted into the equation of a conic, Eq. 3.27, yields

$$r + ex_\omega = p = a(1 - e^2)$$ (3.66)

or, due to the expression for $x_\omega$,

$$r = a(1 - e \cos E).$$ (3.67)

Certainly, since

$$r^2 = x_\omega{}^2 + y_\omega{}^2,$$ (3.68)

solution for $y_\omega$ yields, along with the other two relations, the mappings

$$\begin{aligned} r_\omega = r \qquad &= a(1 - e \cos E) \\ x_\omega = r \cos v &= a(\cos E - e) \\ y_\omega = r \sin v &= a\sqrt{1 - e^2} \sin E. \end{aligned}$$ (3.69)

Furthermore, by direct differentiation,

$$\begin{aligned} \dot{r}_\omega = \dot{r} \qquad\qquad\qquad &= ae\dot{E} \sin E \\ \dot{x}_\omega = \dot{r} \cos v - r\dot{v} \sin v &= -a\dot{E} \sin E \\ \dot{y}_\omega = \dot{r} \sin v + r\dot{v} \cos v &= a\dot{E}\sqrt{1 - e^2} \cos E. \end{aligned}$$ (3.70)

Now, since

$$h\mathbf{W} = \mathbf{r} \times \dot{\mathbf{r}} = \mathbf{r} \times (\dot{\mathbf{r}}_R + \dot{\mathbf{r}}_P),$$ (3.71)

where the subscripts stand for velocity components at right angles and parallel to $\mathbf{r}$, it is possible to verify that

$$h\mathbf{W} = \mathbf{r} \times \dot{\mathbf{r}}_R = \left(rr\dot{v} \sin \frac{\pi}{2}\right)\mathbf{W} = r^2\dot{v}\mathbf{W}.$$ (3.72)

Hence, for convenience repeating Eq. 3.29, the following relations are evident:

$$p = a(1 - e^2) = \frac{h^2}{\mu} = \frac{r^4\dot{v}^2}{\mu} = \frac{(\mathbf{r} \times \dot{\mathbf{r}}) \cdot (\mathbf{r} \times \dot{\mathbf{r}})}{\mu}.$$ (3.73)

The cross product $\mathbf{r} \times \dot{\mathbf{r}}$ referred to the orbital axes $x_\omega$, $y_\omega$ can be formulated as

$$\mu p = (x_\omega \dot{y}_\omega - y_\omega \dot{x}_\omega)^2, \tag{3.74}$$

which, by consequence of Eqs. 3.69 and 3.70, becomes

$$\sqrt{\mu p} = a^{3/2} \sqrt{p} \, (\sin^2 E + \cos^2 E - e \cos E)\dot{E}. \tag{3.75}$$

This equation can be simplified to

$$\frac{\sqrt{\mu}}{a^{3/2}} = (1 - e \cos E) \frac{dE}{d\tau} \tag{3.76}$$

or

$$\frac{\sqrt{\mu}}{a^{3/2}} \int_0^{\tau_t} d\tau = \int_0^{E_t} (1 - e \cos E) \, dE, \tag{3.77}$$

which, upon integration and setting $\tau_t = \tau$ and $E_t = E$, becomes

$$\frac{\sqrt{\mu}}{a^{3/2}} \tau = E - e \sin E. \tag{3.78}$$

Obviously, from the definition of the modified time variable $\tau = k(t - t_0)$ and the integration limits, the epoch time $t_0$ corresponds to the point on the orbit where $E = 0$.  Let this time be called the *time of perifocal passage* denoted by $T$.  Then Eq. 3.78 can be rewritten as

$$n(t - T) = E - e \sin E \tag{3.79}$$

with $n$, called the *mean motion*, defined by

$$n \equiv \frac{k\sqrt{\mu}}{a^{3/2}}. \tag{3.80}$$

Equation 3.79 is known as Kepler's equation and as previously stated relates position in the orbit to time.  The product $n(t - T)$ is called the *mean anomaly* and is usually denoted by $M$.  Furthermore, an orbit determination scheme which determines the position and velocity of a satellite at time $t_0$, enables Eq. 3.79 to be used for the computation of $T$.

The numerical solution of Kepler's equation is a point of interest. Consider the equation

$$M = E - e \sin E. \tag{3.81}$$

Therefore, by differentiation,

$$dM = (1 - e \cos E) \, dE, \tag{3.82}$$

or integration between the adopted bottom limits, 0, and upper limits $E(t) \equiv E_t$, $M(t) \equiv M_t$,

$$\int_0^{E_t} dE = E = \int_0^{M_t} \frac{dM}{1 - e \cos E}.$$  (3.83)

An expansion using Fourier series [9] with

$$a_0 = \frac{1}{P_f} \int_0^{P_f} dE = 1$$  (3.84)

$$a_m = \frac{2}{P_f} \int_0^{P_f} \frac{\cos\left(\frac{2\pi m}{P_f} M\right)}{1 - e \cos E} dM,$$  (3.85)

and noting that $P_f$, the period of the function, is $2\pi$, upon substituting for $dM$, Eq. 3.85 becomes

$$a_m = \frac{1}{\pi} \int_0^{2\pi} \cos\{m(E - e \sin E)\} dE$$  (3.86)

$$= 2J_m(me).$$  (3.87)

$J_m$ is a Bessel function of the first kind of order $m$. For purposes of calculation,

$$J_m(me) = \sum_{n=0}^{\infty} \frac{(-1)^n \left(\frac{me}{2}\right)^{2n+m}}{n!(n+m)!},$$  (3.88)

so that an explicit formula for the eccentric anomaly is given by

$$E = M + 2 \sum_{m=1}^{\infty} \frac{1}{m} J_m(me) \sin(mM).$$  (3.89)

The interested reader is directed to reference [6].

Numerically, at times a few terms can be used to start the solution and then with the first approximation, $E_n$, continue by a Newton procedure,[5] such as

$$E_{n+1} = E_n - \frac{E_n - e \sin E_n - M}{1 - e \cos E_n}, \qquad n = 1, 2, \ldots, p,$$  (3.90)

until $E_p$ no longer varies.

[5] See Section 9.2.3.

*Illustrative Example*
Given the set of orbital elements

$a = 1.5$ e.r.
$e = 0.1$
$T = 1962$ June 22, $16^{hr}$, $1^{min}$, $5^{sec}$
$i = 30°$
$\Omega = 45°$
$\omega = 60°$,

what are the rectangular coordinates of a geocentric satellite in the right ascension-declination **I, J, K** coordinate system on 1962 June 23, $2^{hr}$, $15^{min}$ U.T.?

Utilizing Eqs. 3.43, 3.44, and 3.45, it is possible to compute:

$P_x = \cos 60° \cos 45° - \sin 60° \sin 45° \cos 30°$    $= -0.1767\ 7668$
$P_y = \cos 60° \sin 45° + \sin 60° \cos 45° \cos 30°$    $= +0.8838\ 8346$
$P_z = \sin 60° \sin 30°$    $= +0.4330\ 1270$

$Q_x = -\sin 60° \cos 45° - \cos 60° \sin 45° \cos 30°$  $= -0.9185\ 5864$
$Q_y = -\sin 60° \sin 45° + \cos 60° \cos 45° \cos 30°$  $= -0.3061\ 8622$
$Q_z = \cos 60° \sin 30°$    $= +0.2500\ 0000$

$W_x = \sin 45° \sin 30°$    $= +0.3535\ 5339$
$W_y = -\cos 45° \sin 30°$    $= -0.3535\ 5339$
$W_z = \cos 30°$    $= +0.8660\ 2540.$

Where it is possible to check these values by

$P_x{}^2 + P_y{}^2 + P_z{}^2 = 0.99999996 \cong 1$
$Q_x{}^2 + Q_y{}^2 + Q_z{}^2 = 0.99999997 \cong 1$
$W_x{}^2 + W_y{}^2 + W_z{}^2 = 0.99999999 \cong 1.$

The argument of the Kepler's equation is

$t - T = 10^{hr}\ 13^{min}\ 55^{sec} = 613.9167$ min,

and the mean motion, Eq. 3.80, is

$$n = \frac{0.07436574 \times \sqrt{1}}{(1.5)^{3/2}} = 0.0404\ 7958,$$

so that $M = n(t - T)$, the mean anomaly, is found to be

$M = 24.8510\ 90.$

By an iterative technique, it is possible to solve for $E$ from Kepler's equation 3.79, that is,

$$24.851090 = E - 0.1 \sin E,$$

so that

$$E = 24.820358 \text{ radians} = 1080° + 342° \, 6' \, 6''.33,$$

which upon inserting into Eqs. 3.69, yields

$$x_\omega = 1.5(1 - 0.1 \cos E) \qquad = 1.3572 \, 5952$$
$$y_\omega = 1.5\sqrt{1 - 0.1^2} \sin E = -0.4586 \, 8029$$
$$r_\omega{}^2 = x_\omega{}^2 + y_\omega{}^2 \qquad\qquad = 2.0525 \, 410.$$

The mapping 3.57 then yields the rectangular components as

$$\mathbf{r} = x_\omega \mathbf{P} + y_\omega \mathbf{Q}$$
$$x = \phantom{+}0.1813 \, 9291 \text{ e.r.}$$
$$y = +1.3401 \, 0082 \text{ e.r.}$$
$$z = +0.4730 \, 4053 \text{ e.r.}$$

A check is offered by computing $r$ as

$$r^2 = x^2 + y^2 + z^2 = 2.0525 \, 409,$$

and since $r$ is invariant

$$r_\omega{}^2 = r^2.$$

### 3.5.2  Hyperbolic formulation

Geometrically, the eccentric anomaly can be interpreted by means of Figure 3.10 as a function of the area of sector $OPB$ as follows:

$$E = \frac{2 \times \text{area}}{a^2}. \tag{3.91}$$

Hence, in direct analogy, it is possible to define a new variable for hyperbolic motion as

$$F = \frac{2 \times \text{area}}{a^2}, \tag{3.92}$$

where the area $PBC$ is defined by means of Figure 3.11.

In Figure 3.11, the vehicle or body moving along a hyperbolic trajectory is denoted by $B$.

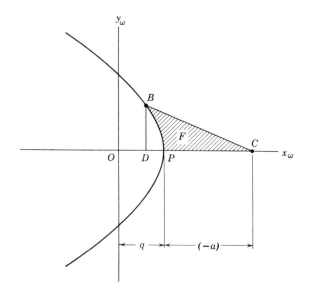

FIGURE 3.11    Hyperbolic reference area.

Certainly then, from the definition of the hyperbolic functions,

$$\overline{DC} = a \cosh F,$$    (3.93)

so that

$$
\begin{aligned}
x_\omega = OD &= q - (-a \cosh F + a) \\
&= a(1 - e) + a \cosh F - a \\
&= a(\cosh F - e).
\end{aligned}
$$    (3.94)

Utilizing Eq. 3.66, that is,

$$r + ex_\omega = a(1 - e^2)$$    (3.95)

and substituting for $x_\omega$ from Eq. 3.94, it is possible to extract

$$r = a(1 - e \cosh F).$$    (3.96)

Finally, from

$$r^2 = x_\omega{}^2 + y_\omega{}^2,$$    (3.97)

upon solving for $y_\omega$ and for convenience repeating the relationships for $r_\omega$ and $x_\omega$

$$
\begin{aligned}
r_\omega &= a(1 - e \cosh F) \\
x_\omega &= a(\cosh F - e) \\
y_\omega &= -a\sqrt{e^2 - 1} \sinh F.
\end{aligned}
$$    (3.98)

By inserting these forms and their derivatives into Eq. 3.74 and repeating the analysis, it is possible to show that

$$M = e \sinh F - F \tag{3.99}$$

with

$$M = n(t - T), \tag{3.100}$$

where the mean motion is, in this case, defined by

$$n \equiv k\sqrt{\mu}/(-a)^{3/2}. \tag{3.101}$$

This is the Kepler equation analogue for hyperbolic motion.

### 3.5.3  Parabolic formulation

Position can be related to time in parabolic orbits by use of

$$r = \frac{2q}{1 + \cos v}, \tag{3.102}$$

that is, the equation of a parabola, derivable from

$$r = \frac{p}{1 + e \cos v}, \tag{3.103}$$

which is Eq. 3.27.   Notice that since $e = 1$,

$$p = a(1 - e)(1 + e) = q(1 + e) = 2q. \tag{3.104}$$

Now, since

$$1 + \cos v = 2 \cos^2 \tfrac{1}{2}v, \tag{3.105}$$

Eq. 3.102 can be rewritten as

$$r = (\sec^2 \tfrac{1}{2}v)q, \tag{3.106}$$

and from Eq. 3.73,

$$\sqrt{2\mu q} = r^2 \dot{v} = q^2(\sec^2 \tfrac{1}{2}v \ \sec^2 \tfrac{1}{2}v)\dot{v}, \tag{3.107}$$

so that

$$\sqrt{2\mu q} \, d\tau = q^2(1 + \tan^2 \tfrac{1}{2}v)(\sec^2 \tfrac{1}{2}v) \, dv. \tag{3.108}$$

Hence,

$$\frac{\sqrt{\mu}}{\sqrt{2} \, q^{3/2}} \int_0^{\tau_t} d\tau = \int_0^{v_t/2} \sec^2 \frac{v}{2} \, d\left(\frac{v}{2}\right) + \int_0^{v_t/2} (\tan^2 \tfrac{1}{2}v)(\sec^2 \tfrac{1}{2}v) \, d\left(\frac{v}{2}\right), \tag{3.109}$$

or by integration, omitting the subscript $t$

$$\frac{\sqrt{\mu}}{\sqrt{2}\,q^{3/2}}\,\tau = \tan\frac{v}{2} + \frac{1}{3}\tan^3\frac{v}{2}. \tag{3.110}$$

Utilizing the definition of $\tau$, Eq. 3.110 becomes

$$\frac{k\sqrt{\mu}\,(t-T)}{\sqrt{2}\,q^{3/2}} = \tan\frac{v}{2} + \frac{1}{3}\tan^3\frac{v}{2}, \tag{3.111}$$

which is the parabolic form of Kepler's equation, known as Barker's equation.

By introduction of the parameter $D$ defined by

$$D \equiv \frac{r\dot{r}}{\sqrt{\mu}} = \sqrt{2q}\,\tan\tfrac{1}{2}v = \sqrt{2q}\,\frac{\sin v}{1 + \cos v}, \tag{3.112}$$

transformation of Eq. 3.111 to a cubic is effected as

$$D^3 + 6qD = 6M \tag{3.113}$$

with

$$M = n(t - T), \tag{3.114}$$

where the parabolic mean motion is defined by

$$n \equiv k\sqrt{\mu}. \tag{3.115}$$

Evidently then, knowing $t$ permits introduction of Cardan's formula[6] (Appendix 3) to yield $D$, which in turn allows the computation of the true anomaly $v$ by means of Eq. 3.112.

### 3.5.4  Modifications to the basic forms

As has been shown, for various types of motion there exist different forms of Kepler's equation, that is,

$$
\begin{array}{lll}
\text{elliptic motion:} & M = E - e\sin E, & \\
\text{hyperbolic motion:} & M = e\sinh F - F, & \tag{3.116}\\
\text{parabolic motion:} & 6M = 6qD + D^3. &
\end{array}
$$

At times, however, it is convenient to express Eqs. 3.116 from some particular epoch $t_0$. Hence, corresponding to $t_0$ or $M_0$ there exist the anomalies $E_0$, $F_0$, and $D_0$. Consider the elliptic case and write

$$M = E - e\sin E \tag{3.117}$$

$$M_0 = E_0 - e\sin E_0. \tag{3.118}$$

[6] This formula was published by Cardan in 1545 as his own work. It was, however, obtained from Tartaglia under the "pledge of secrecy."

Subtraction of Eq. 3.118 from Eq. 3.117 yields

$$M - M_0 = E - E_0 - e \sin E + e \sin E_0 \qquad (3.119)$$

and since

$$e \sin E = e \sin (E - E_0 + E_0)$$
$$= e \sin (E - E_0) \cos E_0 + e \cos (E - E_0) \sin E_0, \qquad (3.120)$$

Eq. 3.119 becomes

$$M - M_0 = E - E_0 - e \cos E_0 \sin (E - E_0)$$
$$- e \sin E_0 \cos (E - E_0) + e \sin E_0 \qquad (3.121)$$

or

$$M - M_0 = E - E_0 + [e \sin E_0][1 - \cos (E - E_0)]$$
$$- [e \cos E_0][\sin(E - E_0)]. \qquad (3.122)$$

Furthermore, upon introduction of the definitions

$$e \sin E_0 \equiv S_e$$
$$e \cos E_0 \equiv C_e, \qquad (3.123)$$

it is possible to express Eq. 3.122 as

$$M - M_0 = E - E_0 + 2S_e \sin^2 \left( \frac{E - E_0}{2} \right) - C_e \sin (E - E_0).$$
$$(3.124)$$

For the hyperbolic case,[7] by an analogous method it can be shown that

$$M - M_0 = -(F - F_0) + 2S_h \sinh^2 \left( \frac{F - F_0}{2} \right) + C_h \sinh (F - F_0)$$
$$(3.125)$$

with

$$e \sinh F_0 \equiv S_h$$
$$e \cosh F_0 \equiv C_h. \qquad (3.126)$$

The parabolic form of Kepler's equation can likewise be expressed as

$$(D - D_0)^3 + 3D_0(D - D_0)^2 + 6r_0(D - D_0) = 6(M - M_0) \qquad (3.127)$$

with

$$D_0 = \sqrt{2q} \tan \tfrac{1}{2}v_0 = \sqrt{2q} \frac{\sin v_0}{1 + \cos v_0}. \qquad (3.128)$$

---

[7] To be precise, a distinction should be made between the elliptic mean anomaly and hyperbolic mean anomaly. Actually, from the definition of the elliptical and hyperbolic functions, it can be shown that $M_e = -\sqrt{-1} M_h$ where the subscripts $e$ and $h$ refer respectively to the elliptic and hyperbolic mean anomaly.

The forms (3.124), (3.125), and (3.127) conclude the discussion of the relationship of position to time. These differenced forms will find direct application in computational procedures for the motion of a vehicle or body from one point in space to another via the two-body equations of motion. It should be noted that when a future (past) time is specified, Eqs. 3.116 will allow computation of $E$, $F$, and $D$ as a function of $M$, depending whether the motion is elliptical, hyperbolic, or parabolic. In contrast, Eqs. 3.124, 3.125, and 3.127 will yield

$$E - E_0, \quad F - F_0, \quad D - D_0, \tag{3.129}$$

at the future (past) time as a function of $M - M_0$. Iterative formulas for obtaining the parameters (3.129) can be derived easily.[8] In passing, it is well to note that the differenced Keplerian forms will be used repeatedly in Chapters 6 and 7.

### 3.6  RELATION BETWEEN SPEED AND POSITION

#### 2.6.1  Vis-viva equation

An extremely important relation of the two-body problem is an energy integral called the vis-viva[9] equation.

Consider the dot product of Eq. 3.4 with $2\dot{\mathbf{r}}$, that is,

$$2\dot{\mathbf{r}} \cdot \ddot{\mathbf{r}} = -2\frac{\mu}{r^3}\dot{\mathbf{r}} \cdot \mathbf{r}. \tag{3.130}$$

Apparently, from Figure 3.12, an explicit evaluation of $\dot{\mathbf{r}} \cdot \mathbf{r}$ yields

$$\dot{\mathbf{r}} \cdot \mathbf{r} = |\dot{\mathbf{r}}| \, |\mathbf{r}| \cos(\angle \dot{\mathbf{r}}, \mathbf{r}) = Vr \cos \psi = rV \cos \psi = r\dot{r}, \tag{3.131}$$

where $|\dot{\mathbf{r}}|$ or the magnitude of the velocity vector is denoted by $V$. Note that $|\dot{\mathbf{r}}| \neq \dot{r}$, since $\dot{r}$ is clearly the radial component of velocity along $r$. Hence the magnitude of the velocity vector can be obtained as the sum of the squares of the radial and tangential velocity components as

$$V^2 = (\dot{r})^2 + (r\dot{v})^2. \tag{3.132}$$

By consequence of relation Eq. 3.131, it is evident that Eq. 3.130 reduces to

$$2\dot{\mathbf{r}} \cdot \ddot{\mathbf{r}} = -2\frac{\mu}{r^3}r\dot{r} = -2\frac{\mu\dot{r}}{r^2}, \tag{3.133}$$

[8] See Exercise 3.3 for a compact iterative form.
[9] From the Latin meaning "living force."

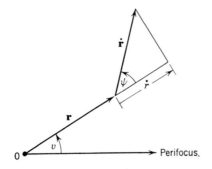

FIGURE 3.12    Position and velocity vectors.

so that

$$\int_0^{\tau_t} 2\dot{\mathbf{r}} \cdot \ddot{\mathbf{r}} \, d\tau = -2 \int_0^{\tau_t} \frac{\mu \dot{r}}{r^2} \, d\tau \tag{3.134}$$

or, upon integration and omission of the $t$ subscript,

$$V^2 - [V^2]_{\tau=0} = \frac{2\mu}{r} - \left[\frac{2\mu}{r}\right]_{\tau=0}. \tag{3.135}$$

If $\tau = 0$ is arbitrarily chosen at the time of perifocal passage or apse, then

$$\frac{dr}{d\tau} = 0, \tag{3.136}$$

and Eq. 3.132 yields

$$[V^2]_{\tau=0} = (r\dot{v})^2 = \frac{\mu p}{r^2}, \tag{3.137}$$

as is evident from Eq. 3.73.    Furthermore, from Figures 3.3, 3.4, and 3.5, it is possible to verify that

$$\left[\frac{2\mu}{r}\right]_{\tau=0} = \frac{2\mu}{q}, \qquad \left[\frac{\mu p}{r^2}\right]_{\tau=0} = \frac{\mu p}{q^2}. \tag{3.138}$$

Equation 3.135 can therefore be evaluated as

$$V^2 = \frac{2\mu}{r} + \frac{\mu p}{q^2} - \frac{2\mu}{q}. \tag{3.139}$$

But $p = a(1 - e^2)$ and $q = a(1 - e)$, so that the vis-viva relation reduces to

$$V^2 = \mu\left(\frac{2}{r} - \frac{1}{a}\right). \tag{3.140}$$

Some important facts can be extracted from Eq. 3.140. For a circle, $r = a$ always, and

$$V_c^2 = \frac{\mu}{a}, \tag{3.141}$$

the subscript $c$ denoting *circular velocity*. For a parabola, the semimajor axis is infinite and

$$V_p^2 = \frac{2\mu}{r}, \tag{3.142}$$

the subscript $p$ denoting *parabolic velocity*. Notice also from Eq. 3.141 that with characteristic units $V$ must have the units of circular satellite speed at the unit distance, that is, $\mu/a = \mu/a_e \approx 1$.

*Illustrative Example*
A satellite in a geocentric orbit has a semimajor axis of 2 e.r. and is 3 e.r. from the center of the Earth, what is its speed?

From Eq. 3.140, working in characteristic units and adopting $\mu = m_1 + m_v = 1$,

$$V^2 = (1)(\tfrac{2}{3} - \tfrac{1}{2}) = \tfrac{1}{6},$$

so that $V$ in characteristic units is

$$V = \frac{1}{\sqrt{6}} \text{ c.s.u.,}$$

which is a speed $1/\sqrt{6}$ times the speed of a circular satellite moving at one earth radii. The speed in ft/sec is given directly by utilizing the conversion factor of Eq. 1.17, so that

$$V = \frac{25936}{\sqrt{6}} = 1058.83 \text{ ft/sec.}$$

### 3.7   MOVEMENT IN SPACE

#### 3.7.1   Selection of orbital elements

Suppose that the position and velocity vectors $\mathbf{r}$, $\dot{\mathbf{r}}$ are known at some epoch time, say $t_0$. Then, as was discussed in Chapter 1, the fundamental constants of the orbit are known and it is uniquely determined.   There are, however, many different sets of fundamental constants that will serve to determine an orbit.   That is, it is possible to definitively know the position and velocity of a space vehicle or object for any other given time from the set

$$[x_0, y_0, z_0, \dot{x}_0, \dot{y}_0, \dot{z}_0]_{t=t_0}, \tag{3.143}$$

or, equally well, the classical parameters

$$[a, e, i, \Omega, \omega, T]. \tag{3.144}$$

The classical parameters are very useful for visualizing a given orbit, but can be equally replaced by the equivalent set

$$[a, e, T, \mathbf{P}, \mathbf{Q}, \mathbf{W}] \tag{3.145}$$

or

$$[a, e, \mathbf{U}_0, \mathbf{V}_0, \mathbf{W}_0]_{t=t_0}, \tag{3.146}$$

where $\mathbf{P}, \mathbf{Q}, \mathbf{U}_0, \mathbf{V}_0, \mathbf{W}_0$ are the orientation unit vectors of Sections 3.4.1 and 3.4.2.   Needless to say, redundant quantities are carried in sets (3.145) and (3.146), since only six "constant parameters" are needed to define a particular orbit.   The expression "constant parameter" perhaps has harsh connotation and needs to be explained.   Consider any parameter $\xi$ of the two-body problem.   Then, if at time $t_0$, the value of this parameter is adopted as an element, that is, symbolically represented by $\xi_0$, it is obvious that it is a constant.   It is for this reason that

$$[a, (e \cos E), (e \sin E), \mathbf{U}, \mathbf{V}]_{t=t_0} \tag{3.147}$$

can be used and, in fact, are a very useful set of elements for an elliptic orbit. It is seen here that $e$ is, of course, always a constant; the eccentric anomaly varies with time but, at some adopted epoch time the product of, for example, $e$ and $\cos E_0$ denoted by $(e \cos E)_0$ is a perfectly valid element.   It is a variable parameter frozen at some epoch.   The set (3.147) can be rewritten as

$$[a, C_e, S_e, \mathbf{U}, \mathbf{V}]_{t=t_0}, \tag{3.148}$$

where

$$\begin{aligned} C_e &= (e \cos E)_0 \\ S_e &\equiv (e \sin E)_0. \end{aligned} \tag{3.149}$$

At times, some sets of elements are preferable to others.   The set (3.144) is very descriptive, but what happens when the orbit is a perfect circle? In this case, perifocus is not defined, due to the fact that all radii are equal with respect to the orbit, and therefore, no minimum radius is defined.

Hence $\omega$ is not defined.    Again, what happens when the inclination is 0 or $\pi$?    In this case, the longitude of the ascending node is not defined. It is, of course, possible to redefine these elements for singular cases, but why not adopt a set such as (3.143) or (3.148), which are better defined?

### 3.7.2   Calculation of orbital elements

Once a set of elements has been chosen, it is possible to proceed along the following lines in order to determine the position and velocity of a given vehicle or object at some desired time $t$.    Let the set (3.148) be adopted, and for an elliptic orbit, for example, given $\mathbf{r}_0$ and $\dot{\mathbf{r}}_0$, compute the following parameters:

$$r_0{}^2 = \mathbf{r}_0 \cdot \mathbf{r}_0 \tag{3.150}$$

$$r_0 \dot{r}_0 = \mathbf{r}_0 \cdot \dot{\mathbf{r}}_0 \tag{3.151}$$

$$\frac{V_0{}^2}{\mu} = \frac{\dot{\mathbf{r}}_0 \cdot \dot{\mathbf{r}}_0}{\mu} \tag{3.152}$$

and from the vis-viva equation obtain

$$\frac{1}{a} = \frac{2}{r_0} - \frac{V_0{}^2}{\mu}. \tag{3.153}$$

From Eq. 3.67, calculate

$$C_e \equiv (e \cos E)_0 = 1 - \frac{r_0}{a}. \tag{3.154}$$

The expression for $S_e$ can be found by solving the first equation of group (3.70) for $(e \sin E)_0$ or $S_e$, that is,

$$S_e \equiv (e \sin E)_0 = \frac{\dot{r}_0}{a\dot{E}_0}. \tag{3.155}$$

As a side calculation, an analytical expression for $\dot{E}$ is required.   Since

$$M = M_0 + n(t - t_0) = M_0 + \sqrt{\mu}\,a^{-\frac{3}{2}}\tau = E - e \sin E, \tag{3.156}$$

differentiation with respect to $\tau$ yields

$$\dot{M} = \sqrt{\mu}\,a^{-\frac{3}{2}} = (1 - e \cos E)\dot{E} \tag{3.157}$$

or

$$\sqrt{\frac{\mu}{a}} = a(1 - e \cos E)\dot{E}. \tag{3.158}$$

Hence it is possible to extract

$$\dot{E} = \frac{1}{r}\sqrt{\frac{\mu}{a}}.$$  (3.159)

By evaluating $\dot{E}$ at $t = t_0$, that is, $\dot{E}_0$, expression (3.155) becomes

$$S_e = \frac{r_0 \dot{r}_0}{\sqrt{\mu a}}.$$  (3.160)

The eccentricity can readily be computed from

$$e^2 = S_e^2 + C_e^2.$$  (3.161)

Proceeding to the orientation vectors of the orbit, $\mathbf{U}_0$ is immediately determined as

$$\mathbf{U}_0 = \frac{\mathbf{r}_0}{r_0}.$$  (3.162)

Next, from the definition of $\mathbf{V}$ and examination of Figure 3.13, a relation between the $\mathbf{U}$ and $\mathbf{V}$ vectors is

$$\dot{\mathbf{r}} = \dot{r}\mathbf{U} + r\dot{v}\mathbf{V}$$  (3.163)

or

$$\dot{\mathbf{r}} = \dot{r}\frac{\mathbf{r}}{r} + r\dot{v}\mathbf{V},$$  (3.164)

hence

$$\mathbf{V} = \frac{r\dot{\mathbf{r}} - \dot{r}\mathbf{r}}{r^2\dot{v}}.$$  (3.165)

If the semiparameter is computed from

$$p = a(1 - e^2),$$  (3.166)

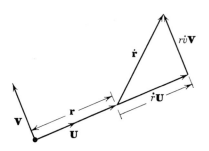

FIGURE 3.13    The U and V unit vectors.

it follows by virtue of Eq. 3.73 that

$$V = \frac{r\dot{r} - \dot{r}r}{\sqrt{\mu p}},$$
(3.167)

or, at epoch time $t_0$, an expression for the companion orientation vector $V_0$, becomes

$$V_0 = \frac{r_0\dot{r}_0 - \dot{r}_0 r_0}{\sqrt{\mu p}}.$$
(3.168)

Equations 3.150–3.154, 3.160–3.162, 3.166, and 3.168 have therefore produced the fundamental set

$$[a, C_e, S_e, U, V]_{t=t_0}$$

from $[r, \dot{r}]_{t=t_0}$.


### 3.7.3   Movement with an adopted set of elements

For any arbitrary time $t$, the desired future or past time, it is possible to calculate the difference in mean motion from Eq. 3.156 so that Eq. 3.124, the differenced Keplerian form, that is,

$$M - M_0 = (E - E_0) + 2S_e \sin^2\left(\frac{E - E_0}{2}\right) - C_e \sin (E - E_0),$$
(3.169)

where

$$M - M_0 = n(t - t_0),$$
(3.170)

can be solved iteratively for $(E - E_0)$.  Now since the first equation of group (3.69) is

$$r = a[1 - e \cos (E - E_0 + E_0)]$$
$$= a[1 - e \cos (E - E_0) \cos E_0 + e \sin (E - E_0) \sin E_0]$$
$$= a[1 - C_e \cos (E - E_0) + S_e \sin (E - E_0)],$$
(3.171)

the radius vector magnitude at future time $t$ can easily be computed. Knowing $r$, $r_0$, it is possible to write Eqs. 3.69 as

$$\cos (v - v_0 + v_0) = \frac{a \cos E - ae}{r}$$
(3.172)

$$\sin (v - v_0 + v_0) = \frac{a\sqrt{1 - e^2} \sin E}{r}.$$
(3.173)

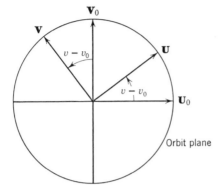

FIGURE 3.14    The **U** and **V** unit vectors after a rotation through an angle $v - v_0$.

Expanding $\cos (v - v_0 + v_0)$ and $\sin (v - v_0 + v_0)$ and solving the linear system for $\cos (v - v_0)$, $\sin (v - v_0)$ yields

$$rr_0 \cos (v - v_0) = a^2 (\cos E - e)(\cos E_0 - e) + a^2(1 - e^2) \sin E \sin E_0 \tag{3.174}$$

$$rr_0 \sin (v - v_0) = a^2 \sqrt{1 - e^2} \, [\sin E(\cos E_0 - e) - \sin E_0(\cos E - e)], \tag{3.175}$$

which permits calculation of the differences in true anomaly as

$$\cos (v - v_0) = 1 - \frac{a^2(1 - e^2)}{rr_0} [1 - \cos (E - E_0)] \tag{3.176}$$

$$\sin (v - v_0) = a^2 \frac{\sqrt{1 - e^2}}{rr_0} [M - M_0 - (E - E_0) + \sin (E - E_0)]. \tag{3.177}$$

It is possible to see from Figure 3.14 that Eqs. 3.176 and 3.177, along with

$$\mathbf{U} = \mathbf{U}_0 \cos (v - v_0) + \mathbf{V}_0 \sin (v - v_0) \tag{3.178}$$

$$\mathbf{V} = \mathbf{V}_0 \cos (v - v_0) - \mathbf{U}_0 \sin (v - v_0), \tag{3.179}$$

determine the **U** and **V** vectors at time $t$.

The radial rate is obtained, like $r$, from the first equation of group (3.70), written as

$$\begin{aligned}
\dot{r} &= ae\dot{E} \sin (E - E_0 + E_0) \\
&= a\dot{E}[e \sin (E - E_0) \cos E_0 + e \cos (E - E_0) \sin E_0] \\
&= a\dot{E}[C_e \sin (E - E_0) + S_e \cos (E - E_0)], \tag{3.180}
\end{aligned}$$

where $\dot{E}$ can be eliminated by virtue of Eq. 3.159, so that

$$\dot{r} = \frac{\sqrt{\mu a}}{r} \left[ C_e \sin (E - E_0) + S_e \cos (E - E_0) \right]. \tag{3.181}$$

The parameters $r$ and $\dot{r}$ are the last two parameters needed, because application of the definition of $\mathbf{U}$ yields

$$\mathbf{r} = r\mathbf{U} \tag{3.182}$$

and from Eq. (3.164),

$$\dot{\mathbf{r}} = \dot{r}\mathbf{U} + \frac{\sqrt{\mu p}}{r} \mathbf{V}. \tag{3.183}$$

Hence, symbolically,

$$\mathbf{r}_0, \, \dot{\mathbf{r}}_0, \, t_0 \rightarrow a, \, C_e, \, S_e, \, \mathbf{U}, \, \mathbf{V}, \, t_0 \rightarrow \mathbf{r}, \, \dot{\mathbf{r}}, \, t, \tag{3.184}$$

that is, from one time $t_0$ movement has been achieved to another time $t$, via a set of intermediate elements. The above procedure will fail for rectilinear orbits since division by $p = 0$ is performed. This difficulty could be removed by defining a new vector $\mathbf{V}_p \equiv \sqrt{p} \, \mathbf{V}$ which would replace $\mathbf{V}$ in the analysis.

A rather lengthy two-body algorithm for motion in space, which is valid for all types of orbits, is presented in Appendix II.

*Illustrative Example*
Given the set of elements $[a, S_e, C_e, \mathbf{U}_0, \mathbf{V}_0]_{t=t_0}$, where

$$a = +2.000000$$
$$S_e = +0.100000$$
$$C_e = +0.173205$$

$$U_{x0} = +0.360000 \qquad V_{x0} = +0.000000$$
$$U_{y0} = +0.640000 \qquad V_{y0} = +0.000000$$
$$U_{z0} = +0.000000 \qquad V_{z0} = +1.000000$$

with epoch time $t_0 = 1963$ October $10^{\text{day}}$ $12^{\text{hr}}$ $20^{\text{min}}$ $00^{\text{sec}}$, compute the position and velocity vectors of a geocentric satellite 0.087265 minutes after epoch.

To solve for $\mathbf{r}$ and $\dot{\mathbf{r}}$ at the future time, it suffices to adopt

$$k = 0.07436574, \qquad \mu = 1.0000000$$

and commence calculating with the following equations:

$$r_0 = a(1 - C_e) = +1.6535900$$
$$e^2 = S_e{}^2 + C_e{}^2 = +0.0399999$$
$$p = a(1 - e^2) = +1.9200002$$
$$n = k\sqrt{\mu}\, a^{-3/2} = +0.0262923$$
$$M - M_0 = n(t - t_0) = +0.0022944.$$

An iterative solution of the modified Keplerian form, that is,

$$M - M_0 = (E - E_0) + 2S_e \sin^2\left(\frac{E - E_0}{2}\right) - C_e \sin(E - E_0)$$

with $M - M_0$ as argument, is effected to yield

$$E - E_0 \qquad = +0.00277463$$
$$\cos(E - E_0) = +0.99999615$$
$$\sin(E - E_0) = +0.00277463.$$

The calculation is continued with

$$r = a[1 - C_e \cos(E - E_0) + S_e \sin(E - E_0)] = +1.6541463$$

$$\dot{r} = \frac{\sqrt{\mu a}}{r}\, [C_e \sin(E - E_0) + S_e \cos(E - E_0)] = +0.0859056.$$

A switch of variables from $E - E_0$ to $v - v_0$ is now accomplished by means of

$$\cos(v - v_0) = 1 - \frac{ap}{rr_0}\, [1 - \cos(E - E_0)] = +0.9999946$$

$$\sin(v - v_0) = a\frac{\sqrt{ap}}{rr_0}\, [M - M_0 - (E - E_0) + \sin(E - E_0)]$$
$$= +0.0032874.$$

The **U** and **V** unit vectors at the future time are obtained from

$$\mathbf{U} = \mathbf{U}_0 \cos(v - v_0) + \mathbf{V}_0 \sin(v - v_0)$$
$$\mathbf{V} = \mathbf{V}_0 \cos(v - v_0) - \mathbf{U}_0 \sin(v - v_0),$$

as

| | |
|---|---|
| $U_x = +0.5999968$ | $V_x = -0.0019724$ |
| $U_y = -0.7999957$ | $V_y = +0.0026299$ |
| $U_z = +0.0032874$ | $V_z = +0.9999946.$ |

A check on these values can be performed, due to the fact that $\mathbf{U} \cdot \mathbf{U} = 1$ and $\mathbf{V} \cdot \mathbf{V} = 1$. If this check is satisfactory, the position can be obtained from

$$\mathbf{r} = r\mathbf{U}$$

as

$$x = rU_x = +0.9924825$$
$$y = rU_y = -1.3233099$$
$$z = rU_z = +0.0054378.$$

Finally, the velocity is determined from

$$\dot{\mathbf{r}} = \dot{r}\mathbf{U} + \frac{\sqrt{\mu p}}{r}\mathbf{V}$$

as

$$\dot{x} = \dot{r}U_x + \frac{\sqrt{\mu p}}{r}V_x = +0.0498908$$

$$\dot{y} = \dot{r}U_y + \frac{\sqrt{\mu p}}{r}V_y = -0.0665211$$

$$\dot{z} = \dot{r}U_z + \frac{\sqrt{\mu p}}{r}V_z = +0.8379551.$$

Hence, the coordinates $\mathbf{r}$, and $\dot{\mathbf{r}}$ have been determined at $t_0 + 0.087265$ minutes. It should be mentioned that an obvious check is provided by recomputing the semimajor axis at the future time from

$$r^2 = x^2 + y^2 + z^2 = +2.7362002$$
$$V^2 = \dot{x}^2 + \dot{y}^2 + \dot{z}^2 = +0.7090829$$
$$\frac{1}{a} = \frac{2}{r} - \frac{V^2}{\mu} = +1.2090828 - 0.7090828 = +0.50000000$$

so that, as expected in Keplerian mechanics,

$$a = +2.0000000.$$

### 3.8   CALCULATION OF ORIENTATION ANGLES

#### 3.8.1   Calculation of $i$, $\Omega$, $\omega$

As mentioned in a previous section, calculation of orientation angles or elements such as $i$, $\Omega$, $\omega$ is beneficial in visualization of an orbit in space. There are many methods for the calculation of these angles, the one about to be presented is beneficial because it avoids low eccentricity inaccuracies at the expense of a little additional computation and proceeds to generate valid elements when $e = 0$, $i = 0$, or $\pi$, that is, for singular cases of $\omega$ and $\Omega$.

It is evident from the $z$ component of Eqs. 3.43 and 3.44, with $u$ substituted for $\omega$, that

$$U_z = \sin u \sin i \tag{3.185}$$

$$V_z = \cos u \sin i. \tag{3.186}$$

Therefore, if $\mathbf{r}_0$, $\dot{\mathbf{r}}_0$ are known, the $z$ component of Eqs. 3.162 and 3.168 allow the sum of the squares of Eqs. 3.185 and 3.186 to be written as

$$\sin^2 i = U_{z0}{}^2 + V_{z0}{}^2, \tag{3.187}$$

which determines $\sin i$, since $\sin i > 0$.

Furthermore, by introducing the angle $l$, called the *true longitude*, which is defined as

$$l \equiv \Omega + \omega + v = \Omega + u, \tag{3.188}$$

Eqs. 3.43 and 3.44, transformed by the introduction of $u$ and $l$, define $U_x$, $U_y$, $V_x$, $V_y$ as

$$\begin{aligned} U_x &= \cos u \cos (l - u) - \sin u \sin (l - u) \cos i \\ V_y &= -\sin u \sin (l - u) + \cos u \cos (l - u) \cos i \end{aligned} \tag{3.189}$$

$$\begin{aligned} U_y &= \cos u \sin (l - u) + \sin u \cos (l - u) \cos i \\ V_x &= -\sin u \cos (l - u) - \cos u \sin (l - u) \cos i. \end{aligned} \tag{3.190}$$

Expansion of $\cos (l - u)$, $\sin (l - u)$ in Eqs. 3.189, and addition yield

$$(1 + \cos i) \cos l = U_x + V_y. \tag{3.191}$$

Similarly, from Eqs. 3.190, it is possible to obtain

$$(1 + \cos i) \sin l = U_y - V_x. \tag{3.192}$$

Squaring and adding the last two forms produces

$$(1 + \cos i)^2 = (U_x + V_y)^2 + (U_y - V_x)^2 \tag{3.193}$$

or corresponding to $t = t_0$,

$$1 + \cos i = +\sqrt{(U_{x0} + V_{y0})^2 + (U_{y0} - V_{x0})^2}. \tag{3.194}$$

Hence, Eqs. 3.187 and 3.194 determine $i$ from

$$\sin i = +\sqrt{U_{z0}{}^2 + V_{z0}{}^2} \tag{3.195}$$

$$\cos i = +\sqrt{(U_{x0} + V_{y0})^2 + (U_{y0} - V_{x0})^2} - 1. \tag{3.196}$$

Furthermore, the equations

$$\cos l_0 = \frac{U_{x0} + V_{y0}}{1 + \cos i} \tag{3.197}$$

and

$$\sin l_0 = \frac{U_{y0} - V_{x0}}{1 + \cos i}, \tag{3.198}$$

which are valid for all orbital inclinations except $i = \pi$, determine the true longitude of the orbit.   It is evident that if $\Omega$ is desired or calculable,

$$\Omega = l_0 - u_0, \tag{3.199}$$

where, from Eqs. 3.185 and 3.186, $u$ at the time $t_0$ is defined by

$$\sin u_0 = \frac{U_{z0}}{\sin i}$$
$$\cos u_0 = \frac{V_{z0}}{\sin i}. \tag{3.200}$$

The argument of perigee is, of course, not defined for $e = 0$, but for other eccentricities, the equation of a conic immediately allows calculation of

$$C_v \equiv e \cos v_0 = \frac{p}{r_0} - 1. \tag{3.201}$$

By direct differentiation of Eq. 3.201, with $v$ and $r$ as variables, it is possible to obtain

$$S_v \equiv e \sin v_0 = \frac{p \dot{r}_0}{r_0^2 \dot{v}_0} = \dot{r}_0 \sqrt{\frac{p}{\mu}}, \tag{3.202}$$

so that

$$e = \sqrt{S_v^2 + C_v^2} \tag{3.203}$$

with $v_0$ defined by and computable from

$$\cos v_0 = \frac{1}{e} \left( \frac{p}{r_0} - 1 \right) \tag{3.204}$$

$$\sin v_0 = \frac{\dot{r}_0}{e} \sqrt{\frac{p}{\mu}}. \tag{3.205}$$

Therefore, the argument of perifocus is obtained as

$$\omega = u_0 - v_0. \tag{3.206}$$

It is impossible to obtain a set of elements such as $i$, $\Omega$, $\omega$ for all possible orbits. However, as calculation of the orbital elements proceeds, as in the above chain of equations, one could generate the orientation set

$$[i, l_0, \omega], \tag{3.207}$$

in the case of zero or low inclination; the set

$$[i, \Omega, u_0], \tag{3.208}$$

in the case of zero or low eccentricity; or the set

$$[i, \Omega, \omega], \tag{3.209}$$

when both $e$ and $i$ do not create numerical complications. Other combinations are possible.

### 3.9  SOLUTION OF THE FUNDAMENTAL EQUATION BY TIME SERIES

### 3.9.1  f and g series

The solution of the fundamental Eq. 3.4, that is,

$$\ddot{\mathbf{r}} = -\frac{\mu\mathbf{r}}{r^3} \tag{3.210}$$

can also be accomplished by series expansions about some epoch point, say $\mathbf{r}_0$, as a function of the modified time variable.

Consider Eq. 3.210 or for simplification following the development of Moulton [2], let

$$\ddot{\mathbf{r}} = -u\mathbf{r} \tag{3.211}$$

with

$$u \equiv \frac{\mu}{r^3}. \tag{3.212}$$

Theoretically, it can be proved that the solution of Eq. 3.211 can be expressed as

$$\begin{aligned}
\mathbf{r} = \mathbf{r}_0 + \dot{\mathbf{r}}_0\tau + \tfrac{1}{2}\ddot{\mathbf{r}}_0\tau^2 + \tfrac{1}{6}\dddot{\mathbf{r}}_0\tau^3 \\
+ \tfrac{1}{24}\overset{\text{IV}}{\mathbf{r}}_0\tau^4 + \tfrac{1}{120}\overset{\text{V}}{\mathbf{r}}_0\tau^5 + \tfrac{1}{720}\overset{\text{VI}}{\mathbf{r}}\tau^6 \\
+ \tfrac{1}{5040}\overset{\text{VII}}{\mathbf{r}}_0\tau^7 + \tfrac{1}{40320}\overset{\text{VIII}}{\mathbf{r}}_0\tau^8 + 0(\tau^9).
\end{aligned} \tag{3.213}$$

Assuming Eq. 3.213 is a solution, let Eq. 3.211 be differentiated six times, frozen at epoch $t_0$, and $\ddot{\mathbf{r}}_0 = -u_0\mathbf{r}_0$ be substituted as soon as $\ddot{\mathbf{r}}_0$ appears in any subsequent expression, that is,

$$\dddot{\mathbf{r}}_0 = -\dot{u}_0\mathbf{r}_0 - u_0\dot{\mathbf{r}}_0$$

$$\overset{\text{IV}}{\mathbf{r}}_0 = (-\ddot{u}_0 + u_0{}^2)\mathbf{r}_0 - 2\dot{u}_0\dot{\mathbf{r}}_0$$

$$\overset{\text{V}}{\mathbf{r}}_0 = (-\dddot{u}_0 + 4u_0\dot{u}_0)\mathbf{r}_0 - (3\ddot{u}_0 - u_0{}^2)\dot{\mathbf{r}}_0$$

$$\overset{\text{VI}}{\mathbf{r}}_0 = (-\overset{\text{IV}}{u}_0 + 7u_0\ddot{u}_0 - u_0{}^3 + 4\dot{u}_0{}^2)\mathbf{r}_0$$
$$\qquad - (4\dddot{u}_0 - 6u_0\dot{u}_0)\dot{\mathbf{r}}_0 \tag{3.214}$$

$$\overset{\text{VII}}{\mathbf{r}}_0 = (-\overset{\text{V}}{u}_0 + 15\dot{u}_0\ddot{u}_0 + 11u_0\dddot{u}_0 - 9u_0{}^2\dot{u}_0)\mathbf{r}_0$$
$$\qquad - (5\overset{\text{IV}}{u}_0 - 13u_0\ddot{u}_0 - 10\dot{u}_0{}^2 + u_0{}^3)\dot{\mathbf{r}}_0$$

$$\overset{\text{VIII}}{\mathbf{r}}_0 = (-\overset{\text{VI}}{u}_0 + 15\ddot{u}_0{}^2 + 26\dot{u}_0\dddot{u}_0 + 16u_0\overset{\text{IV}}{u}_0 - 28u_0\dot{u}_0{}^2$$
$$\qquad - 22u_0{}^2\ddot{u}_0 + u_0{}^4)\mathbf{r}_0 - (6\overset{\text{V}}{u}_0 - 48\dot{u}_0\ddot{u}_0$$
$$\qquad - 24u_0\dddot{u}_0 + 12u_0{}^2\dot{u}_0)\dot{\mathbf{r}}_0$$

and let these successive derivatives be substituted in expression 3.213. Evidently, then,

$$\mathbf{r} = f\mathbf{r}_0 + g\dot{\mathbf{r}}_0, \tag{3.215}$$

where

$$f \equiv 1 - \tfrac{1}{2}u_0\tau^2 - \tfrac{1}{6}\dot{u}_0\tau^3$$
$$\qquad - \tfrac{1}{24}(\ddot{u}_0 - u_0{}^2)\tau^4 - \tfrac{1}{120}(\dddot{u}_0 - 4u_0\dot{u}_0)\tau^5$$
$$\qquad - \tfrac{1}{720}(\overset{\text{IV}}{u}_0 - 7u_0\ddot{u}_0 + u_0{}^3 - 4\dot{u}_0{}^2)\tau^6$$
$$\qquad - \tfrac{1}{5040}(\overset{\text{V}}{u}_0 - 15\dot{u}_0\ddot{u}_0 - 11u_0\dddot{u}_0 + 9u_0{}^2\dot{u}_0)\tau^7$$
$$\qquad - \tfrac{1}{40320}(\overset{\text{VI}}{u}_0 - 15\ddot{u}_0{}^2 - 26\dot{u}_0\dddot{u}_0 - 16u_0\overset{\text{IV}}{u}_0$$
$$\qquad + 28u_0\dot{u}_0{}^2 + 22u_0{}^2\ddot{u}_0 - u_0{}^4)\tau^8$$

and

$$g \equiv \tau - \tfrac{1}{6}u_0\tau^3 - \tfrac{1}{12}\dot{u}_0\tau^4 - \tfrac{1}{120}(3\ddot{u}_0 - u_0{}^2)\tau^5$$
$$\qquad - \tfrac{1}{360}(2\dddot{u}_0 - 3u_0\dot{u}_0)\tau^6$$
$$\qquad - \tfrac{1}{5040}(5\overset{\text{IV}}{u}_0 - 13u_0\ddot{u}_0 - 10\dot{u}_0{}^2 + u_0{}^3)\tau^7$$
$$\qquad - \tfrac{1}{40320}(6\overset{\text{V}}{u}_0 - 48\dot{u}_0\ddot{u}_0 - 24u_0\dddot{u}_0 + 12u_0{}^2\dot{u}_0)\tau^8.$$

The $f$ and $g$ expressions are, for the present, useless from a practical point of view because the higher derivatives of $u$ have not yet been determined. Lagrange[10] proceeds as follows. Introduce $p$ and $q$ by

$$r^2p \equiv \frac{1}{2}\frac{d(r^2)}{d\tau} \tag{3.216}$$

$$r^2q \equiv \frac{1}{2}\frac{d^2(r^2)}{d\tau^2}, \tag{3.217}$$

where it is evident that[11]

$$p = \frac{r\dot{r}}{r^2} = \frac{\mathbf{r}\cdot\dot{\mathbf{r}}}{r^2} \tag{3.218}$$

$$q = \frac{V^2 - r^2u}{r^2}. \tag{3.219}$$

Furthermore,

$$\dot{u} = -\frac{3\mu}{r^4}\frac{dr}{d\tau} = -\frac{3\mu}{r^4}\frac{1}{2r}\frac{d(r^2)}{d\tau} \tag{3.220}$$

$$\dot{p} = \frac{1}{2r^2}\frac{d^2(r^2)}{d\tau^2} - \frac{1}{r^3}\frac{d(r^2)}{d\tau}\frac{dr}{d\tau} \tag{3.221}$$

$$\dot{q} = -\frac{1}{r^3}\frac{d^2(r^2)}{d\tau^2}\frac{dr}{d\tau} + \frac{1}{2r^2}\frac{d^3(r^2)}{d\tau^3}. \tag{3.222}$$

which become by introduction of Eqs. 3.218 and 3.219

$$\dot{u} = -3up \tag{3.223}$$

$$\dot{p} = q - 2p^2 \tag{3.224}$$

$$\dot{q} = -(up + 2pq). \tag{3.225}$$

Notice that

$$\ddot{u} = -3(u\dot{p} + \dot{u}p), \tag{3.226}$$

which upon substitution of Eqs. 3.223 and 3.224, becomes

$$\ddot{u} = -3[u(q - 2p^2) - 3up^2], \tag{3.227}$$

which is lacking in lower order derivatives of $u$. This differentiation process can be repeated, each time eliminating $\dot{u}$, $\dot{p}$, $\dot{q}$ by means of Eqs.

[10] At twenty-three, Lagrange was acknowledged the equal of the greatest mathematicians of the age—Euler and the Bernoullis. (E. T. Bell—*Men of Mathematics*).
[11] Note that $p$, $q$, and $u$ are not the same variables as previously defined.

3.223, 3.224, and 3.225, as the case demands.  By substituting for the time derivatives of $u$ evaluated at the adopted epoch, the $f$ and $g$ expressions are given by

$$f = 1 - \tfrac{1}{2}u_0\tau^2 + \tfrac{1}{2}u_0p_0\tau^3 + \tfrac{1}{24}(3u_0q_0 - 15u_0p_0^2 + u_0^2)\tau^4$$
$$+ \tfrac{1}{8}(7u_0p_0^3 - 3u_0p_0q_0 - u_0^2p_0)\tau^5$$
$$+ \tfrac{1}{720}(630u_0p_0^2q_0 - 24u_0^2q_0 - u_0^3 - 45u_0q_0^2 - 945u_0p_0^4$$
$$+ 210u_0^2p_0^2)\tau^6$$
$$+ \tfrac{1}{5040}(882u_0^2p_0q_0 - 3150u_0^2p_0^3 - 9450u_0p_0^3q_0$$
$$+ 1575u_0p_0q_0^2 + 63u_0^3p_0 + 10395u_0p_0^5)\tau^7$$
$$+ \tfrac{1}{40320}(1107u_0^2q_0^2 - 24570u_0^2p_0^2q_0 - 2205u_0^3p_0^2$$
$$+ 51975u_0^2p_0^4 - 42525u_0p_0^2q_0^2 + 155925u_0p_0^4q_0$$
$$+ 1575u_0q_0^3 + 117u_0^3q_0 - 135135u_0p_0^6 + u_0^4)\tau^8,$$

$$(3.228)$$

$$g = \tau - \tfrac{1}{6}u_0\tau^3 + \tfrac{1}{4}u_0p_0\tau^4 + \tfrac{1}{120}(9u_0q_0 - 45u_0p_0^2 + u_0^2)\tau^5$$
$$+ \tfrac{1}{360}(210u_0p_0^3 - 90u_0p_0q_0 - 15u_0^2p_0)\tau^6$$
$$+ \tfrac{1}{5040}(3150u_0p_0^2q_0 - 54u_0^2q_0 - 225u_0q_0^2$$
$$- 4725u_0p_0^4 + 630u_0^2p_0^2 - u_0^3)\tau^7$$
$$+ \tfrac{1}{40320}(3024u_0^2p_0q_0 - 12600u_0^2p_0^3 - 56700u_0p_0^3q_0$$
$$+ 9450u_0p_0q_0^2 + 62370u_0p_0^5 + 126u_0^3p_0)\tau^8. \quad (3.229)$$

Thus, if $\mathbf{r}_0$ and $\dot{\mathbf{r}}_0$ are known, it is possible to compute $p_0$ and $q_0$ from Eqs. 3.218 and 3.219, and after evaluating $f$ and $g$ from Eqs. 3.228 and 3.229 for a desired value of $\tau$, obtain the position vector as

$$\mathbf{r} = f\mathbf{r}_0 + g\dot{\mathbf{r}}_0. \tag{3.230}$$

In order to concisely express the series, the following functions are defined:

$$f \equiv f(V, r, \dot{r}, \tau_m) = f_m \tag{3.231}$$
$$g \equiv g(V, r, \dot{r}, \tau_m) = g_m. \tag{3.232}$$

These functions will find considerable use in Chapters 6 and 7.

Since $\mathbf{r}_0$ and $\dot{\mathbf{r}}_0$ are constants, it is possible to differentiate Eq. 3.230 to obtain the velocity vector as

$$\dot{\mathbf{r}} = \dot{f}\mathbf{r}_0 + \dot{g}\dot{\mathbf{r}}_0, \tag{3.233}$$

where

$$\dot{f} \equiv \frac{df}{d\tau}, \qquad \dot{g} \equiv \frac{dg}{d\tau}.$$

Moulton [7] has shown that the proved domain of convergence of expansions of $r$ as a function of $\tau$ about perifocus, that is, a series of the form,

$$r = a(1 - e)\left[1 + \frac{e}{2(1 - e)^3}\tau^2 - \frac{e(1 + 3e)}{24(1 - e)^6}\tau^4 + \cdots\right], \qquad (3.234)$$

is restricted by the inequality

$$|\tau| < \frac{(1 - e)^3[-2e + \sqrt{4e^2 + 3e}][(3 + 2e) - \sqrt{4e^2 + 3e}]^3}{108[e + \sqrt{4e^2 + 3e}]}. \qquad (3.235)$$

The reader interested in convergence problems of this type is directed to an excellent discussion in [7].

Numerical studies by Douglas [11] have indicated that for circular orbits up to $a = 6$ e.r., the number of significant figures obtained in $r$ by predicting forward through $M - M_0$ can be tabulated as shown in Figure 3.15.

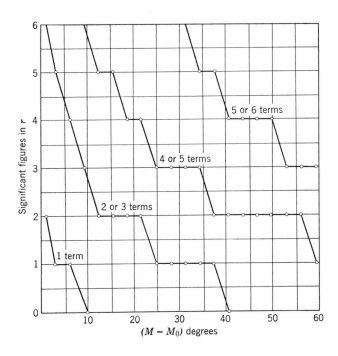

FIGURE 3.15 Expected significant figures in the $f$ and $g$ prediction of $r$ as a function of the number of terms for near-Earth satellites.

**3.10   AN ALTERNATE FORMULATION FOR MOTION IN THE ORBIT PLANE**

### 3.10.1   Closed form expressions for the f and g series

In the previous section, modified time series were developed for the $f$ and $g$ functions. Exact closed form expressions are, however, also derivable.

Consider

$$\mathbf{r} = f\mathbf{r}_0 + g\dot{\mathbf{r}}_0,$$ (3.236)

written for the orbital axes $x_\omega$, $y_\omega$, that is,

$$\mathbf{r}_\omega = f\mathbf{r}_{\omega 0} + g\dot{\mathbf{r}}_{\omega 0}$$ (3.237)

and cross Eq. 3.237 with $\dot{\mathbf{r}}_{\omega 0}$, so that

$$\mathbf{r}_\omega \times \dot{\mathbf{r}}_{\omega 0} = f\mathbf{r}_{\omega 0} \times \dot{\mathbf{r}}_{\omega 0}.$$ (3.238)

However, since $\mathbf{r}_{\omega 0} \times \dot{\mathbf{r}}_{\omega 0}$ can be replaced by $h\mathbf{W}$, as a consequence of Eq. 3.71, it follows that

$$\mathbf{r}_\omega \times \dot{\mathbf{r}}_{\omega 0} = fh\mathbf{W} = f\sqrt{\mu p}\,\mathbf{W}$$ (3.239)

or

$$\begin{vmatrix} \mathbf{P} & \mathbf{Q} & \mathbf{W} \\ x_\omega & y_\omega & 0 \\ \dot{x}_{\omega 0} & \dot{y}_{\omega 0} & 0 \end{vmatrix} = f\sqrt{\mu p}\mathbf{W},$$ (3.240)

which simplifies to

$$(x_\omega \dot{y}_{\omega 0} - y_\omega \dot{x}_{\omega 0})\mathbf{W} = f\sqrt{\mu p}\,\mathbf{W}.$$ (3.241)

Dotting with $\mathbf{W}$ and transposing yields

$$f = \frac{x_\omega \dot{y}_{\omega 0} - y_\omega \dot{x}_{\omega 0}}{\sqrt{\mu p}}.$$ (3.242)

The $g$ coefficient can be obtained by crossing Eq. 3.237 with $\mathbf{r}_{\omega 0}$, so that similarly,

$$g = \frac{y_\omega x_{\omega 0} - x_\omega y_{\omega 0}}{\sqrt{\mu p}}.$$ (3.243)

Expressions for $x_\omega$ and $y_\omega$ are given directly by Eqs. 3.69.  The modified time derivatives are given by 3.70, that is,

$$\dot{x}_\omega = -a\dot{E} \sin E$$
$$\dot{y}_\omega = a\dot{E}\sqrt{1 - e^2} \cos E. \tag{3.244}$$

However, since $\dot{E} = \dfrac{1}{r}\sqrt{\dfrac{\mu}{a}}$, Eq. 3.159, it is possible to write

$$\dot{x}_\omega = -\frac{\sqrt{\mu a}}{r} \sin E \tag{3.245}$$

$$\dot{y}_\omega = \frac{\sqrt{\mu p}}{r} \cos E. \tag{3.246}$$

Evaluating these expressions at the epoch time and inserting into Eqs. 3.242 and 3.243, results in

$$f = \frac{a(\cos E - e)\sqrt{\mu p} \cos E_0 + a\sqrt{\mu p} \sin E \sin E_0}{r_0 \sqrt{\mu p}} \tag{3.247}$$

$$g = \frac{a^2\sqrt{1 - e^2}\,(\cos E_0 - e) \sin E - a^2\sqrt{1 - e^2}\,(\cos E - e) \sin E_0}{\sqrt{\mu p}}, \tag{3.248}$$

which simplify to

$$f = 1 - \frac{a}{r_0}[1 - \cos(E - E_0)] \tag{3.249}$$

$$g = \tau - \frac{a^{3/2}}{\sqrt{\mu}}[(E - E_0) - \sin(E - E_0)]. \tag{3.250}$$

The last two relationships are obtained by expanding $\sin E = \sin(E - E_0 + E_0)$ and utilizing Kepler's equation.

Obviously then, if $\mathbf{r}_0$, $\dot{\mathbf{r}}_0$ are known, it is possible to adopt a set of elements; solve Eq. 3.124 for $(E - E_0)$, enter Eqs. 3.249 and 3.250 and obtain $f$ and $g$.  Naturally then, at modified time $\tau$,

$$\mathbf{r} = f\mathbf{r}_0 + g\dot{\mathbf{r}}_0 \tag{3.251}$$

yields the future (past) position vector.  The corresponding velocity is obtained from

$$\dot{\mathbf{r}} = \dot{f}\mathbf{r}_0 + \dot{g}\dot{\mathbf{r}}_0, \tag{3.252}$$

where $\dot{f}$ and $\dot{g}$ are the modified time derivatives of expressions (3.249) and (3.250), that is,

$$\dot{f} = -\frac{\sqrt{\mu a}}{rr_0} \sin (E - E_0) \qquad (3.253)$$

$$\dot{g} = \frac{a}{r} [\cos (E - E_0) - C_e \cos (E - E_0) + S_e \sin (E - E_0)], \quad (3.254)$$

where $S_e$ and $C_e$ are defined by Eqs. 3.123. Hyperbolic analogues can be obtained by a similar process (see Section 3.12.1).

These closed-form expressions find great use in preliminary orbit determination.

### 3.11   RELATION BETWEEN DYNAMICAL CENTER, SATELLITE, AND OBSERVER

#### 3.11.1   A fundamental vector equation for geocentric orbits

In the previous sections, the controlling equation of two-body motion, Eq. 3.4 has undergone investigation and integration. The dependent vector variable **r** is, of course, a position vector from the dynamical center to the satellite or object moving along a particular orbit. The intent here is to define auxiliary vectors that at times can be used to calculate **r**.

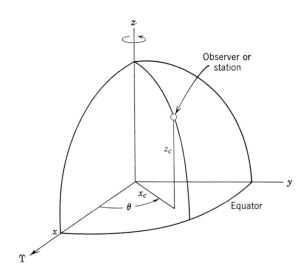

FIGURE 3.16   The observer in a rotating frame.

Consider an observer on the surface of a given geometrically oblate planet, say Earth. Certainly the observer has a definite position with respect to the dynamical center. As a matter of fact, it has been shown in Section 1.4.3 that the observer's geometric coordinates on a given meridian are

$$x_c = G_1 \cos \phi \tag{3.255}$$

$$z_c = G_2 \sin \phi, \tag{3.256}$$

where the $G$ coefficients are functions of the flattening and the geodetic latitude.

The observer's meridian, fixed to the planet, is rotating with an angular velocity equal to $\dot{\theta}$, that is, the sidereal rate of change. As can be seen from Figure 3.16, the rectangular components of the observer in the right ascension-declination coordinate system are given by

$$x_s = x_c \cos \theta$$
$$y_s = x_c \sin \theta \tag{3.257}$$
$$z_s = z_c,$$

where $\theta$ is the sidereal time (Section 1.3.3) and the subscript $s$ refers to a given observer or station. Evidently then, by means of Eqs. 3.255 and 3.256,

$$x_s = G_1 \cos \phi \cos \theta$$
$$y_s = G_1 \cos \phi \sin \theta \tag{3.258}$$
$$z_s = G_2 \sin \phi.$$

Thus, by utilizing the linkage $\theta$ between the rotating Earth-fixed system $(x_c, z_c)$ and inertial or $(x, y, z)$ system, the observer's coordinates can be calculated in the system where the solution of the fundamental equation (3.4) has been formulated.

The vector whose components are given by Eq. 3.258 is, by definition, the negative of the *station coordinate vector* $\mathbf{R}$. That is,

$$\mathbf{R} = \mathbf{R}(X, Y, Z) \equiv \mathbf{R}(-x_s, -y_s, -z_s). \tag{3.259}$$

With this definition, it is possible to draw the vector triangle $ODS$, as shown in Figure 3.17.

Hence $\mathbf{R}$ is a vector from the observer's position to the dynamical center of the planet. The dependent variable of the fundamental equation is, of course, $\mathbf{r}$ and the vector needed to close triangle $ODS$ is $\boldsymbol{\rho}$, which is called the *slant range vector*. The slant range is then the position of the

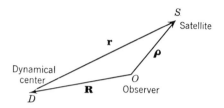

FIGURE 3.17    Vector triangle relating dynamical center, satellite, and observer.

satellite with respect to the observer or ground station. From Figure 3.17, it is evident that

$$\boldsymbol{\rho} = \mathbf{r} + \mathbf{R}. \tag{3.260}$$

Equation 3.260 is of fundamental importance in many orbit determination schemes. The predominating factor at this point is the realization that the vector $\mathbf{R}$ can nearly always be determined at the start of an orbit determination procedure from the known coordinates of the observer as a function of sidereal time.

At times the derivatives of $\mathbf{R}$ are also of importance. They can be directly determined analytically for a given station from Eqs. 3.258. For reference, $\mathbf{R}$ and a few of the derivatives are given by

$$X = -G_1 \cos \phi \cos \theta$$
$$Y = -G_1 \cos \phi \sin \theta \tag{3.261}$$
$$Z = -G_2 \sin \phi$$

or in vector form,

$$\mathbf{R} = \begin{bmatrix} X \\ Y \\ Z \end{bmatrix}, \qquad \dot{\mathbf{R}} = \dot{\theta} \begin{bmatrix} -Y \\ X \\ 0 \end{bmatrix}, \qquad \ddot{\mathbf{R}} = \dot{\theta}^2 \begin{bmatrix} -X \\ -Y \\ 0 \end{bmatrix}$$

$$\dddot{\mathbf{R}} = \dot{\theta}^3 \begin{bmatrix} Y \\ -X \\ 0 \end{bmatrix}, \qquad \overset{\mathrm{IV}}{\mathbf{R}} = \dot{\theta}^4 \begin{bmatrix} X \\ Y \\ 0 \end{bmatrix}, \qquad \overset{\mathrm{V}}{\mathbf{R}} = \dot{\theta}^5 \begin{bmatrix} -Y \\ X \\ 0 \end{bmatrix} = \dot{\theta}^4 \dot{\mathbf{R}}. \tag{3.262}$$

It should be noted that $\dot{\theta} = \dfrac{d\theta}{dt}\dfrac{dt}{d\tau} = \dfrac{1}{k}\dfrac{d\theta}{dt}$ (see Section 1.3.3).

### 3.11.2    Extension of the fundamental vector equation for heliocentric and planetocentric satellites

It is certainly possible to extend the results of the previous section to objects in heliocentric orbits.    Consider a satellite in an orbit about the Sun (Figure 3.18).
    From Figure 3.18,

$$\rho = r + R + R_\odot, \qquad\qquad (3.263)$$

where motion is now relative to a heliocentric inertial frame and $R_\odot$ is a vector of the heliocentric coordinates of the Sun, as obtained from a yearly ephemeris such as the *American Ephemeris and Nautical Almanac* or directly from magnetic tapes for longer spans of time [3].
    A further extension is for planetocentric orbits.    In this case, an observer, say on Earth, observes a satellite moving about another planet, for example, a satellite of the planet Jupiter.
    From Figure 3.19, it is possible to see that

$$\rho = r + R + R_\odot + R_p,$$

where all vectors are, of course, in the same coordinate frame and $R_p$ is a vector of the coordinates of the planet, about which the objective satellite is moving, with respect to the Sun.    In this case, the coordinates $R_p$ would again be obtained from an ephemeris or magnetic tapes [3], and a transformation to a common frame would be made to insure that all the vectors composing $\rho$ are in the same coordinate frame.
    Derivatives of $R_\odot$ and $R_p$ are usually obtained by numerical differentiation of the position vectors.    This will become evident in Chapter 7.

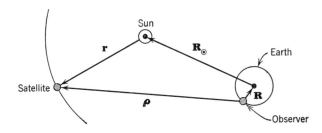

FIGURE 3.18    A heliocentric orbit.

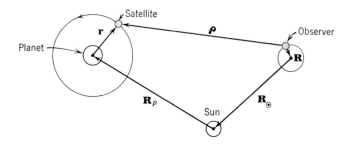

FIGURE 3.19   A planetocentric orbit.


## 3.12   SOME IMPORTANT FORMULAS OF THE TWO-BODY PROBLEM

### 3.12.1   Related formulas

Apart from all the previous formulas that were derived in this chapter, there are other equations which can be developed by means of the preceding relationships. The interested reader may wish to derive them as an exercise.

$$\dot{r} = \sqrt{\frac{\mu}{p}}\, e \sin v \tag{3.264}$$

$$r\dot{v} = \sqrt{\frac{\mu}{p}}\, (1 + e \cos v) \tag{3.265}$$

$$p = (V_0{}^2 - \dot{r}_0{}^2)\frac{r_0{}^2}{\mu} \tag{3.266}$$

$$\cos v = \frac{\cos E - e}{1 - e \cos E} \doteq \frac{e - \cosh F}{e \cosh F - 1} \doteq \frac{2q - D^2}{2q + D^2} \tag{3.267}$$

$$\sin v = \frac{\sqrt{1 - e^2}\, \sin E}{1 - e \cos E} \doteq \frac{\sqrt{e^2 - 1}\, \sinh F}{e \cosh F - 1} \doteq \frac{2\sqrt{2q}\, D}{2q + D^2} \tag{3.268}$$

$$\cos E = \frac{\cos v + e}{1 + e \cos v} \tag{3.269}$$

$$\sin E = \frac{\sqrt{1 - e^2}\, \sin v}{1 + e \cos v} \tag{3.270}$$

$$\cosh F = \frac{\cos v + e}{1 + e \cos v} \tag{3.271}$$

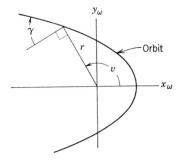

FIGURE 3.20   The flight path angle.

$$\sinh F = \frac{\sqrt{e^2 - 1}\, \sin v}{1 + e \cos v} \tag{3.272}$$

$$\tan \tfrac{1}{2}v = \sqrt{\frac{1 + e}{1 - e}}\, \tan \tfrac{1}{2}E \doteq \sqrt{\frac{e + 1}{e - 1}}\, \tan \text{h}\, \tfrac{1}{2}F \doteq \frac{D}{\sqrt{2q}} \tag{3.273}$$

$$\dot{x}_\omega = -\sqrt{\frac{\mu}{p}}\, \sin v \tag{3.274}$$

$$\dot{y}_\omega = \sqrt{\frac{\mu}{p}}\, (\cos v + e) \tag{3.275}$$

$$\mathbf{P} = \mathbf{U} \cos v_0 - \mathbf{V} \sin v_0 \tag{3.276}$$

$$\mathbf{Q} = \mathbf{U} \sin v_0 + \mathbf{V} \cos v_0 \tag{3.277}$$

$$\mathbf{P} = \left[\frac{\cos E_0}{r_0}\right]\mathbf{r}_0 - \left[\sqrt{\frac{a}{\mu}}\, \sin E_0\right]\dot{\mathbf{r}}_0 \tag{3.278}$$

$$\mathbf{Q} = \left[\frac{\sin E_0}{r_0\sqrt{1 - e^2}}\right]\mathbf{r}_0 + \left[\sqrt{\frac{a}{\mu(1 - e^2)}}\, (\cos E_0 - e)\right]\dot{\mathbf{r}}_0 \tag{3.279}$$

$$\cos \gamma = \frac{1 + e \cos v}{\sqrt{1 + 2e \cos v + e^2}} \tag{3.280}$$

$$\sin \gamma = \frac{e \sin v}{\sqrt{1 + 2e \cos v + e^2}} \tag{3.281}$$

The angle $\gamma$, called the *flight path angle*, is defined by Figure 3.20.

$$\sin (E - E_0) = \frac{r}{\sqrt{ap}}\, \sin (v - v_0) - \frac{r}{p}\, [1 - \cos (v - v_0)]S_e \tag{3.282}$$

$$\cos (E - E_0) = 1 - \frac{rr_0}{ap} [1 - \cos (v - v_0)] \tag{3.283}$$

$$\sinh (F - F_0) = \frac{r}{\sqrt{-ap}} \sin (v - v_0) - \frac{r}{p} [1 - \cos (v - v_0)]S_h \tag{3.284}$$

$$F - F_0 = \log \{\sinh (F - F_0) + [\sinh^2 (F - F_0) + 1]^{1/2}\} \tag{3.285}$$

$$D - D_0 = \frac{rr_0}{(2q)^{3/2}} \{[1 + \cos v_0] \sin (v - v_0)$$

$$- \sin v_0[1 - \cos (v - v_0)]\} \tag{3.286}$$

$$f = 1 - \frac{a}{r_0} [1 - \cos (E - E_0)]$$

$$= 1 - \frac{a}{r_0} [1 - \cosh (F - F_0)] \tag{3.287}$$

$$g = \tau - \frac{a^{3/2}}{\sqrt{\mu}} [(E - E_0) - \sin (E - E_0)]$$

$$= \tau - \frac{(-a)^{3/2}}{\sqrt{\mu}} [\sinh (F - F_0) - (F - F_0)] \tag{3.288}$$

$$\begin{matrix} S_e = e \sin E_0, & S_h = e \sinh F_0 \\ C_e = e \cos E_0, & C_h = e \cosh F_0 \end{matrix} \tag{3.289}$$

$$C_e = \frac{e \cos v_0 + e^2}{1 + e \cos v_0} \doteq C_h \tag{3.290}$$

$$S_e = \frac{[1 - e^2]^{1/2} e \sin v_0}{1 + e \cos v_0} \doteq \frac{[e^2 - 1]^{1/2} e \sin v_0}{1 + e \cos v_0} = S_h \tag{3.291}$$

$$S_v = e \sin v_0, \quad C_v = e \cos v_0 \tag{3.292}$$

$$r = p[1 + C_v \cos (v - v_0) - S_v \sin (v - v_0)]^{-1} \tag{3.293}$$

$$x_v = r \cos (v - v_0) \tag{3.294}$$

$$y_v = r \sin (v - v_0) \tag{3.295}$$

$$\dot{x}_v = \left[\frac{\mu}{p}\right]^{1/2} [S_v - \sin (v - v_0)] \tag{3.296}$$

$$\dot{y}_v = \left[\frac{\mu}{p}\right]^{1/2} [C_v + \cos (v - v_0)]. \tag{3.297}$$

## 3.13   SUMMARY

Utilizing the concept of Newton's gravitational theory has permitted Kepler's laws to be proved in a rigorous manner. Introduction of modified time differentiation has eliminated the gravitational constant from most dynamical equations. Direct integration of the fundamental equation led to an algebraic form that through independent means was shown to be a second-degree algebraic equation or conic. Unit vectors along various axes were introduced in order to define orientation of the plane in which motion occurs. It has been shown how orthogonal transformations or mappings from a two-dimensional to a three-dimensional domain could be effected by means of these unit vectors. Inverse transformations from three space to two space were also introduced. In a two-space domain, the analysis was simplified and various equations for relating angular position to time, were developed. The most famous of these equations is the Kepler equation for elliptic motion. Hyperbolic and parabolic forms are also discussed. Metamorphoses of these basic forms resulted in modified equations whose dependent variable was a difference in the dependent variables of the unaltered equations. These new forms, by adoption of certain orbital elements, permit movement to be made from one state of a trajectory to another without indeterminacies. A very important orbital element and direct index of elliptic, hyperbolic, or parabolic motion which can always be calculated from the vis-viva integral was shown to be the semimajor axis. To uniquely define the overall geometric shape of the trajectory, it was evident that the orbital eccentricity must also be scrutinized. Orientation elements or angles are sometimes used to define the orientation of the orbital plane and fundamental reckoning points.

The fundamental differential equation of Newtonian motion was also shown to possess a solution in terms of modified time series. This attack led to the concept that future position and velocity vectors are linear combinations of position and velocity vectors at a particular epoch. The coefficients of such linear combinations can also be obtained in closed form.

Relationships between the dynamical center, satellite, and hypothetical or actual observer on the surface of a planet were developed. This concept of decomposition of the radius vector into two other vectors, one of which, the station coordinate vector, can always be determined as a function of the observer's position is an important concept. The other vector has been called the slant range vector. It will be used in various orbit determination schemes in the orbit determination process. Some alternate equations, derivable from preceding relationships, were listed for convenience.

**EXERCISES**

1. If the equation of a satellite about the Earth is given by

$$\frac{x^2_{\omega'}}{9} + \frac{y^2_{\omega'}}{4} = 1,$$

where the $x_{\omega}'$ and $y_{\omega}'$ axes are the symmetric axes of the ellipse, obtain:
(a) The distance of the Earth from the $y_{\omega}'$ axis.
(b) The semimajor axis and eccentricity of the orbit.
(c) The semiparameter.
(d) The radius from the dynamical center as a function of semiparameter, eccentricity, true anomaly. Is the launched satellite in a successful orbit?
(e) The tangent speed of the satellite when the true anomaly is 60°.
(f) The period of the orbit.

2. A heliocentric satellite probe has the orbital elements $a = 2$, $e = 0.5$, $i = 30°$, $\Omega = 45°$, $\omega = 60°$, $T = 1963$ December 12, $18^{hr}$, $20^{min}$, $15^{sec}$, with respect to the ecliptic. What are the direction cosines of the radius vector with respect to the ecliptic plane? What are the rectangular components of position with respect to the orbit plane three days after perifocal passage? (Assume the $x$ axis of the heliocentric coordinate system points at the vernal equinox.)

3. Show that

$$M - M_0 = 2g + 2S_e \sin^2 g - 2C_e \sin g \cos g,$$

with

$$g \equiv (E - E_0)/2$$

and apply the Newton formula to obtain the iterative formula

$$g_{n+1} = g_n - \frac{g_n + S_e \sin^2 g_n - C_e \sin g_n \cos g_n - \frac{1}{2}(M - M_0)}{1 + 2S_e \sin g_n \cos g_n - C_e(1 - 2\sin^2 g_n)}.$$

Consider the ease of iteration by means of a set of tables for the square and product of sine and cosine [9].

4. Given the geocentric set $(\mathbf{r}_0, \dot{\mathbf{r}}_0)$ with $t_0 = 1963$ December 12, $18^{hr}$, $20^{min}$, $15^{sec}$, as follows:

$$x_0 = +1.5 \qquad \dot{x}_0 = +0.2$$
$$y_0 = +2.0 \qquad \dot{y}_0 = +0.3$$
$$z_0 = \phantom{+}0.0 \qquad \dot{z}_0 = +0.1$$

obtain the set of elements

$$[a, S_e, C_e, \mathbf{U}, \mathbf{V}]_{t=t_0}.$$

5. Solve for the eccentric anomaly difference when $t = $ 1963 December 45, $18^{hr}$, $20^{min}$, $15^{sec} = $ 1964 January 14, $18^{hr}$, $20^{min}$, $15^{sec}$, using the orbital elements of problem (4) with the formula of problem (3). What are the position and velocity vectors at this time?

6. If the eccentric anomaly of an unknown geocentric orbit is $30°$ and twenty minutes later it is $60°$, what are the eccentricity and semimajor axis if in another twenty minutes the eccentric anomaly is $90°$?

7. When a geocentric orbit has an eccentricity of 0.5, what is the true anomaly corresponding to an eccentric anomaly of $30°$?

8. A parabolic heliocentric orbit has a time of perifocal passage on 1960 June 30, $0^{hr}$, $0^{min}$, $0^{sec}$. What is the true anomaly on 1999 August 24, $0^{hr}$, $0^{min}$, $0^{sec}$, if $q = 2.0$ a.u.?

9. If the components of position and velocity of a satellite in a geocentric orbit are given as in problem (4), obtain the $f$ and $g$ coefficients to terms inclusive of $\tau^3$ for a point 1/192 day after epoch. What accuracy is expected?

10. An observer located on an Earth meridian ($f = 1/298.3$) where $\theta$, (the sidereal time) is $30°$, $\phi'$ (the geocentric latitude) is $60°$, measures the slant range vector of a satellite to be

$$\rho_x = +0.01$$
$$\rho_y = +0.03$$
$$\rho_z = +0.20$$

What is the radius vector to the satellite?

11. Derive Eqs. 3.267 and 3.268. Invert the elliptic case to obtain Eqs. 3.269 and 3.270.

12. Derive Eqs. 3.278 and 3.279.

13. Derive Eqs. 3.280 and 3.281.

14. If the equation of a plane through three points is given by

$$\begin{vmatrix} x & y & z & 1 \\ x_1 & y_1 & z_1 & 1 \\ x_2 & y_2 & z_2 & 1 \\ x_3 & y_3 & z_3 & 1 \end{vmatrix} = 0,$$

verify that the equation of a plane containing the geometric center of the Earth ($x_3$, $y_3$, $z_3$) is

$$Ax + By + Cz = 0,$$

where

$$A = y_1 z_2 - y_2 z_1, \qquad B = x_2 z_1 - x_1 z_2, \qquad C = x_1 y_2 - x_2 y_1$$

and furthermore, that if

$$\Delta_1 \equiv +\sqrt{A^2 + B^2 + C^2}, \qquad \Delta_2 \equiv +\sqrt{A^2 + B^2},$$

then

$$\cos i = \frac{C}{\Delta_1} \qquad \sin i = \frac{\Delta_2}{\Delta_1}$$

$$\cos \Omega = -\frac{B}{\Delta_2} \qquad \sin \Omega = \frac{A}{\Delta_2}, \quad i \leq 90°$$

$$\cos \Omega = \frac{B}{\Delta_2} \qquad \sin \Omega = -\frac{A}{\Delta_2}, \quad i > 90°.$$

**15.** An orbit determination process for a near-Earth satellite ($a = 1.5$) yields a true anomaly of 30° and an eccentricity of 0.5. If the epoch universal time of the determination process was 1984 January 15, $10^{hr}$, $10^{min}$, $5^{sec}$, what was the time of perifocal passage?

**REFERENCES**

1. L. Brand, *Vector Analysis*, John Wiley and Sons, New York, 1957.
2. F. R. Moulton, *An Introduction to Celestial Mechanics*, The Macmillan Company, New York, 1914.
3. R. M. L. Baker, Jr., and M. W. Makemson, *An Introduction to Astrodynamics*, Academic Press, New York, 1960.
4. T. E. Sterne, *An Introduction to Celestial Mechanics*, Interscience Publishers Inc., New York, 1960.
5. W. M. Smart, *Celestial Mechanics*, Longmans, Green and Co., London, 1953.
6. F. Bowman, *Introduction to Bessel Functions*, Dover Publications, New York, 1958, p. 122.
7. F. R. Moulton, *Differential Equations*, Dover Publications Inc., New York, 1958.
8. L. A. Pipes, *Matrix Methods for Engineering*, Prentice-Hall, Englewood Cliffs, N.J., 1963.
9. *Standard Mathematical Tables*, Chemical Rubber Publishing Company, tenth edition, 1959.
10. A. Berry, *A Short History of Astronomy*, Dover Publications, New York, 1961.
11. B. Douglas, TRW Space Technology Laboratories, private communication.

# 4 Astrodynamic coordinate systems

PLATO [6]

## 4.1 COORDINATE SYSTEMS IN GENERAL

Of rather basic importance in the fields of astronomy and astrodynamics is a clear understanding of the coordinate systems used in the analytic solution of occurring problems.

As mentioned briefly in Section 1.1, preliminary orbit determination is, in part, a process of coordinate transformations. This is said in light of the fact that observations of an object in space are very frequently not in a preferred coordinate system for performing the necessary analysis. Needless to say, a great saving of time and effort can be realized by choosing the proper coordinate system in the solution of an existing problem. At times, of course, the analyst is at the unfortunate point of being given data in a particular coordinate frame and thus a transformation must be effected to the fitting and proper system in which the analysis is to be continued. Again, it often happens that the predominating reason for a transformation is the desirability of performing analysis in an *inertial* or fixed coordinate system.

Two phrases of importance in describing a particular coordinate system are *fundamental plane* and *principal axis*. The fundamental plane is the main plane of reference. It is an adopted plane above, below, and in which all measurements are made. The equatorial plane of the planet Earth extended to infinity is an example of a very important fundamental plane. Within the fundamental plane it is also necessary to fix or give direction to a particular axis of the adopted coordinate system. Usually, the principal axis of a coordinate system is denoted by $x$ and is given a very definite orientation within the fundamental plane. The orientation of such an axis is usually made as conveniently as possible.

**125**

Even the most common coordinate system, that is, the right ascension-declination frame introduced briefly in Chapter 1, is not truly inertial unless it is frozen or held fixed at some particular epoch. The principal or fundamental axis of this system undergoes a slow precession. Solar and lunar perturbations acting on the Earth's equatorial bulge cause westward motion of fundamental reckoning points. Actually, the equator and equinox of a specific point in space must be known in order to have an absolute reference. But even the location in space of the fundamental plane and axis must be carefully delineated. The retrograde motion of the vernal equinox has a steady precession rate with a period of about 26,000 years. There are also variations due to the Moon's influence with a period of about 18.6 years. The short-period variations are called *nutation*. Hence reference is made to a *mean equinox and equator of date* which is nothing more than a system in which only the steady precession corrections have been applied. The *true equinox and equator of date* has both corrections applied.

Hence, an *ephemeris* or tabulation of a planet's position, say Earth, is referred to some specific location or epoch of the fundamental axis. Obviously then, the location of an object, here taken to be the Earth in the year $X$, that is, the year or date in which the fundamental axis was frozen in order to achieve a completely inertial system, may have to be "brought forward in time" to be of any use in the analysis. These transformations of coordinates from an initial epoch are termed precession transformations, and rightly fall in the domain of coordinate transformations [5].

At any rate, it seems convenient to have a concise tabulation of the commonly used coordinate systems and the transformations which link them together. The purpose of this chapter is to perform such a tabulation and to define the variables and coordinates of the familiar standardized systems.

The analytical transformations to and from all these systems are presented in Appendix I in a form ready for practical calculations. The user is directed to the symbolic outline of Appendix I for a rapid method of locating the desired transformation.

### 4.1.1 Transformation of position, velocity, and acceleration

Consider two rectangular coordinate systems, as illustrated in Figure 4.1. The system $I(x_I, y_I, z_I)$ is inertially fixed in space, but, in contrast, the system $R(x_R, y_R, z_R)$ is rotating with respect to $I$ with an angular velocity vector $\boldsymbol{\omega}$.

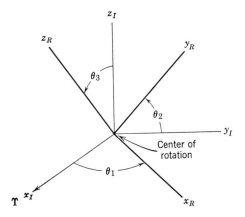

FIGURE 4.1   Superposition of a rotating coordinate system upon an inertial coordinate system.

As shown in Section 3.4.3 for orthogonal transformations, it is possible to transform from system $I$ to $R$ by means of

$$\begin{bmatrix} x_R \\ y_R \\ z_R \end{bmatrix} = [M] \begin{bmatrix} x_I \\ y_I \\ z_I \end{bmatrix}, \qquad (4.1)$$

where $[M]$ is the matrix of the transformation, that is, in this case, a square $3 \times 3$ matrix, whose elements $a_{ij}$ are the direction cosines of the $x_R, y_R, z_R$ axes with respect to the $x_I, y_I, z_I$ axes.   To be more explicit, if a set of orthogonal unit vectors is introduced along the $x_I, y_I, z_I$ axes, denoted by $\mathbf{I, J, K}$, respectively, and another set of orthogonal unit vectors is taken along $x_R, y_R, z_R$, denoted by $\mathbf{I', J', K'}$, then, since $\mathbf{I' \cdot I} = \cos (< \mathbf{I'}, \mathbf{I}) = \cos \theta_1$, and so on, it is possible to write the transformation between $I$ and $R$ as

$$\begin{bmatrix} x_R \\ y_R \\ z_R \end{bmatrix} = \begin{bmatrix} \mathbf{I' \cdot I} & \mathbf{I' \cdot J} & \mathbf{I' \cdot K} \\ \mathbf{J' \cdot I} & \mathbf{J' \cdot J} & \mathbf{J' \cdot K} \\ \mathbf{K' \cdot I} & \mathbf{K' . J} & \mathbf{K' \cdot K} \end{bmatrix} \begin{bmatrix} x_I \\ y_I \\ z_I \end{bmatrix}. \qquad (4.2)$$

To give definiteness to such a matrix transformation, suppose for the present that the $R$ system is not rotating with respect to the $I$ system.

Then, an important example of such a matrix mapping is given by Eq. 3.48, that is,

$$\begin{bmatrix} x_\omega \\ y_\omega \\ z_\omega \end{bmatrix} = \begin{bmatrix} P_x & P_y & P_z \\ Q_x & Q_y & Q_z \\ W_x & W_y & W_z \end{bmatrix} \begin{bmatrix} x \\ y \\ z \end{bmatrix}, \qquad (4.3)$$

a position transformation from one inertial system to another. In this case, the $a_{ij}$ coefficients of the transformation matrix of Eq. 4.3 are constants. Let a matrix whose elements are constants, be defined by

$$[M]_c \equiv \begin{bmatrix} C_{1x} & C_{1y} & C_{1z} \\ C_{2x} & C_{2y} & C_{2z} \\ C_{3x} & C_{3y} & C_{3z} \end{bmatrix}. \qquad (4.4)$$

Generally speaking, then, Eq. 4.3 can be written as

$$\begin{bmatrix} x_\omega \\ y_\omega \\ z_\omega \end{bmatrix} = [M]_c \begin{bmatrix} x \\ y \\ z \end{bmatrix}, \qquad (4.5)$$

and, if one is interested in velocity transformations,

$$\begin{bmatrix} \dot{x}_\omega \\ \dot{y}_\omega \\ \dot{z}_\omega \end{bmatrix} = [M]_c \begin{bmatrix} \dot{x} \\ \dot{y} \\ \dot{z} \end{bmatrix} + \frac{d[M]_c}{d\tau} \begin{bmatrix} x \\ y \\ z \end{bmatrix}, \qquad (4.6)$$

where, since the elements of $[M]_c$ are constants, the derivative of each element of $[M]_c$ is equal to zero or

$$\begin{bmatrix} \dot{x}_\omega \\ \dot{y}_\omega \\ \dot{z}_\omega \end{bmatrix} = [M]_c \begin{bmatrix} \dot{x} \\ \dot{y} \\ \dot{z} \end{bmatrix}. \qquad (4.7)$$

Similarly, accelerations are transformed according to

$$\begin{bmatrix} \ddot{x}_\omega \\ \ddot{y}_\omega \\ \ddot{z}_\omega \end{bmatrix} = [M]_c \begin{bmatrix} \ddot{x} \\ \ddot{y} \\ \ddot{z} \end{bmatrix}. \qquad (4.8)$$

Let a matrix of transformation whose elements are functions of a parameter, such as modified time, be denoted by

$$[M]_\tau \equiv \begin{bmatrix} C_{1x}(\tau) & C_{1y}(\tau) & C_{1z}(\tau) \\ C_{2x}(\tau) & C_{2y}(\tau) & C_{2z}(\tau) \\ C_{3x}(\tau) & C_{3y}(\tau) & C_{3z}(\tau) \end{bmatrix}. \tag{4.9}$$

Certainly then,

$$\frac{d[M]_\tau}{d\tau} = \begin{bmatrix} \dot{C}_{1x}(\tau) & \dot{C}_{1y}(\tau) & \dot{C}_{1z}(\tau) \\ \dot{C}_{2x}(\tau) & \dot{C}_{2y}(\tau) & \dot{C}_{2z}(\tau) \\ \dot{C}_{3x}(\tau) & \dot{C}_{3y}(\tau) & \dot{C}_{3z}(\tau) \end{bmatrix}, \tag{4.10}$$

where the overhead dots denote, as usual, differentiation with respect to modified time.

Returning now to the general problem, namely, the transformation of coordinates from a fixed or inertial system to a rotating system, Eq. 4.1 can be more correctly written as

$$\begin{bmatrix} x_R \\ y_R \\ z_R \end{bmatrix} = [M]_\tau \begin{bmatrix} x_I \\ y_I \\ z_I \end{bmatrix}. \tag{4.11}$$

Hence, by direct differentiation,

$$\begin{bmatrix} \dot{x}_R \\ \dot{y}_R \\ \dot{z}_R \end{bmatrix} = [M]_\tau \begin{bmatrix} \dot{x}_I \\ \dot{y}_I \\ \dot{z}_I \end{bmatrix} + [\dot{M}]_\tau \begin{bmatrix} x_I \\ y_I \\ z_I \end{bmatrix}, \tag{4.12}$$

which is the manner that velocities from an inertial system transform into a rotating system.

By differentiation, it can be seen that accelerations transform from $I$ to $R$ according to

$$\begin{bmatrix} \ddot{x}_R \\ \ddot{y}_R \\ \ddot{z}_R \end{bmatrix} = [M]_\tau \begin{bmatrix} \ddot{x}_I \\ \ddot{y}_I \\ \ddot{z}_I \end{bmatrix} + 2[\dot{M}]_\tau \begin{bmatrix} \dot{x}_I \\ \dot{y}_I \\ \dot{z}_I \end{bmatrix} + [\ddot{M}]_\tau \begin{bmatrix} x_I \\ y_I \\ z_I \end{bmatrix}. \tag{4.13}$$

The rate of change of acceleration or *jerk* and higher derivatives would be obtained by differentiation of Eq. 4.13.

*Illustrative Example*

If rotation of one coordinate system with respect to another occurs counterclockwise only about the positive $z$ axis, with a constant angular velocity $\dot{\theta}$, what are the velocity and acceleration transformations from the fixed to the rotating system?

Examination of the coincident $x$, $y$ planes of both coordinate systems (Figure 4.2) will yield the following relationship

$$x_R = \quad x_I \cos\theta + y_I \sin\theta$$
$$y_R = -x_I \sin\theta + y_I \cos\theta$$
$$z_R = \quad z_I$$

or, in matrix form,

$$\begin{bmatrix} x_R \\ y_R \\ z_R \end{bmatrix} = \begin{bmatrix} \cos\theta & \sin\theta & 0 \\ -\sin\theta & \cos\theta & 0 \\ 0 & 0 & 1 \end{bmatrix} \begin{bmatrix} x_I \\ y_I \\ z_I \end{bmatrix},$$

where the transformation matrix is $[M]_t$. Differentiation of the transformation matrix results in

$$[\dot{M}]_t = \dot{\theta} \begin{bmatrix} -\sin\theta & \cos\theta & 0 \\ -\cos\theta & -\sin\theta & 0 \\ 0 & 0 & 0 \end{bmatrix}$$

and application of Eq. 4.12 yields

$$\begin{bmatrix} \dot{x}_R \\ \dot{y}_R \\ \dot{z}_R \end{bmatrix} = \begin{bmatrix} \cos\theta & \sin\theta & 0 \\ -\sin\theta & \cos\theta & 0 \\ 0 & 0 & 1 \end{bmatrix} \begin{bmatrix} \dot{x}_I \\ \dot{y}_I \\ \dot{z}_I \end{bmatrix}$$

$$+ \dot{\theta} \begin{bmatrix} -\sin\theta & \cos\theta & 0 \\ -\cos\theta & -\sin\theta & 0 \\ 0 & 0 & 0 \end{bmatrix} \begin{bmatrix} x_I \\ y_I \\ z_I \end{bmatrix},$$

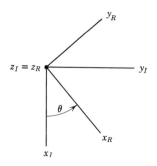

FIGURE 4.2   A common rotation in the $x - y$ plane.

so that upon performing the indicated matrix multiplications,

$$\dot{x}_R = \dot{x}_I \cos \theta + \dot{y}_I \sin \theta + \dot{\theta}(-x_I \sin \theta + y_I \cos \theta)$$
$$\dot{y}_R = -\dot{x}_I \sin \theta + \dot{y}_I \cos \theta - \dot{\theta}(\ x_I \cos \theta + y_I \sin \theta)$$
$$\dot{z}_R = \dot{z}_I.$$

It can also be noted that if the velocity is transformed from $I$ to $R$ according to $[M]_t$ and if $\boldsymbol{\omega}$ is taken as the row vector $[0, 0, \dot{\theta}]$, the fundamental identification of Eq. 4.12 with

$$\dot{\mathbf{r}}_R = [M]_t \dot{\mathbf{r}}_I - \boldsymbol{\omega} \times \mathbf{r}_R,$$

can also be used to obtain the velocities in the rotating system, that is,

$$-\boldsymbol{\omega} \times \mathbf{r}_R = - \begin{bmatrix} I' & J' & K' \\ 0 & 0 & \dot{\theta} \\ x_R & y_R & z_R \end{bmatrix} = \dot{\theta} y_R I' - \dot{\theta} x_R J'.$$

Acceleration transformations can now be obtained by differentiation of $[\dot{M}]_t$ and application of Eq. 4.13.   Accordingly,

$$[\ddot{M}]_t = \dot{\theta}^2 \begin{bmatrix} -\cos \theta & -\sin \theta & 0 \\ \sin \theta & -\cos \theta & 0 \\ 0 & 0 & 0 \end{bmatrix},$$

and since $[M]_t$, $[\dot{M}]_t$ have already been evaluated,

$$\begin{bmatrix} \ddot{x}_R \\ \ddot{y}_R \\ \ddot{z}_R \end{bmatrix} = \begin{bmatrix} \cos \theta & \sin \theta & 0 \\ -\sin \theta & \cos \theta & 0 \\ 0 & 0 & 1 \end{bmatrix} \begin{bmatrix} \ddot{x}_I \\ \ddot{y}_I \\ \ddot{z}_I \end{bmatrix}$$

$$+ 2\dot{\theta} \begin{bmatrix} -\sin \theta & \cos \theta & 0 \\ -\cos \theta & -\sin \theta & 0 \\ 0 & 0 & 0 \end{bmatrix} \begin{bmatrix} \dot{x}_I \\ \dot{y}_I \\ \dot{z}_I \end{bmatrix}$$

$$+ \dot{\theta}^2 \begin{bmatrix} -\cos \theta & -\sin \theta & 0 \\ \sin \theta & -\cos \theta & 0 \\ 0 & 0 & 0 \end{bmatrix} \begin{bmatrix} x_I \\ y_I \\ z_I \end{bmatrix}$$

is the relation between accelerations in the $I$ and $R$ systems.   Evaluating the matrices yields each component equation as

$$\ddot{x}_R = \ddot{x}_I \cos \theta + \ddot{y}_I \sin \theta + 2\dot{\theta}(-\dot{x}_I \sin \theta + \dot{y}_I \cos \theta)$$
$$- \dot{\theta}^2(\ x_I \cos \theta + y_I \sin \theta)$$
$$\ddot{y}_R = -\ddot{x}_I \sin \theta + \ddot{y}_I \cos \theta - 2\dot{\theta}(\ \dot{x}_I \cos \theta + \dot{y}_I \sin \theta)$$
$$- \dot{\theta}^2(-x_I \sin \theta + y_I \cos \theta)$$
$$\ddot{z}_R = \ddot{z}_I$$

or  $\ddot{x}_R = \quad \ddot{x}_I \cos \theta + \ddot{y}_I \sin \theta + 2\dot{\theta}\dot{y}_R + \dot{\theta}^2 x_R$

$\ddot{y}_R = -\ddot{x}_I \sin \theta + \ddot{y}_I \cos \theta - 2\dot{\theta}\dot{x}_R + \dot{\theta}^2 y_R$

$\ddot{z}_R = \quad \ddot{z}_I.$

Here again, it is possible to associate Eq. 4.13 with

$$\ddot{\mathbf{r}}_R = [M]_\tau \ddot{\mathbf{r}}_I - 2\boldsymbol{\omega} \times \dot{\mathbf{r}}_R - \boldsymbol{\omega} \times (\boldsymbol{\omega} \times \mathbf{r}_R),$$

as an alternate means of computing the accelerations. To verify this, it is possible to evaluate

$$-2\boldsymbol{\omega} \times \dot{\mathbf{r}}_R = - \begin{bmatrix} \mathbf{I}' & \mathbf{J}' & \mathbf{K}' \\ 0 & 0 & \dot{\theta} \\ \dot{x}_R & \dot{y}_R & \dot{z}_R \end{bmatrix} = 2\dot{\theta}\dot{y}_R \mathbf{I}' - 2\dot{\theta}\dot{x}_R \mathbf{J}',$$

$$-\boldsymbol{\omega} \times (\boldsymbol{\omega} \times \mathbf{r}_R) = - \begin{bmatrix} \mathbf{I}' & \mathbf{J}' & \mathbf{K}' \\ 0 & 0 & \dot{\theta} \\ -\dot{\theta}y_R & \dot{\theta}x_R & 0 \end{bmatrix} = \dot{\theta}^2 x_R \mathbf{I}' + \dot{\theta}^2 y_R \mathbf{J}',$$

which, when added to the rotated acceleration vector, denoted by $[M]_\tau \ddot{\mathbf{r}}_I$, yield the same equations.

If inverse transformations are desired, that is, from the rotating frame into the inertial frame, then it is possible to premultiply Eq. 4.11 by $[M]_\tau^{-1}$, the inverse of $[M]_\tau$, to obtain in this case

$$\begin{bmatrix} x_I \\ y_I \\ z_I \end{bmatrix} = [M]_\tau^{-1} \begin{bmatrix} x_R \\ y_R \\ z_R \end{bmatrix}.$$

More explicitly, since the transformation is orthogonal, the inverse is equal to the transpose of the matrix and differentiation of the relation

$$\begin{bmatrix} x_I \\ y_I \\ z_I \end{bmatrix} = \begin{bmatrix} \cos \theta & -\sin \theta & 0 \\ \sin \theta & \cos \theta & 0 \\ 0 & 0 & 1 \end{bmatrix} \begin{bmatrix} x_R \\ y_R \\ z_R \end{bmatrix}$$

will yield the appropriate velocity and acceleration transformations.

### 4.2 THE AZIMUTH-ELEVATION COORDINATE SYSTEM

#### 4.2.1 System 1

An observer standing on a particular meridian on the surface of a rotating planet sees all objects (taken to be of infinitesimal dimensions) in a rotating

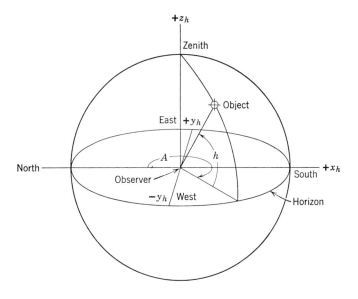

FIGURE 4.3   Azimuth-elevation coordinate system.

coordinate system.  In this system, the observer is at the origin of the coordinate system and the fundamental plane is the local horizon, that is, a *topocentric* system (Figure 4.3).  The principal axis or direction is taken as pointing due South.

The two angles needed to define the location of an object along some ray from the origin are defined as follows.

*h* (*Elevation*).  Angular elevation of an object, above a tangent plane to the observer's meridian, at the observer's position.

*A* (*Azimuth*).  The angle from the North to the object's meridian, measured in the tangent plane to the observer's meridian, at the observer's position.

Distance from the observer to the object is defined as slant range and is symbolized by:

$\rho_h$ (*Slant Range*).  The distance or extension between the origin of the coordinate system and the location of a point (object) within the coordinate system.

The following convention is usually adopted.

| VARIABLE | SENSE | RANGE |
|---|---|---|
| $h$ | Positive above horizon | $-90° \le h \le 90°$ |
| $A$ | Positive to East from North | $0° \le A \le 360°$ |
| $\rho_h$ | A positive length | $\rho_h \ge 0$ |

### 4.3 THE RIGHT ASCENSION-DECLINATION COORDINATE SYSTEM

### 4.3.1 System 2

Calculations in space are best carried out in an inertial or fixed coordinate system. The right ascension-declination coordinate system is the basic astronomical system. In this system, the Earth's center is usually taken to be the origin, that is, a *geocentric* system. The fundamental plane is the equatorial plane and the principal axis is assumed pointing to the vernal equinox (Figure 4.4).

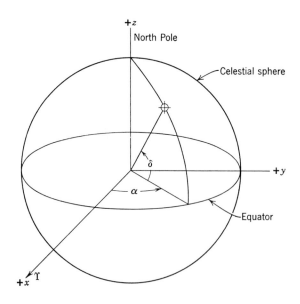

FIGURE 4.4    Right ascension-declination coordinate system.

The two angles needed to define the location of an infinitesimal object along some ray from the origin are defined as follows.

$\alpha$ (*Right Ascension*).   The angle measured in the plane of the equator from a fixed inertial axis in space (vernal equinox), to a plane normal to the equator (meridian) which contains the object.

$\delta$ (*Declination*).   The angle between object and equator measured in a plane normal to the equator, which contains the object and the origin.

Distance from the center of the Earth to the object is symbolized by:

$r$ (*Radial Distance*).   The distance or extension between the origin of the coordinates and the location of a point (object) within the coordinate system.

The following convention is usually adopted.

| VARIABLE | SENSE | RANGE |
|---|---|---|
| $\alpha$ | Positive counterclockwise as seen from $+z$ | $0° \leq \alpha \leq 360°$ |
| $\delta$ | Positive above equator | $-90° \leq \delta \leq 90°$ |
| $r$ | A positive length | $r \geq 0$ |

## 4.4   THE LATITUDE–LONGITUDE COORDINATE SYSTEM

### 4.4.1   System 3

Usually, on Earth, the location of a given object is referenced by two angular coordinates (latitude–longitude) and the altitude above (below) the adopted reference ellipsoid.

The origin of the latitude-longitude coordinate system is the geocenter, that is, a geocentric system (Figure 4.5).   The fundamental plane is the equator and the principal axis is taken in the fundamental plane pointing towards the Greenwich meridian.   It should be noted that because of the flattening and other irregularities, three kinds of latitudes are of possible interest to the analyst.   Even though they were given in Chapter 1, these definitions are repeated here for convenience.

$\phi'$ (*Geocentric Latitude*).   The acute angle measured perpendicular to the equatorial plane, between the equator and a line connecting the geometric center of the coordinate system, with a point on the surface of the reference ellipsoid.

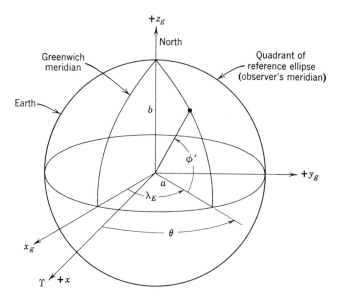

FIGURE 4.5   Latitude-longitude coordinate system.

$\phi$ (*Geodetic Latitude*).   The acute angle measured perpendicular to the equatorial plane, between a line normal to a tangent plane touching the reference ellipsoid, and the equatorial plane.[1]

$\phi_a$ (*Astronomical Latitude*).   The acute angle measured perpendicular to the equatorial plane formed by the intersection of a gravity ray (plumb bob) with the equatorial plane.[1]

Transformation of geocentric latitude to geodetic latitude is accomplished by

$$\phi = \tan^{-1} \left( \frac{1}{(1-f)^2} \tan \phi' \right) \tag{4.14}$$

or inversely,

$$\phi' = \tan^{-1} \left( (1-f)^2 \tan \phi \right). \tag{4.15}$$

The transformation of astronomical latitude to either geodetic or geocentric latitude requires special knowledge of the direction of the gravitational acceleration.

In essence, the angular coordinates necessary to locate an observer on the surface of the Earth (Figure 4.5) are: $\phi$ or $\phi'$, and

---

[1] See Section 1.4.

$\lambda_E$ (*East Longitude*). The angle measured towards the East, in the equatorial plane, between the prime meridian and the meridian containing the surface point.[2]

$H$ (*Altitude*). The distance of the observer above (below) the reference ellipsoid.

The following convention is usually adopted.

| VARIABLE | SENSE | RANGE |
|---|---|---|
| $\phi'$ | Positive above equator | $-90° \leq \phi' \leq 90°$ |
| $\phi$ | Positive above equator | $-90° \leq \phi \leq 90°$ |
| $\lambda_E$ | Positive clockwise, as seen from $-z_g$ | $0° \leq \lambda_E \leq 360°$ |
| $H$ | Positive above the surface of the reference ellipsoid | |

The connection of the observer's coordinate system to the fixed inertial axis ♈ of the right ascension-declination coordinate system (Figure 4.5) is the angle $\theta$, the sidereal time. Thus, as defined in Chapter 1:

$\theta$ (*Sidereal Time*). The angle measured in the equatorial plane from the fixed inertial axis (vernal equinox) to the observer's meridian.

The following convention is usually adopted.

| VARIABLE | SENSE | RANGE |
|---|---|---|
| $\theta$ | Positive counterclockwise, as seen from $+z$ or $+z_g$ | $0^{hr}$ to $24^{hr}$ |

### 4.5  THE HOUR ANGLE-DECLINATION COORDINATE SYSTEM

#### 4.5.1  System 4

Of particular interest is a rotating coordinate system in which infinitesimal objects are reckoned from the observer's meridian. In this coordinate system the origin is at the geocenter, the fundamental plane is the equator, and the principal axis is taken to lie in the equatorial plane at the observer's meridian, that is, a geocentric system.

[2] Preference at times dictates the use of $\lambda_W$, the west longitude which is nothing more than $360° - \lambda_E$.

The two angles needed to define the location of an object (Figure 4.6) along some ray from the origin are defined as follows.

*HA* (*Hour Angle*). The angle measured towards the West, in the equatorial plane, between the observer's meridian and the meridian containing the object.

δ (*Declination*). The angle measured perpendicular to the equatorial plane, between the equator and a line connecting the object and the coordinate origin.

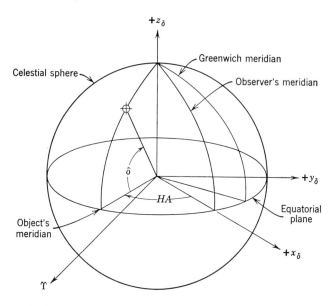

FIGURE 4.6    Hour angle-declination coordinate system.

Distance from the center of the Earth to the object is symbolized by:

*r* (*Radial Distance*). The distance or extension between the origin of the coordinate system and the location of a point (object) within the coordinate system.

The following convention is usually adopted.

| VARIABLE | SENSE | RANGE |
|---|---|---|
| *HA* | Positive clockwise to West, as seen from $+z_\delta$ | $0^{hr}$ to $24^{hr}$ |
| δ | Positive above equatorial plane | $-90° \leq \delta \leq 90°$ |
| *r* | A positive length | $r \geq 0$ |

## 4.6   THE CELESTIAL LATITUDE–LONGITUDE COORDINATE SYSTEM

### 4.6.1   System 5

Another frequently used coordinate system is the celestial latitude–longitude coordinate system.   The origin is at the center of the Sun and the fundamental plane is the plane of the ecliptic.[3]   A principal axis pointing to the vernal equinox is assumed, that is, a heliocentric system (Figure 4.7).

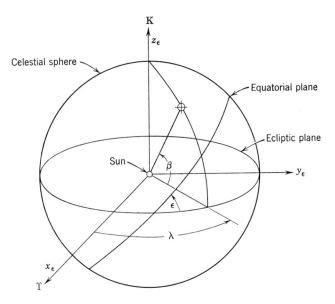

FIGURE 4.7    Celestial latitude-longitude coordinate system.

The angles needed to define the location of some infinitesimal object along some ray from the origin are defined as follows.

$\beta$ (*Celestial Latitude*).   The angle measured normal to the ecliptic plane, between a line connecting the object with the origin, and the ecliptic plane.

$\lambda$ (*Celestial Longitude*).   The angle measured in the plane of the ecliptic from a fixed inertial axis in space (vernal equinox) to a plane normal to the ecliptic plane which contains the object.

---

[3] The plane defined by the apparent motion of the Sun as it moves through space. See Section 1.1.

Distance from the center of the Sun to the object is symbolized by:

$r_\epsilon$ (*Heliocentric Radial Distance*).   The distance or extension between the origin of the coordinates and the location of a point with the co-ordinate system.

The following convention is usually adopted.

| VARIABLE | SENSE | RANGE |
|---|---|---|
| $\beta$ | Positive above the ecliptic plane | $-90° \leq \beta \leq 90°$ |
| $\lambda$ | Positive counterclockwise, as seen from $+K$ | $0° \leq \lambda \leq 360°$ |
| $r_\epsilon$ | A positive length | $r_\epsilon \geq 0$ |

The angle between the equatorial plane and the ecliptic plane is called the *obliquity of the ecliptic* and is denoted by $\epsilon$, $\epsilon < 90°$.   See Appendix I, Transformation 26, for numerical values.

## 4.7   THE VEHICLE-CENTERED COORDINATE SYSTEM

### 4.7.1   System 6

Orientation of a vehicle is usually specified by a relative coordinate system carried along with the vehicle.   The origin of this system is the vehicle's center of gravity, and the fundamental plane is the local horizon.[4]   A principal axis pointing South is usually assumed (Figure 4.8).

The two angles needed to define the orientation of an object, relative to a ray from the origin are defined as follows.

$\gamma$ (*Flight Path Angle*).   The angle between the velocity vector and local horizontal, measured in a plane perpendicular to the local horizon.

$A$ (*Azimuth*).   The angle from the North measured in the plane of the local horizontal to the projection of the velocity vector on the local horizontal plane.

Distance from the center of the Earth to the vehicle is symbolized by:

$r$ (*Radial Distance*).   The distance or extension between the origin of the coordinate system and the location of the vehicle (point) with respect to the geocenter.

---

[4] A plane at the position of the vehicle that is normal to the radial distance.

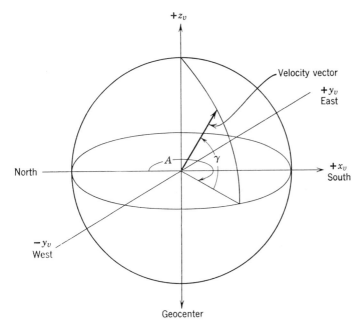

FIGURE 4.8  Vehicle-centered coordinate system.

The following convention is usually adopted.

| VARIABLE | SENSE | RANGE |
|---|---|---|
| $\gamma$ | Position above local horizontal plane | $-90° \leq \gamma \leq 90°$ |
| $A$ | Positive to East from North | $0° \leq A \leq 360°$ |
| $r$ | A positive length | $r \geq 0$ |

## 4.8  THE SELENOGRAPHIC COORDINATE SYSTEM

### 4.8.1  System 7

For calculations of a vehicle's position and velocity relative to the Moon, a rotating selenographic coordinate system is usually used.  In this system, the Moon's equatorial plane is taken to be the fundamental plane.

The origin is the selenocenter and the principal axis is taken in the Moon's equatorial plane pointing towards the Moon's prime meridian.

By definition, the Moon's prime meridian is taken to pass through the surface point on the Moon, intersected by a line connecting the seleno-center and geocenter when the Moon is at the mean ascending node, and when the node is coincident with the mean perigee or apogee. Actually, this is a cumbersome definition and it is simpler to take a landmark on the

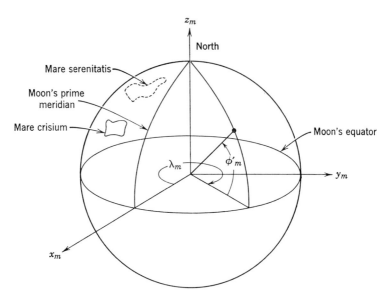

FIGURE 4.9    Selenographic coordinate system.

Moon, such as craterlet Mösting A, or a given distance from this landmark as the point where the prime meridian passes (Figure 4.9).

For purposes of clarity, the relation of the fundamental or principal axis to the right ascension-declination coordinate system is illustrated in Figure 4.10.

Since objects in this reference frame are fixed relative to the Moon's equator, the object's position is free from the geometric and physical *librations* or fluctuations of the Moon. In contrast, a *selenocentric* coordi-nate system or a translated right ascension-declination coordinate system, whose new origin is the Moon's center, will have a tendency to wobble. The selenocentric frame finds use in the study of certain Moon-centered or *lunicentric* satellite observation problems.

The two angles necessary to define the location of some infinitesimal object located along some ray from the origin are defined as follows.

$\phi_m'$ (*Selenographic Latitude*). The acute angle measured normal to the Moon's equator between the equator and a line connecting the geometrical center of the coordinate system with a point on the surface of the Moon.

$\lambda_m$ (*Selenographic Longitude*). The angle measured towards the West, in the Moon's equatorial plane, from the lunar prime meridian to the object's meridian.

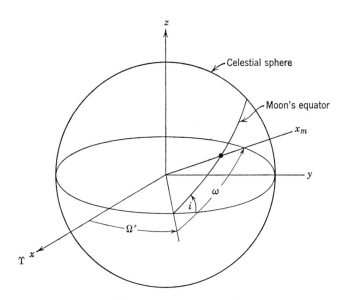

FIGURE 4.10   Location of the fundamental axis of the selenographic system in the right ascension-declination system.

| VARIABLE | SENSE | RANGE |
|---|---|---|
| $\phi_m'$ | Positive towards the North | $-90° \leq \phi_m' \leq 90°$ |
| $\lambda_m$ | Positive towards the West | $0° \leq \lambda_m \leq 360°$ |
| North | Section above lunar equator containing Mare Serenitatis | |
| West | Measured towards Mare Crisium | |

The transformation into and out of the selenographic system is very complex and is stated as an algorithm in Appendix I; reference [4] will be of benefit to the interested reader.

## 4.9   THE ORBIT PLANE COORDINATE SYSTEM

### 4.9.1   System 8

The ease and facility with which analysis can be performed in the plane defined by the orbit of a vehicle is the basis for the selection of an orbit plane coordinate system. The origin of this inertial system is the geocenter. The fundamental plane is the orbit plane at some epoch time. It should be noted that in Keplerian mechanics this plane is fixed in inertial space,

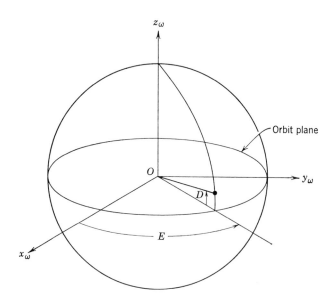

FIGURE 4.11   Orbit plane coordinate system.

otherwise it will gradually drift from the epoch position owing to existing perturbations. A principal axis pointing towards *perifocus* or physically smallest radius is usually assumed. If the orbit is a perfect circle, the principal axis can be chosen in some convenient manner. See Figure 4.11.

The two angles needed in order to locate an infinitesimal object along some ray from the origin are defined as follows.

*E* (*Eccentric Anomaly*).   The angle measured in the fundamental plane from the principal axis to a meridian which contains at its remote base point the outward projection (normal to principal axis) of the vehicle on a circle that circumscribes the actual ellipse of motion.

*D* (*Angular Deviation*).   The angle measured normal to the fundamental plane between the object and the fundamental plane.   (Usually *D* is taken to be zero, hence Figure 4.11 reduces to Figure 4.12.)

The distance from the center of the Earth to the object or vehicle is symbolized by:

$r_\omega$ (*Radial Distance*).   The distance or extension between the origin of the coordinate system and the location of the vehicle (point) within the coordinate system.

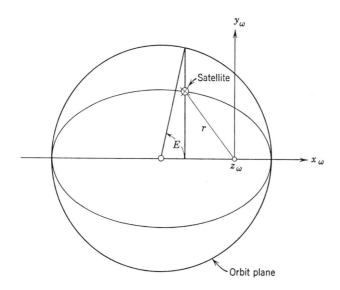

FIGURE 4.12   Orbit plane coordinate system for *D* = 0, that is, Keplerian mechanics.

The following convention is usually adopted.

| VARIABLE | SENSE | RANGE |
|---|---|---|
| *E* | Positive counterclockwise, as seen from $+z_\omega$ | $0° \leq E \leq 360°$ |
| *D* | Positive above fundamental plane | $-90° \leq D \leq 90°$ |

## 4.10   THE OBLATE SPHEROIDAL COORDINATE SYSTEM

### 4.10.1   System 9

A very interesting coordinate system is the oblate spheroidal coordinate system.   It will find substantial use in perturbation theory and is presented for the sake of completeness.   The origin of this system is the geocenter, the fundamental plane is the equator and the principal axis is taken to be pointing towards the vernal equinox (Figure 4.13).

Surfaces of constant $\xi$ are oblate spheroids (circles perpendicular to $z_0$ and ellipsoids for meridian sections).   Surfaces of constant $\eta$ are one-sheet hyperboloids of revolution.   Finally surfaces of constant $\alpha$ (right ascension) are planes which contain the polar axis.

The coordinates needed to define the location of some object relative to the origin are defined as follows.

$\xi$ (*Pseudo Radius Vector*).   A coordinate that for large values of the radial distance behaves like the radial distance of the right ascension-declination coordinate system.

$\eta$ (*Pseudo Declination*).   A coordinate that for large values of the radius distance behaves like the sine of the declination of the right ascension-declination coordinate system.

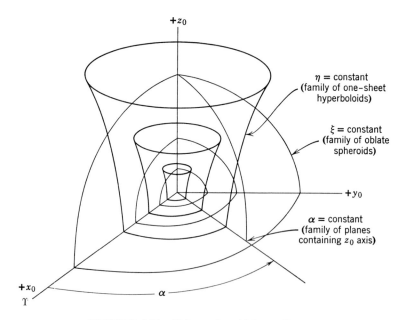

FIGURE 4.13   Oblate spheroidal coordinates.

$\alpha$ (*Right Ascension*).   The angle measured in the equatorial plane from the fixed or principal axis in space to a meridian containing the object (point).

The following convention is usually adopted.

| VARIABLE | SENSE | RANGE |
|---|---|---|
| $\xi$ | Always positive | $\xi > 0$ |
| $\eta$ | Positive above fundamental plane | $-1 \leq \eta \leq +1$ |
| $\alpha$ | Positive counterclockwise, as seen from $+z_0$ | $0° \leq \alpha \leq 360°$ |

## 4.11   THE AREOCENTRIC COORDINATE SYSTEM

### 4.11.1   System 10

Voyages to Mars will be occasioned in the near future.   The areocentric or Mars-centered inertial coordinate system will find increased use as the exploration of Mars is undertaken.   In the areocentric system, the fundamental plane is the Martian equatorial plane, and the principal axis

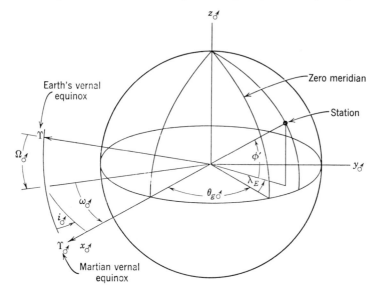

FIGURE 4.14   The areocentric right ascension-declination coordinate system.

is taken as pointing towards the Martian vernal equinox denoted by $\Upsilon_\delta$. Figure 4.14 illustrates the Martian coordinate system.   A full discussion of this coordinate system is presented in [5].   The mappings into and out of the areocentric system are presented in Appendix I.   Analytical expressions for $\Omega_\delta$, $i_\delta$, $\omega_\delta$, that is, the standard Euler rotation angles of the Martian vernal equinox $\Upsilon_\delta$, with respect to the Earth's vernal equinox are also tabulated.

The angular coordinates $\lambda_E$ and $\phi'$ are defined in exactly the same manner and sense as for the Earth (System 3) except, of course, these angles are relative to Mars.

### 4.12   SUMMARY

A tabulation of the most commonly used coordinate systems in astro-dynamics and preliminary orbit determination have been presented and defined.   Velocity and acceleration transformations from rotating to inertial systems have been examined and appropriate formulas to accomplish the transformations have been derived.   Care has been exercised to define all the principal angles and their respective ranges.   The reader would do well to acquaint himself with each particular system and its associated nomenclature.   The analytical transformation from each coordinate system and its inverse is given in Appendix I.

### EXERCISES

1. Of all the systems presented, which can be considered inertial?
2. An observer on a given meridian with the coordinates

$$\phi' = 60°$$
$$\lambda_E = 270°$$
$$H = 1000 \text{ meters}$$

   on January 15, 1970, at 11:30 in the evening (Eastern Standard Time), sees a bright light in the heavens and obtains its azimuth and elevation as 120° and 30°, respectively.   He wants to check its coordinates with a star catalog and thus needs to calculate the right ascension and declination.   What should these angles be? (*Hint:* use Appendix I.)
3. A space vehicle is located in the right ascension-declination coordinate system by

$$x = 1.5 \text{ e.r.}$$
$$y = 0.5 \text{ e.r.}$$
$$z = 0.3 \text{ e.r.}$$

at a U.T. of 1962 June 5, $10^{hr}$, $15^{min}$, $10^{sec}$.  Where is it with respect to the latitude–longitude coordinate system?

**4.** Derive Transformation 1 of Appendix I.

**5.** Derive Transformation 12 of Appendix I.

**6.** A rocket near the Earth ($f = 1/298.3$) at burnout has the missile coordinates $V$ (inertial velocity), $H_s$ (normal height above adopted ellipsoid), $\gamma$ (angle with local horizontal), $A$ (azimuth angle), $\phi_s'$ (geocentric subvehicle latitude), $\lambda_E$ (subvehicle longitude) on 1968 December 23, $22^{hr}$, $85.2^{min}$ given by

$$V = 18{,}000 \text{ ft/sec}$$
$$H_s = 500{,}000 \text{ ft}$$
$$\gamma = 30°$$
$$A = 120°$$
$$\phi_s' = 60°$$
$$\lambda_E = 270°.$$

What are the rectangular components of position in the right ascension–declination coordinate frame? What are these components in the year 1960 (referred to as epoch)? What are the rectangular position components in the celestial latitude–longitude coordinate system? (See Appendix I.)

**7.** If velocity transformations from one epoch to another are desired, consider the differentiation of the precession transformation of Appendix I.

**REFERENCES**

1. W. Chauvenet, *A Manual of Spherical and Practical Astronomy*, Vol. I, Dover Publications, New York, 1960.

2. S. Newcomb, *A Compendium of Spherical Astronomy*, Dover Publications, New York, 1960.

3. J. P. Vinti, "New Method for Unretarded Satellite Orbits," *Journal of Research of the National Bureau of Standards*, Vol. 62B, No. 2, October–December, 1959.

4. R. C. Hutchinson, *Inertial Orientation of the Moon*, Instrumentation Laboratory, Massachusetts Institute of Technology, R-385, Cambridge 39, Massachusetts, October, 1962.

5. *Explanatory Supplement to the Astronomical Ephemeris and the American Ephemeris and Nautical Almanac*, Her Majesty's Stationery Office, London, 1961.

6. E. T. Bell, *Men of Mathematics*, Simon Schuster, New York, 1937.

# 5 Analytics of the two-body problem

*Every new body of discovery is mathematical in form, because there is no other guidance we have.*

C. G. DARWIN [6]

## 5.1 APPLICATIONS OF TWO-BODY THEORY

In this chapter, various aspects of two-body mechanics are analyzed. The context internal to this chapter is aimed towards what might be termed "Keplermanship," the art of manipulation of the two-body formulas.

It should be apparent that judicious use of two-body analysis is of paramount importance in the development of a zero order, or first approximation technique. These techniques, whatever they may be, are very often the sensible way to solve a problem with minimum effort. Furthermore, the first approximation lends a great deal of insight into the physical problem whose solution is desired.

Fundamentally, it is unfortunate that most problems are immediately subjected to solution by direct numerical techniques without regard to a first-order theory. Even on high-speed digital computers, a saving in computational speed, a closed solution, a direct solution, or even a first guess supplied to the general problem, exhibits a sophistication of analysis and thus a better understanding of the physical problem.

As an example to the previous statements, consider a satellite in an elliptical orbit about the Earth. What are the times when the satellite passes through the ascending and descending nodes, the times into and out of the shadow of the Earth, the times of rise and set with respect to a particular ground station? Certainly all these problems can be solved by subjection to the cannonade of numerical analysis, that is, compute the trajectory point by point and check for the above criteria or event.

**150**

Obviously a solution is possible by this process. Consider, however, two-body solutions to these and other problems. By appropriate choice of coordinate systems and variables, direct solutions are possible. The objection may be raised that the two-body solution is an approximation, and thereby it does not provide sufficient accuracy. However, if general perturbation procedures are brought into play, as shown in Chapter 10, it is very expedient to solve the two-body problem and then obtain the corresponding time and update, or correct by series expressions the value of the not-truly constant or perturbed two-body elements used in the analysis. Using these improved elements that control the solution of the two-body problem, the two-body problem may be resolved so that a better approximation is obtained. The process could then be continued until a sufficient degree of accuracy is reached. In most cases, this type of approach will result in a manifold increase in computing speed. Even when the two-body theory is not of specifically sufficient accuracy, it is possible to predict a particular point (here used in the sense of event) in the physical problem and then run the general numerical solution to within an arbitrary domain of this event. It is at these critical points that the rigorous checking procedure for the particular event begins. Again, a great deal of time and calculation is saved by avoidance of the point-by-point check procedure at each integration step where the event cannot possibly occur.

It is hoped that the selected topics will clarify and present the use of some of the equations of the two-body problem in fields related to orbit determination processes.

### 5.2   DIRECT VISIBILITY OF A PLANETARY SURFACE

In a Newtonian or two-body system, that is, a given satellite and planet, the determination of the universal times when the satellite with adopted elements $a$, $e$, $i$, $\Omega$, $\omega$, $T$, where

$a = $ semimajor axis of the orbit,

$e = $ orbital eccentricity,

$i = $ orbital inclination to the equator,

$\Omega = $ longitude of the ascending node,

$\omega = $ argument of perigee,

$T = $ latest time of perifocal passage,

will have a view of the planet's surface that is bathed in direct sunlight is of fundamental importance. Specifically, for planetary probes, interest in photographic limits or on–off camera times requires that a method be available for predicting when to activate the camera or transmission equipment. It should be noted that in the analysis to be developed, the adopted elements are relative to the central planet about which the satellite moves. The analysis is formulated for elliptic motion.

### 5.2.1    Development of the controlling equation which defines the entrance and departure eccentric anomalies

As can be seen from Figure 5.1, it is desirable to restrict the angle between the satellite's position vector $\mathbf{r}$ and the Sun's position vector $\mathbf{R}_\odot$ to some specific angle, that is,

$$\mathbf{r} \cdot \mathbf{R}_\odot = r R_\odot \cos \psi, \tag{5.1}$$

where $\psi$ is a specified angle.

The satellite's position vector is given by the vector equation (Section 3.4.3)

$$\mathbf{r} = x_\omega \mathbf{P} + y_\omega \mathbf{Q} \tag{5.2}$$

with

$$x_\omega = a(\cos E - e)$$
$$y_\omega = a\sqrt{1 - e^2} \sin E$$
$$r = r_\omega = a(1 - e \cos E).$$

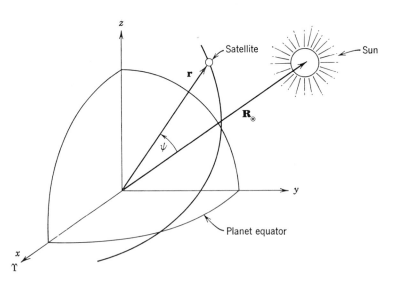

FIGURE 5.1    Orbit geometry.

Equation 5.2 has the **P** and **Q** unit vectors (Section 3.4.1) defined by

$$P_x = \cos \omega \cos \Omega - \sin \omega \sin \Omega \cos i$$
$$P_y = \cos \omega \sin \Omega + \sin \omega \sin \Omega \cos i \qquad (5.3)$$
$$P_z = \sin \omega \sin i$$

$$Q_x = -\sin \omega \cos \Omega - \cos \omega \sin \Omega \cos i$$
$$Q_y = -\sin \omega \sin \Omega + \cos \omega \cos \Omega \cos i \qquad (5.4)$$
$$Q_z = \cos \omega \sin i$$

with the understanding that if the orbit is circular, $\omega$ must be arbitrarily defined, say $\omega = 0$. The angle $\Omega$ must also be arbitrarily defined as zero or some convenient value if $i = 0$ or $\pi$.

Direct substitution of Eq. 5.2 into Eq. 5.1 results in

$$(\cos E - e)\mathbf{P} \cdot \mathbf{R}_\odot + (\sqrt{1 - e^2} \sin E)\mathbf{Q} \cdot \mathbf{R}_\odot$$
$$= (1 - e \cos E)R_\odot \cos \psi. \qquad (5.5)$$

Consider the definitions,

$$\beta \equiv \frac{\mathbf{P} \cdot \mathbf{R}_\odot}{R_\odot} = \frac{X_\odot P_x + Y_\odot P_y + Z_\odot P_z}{\sqrt{X_\odot{}^2 + Y_\odot{}^2 + Z_\odot{}^2}},$$

$$\xi \equiv \frac{\mathbf{Q} \cdot \mathbf{R}_\odot}{R_\odot} = \frac{X_\odot Q_x + Y_\odot Q_y + Z_\odot Q_z}{\sqrt{X_\odot{}^2 + Y_\odot{}^2 + Z_\odot{}^2}}, \qquad (5.6)$$

with the knowledge that $\mathbf{R}_\odot$ varies very slowly over a single revolution of the satellite about the central planet. The components of $\mathbf{R}_\odot$, at least for the Earth, are conveniently tabulated in the *American Ephemeris and Nautical Almanac* [5]. Hence, with small error, $\beta$ and $\xi$ can be considered as constants over an orbital period.[1] Equation 5.5 can thus be rewritten as

$$(\beta + e \cos \psi) \cos E + (\xi \sqrt{1 - e^2}) \sin E = \beta e + \cos \psi. \qquad (5.7)$$

This is, in effect, the controlling equation of the direct visibility problem.

### 5.2.2  Solution of the controlling equation

Introduction of the auxiliary angle $\tilde{\gamma}$ defined by

$$\cos \tilde{\gamma} \equiv \frac{\beta + e \cos \psi}{\sqrt{(\beta + e \cos \psi)^2 + (1 - e^2)\xi^2}}$$

$$\sin \tilde{\gamma} \equiv \frac{\xi \sqrt{1 - e^2}}{\sqrt{(\beta + e \cos \psi)^2 + (1 - e^2)\xi^2}}, \qquad (5.8)$$

---

[1] If more accuracy is desired once the problem is solved with this approximation, $\beta$ and $\xi$ can be re-evaluated.

reduces the controlling equation to the form

$$\cos \tilde{\gamma} \cos E + \sin \tilde{\gamma} \sin E = \frac{\beta e + \cos \psi}{\sqrt{(\beta + e \cos \psi)^2 + (1 - e^2)\xi^2}} \qquad (5.9)$$

or

$$\cos (E - \tilde{\gamma}) = \frac{\beta e + \cos \psi}{\sqrt{(\beta + e \cos \psi)^2 + (1 - e^2)\xi^2}}, \qquad (5.10)$$

which admits solution as

$$E = \tilde{\gamma} \pm \cos^{-1}\left[\frac{\beta e + \cos \psi}{\sqrt{(\beta + e \cos \psi)^2 + (1 - e^2)\xi^2}}\right], \quad 0 \le E \le 2\pi. \qquad (5.11)$$

As can be seen from Figure 5.1, once $\psi$ has been specified, the satellite will reach a point where the angle between its radius vector and the Sun's radius vector $\psi'$ will precisely equal $\psi$. From this point on, $\psi'$ will decrease for a while and then increase until $\psi' = \psi$. Hence, Eq. (5.11) provides the two limiting values of the eccentric anomalies corresponding to the critical on–off camera times. This line of reasoning is correct if a solution to the physical situation exists; the arc-cosine in Eq. 5.11 must be real, or

$$\frac{(\beta e + \cos \psi)^2}{(\beta + e \cos \psi)^2 + (1 - e^2)\xi^2} \le 1, \qquad (5.12)$$

which implies for all $\psi < \pi/2$,

$$\cos \psi \le + \sqrt{\beta^2 + \xi^2}, \qquad (5.13)$$

with the equal sign holding if Eq. 5.11 only has two double zeros, or if the chosen $\psi$ corresponds to the exact achievable minimum angle between $r$ and $R_\odot$.

### 5.2.3   Determination of the corresponding universal times

Once the limiting eccentric anomalies have been found, it is necessary to determine which eccentric anomaly corresponds to entrance into the region of visibility. Evidently, from the previous reasoning, the $E$ which causes $\cos \psi$ to increase when $E_i$, $i = 1, 2$ is increased by a small positive increment, is the entrance eccentric anomaly. This check can be easily made by incrementing $E_i$ and using Eq. 5.2 to yield the test $\mathbf{r}_i$. Equation 5.1

can now be utilized to obtain the test $\cos \psi_i$. Since the correct angular association between entrance and departure conditions and the corresponding eccentric anomalies have been made, the universal on–off camera times may be obtained from Kepler's equation

$$t_i = \frac{E_i - e \sin E_i}{n} + T, \tag{5.14}$$

with $n = k\sqrt{\mu}\,a^{-3/2}$.

### 5.3  ORBITAL ENTRANCE AND EXIT OF A SATELLITE FROM THE SHADOW OF THE EARTH

Transit into the shadow of the Earth and the duration of eclipse are important considerations for a number of basic problems such as optical tracking and the determination of viewing times from approximate data in order to improve the orbit. In this section, a general technique is developed for determining the entrance and exit true anomaly and the time of total eclipse.

Even though the dynamic analysis is strictly Keplerian or two-body, this is a good problem with which to demonstrate the rigorous inclusion of all geometric constraints peculiar to such a task.

### 5.3.1  The quartic solution

The analysis of eclipse times can be divided conveniently into two sections. The first section determines the entrance and exit true anomalies, assuming no flattening of the Earth and no shift of the Earth in its orbit. Umbra and penumbra effects are also neglected. These assumptions will result in a quartic equation in the cosine of the entrance and exit true anomalies. The second section, using the approximate true anomalies from the first section as an initial approximation, will take into consideration all the idealizations imposed upon the problem in order to obtain a closed-form solution.

Adopting the classical orbital elements as a convenient starting point, one can proceed with the development of the first section as follows.
Given

$$a, \quad e, \quad i, \quad \Omega, \quad \omega, \quad T \tag{5.15}$$

or, equivalently, the elements

$$a, \quad e, \quad \mathbf{P}, \quad \mathbf{Q}, \quad T, \tag{5.16}$$

where the unit vectors $\mathbf{P}$ and $\mathbf{Q}$ are defined by Eqs. 5.3 and 5.4, a given ellipse is fully defined as to dimensional size and orientation in the equatorial or right ascension-declination coordinate system (Chapter 4, System 2). It should be noted that $\mathbf{P}$ is a vector that points toward perifocus and is therefore not defined for a circular orbit. If the analysis is to be performed for a circular orbit, then $\mathbf{P}$ should be arbitrarily defined, for example, $\mathbf{P}$ can be taken pointing along the intersection of the orbital and equatorial planes.[2]

The following vector relationship is obtained from Figure 5.2

$$\mathbf{d} + \mathbf{a} = \mathbf{r}. \tag{5.17}$$

The geometric constraint of the problem can be obtained by realizing that upon entrance to or exit from the shadow,

$$\mathbf{R}_\odot \cdot \mathbf{d} = -R_\odot d \tag{5.18}$$

or

$$\mathbf{R}_\odot \cdot (\mathbf{r} - \mathbf{a}) = -R_\odot d, \tag{5.19}$$

since $\mathbf{R}_\odot$ is perpendicular to $\mathbf{a}$. Therefore, the angle between the radius vector to the Sun and the radius vector to the satellite at entrance or at exit points is given by

$$\cos \psi = \frac{-(r^2 - a_e^2)^{1/2}}{r}. \tag{5.20}$$

The angle $\psi$ is taken to be in the interval $\pi/2 \le \psi \le 3\pi/2$, since this is the only domain where a shadow exists.

At all times, the angle $\psi$ can be obtained from the equation

$$\cos \psi = (\mathbf{R}_\odot \cdot \mathbf{r})/R_\odot r. \tag{5.21}$$

The components of $\mathbf{R}_\odot$ are the geocentric coordinates of the Sun, as found in the *American Ephemeris and Nautical Almanac* [5]. Therefore, by using the vector equation (Section 3.4.3),

$$\mathbf{r} = x_\omega \mathbf{P} + y_\omega \mathbf{Q}, \tag{5.22}$$

which maps the radius vector to the satellite from the orbital to the equatorial coordinate system, $\cos \psi$ can be obtained as follows:

$$\cos \psi = \frac{(x_\omega \mathbf{R}_\odot \cdot \mathbf{P} + y_\omega \mathbf{R}_\odot \cdot \mathbf{Q})}{R_\odot r}. \tag{5.23}$$

[2] If $i = 0$ or $\pi$, $\mathbf{P}$ should also be redefined in a convenient manner.

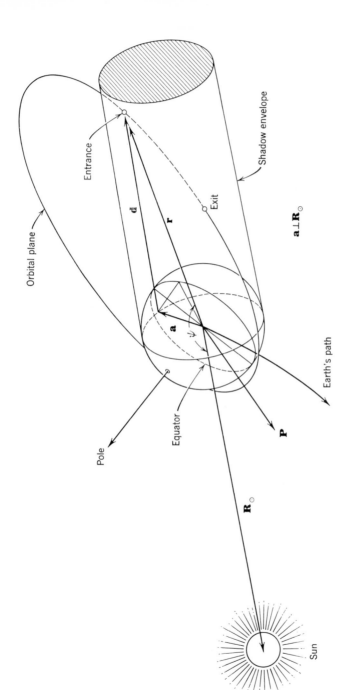

FIGURE 5.2   Orbit geometry.

If the dot products in Eq. (5.23) are defined by

$$\beta \equiv \frac{X_\odot P_x + Y_\odot P_y + Z_\odot P_z}{(X_\odot{}^2 + Y_\odot{}^2 + Z_\odot{}^2)^{\frac{1}{2}}}$$

$$\xi \equiv \frac{X_\odot Q_x + Y_\odot Q_y + Z_\odot Q_z}{(X_\odot{}^2 + Y_\odot{}^2 + Z_\odot{}^2)^{\frac{1}{2}}}, \tag{5.24}$$

where the coordinates of $R_\odot$ are taken at some convenient time, say the time of latest perifocal passage, and the substitutions

$$x_\omega = r \cos v, \qquad y_\omega = r \sin v, \tag{5.25}$$

are performed, there results from Eq. 5.23

$$\cos \psi = \beta \cos v + \xi \sin v. \tag{5.26}$$

When the squares of Eqs. 5.20 and 5.26 are equated, and the relation (Section 3.3)

$$r = p/(1 + e \cos v) \tag{5.27}$$

employed, the shadow function $S$ is produced, that is,

$$S \equiv a_e{}^2(1 + e \cos v)^2 + p^2(\beta \cos v + \xi \sin v)^2 - p^2, \tag{5.28}$$

where $S = 0$ is the condition for entrance or exit from the shadow. It should be noted that only those solutions of Eq. 5.28 obtained when

$$\beta \cos v + \xi \sin v < 0 \tag{5.29}$$

are of any physical meaning, that is, $\cos \psi \leq 0$.

Eq. 5.28 is of fourth degree in the cosine of the true anomaly which is bounded in the interval $0 \leq v \leq 2\pi$. Transformation to standard form may be effected by using the coefficients,

$$A_0 = [(a_e/p)^4 e^4 - 2(a_e/p)^2(\xi^2 - \beta^2)e^2 + (\beta^2 + \xi^2)^2]$$

$$A_1 = [4(a_e/p)^4 e^3 - 4(a_e/p)^2(\xi^2 - \beta^2)e]$$

$$A_2 = [6(a_e/p)^4 e^2 - 2(a_e/p)^2(\xi^2 - \beta^2) - 2(a_e/p)^2(1 - \xi^2)e^2$$
$$\qquad + 2(\xi^2 - \beta^2)(1 - \xi^2) - 4\beta^2\xi^2] \tag{5.30}$$

$$A_3 = [4(a_e/p)^4 e - 4(a_e/p)^2(1 - \xi^2)e]$$

$$A_4 = [(a_e/p)^4 - 2(a_e/p)^2(1 - \xi^2) + (1 - \xi^2)^2],$$

so that $S$ becomes

$$S^* = A_0 \cos^4 v + A_1 \cos^3 v + A_2 \cos^2 v + A_3 \cos v + A_4, \tag{5.31}$$

which is solvable in closed form by quadratic radicals.[3]  Rejection of spurious roots is accomplished by Eqs. 5.28 and 5.29.

---

[3] The solution is presented in Appendix III.

It should be noticed that when

$$\beta \cos v + \xi \sin v = 0, \tag{5.32}$$

the satellite, for all practical cases, will be in direct sunlight, and Eq. 5.28 reduces to

$$S = S_0 = a_e^2 (1 + e \cos v)^2 - p^2 < 0. \tag{5.33}$$

Therefore, if the satellite is entering the shadow, $S$ must change sign from minus to plus. Exit from the shadow will in opposite fashion be characterized by $S$, changing sign from plus to minus.

### 5.3.2 Correction for flattening of Earth

Examination of Figure 5.2 shows that the shadow ray $\mathbf{d}$ departs from the Earth at some particular geocentric latitude so that the magnitude of $\mathbf{a}$, the local radius of the Earth associated with this latitude, is directly involved in the eclipse calculation. An iterative solution for determining the local value of the magnitude of the $\mathbf{a}$ vector will now be developed.

Consider the vector equation

$$-\frac{\mathbf{R}_\odot}{R_\odot} d + \mathbf{a} = \mathbf{r}, \tag{5.34}$$

obtained from examination of Figure 5.2. To be more explicit, by writing the $z$ component of Eq. 5.34 and using Eq. 5.22, it is possible to write

$$-\frac{Z_\odot}{R_\odot} d + a_z = x_\omega P_z + y_\omega Q_z \tag{5.35}$$

or by means of Eqs. 5.20, 5.25, and 5.27, solving for $a_z$,

$$a_z = p \frac{(P_z \cos v + Q_z \sin v - Z_\odot \cos \psi / R_\odot)}{1 + e \cos v}. \tag{5.36}$$

However, $a_z$ is nothing more than the $z$ component of the negative station coordinate vector $-\mathbf{R}$ (Section 3.11), whose magnitude is equal to

$$a_z = \frac{a_e \sqrt{1 - (2f - f^2)} \sin \phi'}{\sqrt{1 - (2f - f^2) \cos^2 \phi'}}. \tag{5.37}$$

Let this equation be solved for $\cos^2 \phi'$, that is,

$$\cos^2 \phi' = \frac{a_e^2 [1 - (2f - f^2)] - a_z^2}{a_e^2 [1 - (2f - f^2)] - a_z^2 (2f - f^2)}. \tag{5.38}$$

For purposes of simplification, let

$$G_3 \equiv 1 - (2f - f^2) \tag{5.39}$$

and substitute the value of $a_z$ from Eq. 5.36 into Eq. 5.38, so that

$$\cos^2 \phi_j' =$$
$$\frac{a_e^2 G_3 (1 + e \cos v_j)^2 - p^2 (P_z \cos v_j + Q_z \sin v_j - Z_\odot \cos \psi_j/R_\odot)^2}{a_e^2 G_3 (1 + e \cos v_j)^2 - (1 - G_3) p^2 (P_z \cos v_j + Q_z \sin v_j - Z_\odot \cos \psi_j/R_\odot)^2} \tag{5.40}$$

where the $j$ subscript denotes entrance and exit conditions.

In terms of the acceptable roots of the quartic solution, the values of the squares of the geocentric latitudes associated with the magnitudes of the entrance and exit **a** vectors can be directly calculated from Eq. 5.40. However, from Eqs. 1.46 and 1.47

$$|\mathbf{a}_j| \equiv a_{sj} = \sqrt{x_{cj}^2 + z_{cj}^2} = \frac{a_e \sqrt{1 - (2f - f^2)}}{\sqrt{1 - (2f - f^2) \cos^2 \phi_j'}}, \tag{5.41}$$

so that $a_{sj}$, the magnitude of the Earth's radius at the departure points of **d**, can be recalculated. That is, obtain $\cos^2 \phi_j'$ from Eq. 5.40 and calculate $a_{sj}$ from Eq. 5.41.

Hence, using the first approximation for the entrance and exit true anomalies from the quartic and obtaining by these same estimates the $a_{sj}$, replace $a_e$ in Eq. 5.28 by $a_{sj}$. Note that two separate equations must be written, one for $a_s$ corresponding to entrance, and another for exit. By a Newton procedure, solve each of these equations for corrected values of the entrance and exit true anomalies. These corrected values of $v_j$ will yield improved values of $a_{sj}$ and the process repeated until the $a_{sj}$ do not vary within a given tolerance.

### 5.3.3  Umbra-penumbra corrections

Consideration of Figure 5.3 shows that the angles $\delta_u$ and $\delta_p$, where the subscripts denote umbra and penumbra, are given by the relations

$$\cos \delta_u = \frac{[R_\odot^2 - (a_\odot - a_e)^2]^{1/2}}{R_\odot}, \qquad \sin \delta_u = \frac{a_\odot - a_e}{R_\odot},$$
$$\cos \delta_p = \frac{[R_\odot^2 - (a_\odot + a_e)^2]^{1/2}}{R_\odot}, \qquad \sin \delta_p = \frac{a_\odot + a_e}{R_\odot}, \tag{5.42}$$

where $a_\odot$ denotes the radius of the Sun, and the assumption that the Sun and Earth are perfect spheres is inherent. This assumption actually does not invalidate the results because the variations caused by the flattening

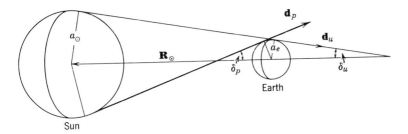

FIGURE 5.3    Shadow geometry.

of the Sun and Earth affect the angles $\delta_u$ and $\delta_p$ only infinitesimally.    The relation between $r$, $a_e$, and $d$ is obtained from

$$r_i^2 = (\mathbf{d}_i + \mathbf{a}_i) \cdot (\mathbf{d}_i + \mathbf{a}_i) = d_i^2 + a_i^2, \tag{5.43}$$

where $i$ denotes umbra and penumbra distances.

It can be shown by simple geometric relationships that the cosine of the angle between the satellite radius vector and the radius vector to the Sun is given by

$$\cos \psi_i = -(d_i/r_i) \cos \delta_i \pm (a_{si}/r_i) \sin \delta_i \tag{5.44}$$

with the convention that the upper sign be taken for penumbra entrance and $0 \le \delta_i \le \pi/2$.    Hence, for the umbra-penumbra effects, Eq. 5.20 is replaced by

$$\cos \psi_i = -[(r_i^2 - a_{si}^2)^{1/2}/r_i] \cos \delta_i \pm (a_{si}/r_i) \sin \delta_i. \tag{5.45}$$

The shadow function $S$ (Eq. 5.28) is therefore more accurately written as

$$\bar{S}_i = a_{si}^2(1 + e \cos v_i)^2 + p^2(\beta \cos v_i + \xi \sin v_i)^2 - p^2$$
$$\mp 2 p a_{si}(\beta \cos v_i + \xi \sin v_i)(1 + e \cos v_i) \sin \delta_i. \tag{5.46}$$

A Newton iteration procedure applied to Eq. 5.46, with the estimates obtained from Eq. 5.31, will converge very rapidly to the desired root.

Evidently, if flattening were also a consideration, the variables with an $i$ subscript would also possess a $j$ subscript, as in the previous section. The flattening correction would then be internal to the umbra-penumbra corrections.

### 5.3.4    Movement of the Earth

The dot products $\beta$ and $\xi$, the parameter $a_z$, and the angles $\delta_i$, are all functionally dependent upon the position of the Sun relative to the Earth. Again, if the preliminary true anomaly estimates (cylindrical shadow assumption) from Eq. 5.31 are known, it is possible to calculate the time at a particular true anomaly from

$$t = [a^{3/2}/(k_e\sqrt{\mu})]\cdot(E - e\sin E) + T, \tag{5.47}$$

where the eccentric anomaly is defined by

$$\sin E = [(1 - e^2)^{1/2}\sin v]/(1 + e\cos v)$$
$$\cos E = [\cos v + e]/(1 + e\cos v). \tag{5.48}$$

An interpolation in the table of the Sun's coordinates, with the improved value of $t$, will now yield almost the exact values of $\beta$, $\xi$, $a_z$, and $\delta_i$.

### 5.3.5   Transit time spent in Earth shadow

From a Keplerian point of view, the equation

$$\Delta t = \frac{a^{3/2}}{k_e\sqrt{\mu}}\left[\tan^{-1}\left(\frac{\sin E_2}{\cos E_2}\right) - \tan^{-1}\left(\frac{\sin E_1}{\cos E_1}\right) + \right.$$
$$\left. e(\sin E_1 - \sin E_2)\right], \tag{5.49}$$

where the correct quadrant of $E$ is to be determined by examination of the numerator and denominator of the arctangents, will yield the time spent in the shadow of the Earth.   If $\Delta t$ is negative, then the desired time is actually $P - \Delta t$, where $P$ is the period of the orbit.

### 5.3.6   General remarks

It has been seen how solution of Eq. 5.31 yields a first closed approximation to the general shadow function $\bar{S}$, Eq. 5.46.   Within the solution of this function, by iterative means, it is also possible to correct for the flattening and shift of the Earth in its orbit about the Sun.   Apparently then, if perturbations or the influences of other disturbing forces were included in the elements, every time a correction is applied for the shift of the Earth it would be possible at this time and with perturbation theory to replace the old elements by new elements and to resolve the problem with much greater accuracy.   This will become evident in Chapter 10.

### 5.4   RISE-AND-SET TIME OF A SATELLITE ABOUT AN OBLATE PLANET

The purpose of this section is to present a Keplerian closed-form solution to the rise-and-set time problem.   In effect, this problem usually involves the calculation of the rise-and-set universal time of a given satellite from a specific ground station.    The analysis has important application in orbit improvement and refinement.

In the past, it has been the custom to solve the problem by letting the satellite run through its ephemeris, and checking at each instant to see whether the elevation angle $h$ of the satellite, with respect to a ground station, was greater than some minimum value.    However, by attacking the problem from a different point of view, that is, with the eccentric anomaly taken to be the independent variable, it is possible to obtain a closed-form solution to the satellite visibility problem.    Specifically, the closed-form solution is a single transcendental equation in the eccentric anomalies corresponding to a rise-and-set time for a given orbital pass of a satellite.    It is more difficult to solve the controlling equation than the standard Keplerian equation.    However, the method offers the advantage that the controlling equation is solved only once per orbital period as contrasted with the hundreds of times the Keplerian equation must be solved with the standard step-by-step technique.

If the orbital elements and the station coordinates, as well as the minimum value of station elevation angle $h$ are known, it will be possible to obtain a single transcendental equation in the eccentric anomalies corresponding to the rise-and-set times.    Hence the orbital elements $a$, $e$, $i$, $\Omega$, $\omega$, and $T$, as defined in the first paragraph of Section 5.2, and the station coordinates $\theta_0$, $\phi$, $H$ and $\lambda_E$, defined as follows,

$\theta_0 = $ station sidereal time at some epoch time,

$\phi = $ station geodetic latitude,

$H = $ station height above and measured normal to the surface of the adopted ellipsoid,

$\lambda_E = $ station east longitude,

must be known in order to commence solution of the rise-and-set problem.

### 5.4.1   Development of the controlling equation which defines the rise-and-set eccentric anomalies

From a ground station located in a rotating topocentric coordinate frame (Figure 5.4), that is, the azimuth-elevation system (Chapter 4, System 1), the sine of the elevation angle is given by

$$\frac{\mathbf{\rho}}{\rho} \cdot \mathbf{Z} = \sin h \tag{5.50}$$

or

$$\rho_x Z_x + \rho_y Z_y + \rho_z Z_z = \rho \sin h. \tag{5.51}$$

The components of the unit vector $\mathbf{Z}$, which points toward the geodetic zenith, referred to an inertial coordinate frame (Figure 5.5), that is, the

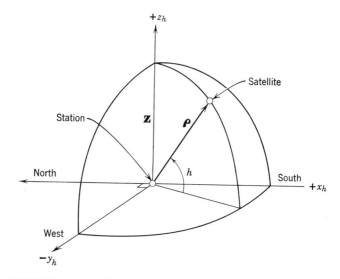

FIGURE 5.4    Satellite location in a topocentric coordinate system.

right ascension-declination coordinate system (Chapter 4, System 2), are given directly by

$$Z_x = \cos\theta \cos\phi$$
$$Z_y = \sin\theta \cos\phi$$
$$Z_z = \sin\phi,$$

(5.52)

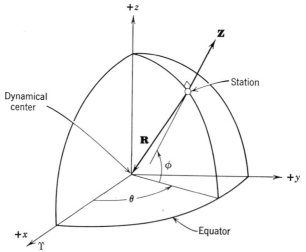

FIGURE 5.5    Station coordinate system in a geocentric coordinate system.

where, for the sake of definiteness,

$\theta$ = station sidereal time,

$\phi$ = station geodetic latitude.

The relationship between the observation station, satellite, and dynamical center is given by

$$\rho = \mathbf{r} + \mathbf{R}, \tag{5.53}$$

where, as explained in Section 3.11,

$\rho$ = slant range vector,

$\mathbf{r}$ = orbit radius vector,

$\mathbf{R}$ = station coordinate vector.

Hence, in terms of the geodetic latitude, the components of the station radius vector $\mathbf{R}$ for an oblate spheroid are given by

$$X = -G_1 \cos \phi \cos \theta$$
$$Y = -G_1 \cos \phi \sin \theta$$
$$Z = -G_2 \sin \phi, \tag{5.54}$$

where the $G$ coefficients are defined from Eqs. 1.64 and 1.65 as

$$G_1 \equiv \frac{a_e}{\sqrt{1 - (2f - f^2) \sin^2 \phi}} + H$$

$$G_2 \equiv \frac{(1 - f)^2 a_e}{\sqrt{1 - (2f - f^2) \sin^2 \phi}} + H$$

and

$a_e$ = equatorial radius of the planet,

$f$ = flattening of the adopted ellipsoid,

$H$ = station elevation above and measured normal to the surface of the adopted ellipsoid,

$\theta$ = local sidereal time.

Having defined the necessary variables and coordinate systems, it is now possible to substitute Eq. 5.53 into Eq. 5.51 so that

$$(x + X)Z_x + (y + Y)Z_y + (z + Z)Z_z = \rho \sin h. \tag{5.55}$$

Introducing the unit vector $\mathbf{Z}$ and the station coordinates into Eq. 5.55, it is possible to write

$$[x - G_1 \cos \phi \cos \theta] \cos \phi \cos \theta + [y - G_1 \cos \phi \sin \theta] \cos \phi \sin \theta$$
$$+ [z - G_2 \sin \phi] \sin \phi = \rho \sin h \tag{5.56}$$

or, upon rearrangement,

$$x \cos \phi \cos \theta + y \cos \phi \sin \theta + z \sin \phi = \rho \sin h + G, \qquad (5.57)$$

where[4]

$$G \equiv G_1 \cos^2 \phi + G_2 \sin^2 \phi. \qquad (5.58)$$

Equation 5.57 is, in effect, the geometric constraint which comprises the controlling equation.

### 5.4.2  Analytic formulation of the controlling equation when the satellite is on the geodetic horizon

When the elevation angle at the ground station is taken to be zero, the controlling equation can be written as

$$x \cos \phi \cos \theta + y \cos \phi \sin \theta + z \sin \phi = G. \qquad (5.59)$$

Introducing the vector equation (Section 3.4.3),

$$\mathbf{r} = x_\omega \mathbf{P} + y_\omega \mathbf{Q}, \qquad (5.60)$$

where $\mathbf{P}$ and $\mathbf{Q}$ unit vectors given by Eqs. 5.3 and 5.4 as a function $i$, $\Omega$, $\omega$, transforms Eq. 5.59 into an equation in which $z$ is lacking, that is, in which analysis is now being performed in the orbital plane. Therefore, the controlling equation can be expressed as follows:

$$[P_x \cos \phi \cos \theta + P_y \cos \phi \sin \theta + P_z \sin \phi]x_\omega$$
$$+ [Q_x \cos \phi \cos \theta + Q_y \cos \phi \sin \theta + Q_z \sin \phi]y_\omega = G,$$

or more concisely as

$$\mathbf{P} \cdot \mathbf{Z} x_\omega + \mathbf{Q} \cdot \mathbf{Z} y_\omega = G. \qquad (5.61)$$

Since the coordinates in the orbit plane (Section 3.5) are given by

$$x_\omega = a(\cos E - e)$$
$$y_\omega = a\sqrt{1 - e^2} \sin E, \qquad (5.62)$$

substitution converts Eq. 5.61 to the form

$$F \equiv a(\cos E - e)\mathbf{P} \cdot \mathbf{Z} + (a\sqrt{1 - e^2} \sin E)\mathbf{Q} \cdot \mathbf{Z} - G = 0. \qquad (5.63)$$

Note that the dot products $\mathbf{P} \cdot \mathbf{Z}$ and $\mathbf{Q} \cdot \mathbf{Z}$ are functions of time in Eq. 5.63 and in order to write $F$ as a function of $E$ alone, it is necessary to eliminate the time dependency of the unit $\mathbf{Z}$ vector.

---

[4] The $G$ coefficient, Eq. 5.58, can be conveniently tabulated for stations.

Equations 5.52, by virtue of Eq. 1.30, can be written as follows

$$Z_x = \cos \phi \cos \left[ \theta_0 + \frac{d\theta}{dt} (t - t_0) \right]$$

$$Z_y = \cos \phi \sin \left[ \theta_0 + \frac{d\theta}{dt} (t - t_0) \right] \qquad (5.64)$$

$$Z_z = \sin \phi,$$

where

$\theta_0$ = epoch sidereal station time in radians,

$\dfrac{d\theta}{dt}$ = sidereal rate of change,

$t_0$ = epoch universal time,

$t$ = universal time.

Introducing Kepler's equation for elliptic motion (Section 3.5), that is,

$$t = \frac{E - e \sin E}{n} + T, \qquad (5.65)$$

where

$n$ = mean motion = $k\sqrt{\mu}\, a^{-\frac{3}{2}}$,

$T$ = time of latest perifocal passage,

$k\sqrt{\mu}$ = dynamical constant,

the **Z** vector becomes

$$Z_x = \cos \phi \cos \left( \theta_0 + \frac{d\theta}{dt} \left[ \frac{E - e \sin E}{n} + T - t_0 \right] \right)$$

$$Z_y = \cos \phi \sin \left( \theta_0 + \frac{d\theta}{dt} \left[ \frac{E - e \sin E}{n} + T - t_0 \right] \right) \qquad (5.66)$$

$$Z_z = \sin \phi,$$

in which time has been eliminated. Therefore, Eq. 5.63 becomes only a function of eccentric anomaly when **Z** is defined by means of Eq. 5.66. Examination of Eq. 5.63, the controlling function, as a function of $E$, produces a curve which has two real roots (Figure 5.6) if the satellite is visible. One of the roots corresponds to the eccentric anomaly at rise, while the remaining one defines the set eccentric anomaly.

It can be shown that when the satellite is visible, $F > 0$ so that when $F$ changes sign from negative to positive, the satellite is rising. A set is oppositely characterized by $F$'s, changing sign from positive to negative. This, in effect, can be seen by consideration of the controlling function $F$ in its simplest form,

$$F \equiv \frac{\rho}{\rho} \cdot \mathbf{Z} - \sin h. \qquad (5.67)$$

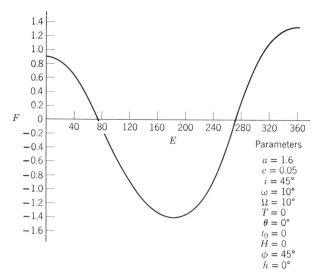

FIGURE 5.6   *F* function versus *E*.

Hence, by replacing $\dfrac{\boldsymbol{\rho}}{\rho}$ by its unit vector counterpart **L**, it is possible to write

$$F \equiv \mathbf{L} \cdot \mathbf{Z} - \sin h \tag{5.68}$$

or

$$F \equiv \cos (\angle \mathbf{L}, \mathbf{Z}) - \sin h. \tag{5.69}$$

However, when the satellite is directly overhead, $\angle \mathbf{L}$, $\mathbf{Z} = 0$ and $F = 1 - \sin h > 0$, if $h < 90°$.

### 5.4.3   Preliminary estimates of the rise-and-set eccentric anomalies

The solution of the controlling equation $F(E)$ can be greatly facilitated if some good preliminary estimates for the values of the rise-and-set eccentric anomalies are known.

Examination of the controlling function $F$ at $E = 0$ and at $E = 2\pi$, produces the following two equations:

$$F(0) = \mathbf{P} \cdot \mathbf{Z}_0 a - \mathbf{P} \cdot \mathbf{Z}_0 ae - G = 0 \tag{5.70}$$

$$F(2\pi) = \mathbf{P} \cdot \mathbf{Z}_{2\pi} a - \mathbf{P} \cdot \mathbf{Z}_{2\pi} ae - G = 0, \tag{5.71}$$

in which it is to be noted that if the **Z** vector were constant, the controlling function $F$ would be periodic.   Therefore, the effect of **Z** is to vary the amplitude of the $F$ function. For near-Earth satellites, this effect is quite small. It is therefore possible to define an average $\mathbf{Z}$ vector $\bar{\mathbf{Z}}$ by[5]

$$\bar{\mathbf{Z}} \equiv (\mathbf{Z}_0 + \mathbf{Z}_{2\pi})/2. \tag{5.72}$$

Equation 5.63 can then be written as

$$\mathbf{P} \cdot \bar{\mathbf{Z}} a \cos E + \mathbf{Q} \cdot \bar{\mathbf{Z}} a \sqrt{1 - e^2} \sin E = G + \mathbf{P} \cdot \bar{\mathbf{Z}} a e, \tag{5.73}$$

which, upon defining the angle $\beta$ by

$$\cos \beta \equiv \frac{\mathbf{P} \cdot \bar{\mathbf{Z}}}{\sqrt{(\mathbf{P} \cdot \bar{\mathbf{Z}})^2 + (\mathbf{Q} \cdot \bar{\mathbf{Z}})^2(1 - e^2)}}$$

$$\sin \beta \equiv \frac{\mathbf{Q} \cdot \bar{\mathbf{Z}} \sqrt{1 - e^2}}{\sqrt{(\mathbf{P} \cdot \bar{\mathbf{Z}})^2 + (\mathbf{Q} \cdot \bar{\mathbf{Z}})^2(1 - e^2)}}, \tag{5.74}$$

reduces to

$$\cos \beta \cos E + \sin \beta \sin E = \frac{1}{a} [G + \mathbf{P} \cdot \bar{\mathbf{Z}} a e] \frac{\cos \beta}{\mathbf{P} \cdot \bar{\mathbf{Z}}} \tag{5.75}$$

or

$$E = \beta - \cos^{-1} \left[ \frac{G + \mathbf{P} \cdot \bar{\mathbf{Z}} a e}{a \sqrt{(\mathbf{P} \cdot \bar{\mathbf{Z}})^2 + (\mathbf{Q} \cdot \bar{\mathbf{Z}})^2(1 - e^2)}} \right]. \tag{5.76}$$

Equation 5.76 is a direct expression of the value of the rise-and-set eccentric anomalies with the assumption that the planet's rotation is negligible. If the satellite is visible, this equation will have two roots. Should the argument of the arccosine be greater than unity in absolute value, it should be truncated to unity with the correct sign attached. It is possible that this will happen if the rise-and-set times are very close together.

It may be evident that the location of the approximate zeros of the $F$ function is a complicated procedure. Equation 5.76 can be utilized with very good success if it is possible to assert that the satellite is visible. In general, however, it will be necessary to catalog the rise-and-set function $F$. Examination of Figure 5.7 indicates that for near-Earth satellites, six possible forms of the $F$ function can occur.

If the rise-and-set function is evaluated at 0 and $2\pi$ by means of Eq. 5.63, and $F$ is possessed of opposite signs at the two extremes, cases $C$ and $F$, it is evident that only one root lies in the interval in question. This situation arises, for example, if the rise-and-set computations are initiated when the satellite is visible. Equation 5.76 can then be directly

---

[5] The averaging technique proposed by approximation 5.72 will produce negative estimates (Eq. 5.76) when $E$ is either very small, nearly zero, or when very large, nearly $2\pi$. If this should happen, it will then be advantageous to set $\bar{\mathbf{Z}}$ equal to $\mathbf{Z}(0)$ or $\bar{\mathbf{Z}}$ equal to $\mathbf{Z}(2\pi)$, so that better estimates will result.

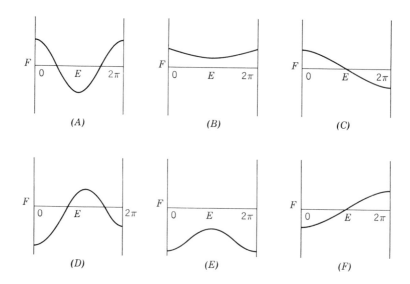

FIGURE 5.7    Catalog of rise-and-set function.

employed to yield the approximate eccentric anomalies.    If the rise-and-set function is evaluated at 0 and $2\pi$ and $F$ is possessed of the same sign, then either cases $A$, $B$ or $D$, $E$ describe the physical situation at hand. In these cases, it is better to directly obtain the minimum or maximum value of $F$ in the interval $0 \leq E \leq 2\pi$.    Hence, by direct differentiation of Eq. 5.73,

$$F' = -\mathbf{P} \cdot \bar{\mathbf{Z}}a \sin E + \mathbf{Q} \cdot \bar{\mathbf{Z}}a\sqrt{1 - e^2} \cos E \qquad (5.77)$$

$$F'' = -\mathbf{P} \cdot \bar{\mathbf{Z}}a \cos E - \mathbf{Q} \cdot \bar{\mathbf{Z}}a\sqrt{1 - e^2} \sin E \qquad (5.78)$$

and $F' = 0$, yields

$$\tan E = \frac{\mathbf{Q} \cdot \bar{\mathbf{Z}}}{\mathbf{P} \cdot \bar{\mathbf{Z}}} \sqrt{1 - e^2}. \qquad (5.79)$$

By determining both values of $E$, obtainable from Eq. 5.79 and substituting into Eq. 5.78 to assure that $F'' > 0$ for cases $A$ and $B$, or $F'' < 0$ for cases $D$ and $E$, an approximate value of $E$ can be obtained which corresponds to the maximum or minimum value of $F$ in the interval $0 \leq E \leq 2\pi$. Using the desired value of $E$, an iteration employing Eq. 5.81 will yield a precise value of the eccentric anomaly corresponding to $F$ minimum or maximum.    Evidently, if $F(E_m)$, where the subscript denotes min-max conditions is different in sign from $F(0)$ or $F(2\pi)$, Eq. 5.76 will yield the approximate rise-and-set eccentric anomalies; otherwise, the satellite is not visible in the local $0 \leq E \leq 2\pi$ interval. For nearby satellites, numerical results have shown that Eq. 5.76 yields excellent results. If, however, the satellite is very far away, it will be necessary to hunt for the zeros of Eq. 5.63 directly. In this case, a hunt with the derivative of Eq. 5.63, that is, $F'(E)$, instead of $F(E)$ will be beneficial.

### 5.4.4   Numerical solution of the controlling equation

Since Eq. 5.63 possesses at least a single root (if the satellite is visible) in the interval $0 \leq E \leq 2\pi$, the following procedure is recommended. Once an estimate of $E$ is available, Newton's method provides a better or improved estimate by means of the following formula:

$$E_{n+1} = E_n - \frac{F(E_n)}{F'(E_n)}, \quad n = 1, 2, \ldots p, \qquad (5.80)$$

where, by differentiation of Eq. 5.63, the $Z$'s being obtained from Eq. 5.66, $F'$ is given by

$$F'(E) = [a(\cos E - e)(P_y Z_x - P_x Z_y) + a\sqrt{1 - e^2} \sin E(Q_y Z_x - Q_x Z_y)]$$
$$\times \frac{(1 - e\cos E)}{n}\dot{\theta} + \mathbf{Q} \cdot \mathbf{Z}a\sqrt{1 - e^2}\cos E - \mathbf{P} \cdot \mathbf{Z}a\sin E. \qquad (5.81)$$

Note that the new estimate of $E_{n+1}$ should not be allowed to change by more than a few per cent of the previous value. The correction should be bounded. The Newton procedure is quadratically convergent and yields very rapid results.[6]

### 5.4.5   Solution of the controlling equation
### when the satellite is above the geodetic horizon

Usually a particular station imposes a minimum elevation angle constraint with respect to the rise-and-set times, for example, a mountain range may be in the direct line of sight. Consequently, it is necessary to evaluate $\rho$ in Eq. 5.57 as a function of $E$, and thus express the controlling equation as a function of a single parameter.

   Since the slant range is given by

$$\rho = [(x + X)^2 + (y + Y)^2 + (z + Z)^2]^{1/2}, \qquad (5.82)$$

---

[6] See Section 9.2.3 for a discussion of the Newton procedure.

or, by using Eqs. 5.54,

$$\rho = [x^2 + y^2 + z^2 + G_0{}^2 - (2G_1 \cos \phi \cos \theta)x$$
$$- (2G_1 \cos \phi \sin \theta)y - (2G_2 \sin \phi)z]^{1/2}, \quad (5.83)$$

it is possible to express $\rho$ as a function of eccentric anomaly with the aid of Eqs. 5.52 and 5.60 as

$$\rho(E) = \{[a^2(1 - e \cos E)^2 + G_0{}^2]$$
$$- 2G_1 Z_x[a(\cos E - e)P_x + a\sqrt{1 - e^2} \sin EQ_x]$$
$$- 2G_1 Z_y[a(\cos E - e)P_y + a\sqrt{1 - e^2} \sin EQ_y]$$
$$- 2G_2 Z_z[a(\cos E - e)P_z + a\sqrt{1 - e^2} \sin EQ_z]\}^{1/2}, $$
$$(5.84)$$

where

$$G_0 \equiv (G_2{}^2 \sin^2 \phi + G_1{}^2 \cos^2 \phi)^{1/2}$$

with the understanding that $\mathbf{Z}$ is obtained from Eqs. 5.66.

In brief, if estimates for the rise-and-set eccentric anomalies are known, for example, from the approximate formula, Eq. 5.76, it is possible to compute the rise-and-set slant ranges from Eq. 5.84. Then, if the right side of Eq. 5.57 is redefined to be a new constant, that is,

$$S_k \equiv \rho_k \sin h_k + G, \quad k = 1, 2, \quad (5.85)$$

where the subscript $k$ refers to rise-and-set conditions, it is possible to write Eq. 5.63 with $S_k$ replacing $G$. Therefore, two independent equations, one for a rise eccentric anomaly and the other for a set eccentric anomaly, are obtained. The solution of Eq. 5.63, however, has already been discussed. The new values of $E_k$ yield a better $\rho_k$, etc.

### 5.4.6 Calculation of rise-and-set time

Once the rise-and-set anomalies $E_k$ are known, where $k = 1, 2$, it is possible to solve Kepler's equation the easy way for $t_k$, that is, determine the rise-and-set time by means of

$$t_k = \frac{E_k - e \sin E_k}{n} + T, \quad k = 1, 2, \quad (5.86)$$

where $T$ = time of latest perifocal passage.

By adding the period or multiples of it to the latest time of perifocal passage, it is possible to solve for future rise-and-set times.

### 5.4.7    General remarks and results

A general set of equations have been developed for calculating the rise-and-set time of a satellite about a geometrically oblate planet. The analysis was programmed on an IBM 7090 computer in Fortran. The secular variations[7] in $\Omega$, $\omega$, and $M_0$ were added to the analysis, and the results were compared to a fully rigorous numerical integration of the equations of motion and a point-by-point check procedure. A tabulation of the comparison follows.

$$a = 1.0346400 \text{ earth-radii}$$
$$e = 0.0004648$$
$$i = 91.995912 \text{ degrees}$$
$$\Omega = 311.45905 \text{ degrees}$$
$$\omega = 128.31922 \text{ degrees}$$
$$T = 1371.0420 \text{ minutes}$$

| REVOLUTION NUMBER | RISE TIME (closed-form solution) Day Hour Minute | | | RISE TIME (integrated solution) Day Hour Minute | | |
|---|---|---|---|---|---|---|
| 17 | 1 | 0 | 9.84 | 1 | 0 | 9.88 |
| 20 | 1 | 4 | 31.96 | 1 | 4 | 31.98 |
| 30 | 1 | 19 | 25.80 | 1 | 19 | 25.93 |
| | SET TIME | | | SET TIME | | |
| 17 | 1 | 0 | 13.13 | 1 | 0 | 13.04 |
| 20 | 1 | 4 | 37.21 | 1 | 4 | 37.15 |
| 30 | 1 | 19 | 32.00 | 1 | 19 | 32.10 |

STATION LOCATION
21 June 1962

$$\lambda_E = 291.5 \text{ degrees} \qquad \phi = 76.5 \text{ degrees}$$
$$h = 3.0 \text{ degrees} \qquad H = 900 \text{ feet}$$

Some of the slight discrepancies in the rise-and-set times result from the fact that the integration technique includes more extensive perturbations;

[7] See Chapter 10.

the remaining discrepancies stem from the use of an integration method which performs a linear interpolation for the rise-and-set times between two integration intervals.

On the average, numerical results have shown that the computing speed for the closed-form solution is approximately twenty-five times faster than the computing speed for the integration procedure. Needless to say, if more perturbations are added to the analysis, the rise-and-set times will be computed to greater accuracy at little expense in machine time.

### 5.5  SELECTION OF AN ORBIT PASSING OVER A SPECIFIC GROUND STATION ON AN OBLATE PLANET

Station flyover is the name given to the problem of selecting a set of orbital orientation elements such that at some specified future time the orbit of the satellite defined by the selected set of elements will pass directly over a specified ground station. This, in effect, is a problem in orbit selection rather than orbit determination.

A method is presented for the solution of the flyover problem in closed-form. In effect, a set of formulas are developed which allow computation of the orientation and dimensional elements of an orbit such that at some specified time the satellite will be at some specified geocentric altitude directly above the station. In the solution of the problem, the rate of change of the station or target out of the orbit plane is made to vanish at the flyover point. Obviously the ability to determine such an orbit is of great importance in the fields of reconnaissance, communications, and photogrammetry.

Apparently, solution to this problem can be achieved by assuming a set of starting orbital elements and integrating forward till the desired time; at this point the original elements, if in error, are "backed up" and the process repeated until the satellite is over the desired ground point at the desired time. The analysis to be presented is a closed-form, explicit solution to the flyover problem. Inherent in the analysis is the assumption of two-body Newtonian mechanics, but the surface geometry of the central planet is taken to be an oblate ellipsoid. Here again, a problem which can be solved by the introduction of direct trajectory integration is reduced to some simple equations. Once the two-body elements have been determined, it is an easy extension to add in or incorporate perturbative influences (Chapter 10).

### 5.5.1  The geometric constraining equation of the flyover problem

It is possible to reduce the difficulty of the problem a substantial amount by stating the flyover criterion in the following manner. A satellite is

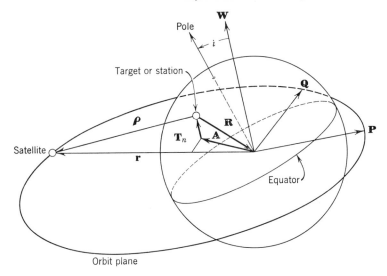

FIGURE 5.8    Orbit geometry.

said to have overflown the target where the target is defined as the specified ground station at some time $t$, if the magnitude of the normal from the orbit plane that intersects the station is identically zero.[8]  The orbit geometry is defined in Figure 5.8.

   In this light, it is possible to proceed as follows.  Introduce the usual right-handed set of unit vectors, $\mathbf{P}$, $\mathbf{Q}$, $\mathbf{W}$, into the right ascension–declination coordinate system (Chapter 4, System 2), such that $\mathbf{P}$ and $\mathbf{Q}$ define the orientation of the desired orbit plane.  $\mathbf{P}$ is taken in the perifocal direction, and $\mathbf{Q}$ is advanced by a right angle to $\mathbf{P}$ in the direction of motion; $\mathbf{W}$ is taken normal to the orbit plane.

   Examination of Figure 5.8 permits the following vector equation to be written.

$$\mathbf{R} + \mathbf{A} + \mathbf{T}_n = \mathbf{0}, \tag{5.87}$$

where $\mathbf{R}$ is the station coordinate vector from the specified target station to the dynamical center, $\mathbf{A}$ is a vector from the dynamical center to $\mathbf{T}_n$ in the unknown orbit plane, and $\mathbf{T}_n$ is a vector normal to the orbit plane which intersects the target station.  Hence, by dotting Eq. 5.87 with $\mathbf{W}$, it is possible to write

$$\mathbf{W} \cdot \mathbf{R} + \mathbf{W} \cdot \mathbf{A} + \mathbf{W} \cdot \mathbf{T}_n = 0. \tag{5.88}$$

---

[8] Once the orientation plane is correctly aligned, it is a simple extension to place the satellite in the proper position.  This will be done in a later section.

But

$$\mathbf{W} \cdot \mathbf{A} = 0, \tag{5.89}$$

since $\mathbf{W}$ is perpendicular to $\mathbf{A}$, and

$$\mathbf{W} \cdot \mathbf{T}_n = T_n, \tag{5.90}$$

since $\mathbf{W}$ is a unit vector parallel to $\mathbf{T}_n$, and the angle between $\mathbf{W}$ and $\mathbf{T}_n$ is zero. Therefore, Eq. 5.88 states that

$$T_n = -\mathbf{W} \cdot \mathbf{R}. \tag{5.91}$$

Before evaluating Eq. 5.91, a slight digression into the station coordinates of the target station is required. In terms of the geodetic latitude $\phi$, the components of the station radius vector $\mathbf{R}$ for an oblate spheroid are given by Section 3.11.

$$
\begin{aligned}
X &= -G_1 \cos \phi \cos \theta \\
Y &= -G_1 \cos \phi \sin \theta \\
Z &= -G_2 \sin \phi,
\end{aligned}
\tag{5.92}
$$

where the $G$ coefficients are defined from Eqs. 1.64 and 1.65 as

$$G_1 \equiv \frac{a_e}{\sqrt{1 - (2f - f^2) \sin^2 \phi}} + H$$

$$G_2 \equiv \frac{a_e(1 - f)^2}{\sqrt{1 - (2f - f^2) \sin^2 \phi}} + H$$

and, as usual,

$a_e$ = equatorial radius of planet,

$f$ = flattening of adopted ellipsoid,

$H$ = station elevation above and measured normal to the surface of the adopted ellipsoid,

$\theta$ = local sidereal time.

Therefore, by evaluating the dot product defined by Eq. 5.91, it is possible to express the constraining equation as

$$T_n = -(W_x X + W_y Y + W_z Z), \tag{5.93}$$

or more exactly as

$$T_n = G_1 W_x \cos \phi \cos \theta + G_1 W_y \cos \phi \sin \theta + G_2 W_z \sin \phi. \tag{5.94}$$

Equation 5.94 is the sought-for constraint.

### 5.5.2   Solution of the constraining equation

It is obvious that if $T_n$ is set equal to zero, a relationship will exist between $W_x$, $W_y$, and $W_z$ such that the station or target will be in plane of the orbit. Furthermore, the components of the **W** unit vector are related by means of

$$W_x{}^2 + W_y{}^2 + W_z{}^2 = 1. \tag{5.95}$$

Simultaneous solution of Eqs. 5.94 and 5.95, with $T_n$ set equal to zero, will then solve the orientation part of the flyover problem. However, for most applications (photogrammetry, etc.), it will also be beneficial to make the rate of change the scalar $T_n$ (the normal to the orbit plane) with respect to $\theta$ (the sidereal time) equal to zero at flyover point. Naturally, this will result in a better photograph of the target site.[9] Therefore, from Eq. 5.94,

$$\frac{dT_n}{d\theta} = -G_1 W_x \cos\phi \sin\theta + G_1 W_y \cos\phi \cos\theta, \tag{5.96}$$

and

$$\frac{d^2 T_n}{d\theta^2} = -G_1 W_x \cos\phi \cos\theta - G_1 W_y \cos\phi \sin\theta. \tag{5.97}$$

So that from Eq. 5.96, setting $dT_n/d\theta = 0$,

$$-W_x \sin\theta + W_y \cos\theta = 0, \tag{5.98}$$

or

$$\tan\theta = \frac{W_y}{W_x}. \tag{5.99}$$

It must be remembered that $W_x$ and $W_y$ must be chosen such that

$$\frac{d^2 T_n}{d\theta^2} = -G_1 \cos\phi[W_x \cos\theta + W_y \sin\theta] > 0, \tag{5.100}$$

in order to insure a minimum value for the magnitude of $T_n$ at the flyover point.

[9] There is evidently a conflict between a speed constraint, that is, slowest speed over the station, and a height constraint. Therefore, if the speed of the satellite is decreased, the height will be increased. These are dynamical constraints and will not be discussed at this point. In passing, it is well to note that there are an infinite number of orbits with $|\mathbf{T}_n| = 0$. However, it certainly appears feasible to have the normal component $(dT_n/d\theta)$ of station velocity equal to zero by proper choice of elements.

Substituting Eqs. 5.95 and 5.99 into Eq. 5.94 results in the following expression:

$$G_1 W_x \cos \phi \cos \theta + G_1 W_x \cos \phi \tan \theta \sin \theta$$
$$\pm G_2 \sin \phi (1 - W_x^2 - W_x^2 \tan^2 \theta)^{1/2} = 0 \quad (5.101)$$

or

$$\frac{G_1 W_x \cos \phi}{\cos \theta} \pm G_2 \sin \phi (1 - W_x^2 \sec^2 \theta)^{1/2} = 0. \quad (5.102)$$

By transposing, squaring both sides, and collecting terms, the $W_x$ component of the **W** vector is therefore found to be

$$W_x = \pm \frac{G_2 \sin \phi \cos \theta}{G_0} \quad (5.103)$$

with

$$G_0^2 \equiv G_2^2 \sin^2 \phi + G_1^2 \cos^2 \phi. \quad (5.104)$$

Then, from Eq. 5.99, it is possible to obtain

$$W_y = \pm \frac{G_2 \sin \phi \sin \theta}{G_0}. \quad (5.105)$$

Finally, Eq. 5.95 yields

$$W_z = \pm \frac{\sqrt{G_0^2 - G_2^2 \sin^2 \phi}}{G_0} = \pm \frac{G_1}{G_0} \cos \phi. \quad (5.106)$$

In order to insure a minimum value for the rate of change of $T_n$, it is possible to show that $W_x$ and $W_y$ take the lower signs if a station is above the equator, and the upper signs if a station is below the equator. This can be seen by substitution of Eqs. 5.103 and 5.105 into Eq. 5.100.

$$\frac{d^2 T_n}{d\theta^2} = -\frac{1}{2} \frac{G_1 G_2}{G_0} \sin 2\phi \, [\pm \cos^2 \theta \pm \sin^2 \theta], \quad (5.107)$$

so that if $\phi > 0$ taking the lower sign,

$$\frac{d^2 T_n}{d\theta^2} = \frac{1}{2} \frac{G_1 G_2}{G_0} \sin 2\phi > 0,$$

and likewise for $\phi < 0$ taking the upper sign,

$$\frac{d^2 T_n}{d\theta^2} = -\frac{1}{2} \frac{G_1 G_2}{G_0} \sin 2\phi > 0.$$

The sign of $W_z$ is taken as desired, since both retrograde ($W_z < 0$) and direct orbits ($W_z \geq 0$) can be used to solve the flyover problem.[10]

[10] A retrograde orbit will, of course, increase the relative velocity between station and satellite.

Equations 5.103, 5.105, and 5.106 can be conveniently rewritten as

$$W_x = \pm \frac{G_2}{G_0} \sin \phi \cos \left[ \theta_0 + \frac{d\theta}{dt} (t - t_0) \right]$$

$$W_y = \pm \frac{G_2}{G_0} \sin \phi \sin \left[ \theta_0 + \frac{d\theta}{dt} (t - t_0) \right] \qquad (5.108)$$

$$W_z = \pm \frac{G_1}{G_0} \cos \phi$$

which, as shall be presently shown, in effect completely solves the orientation problem with due regard for the sign of each quantity as indicated previously, and where

$t$ = desired station universal flyover time,

$t_0$ = station universal time at epoch,

$\dfrac{d\theta}{dt}$ = sidereal rate of change,

$\theta_0$ = station sidereal time at epoch.

The unit vector $\mathbf{W}$ is related to the classical orientation angles (Section 3.4) by means of

$$W_x = \sin \Omega \sin i, \qquad 0 \le \Omega \le 2\pi,$$
$$W_y = - \cos \Omega \sin i, \quad 0 \le i \le \pi, \qquad (5.109)$$
$$W_z = \cos i,$$

so that

$$\sin i = + \sqrt{1 - W_z^2}$$
$$\cos i = W_z$$
$$\sin \Omega = \frac{W_x}{\sin i} \qquad (5.110)$$
$$\cos \Omega = - \frac{W_y}{\sin i}.$$

This completely determines $i$, the orbital inclination, and $\Omega$, the longitude of the ascending node. It is evident from the analysis that only these two angles are needed to solve the flyover problem. Therefore, $\omega$, the argument of perigee, which is the third orientation element of the classical set, $i$, $\Omega$, $\omega$ can be picked as desired. Having picked $\omega$, it is possible to calculate the vectors $\mathbf{P}$ and $\mathbf{Q}$ by Eqs. 5.3 and 5.4. Advantage can be taken by choosing $\omega = 0$ because the calculation of $\mathbf{P}$ simplifies greatly. $\mathbf{Q}$ can always be obtained from $\mathbf{Q} = \mathbf{W} \times \mathbf{P}$. These vectors are calculated here because they will find use presently.

### 5.5.3    The dimensional elements

In the previous section, the orientation elements $i$, $\Omega$, and $\omega$ have been determined such that the station or target is in the plane of the orbit at the desired time $t$. The dimensional elements,

$$a, \quad e, \quad T,$$

where

$a$ = semimajor axis,
$e$ = orbital eccentricity,
$T$ = time of perifocal passage,

are still undetermined. Actually, no explicit relationship is imposed upon these elements in the orientation solution of the flyover problem. However, a useful extension to the flyover problem is the added conditional constraint that the satellite, which is now in a predetermined plane, shall be directly over the station at a specified time and at a specified altitude $H_s$.[11]

To be more specific, if the altitude of the satellite (above and measured normal to the surface of the adopted ellipsoid) is a given constraint, which is to be in effect at time $t$, it is possible to compute the magnitude of the radius vector (Appendix I, Transformation 4) as

$$r = \sqrt{r_c^2 + H_s^2 + 2r_c H_s \cos(\phi_s - \phi_s')}, \tag{5.111}$$

where the geocentric latitude $\phi_s'$ of the station is obtained as a function of the flattening $f$ by

$$\phi_s' = \tan^{-1}[(1 - f)^2 \tan \phi_s], \quad -90° \le \phi_s' \le 90° \tag{5.112}$$

and the distance from the dynamical center to the ellipsoid, $r_c$, (Section 1.4) is obtained as

$$r_c^2 = \frac{a_e^2[1 - (2f - f^2)]}{1 - (2f - f^2) \cos^2 \phi_s'}. \tag{5.113}$$

Hence, given $H_s$, it is certainly possible to compute the magnitude of the radius vector $r$ to the satellite.

The true anomaly $v$ of the satellite can be directly calculated if it is realized that at the flyover point the station coordinate vector is in the plane of the orbit. Therefore, by defining the unit vector $\mathbf{U}^*$ as

$$\mathbf{U}^* \equiv -\frac{\mathbf{R}}{R}, \tag{5.114}$$

[11] The subscript $s$ refers to subvehicle point.

that is, a unit vector pointing directly to the satellite at the flyover point, it follows that

$$\cos v = \mathbf{P} \cdot \mathbf{U}^* \tag{5.115}$$

and

$$\mathbf{W} \sin v = \mathbf{P} \times \mathbf{U}^*. \tag{5.116}$$

It should be noticed that $\mathbf{P}$ is defined by means of Eq. 5.3 and that only one component of Eq. 5.116 is needed.[12]

Now since no further conditions are imposed upon the specific orbit, for example, minimum time to the station from a given position in the orbit, etc., it is possible arbitrarily to pick a dimensional element; let it be $e$, the eccentricity. By means of the mappings,

$$\cos E = \frac{\cos v + e}{1 + e \cos v}, \qquad \sin E = \frac{\sqrt{1 - e^2} \sin v}{1 + e \cos v}, \tag{5.117}$$

the eccentric anomaly $E$ is readily computed, and thus the semimajor axis of the orbit, $a$, can be determined from

$$a = \frac{r}{1 - e \cos E}. \tag{5.118}$$

Then utilizing Kepler's equation in the form

$$T = t - \left[ \frac{E - e \sin E}{k \sqrt{\mu}} \right] a^{3/2}, \tag{5.119}$$

where[13] $k$ = gravitation constant of the planet, $\mu$ = sum of the masses of the two bodies, allows the determination of the time of perifocal passage $T$.

This satellite, with elements of orientation $i$ and $\Omega$, from Eq. 5.110, an arbitrary value of $\omega$, along with the dimensional element $a$ from Eq. 5.118, the $T$ obtained from Eq. 5.119, with arbitrary $e$, will be directly over the station or target at time $t$ with altitude $H_s$.

### 5.5.4  Solution with fixed orbital inclination

Since the constraint of a fixed inclination is quite strong, a solution to this problem is presented for the sake of completeness.

[12] Obviously, the largest component of $\mathbf{W}$ should be used to yield the greatest accuracy. Notice that $\sin v$ can also be determined as $\sin v = \mathbf{W} \cdot (\mathbf{P} \times \mathbf{U}^*)$.
[13] The time, $t$, in Eq. 5.119 should be the universal time. However, if this is understood it suffices to use $t$ in minutes measured from $t_0$.

It follows that if $i$ is specified then Eq. 5.95 yields

$$W_x^2 + W_y^2 = 1 - \cos^2 i = 1 - W_{z0}^2, \qquad (5.120)$$

where the zero subscript means that $W_z$ is held constant. The condition $T_n = 0$ produces the following relationship from Eq. 5.94

$$G_1 W_x \cos \phi \cos \theta + G_1 W_y \cos \phi \sin \theta = -G_2 W_{z0} \sin \phi. \qquad (5.121)$$

This, in effect, is the solution of the problem, for $W_x$ and $W_y$ are determined as the solutions of the intersection of a straight line, Eq. 5.121, and the circle defined by Eq. 5.120. Substitution of $W_y$ from Eq. 5.121 into Eq. 5.120 produces the quadratic resolvent in $W_x$:

$$W_x^2 + 2\left[\left(\frac{G_2}{G_1}\right) W_{z0} \tan \phi \cos \theta\right] W_x + \left[\left(\frac{G_2}{G_1}\right)^2 W_{z0}^2 \tan^2 \phi\right.$$
$$\left. - (1 - W_{z0}^2) \sin^2 \theta\right] = 0. \qquad (5.122)$$

Hence, after obtaining a root of Eq. 5.122, $W_y$ is obtained from the linear constraint Eq. 5.121. The solution then continues as indicated previously starting with Eqs. 5.110.

*Illustrative Example*

Determine the orbital elements of a satellite that is to be selected such that it will pass directly over New York at an altitude of 100 nautical miles exactly three days after injection. Injection occurred from Cape Kennedy at midnight (0 hr) on August 24, 1963. The coordinates of New York are $\phi = 40°.7$, $\lambda_E = 286°.0$, $H = 0$.

In order to perform the indicated analysis, it suffices to adopt:

$$f = 0.0033523$$
$$a_e = 1.0000000 \text{ e.r.}$$
$$k_e = 0.0743657 \text{ (e.r.)}^{3/2}/\text{min}$$
$$\frac{d\theta}{dt} = 4.375269 \times 10^{-3} \text{ rad/min},$$

and from the problem:

$$H = 0.0000000 \text{ e.r.}$$
$$\phi = 40.700000 \text{ degrees}$$
$$\lambda_E = 286.00000 \text{ degrees}$$
$$H_s = 0.0290562 \text{ e.r.}$$
$$t - t_0 = 4320.0000 \text{ min}$$

The Greenwich sidereal time for August 24, 1963, is obtained from the *American Ephemeris and Nautical Almanac* [5], or Eq. 1.27 as

$$\theta_g = 22^{hr} 06^{min} 12.550^{sec}.$$

Hence, utilizing the East longitude of New York the epoch sidereal time is obtainable as

$$\theta_g + \lambda_E = \theta_0 = 257°55229.$$

Having calculated the shape coefficients $G_1$, $G_2$, and $G_0$ from Eqs. 5.92, the **W** vector is obtained by Eq. 5.108.   Selecting arbitrarily,

$e = 0.2000000$

$\omega = 0.0000000$ degrees,

Eqs. 5.110 yield

$\Omega = 170.51304$ degrees

$i = 40.509856$ degrees.

The **P** and **Q** vectors are calculated next by means of Eqs. 5.3 and 5.4, and the true anomaly is obtained by Eqs. 5.114, 5.115, and 5.116.   Hence, by virtue of Eqs. 5.111 and 5.117, the semimajor axis is calculated from Eq. 5.118 as

$a = 1.0704443$ e.r.

The time of perifocal passage is finally obtained from Eq. 5.119,

$T = 4320.0000$ min.

If these are the correct orbital elements, then at midnight on August 27, 1963, the cross product of the satellite radius vector and slant range vector must vanish, thus

$$\boldsymbol{\rho} \times \mathbf{r} = \mathbf{0},$$

since the angle between $\boldsymbol{\rho}$ and $\mathbf{r}$ is zero.

Computing $\boldsymbol{\rho}$ and $\mathbf{r}$, and evaluating their cross product, yields

$$\rho_y z - \rho_z y = 0.00000$$

$$\rho_z x - \rho_x z = 0.00000$$

$$\rho_x y - \rho_y x = 0.00000.$$

### 5.5.5   General remarks

A set of expressions has been developed that enables the orientation elements of an orbit to be determined such that at some future (past) time a specified ground station will be in the plane of the orbit.   Furthermore, the lateral rate of change of the station out of the orbit plane is taken to be zero in order to obtain a smoother passage.   As an added extension, a technique has been developed that will place the satellite at a specified height above the desired station or target at the specified time. Solution of the complete flyover problem as developed in this section requires that two elements of the orbit be arbitrarily chosen as the problem at hand best decrees. The other four are defined by the developed equations.

A solution with a fixed inclination has also been found. Since the solution is achieved in closed form a great saving in machine time will be realized. Perturbations to the elements can easily be incorporated.


### 5.6  SUMMARY

This chapter has presented the solution of certain problems related to preliminary orbit determination with the objective of familiarizing the reader with the manipulation of the two-body equations.

As an introduction to Keplerian analysis, the problem of direct visibility of a planetary surface for Earth satellites and space probes was solved in a simple manner.

Within the field of two-body or Keplerian mechanics, the eclipse problem of a satellite in an elliptic orbit was formulated and its solution attained by means of a quartic equation. Corrections for the flattening, umbra-penumbra, and Earth shift or movement were incorporated by iterative techniques.

The rise-and-set time problem of a satellite about an oblate planet, or the question of when a satellite comes into view from a specified ground station, was analyzed from the two-body aspect.

Finally, a problem in orbit selection was studied and analyzed. Thus it was seen that two-body formulas can be used directly to pick a set of orbital elements such that a satellite will be directly over a specified ground station at some desired future time.

As can be seen, a great variety of problems can be solved by the use of two-body theory. When more accuracy is desired, perturbative influences can be incorporated.


### EXERCISES

1. Nodal crossing times of a satellite in orbit around a central planet are very useful as reference points. The definition of ascending nodal crossing is taken to be the time when a satellite is passing through the equatorial plane with a positive velocity component in the $z$ direction

(System 2, Chapter 4); the definition of descending nodal crossing is characterized by a component of velocity in the $-z$ direction. Develop a method of obtaining these fundamental reckoning points and apply the analysis to determine the times of nodal crossing of a satellite whose orbital elements are

$$a = 2, \quad e = 0.3, \quad i = 60°,$$
$$\Omega = 30°, \quad \omega = 30°, \quad T = 1962 \text{ Jan 2, } 3000^{\text{min}}.$$

2. Determine the true anomalies at the entrance and exit shadow points of a satellite with the elements:

$$a = 2.0, \quad e = 0.5, \quad i = 5°,$$
$$\Omega = 45°, \quad \omega = 60°, \quad T = 1963 \text{ Dec 23, } 0^{\text{hr}}, 0^{\text{min}}, 0^{\text{sec}},$$

if

$$X_\odot = +0.0040829 \text{ a.u.}$$
$$Y_\odot = -0.9024311 \text{ a.u.}$$
$$Z_\odot = -0.3913413 \text{ a.u.}$$

Assume a cylindrical shadow, no flattening corrections, and no Earth shift.

3. A ground station located in the twilight zone observes the satellite in problem 2 enter the shadow of the Earth, assuming that $f = 1/298.3$, $a_e = 1$, what is the latitude of the station?

4. Assuming the Earth does not rotate, what are the first rise-and-set eccentric anomalies after the time of perifocal passage of a satellite with elements:

$$a = 1.2, \quad e = 0.05, \quad i = 45°$$
$$\Omega = 45°, \quad \omega = 45°, \quad T = 1962 \text{ Jan 2, } 3000^{\text{min}}$$

from Addis Ababa, Ethiopia, with station coordinates

$$\phi = 9°, \quad \lambda_E = 38°.75, \quad H = 7628 \text{ ft}$$

5. What are the exact two-body rise-and-set times of problem 4?

6. Select an elliptic orbit which passed over Olifantsfontein, Africa ($\phi = -25°.9594$, $\lambda_E = 28°.2483$, $H_s = 500$ km) on 1965 January 15, $10^{\text{hr}} 5^{\text{min}} 55^{\text{sec}}$ universal time, if injection occurred on 1964, June 1, $0^{\text{hr}}, 0^{\text{min}}, 0^{\text{sec}}$. Assume $e = 0.05$, $\omega = 0°$.

7. Show that for a circular orbit, with elements the same as problem 1 except that $e = 0$, the solution of the eclipse problem reduces to a biquadratic equation in which cubic and linear terms are lacking. By redefining $\mathbf{P}$ as being equal to a unit vector along the line of nodes and using $T_\Omega = 1962 \text{ Jan 2, } 1440^{\text{min}}$, obtain the entrance and exit

true anomalies and corresponding times.   Obtain the position of the Sun from the *American Ephemeris and Nautical Almanac*.

8. Develop an analytical expression for determining the sidereal time, $\theta$, when a satellite with known elements $i$, $\Omega$, $\omega$ will be directly over a specified ground station.   Assume that geometrical flattening is an important consideration.

9. The world is eagerly awaiting news concerning the assassination of Count Alucard of Transylvania.   Satellite Omega-7 with orbital elements $a$, $e$, $i = 0$, $\Omega$, $\omega$, $T$ is to televise direct coverage of this event to New York.   The relays of the satellite must be activated when Omega-7 is midway between the meridian of Transylvania, $\lambda_{E1}$, and New York, $\lambda_{E2}$.   Show that the eccentric anomaly of initial transmission is defined by the zero of the equation

$$F = (\cos E - e)\{P_x \cos \hat{\theta} + P_y \sin \hat{\theta}\} +$$
$$\sqrt{1 - e^2} \sin E\{Q_x \cos \hat{\theta} + Q_y \cos \hat{\theta}\} - (1 - e \sin E),$$

where

$$\hat{\theta} = \theta_{g0} + \lambda_{E2} + \tfrac{1}{2}(\lambda_{E1} - \lambda_{E2}) + \hat{\theta}\left\{\frac{1}{n}(E - e \sin E) + T\right\}$$

and **P** and **Q**, are the usual unit vectors (Chapter 3).

10. Determine a single iterative equation in the eccentric anomaly of an Earth satellite which will determine the point of closest approach to a specified ground station.

**REFERENCES**

1. T. R. Oppolzer, *Canon of Eclipses*, Dover Publications, New York, 1962.
2. P. R. Escobal, "Orbital Entrance and Exit from the Shadow of the Earth," *ARS Journal*, December 1962.
3. P. R. Escobal, "Rise and Set Time of a Satellite About an Oblate Planet," *AIAA Journal*, Vol. I, No. 10, October 1963.
4. P. R. Escobal, *An Optimum Explicit Solution to the Station Flyover Problem*, LTM 50285, Lockheed California Company, December 1962.
5. *American Ephemeris and Nautical Almanac*, U.S. Government Printing Office, Washington, D.C., 1960, 1961, 1962, 1963, etc.
6. E. T. Bell, *Men of Mathematics*, Simon Schuster, New York, 1937.

# 6 Determination of an orbit from two position vectors and time

*A new planet had been discovered in a position which made it extraordinarily difficult of observation. To compute an orbit from the meager data available was a task which might have exercised Laplace, himself. Newton had declared that such problems are among the most difficult in mathematical astronomy. The mere arithmetic necessary to establish an orbit with accuracy sufficient to ensure that Ceres on her whirl around the Sun should not be lost to telescopes might well deter an electrically-driven calculating machine even today; but to the young man Gauss, whose inhuman memory enabled him to dispense with a table of logarithms when he was hard pressed or too lazy to reach for one, all this endless arithmetic—logistica, not arithmetica—was the sport of an infant.*

E. T. BELL [7]

## 6.1 THE TWO POSITION VECTORS AND TIME INTERVAL PROBLEM

Let it be assumed that two position vectors $r_1$ and $r_2$ of an object in a Newtonian force field are known. Furthermore, let the time interval required by the object to move from $r_1$ to $r_2$ or $t_2 - t_1$ be known. It will be shown that determination of an orbit satisfying these boundary conditions can be determined by a number of different techniques.

Modern ideology of scientific investigation has engendered considerable interest in the two position vectors and time interval problem. Apart from the direct application for the determination of an unknown orbit from angular observations, these schemes can be of great use in the solution of intercept, targeting, and rendezvous trajectory problems. For example, the intercept problem could be solved by direct orbit calculation utilizing some of the techniques presented herein, where the initial data could very well be two position vectors. Since there are an infinite number of orbits that can be passed through two position vectors, with this type of application a given variable is usually considered in an objective function and a minimum time, velocity increment, etc., trajectory found to determine the unique orbit and satisfy the mission.

**187**

The other aspect, determination of the orbit from direct observations, can be handled by a remarkable transformation which reduces the given angular observations to radius or position vectors. This transformation will be developed and discussed in Chapter 7.

In this chapter a number of different techniques for preliminary orbit determination from two position vectors and respective time interval will be developed. For each method, except the last, the theory will be presented and then an algorithm for practical use and clarification of the equations particular to the technique will be stated. The last technique, owing to its newness, is not stated in algorithm form. With the exception of the last two methods, only elliptical formulations are considered. Hyperbolic extensions can be formulated in much the same manner.

## 6.2    GAUSSIAN PRELIMINARY ORBIT DETERMINATION

### 6.2.1    Episode

January 1, 1801, was an eventful day from an astronomical point of view. The first minor planet, Ceres, had just been discovered. Or was it a planet? It had been observed for only a few weeks and then lost. The problem of determining the orbit from the meager data was one of great difficulty, and marked the explosive entry of twenty-four year old Carl Friederick Gauss (1777–1855) into the realm of mathematical astronomy. In a short time Gauss devised a scheme for determination of the orbit, and Ceres was recovered at the end of the year in the predicted position. Ceres was indeed a minor planet.

### 6.2.2    Ratio of sector to triangle

It will become evident that orbit determination is a judicious balancing of geometric and dynamical concepts. Consider, for example, the orbit of a planet or satellite moving about a central body as shown in Figure 6.1.

As can be seen, the ratio of the sector $ABC$ to the triangle $ABC$ is small. To be more explicit, the parameter of the ellipse $p$ is analytically expressible as

$$p = \frac{r^4 \dot{v}^2}{\sqrt{\mu}}.$$    (6.1)

But the angular momentum vector $\mathbf{h}$ is given by

$$\mathbf{h} = \frac{\mathbf{r} \times \dot{\mathbf{r}}}{\sqrt{\mu}}$$    (6.2)

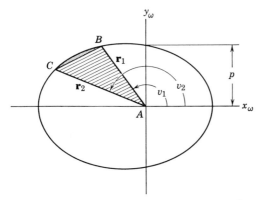

FIGURE 6.1   Triangle superimposed upon a sector of an ellipse.

with the understanding that the magnitude of **h** is equal to $\sqrt{\mu p}$. There-fore, if Eq. 6.2 is written for the orbit plane coordinate system (System 8, Chapter 4), it is possible to write

$$\sqrt{\mu p} = x_\omega \dot{y}_\omega - y_\omega \dot{x}_\omega = 2\frac{dA}{d\tau},\tag{6.3}$$

where $dA/d\tau$ is the *areal velocity* or rate of change of the enclosed area in Figure 6.1.   It follows that the area of the sector $ABC$ is given by

$$A_s = \tfrac{1}{2}\int_0^\tau \sqrt{\mu p}\ d\bar\tau = \tfrac{1}{2}\sqrt{\mu p}\ \tau.\tag{6.4}$$

The area of the triangle $ABC$ is one-half the product of the base and altitude, or

$$A_T = \tfrac{1}{2}r_2 r_1 \sin (v_2 - v_1).\tag{6.5}$$

Therefore, the ratio of sector to triangle is

$$y = \frac{\sqrt{\mu p}\cdot \tau}{r_2 r_1 \sin (v_2 - v_1)}.\tag{6.6}$$

This ratio, $y$, is a very important parameter in the method of Gauss. Notice the vanishing of the denominator of $y$ at a radius vector spread of $\pi$ radians.

### 6.2.3   A relation between the ratio of sector to triangle and the difference in eccentric anomalies

Having the concept of sector to triangle ratio at hand, a relation between this ratio and the difference in eccentric anomalies corresponding to the known difference in true anomalies, that is, $v_2 - v_1$, will now be sought.

The equation of a conic in polar form is given by

$$r = \frac{p}{1 + e \cos v}. \tag{6.7}$$

Writing this equation at the times $t_2$ and $t_1$, corresponding to the modified time variable $\tau$ and adding, yields

$$p\left(\frac{1}{r_1} + \frac{1}{r_2}\right) = 2 + e(\cos v_1 + \cos v_2) \tag{6.8}$$

or, summing the cosines,

$$p\left(\frac{1}{r_1} + \frac{1}{r_2}\right) = 2 + 2e \cos\left(\frac{v_2 + v_1}{2}\right) \cos\left(\frac{v_2 - v_1}{2}\right). \tag{6.9}$$

Equation 6.9 contains the factor $e \cos\left(\dfrac{v_2 + v_1}{2}\right)$ which is unknown, and which must therefore be eliminated. Equations 6.10 through 6.18 are used in the elimination of this factor.

Utilizing the trigonometric half-angle formulas multiplied by $\sqrt{r}$, it is possible to see that

$$\sqrt{r} \cos \frac{v}{2} = \pm\sqrt{\frac{r(1 + \cos v)}{2}}, \quad \sqrt{r} \sin \frac{v}{2} = \pm\sqrt{\frac{r(1 - \cos v)}{2}} \tag{6.10}$$

and introducing

$$r = a(1 - e \cos E) \tag{6.11}$$

$$r \cos v = a(\cos E - e) \tag{6.12}$$

the following half-angle mappings are obtainable between true and eccentric anomalies via the dimensional elements $a$ and $e$:

$$\sqrt{r} \cos \frac{v}{2} = \sqrt{a(1 - e)} \cos \frac{E}{2} \tag{6.13}$$

$$\sqrt{r} \sin \frac{v}{2} = \sqrt{a(1 + e)} \sin \frac{E}{2}. \tag{6.14}$$

Consider the factors $\cos\left(\dfrac{v_2 - v_1}{2}\right)$ and $\cos\left(\dfrac{v_2 + v_1}{2}\right)$. These can certainly be multiplied by $\sqrt{r_2 r_1}$ and expanded as

$$\sqrt{r_2 r_1} \cos\left(\frac{v_2 \pm v_1}{2}\right) = \left[\sqrt{r_2} \cos \frac{v_2}{2}\right]\left[\sqrt{r_1} \cos \frac{v_1}{2}\right]$$
$$\mp \left[\sqrt{r_2} \sin \frac{v_2}{2}\right]\left[\sqrt{r_1} \sin \frac{v_1}{2}\right]. \tag{6.15}$$

Then, by virtue of Eqs. 6.13 and 6.14, after multiplying out and regrouping terms,

$$\sqrt{r_2 r_1} \cos\left(\frac{v_2 - v_1}{2}\right) = a \cos\left(\frac{E_2 - E_1}{2}\right) - ae \cos\left(\frac{E_2 + E_1}{2}\right) \quad (6.16)$$

$$\sqrt{r_2 r_1} \cos\left(\frac{v_2 + v_1}{2}\right) = -ae \cos\left(\frac{E_2 - E_1}{2}\right) + a \cos\left(\frac{E_2 + E_1}{2}\right). \tag{6.17}$$

Multiplying the last equation by $e$ and adding it to the first produces

$$\sqrt{r_2 r_1} \left[ \cos\left(\frac{v_2 - v_1}{2}\right) + e \cos\left(\frac{v_2 + v_1}{2}\right) \right]$$

$$= a \cos\left(\frac{E_2 - E_1}{2}\right) - ae^2 \cos\left(\frac{E_2 - E_1}{2}\right) \quad (6.18)$$

or

$$e \cos\left(\frac{v_2 + v_1}{2}\right) = \frac{p}{\sqrt{r_2 r_1}} \cos\left(\frac{E_2 - E_1}{2}\right) - \cos\left(\frac{v_2 - v_1}{2}\right). \tag{6.19}$$

This relation can be substituted into Eq. 6.9, thus eliminating $e \cos\left(\frac{v_2 + v_1}{2}\right)$, that is,

$$p\left(\frac{1}{r_1} + \frac{1}{r_2}\right) = 2 + \frac{2p}{\sqrt{r_2 r_1}} \cos\left(\frac{E_2 - E_1}{2}\right) \cos\left(\frac{v_2 - v_1}{2}\right)$$

$$- 2\cos^2\left(\frac{v_2 - v_1}{2}\right). \tag{6.20}$$

But

$$p = \frac{y^2 r_2{}^2 r_1{}^2 \sin^2(v_2 - v_1)}{\mu \tau^2} \tag{6.21}$$

from the sector to triangle ratio, so that substituting $p$ into Eq. 6.20 yields

$$y^2 = \frac{\mu \tau^2 \sec^2\left(\dfrac{v_2 - v_1}{2}\right)}{2r_1 r_2 \left[ r_1 + r_2 - 2\sqrt{r_1 r_2} \cos\left(\dfrac{v_2 - v_1}{2}\right) \cos\left(\dfrac{E_2 - E_1}{2}\right) \right]}. \tag{6.22}$$

Therefore, by means of the definitions,

$$l \equiv \frac{r_1 + r_2}{4\sqrt{r_1 r_2} \cos\left(\dfrac{v_2 - v_1}{2}\right)} - \frac{1}{2} \tag{6.23}$$

$$m \equiv \frac{\mu \tau^2}{\left[ 2\sqrt{r_1 r_2} \cos\left(\dfrac{v_2 - v_1}{2}\right) \right]^3} \tag{6.24}$$

$$x \equiv \frac{1}{2}\left[ 1 - \cos\left(\frac{E_2 - E_1}{2}\right) \right] = \sin^2\left(\frac{E_2 - E_1}{4}\right), \tag{6.25}$$

the first equation of Gauss or the reduction of Eq. 6.22 is obtained

$$y^2 = \frac{m}{l + x}. \qquad (6.26)$$

A relation is now known between the ratio of sector to triangle, and the difference in eccentric anomalies. Note that the parameters $m$ and $l$ are immediately determined from the two radius vectors of the problem, but $x$ is, of course, still an unknown.

### 6.2.4   Introduction of Kepler's equation

The development so far has been free of any relation involving time and angular position in the form of Kepler's equation, that is,

$$\frac{\sqrt{\mu}\,k}{a^{3/2}}\,(t - T) = E - e \sin E. \qquad (6.27)$$

Hence, by writing the Keplerian form for times $t_2$ and $t_1$ corresponding to $v_2 - v_1$ and differencing, yields

$$\frac{\sqrt{\mu}\,k(t_2 - t_1)}{a^{3/2}} = E_2 - E_1 - e(\sin E_2 - \sin E_1). \qquad (6.28)$$

The formulas for the difference of two sines and modified time variable produce

$$\frac{\sqrt{\mu}\,\tau}{a^{3/2}} = E_2 - E_1 - 2e \sin\left(\frac{E_2 - E_1}{2}\right) \cos\left(\frac{E_2 + E_1}{2}\right). \qquad (6.29)$$

But, by Eq. 6.16,

$$e \cos\left(\frac{E_2 + E_1}{2}\right) = \cos\left(\frac{E_2 - E_1}{2}\right) - \frac{\sqrt{r_2 r_1}}{a} \cos\left(\frac{v_2 - v_1}{2}\right),$$

so that the differenced Keplerian form becomes

$$\frac{\sqrt{\mu}\,\tau}{a^{3/2}} = E_2 - E_1 - \sin(E_2 - E_1)$$

$$+ 2 \frac{\sqrt{r_2 r_1}}{a} \sin\left(\frac{E_2 - E_1}{2}\right) \cos\left(\frac{v_2 - v_1}{2}\right). \qquad (6.30)$$

Now, since

$$\sin\left(\frac{E_2 - E_1}{2}\right) = \sin\frac{E_2}{2}\cos\frac{E_1}{2} - \cos\frac{E_2}{2}\sin\frac{E_1}{2} \tag{6.31}$$

or by Eqs. 6.13 and 6.14,

$$\sin\left(\frac{E_2 - E_1}{2}\right) = \frac{\sqrt{r_2 r_1}}{\sqrt{ap}}\left(\sin\frac{v_2}{2}\cos\frac{v_1}{2} - \cos\frac{v_2}{2}\sin\frac{v_1}{2}\right) \tag{6.32}$$

$$\sin\left(\frac{E_2 - E_1}{2}\right) = \frac{\sqrt{r_2 r_1}}{\sqrt{ap}}\sin\left(\frac{v_2 - v_1}{2}\right), \tag{6.33}$$

substitution of Eq. 6.33 into Eq. 6.30 produces

$$\tau = \frac{a^{3/2}}{\sqrt{\mu}}[E_2 - E_1 - \sin(E_2 - E_1)] + \frac{r_2 r_1 \sin(v_2 - v_1)}{\sqrt{\mu p}}. \tag{6.34}$$

If it is noticed that, by consequence of Eq. 6.6, the inverse of the ratio of sector to triangle is

$$\frac{1}{y} = \frac{r_2 r_1 \sin(v_2 - v_1)}{\sqrt{\mu p}\,\tau}, \tag{6.35}$$

then, by substituting the expression for $\sin(v_2 - v_1)$ from Eq. 6.34 into the $1/y$ expression, it is possible to see that

$$1 - \frac{1}{y} = \frac{a^{3/2}}{\tau\sqrt{\mu}}[E_2 - E_1 - \sin(E_2 - E_1)]. \tag{6.36}$$

Consider the double angle relationship

$$\sin(v_2 - v_1) = 2\sin\left(\frac{v_2 - v_1}{2}\right)\cos\left(\frac{v_2 - v_1}{2}\right), \tag{6.37}$$

or, by Eq. 6.33,

$$\sin(v_2 - v_1) = \frac{2\sqrt{ap}}{\sqrt{r_2 r_1}}\sin\left(\frac{E_2 - E_1}{2}\right)\cos\left(\frac{v_2 - v_1}{2}\right). \tag{6.38}$$

It is now possible to verify with the aid of Eq. 6.6 that the ratio of sector to triangle becomes

$$y = \frac{\sqrt{\mu p}\,\tau}{r_2 r_1 \sin(v_2 - v_1)} = \frac{\sqrt{\mu}\,\tau}{2\sqrt{a}\sqrt{r_2 r_1}\sin\left(\dfrac{E_2 - E_1}{2}\right)\cos\left(\dfrac{v_2 - v_1}{2}\right)}. \tag{6.39}$$

Elimination of $a$ from Eqs. 6.36 and 6.39 will now yield the second equation of Gauss. Thus, by cubing the last equation and multiplying it into Eq. 6.36,

$$y^3\left(1 - \frac{1}{y}\right) = \frac{\mu\tau^2}{\left[2\sqrt{r_2 r_1}\cos\left(\dfrac{v_2 - v_1}{2}\right)\right]^3}\left[\frac{E_2 - E_1 - \sin(E_2 - E_1)}{\sin^3\left(\dfrac{E_2 - E_1}{2}\right)}\right]$$

(6.40)

in which the first factor on the right is recognizable as $m$ and the other factor is defined as $X$, that is,

$$X \equiv \frac{E_2 - E_1 - \sin(E_2 - E_1)}{\sin^3\left(\dfrac{E_2 - E_1}{2}\right)}.$$

(6.41)

Hence it is possible to write compactly

$$y^2(y - 1) = mX.$$

(6.42)

### 6.2.5  Compendium of the basic equations

The preceding analysis has yielded the three forms:

(a) *Ratio of sector to triangle*

$$y = \frac{\sqrt{\mu p}\cdot\tau}{r_2 r_1 \sin(v_2 - v_1)}$$

(6.43)

(b) *First equation of Gauss*

$$y^2 = \frac{m}{l + x}$$

(6.44)

(c) *Second equation of Gauss*

$$y^2(y - 1) = mX$$

(6.45)

### 6.2.6  Solution of the equations

If the value of the square of the sector to triangle ratio from Eq. 6.44 is replaced in Eq. 6.45, it is possible to see that

$$y = 1 + X(l + x).$$

(6.46)

Knowing $\mathbf{r}_1$, $\mathbf{r}_2$, $\tau$ it follows that $m$ and $l$ are calculable from Eqs. 6.23 and 6.24. From the first equation of Gauss, it is possible to guess $y \approx 1$ and obtain

$$x = \frac{m}{y^2} - l.$$

(6.47)

Hence, having $x$, an iterative scheme can be initiated, and it is possible to continue with

$$\cos \left(\frac{E_2 - E_1}{2}\right) = 1 - 2x \tag{6.48}$$

by consequence of Eq. 6.25. Then, since $(E_2 - E_1)/2$ is bounded in the interval $0 \le (E_2 - E_1)/2 \le \pi$,

$$\sin \left(\frac{E_2 - E_1}{2}\right) = + \sqrt{4x(1 - x)}. \tag{6.49}$$

Therefore $(E_2 - E_1)$ is uniquely determined. From Eq. 6.41, $X$ is found as

$$X = \frac{E_2 - E_1 - \sin (E_2 - E_1)}{\sin^3 \left(\dfrac{E_2 - E_1}{2}\right)}. \tag{6.50}$$

Then, from Eq. 6.46,

$$y = 1 + X(l + x) \tag{6.51}$$

which can be substituted back into Eq. 6.47. When the loop is repeated, Eqs. 6.47 through 6.51 produce a better value of $y$, etc. Finally, when $y$ stops changing within a specified tolerance,

$$\sqrt{a} = \frac{\tau \sqrt{\mu}}{2y \sqrt{r_2 r_1} \cos \left(\dfrac{v_2 - v_1}{2}\right) \sin \left(\dfrac{E_2 - E_1}{2}\right)} \tag{6.52}$$

by consequence of Eq. 6.39.

Utilization of the closed-form $f$ and $g$ series (Section 3.10), i.e.,

$$f = 1 - \frac{a}{r_1} [1 - \cos (E_2 - E_1)] \tag{6.53}$$

$$g = \tau - \frac{a^{3/2}}{\sqrt{\mu}} [E_2 - E_1 - \sin (E_2 - E_1)], \tag{6.54}$$

along with the vector mapping from Section 3.9, permits the radius vector $\mathbf{r}_2$ to be written as

$$\mathbf{r}_2 = f \mathbf{r}_1 + g \dot{\mathbf{r}}_1 \tag{6.55}$$

or

$$\dot{\mathbf{r}}_1 = \frac{\mathbf{r}_2 - f \mathbf{r}_1}{g} \tag{6.56}$$

yields the value of the velocity vector at time $t_1$. The fundamental position and velocity set

$$\mathbf{r} \text{ and } \dot{\mathbf{r}} \tag{6.57}$$

have been determined at given epoch $t_1$ and the orbit can be considered as known.

### 6.2.7   Computational algorithm

Given $\mathbf{r}_1(x_1, y_1, z_1)$, $\mathbf{r}_2(x_2, y_2, z_2)$ and their corresponding universal times, $t_1$ and $t_2$, along with an indication of whether the orbit is direct or retrograde, proceed as follows

$$\tau = k(t_2 - t_1) \tag{6.58}$$

$$r_1 = \sqrt{\mathbf{r}_1 \cdot \mathbf{r}_1} \tag{6.59}$$

$$r_2 = \sqrt{\mathbf{r}_2 \cdot \mathbf{r}_2} \tag{6.60}$$

$$\cos(v_2 - v_1) = \frac{\mathbf{r}_2 \cdot \mathbf{r}_1}{r_2 r_1}, \quad (v_2 - v_1) \neq \pi. \tag{6.61}$$

For direct motion,[1] that is, $W_z \geq 0$, calculate

$$\sin(v_2 - v_1) = \frac{x_1 y_2 - x_2 y_1}{|x_1 y_2 - x_2 y_1|} \cdot \sqrt{1 - \cos^2(v_2 - v_1)}. \tag{6.62}$$

For retrograde motion, that is, $W_z < 0$, calculate

$$\sin(v_2 - v_1) = -\frac{x_1 y_2 - x_2 y_1}{|x_1 y_2 - x_2 y_1|} \cdot \sqrt{1 - \cos^2(v_2 - v_1)}. \tag{6.63}$$

Obtain the constants

$$l = \frac{r_1 + r_2}{4\sqrt{r_1 r_2}\cos\left(\dfrac{v_2 - v_1}{2}\right)} - \frac{1}{2} \tag{6.64}$$

$$m = \frac{\mu \tau^2}{\left[2\sqrt{r_1 r_2}\cos\left(\dfrac{v_2 - v_1}{2}\right)\right]^3}. \tag{6.65}$$

---

[1] As indicated in Section 3.4, a direct orbit is characterized by $\cos i = W_z \geq 0$ in contrast to $W_z < 0$ for a retrograde orbit.   Certainly if this characteristic is known it is possible to use the $z$ component of the cross product of $\mathbf{r}_1$ and $\mathbf{r}_2$ to determine $\sin(v_2 - v_1)$.   It should be noted that if the radius vectors are given, $\mathbf{W} = (\mathbf{r}_1 \times \mathbf{r}_2)/[r_1 r_2 \sin(v_2 - v_1)]$.

As a first approximation, set

$$y = 1, \tag{6.66}$$

and continue calculating with

$$x = \frac{m}{y^2} - l \tag{6.67}$$

$$\cos\left(\frac{E_2 - E_1}{2}\right) = 1 - 2x \tag{6.68}$$

$$\sin\left(\frac{E_2 - E_1}{2}\right) = +\sqrt{4x(1 - x)} \tag{6.69}$$

$$X = \frac{E_2 - E_1 - \sin(E_2 - E_1)}{\sin^3\left(\frac{E_2 - E_1}{2}\right)} \tag{6.70}$$

$$y = 1 + X(l + x). \tag{6.71}$$

If $y$ is now equal to the assumed value within some tolerance, continue with Eq. 6.72, if it is not, place the value of $y$ from Eq. 6.71 into Eq. 6.67 and repeat equational loop (6.67) through (6.71). Continue calculating with

$$\sqrt{a} = \frac{\tau\sqrt{\mu}}{2y\sqrt{r_2 r_1} \cos\left(\frac{v_2 - v_1}{2}\right) \sin\left(\frac{E_2 - E_1}{2}\right)} \tag{6.72}$$

$$f = 1 - \frac{a}{r_1}[1 - \cos(E_2 - E_1)] \tag{6.73}$$

$$g = \tau - \frac{a^{3/2}}{\sqrt{\mu}}[E_2 - E_1 - \sin(E_2 - E_1)] \tag{6.74}$$

$$\dot{\mathbf{r}}_1 = \frac{\mathbf{r}_2 - f\mathbf{r}_1}{g}. \tag{6.75}$$

Hence $\mathbf{r}_1$ and $\dot{\mathbf{r}}_1$ are known, and the orbit is considered determined.

### 6.3 LAMBERT–EULER PRELIMINARY ORBIT DETERMINATION

### 6.3.1 Episode

Euler, perhaps the most prolific mathematician in history, was the first to propose in 1744 a pure analytical method for the determination of open cometary or parabolic orbits. One is completely intrigued by the image of a man possessing the mathematical prowess of Euler. Here was a man who shortly after the age of 59 succumbed to blindness, and yet he was able to attack one of Newton's prime headaches, the lunar theory, by performing the complicated analysis mentally. His entry into the field of mathematical astronomy, aided by the calculus of Newton, was the beginning of a new era in analytical mechanics. Lambert, who was mainly a geometer at heart, extended Euler's developments to elliptical and hyperbolic orbits. It was not, however, until publications of Lagrange in 1788 that a complete solution was imminent.

### 6.3.2   Chord length as a function of the eccentric anomalies

Consider the orbit illustrated in Figure 6.2, in which the chord length $c$ between radius vectors $\mathbf{r}_2$ and $\mathbf{r}_1$ is a parameter. Certainly then,

$$c^2 = (\mathbf{r}_2 - \mathbf{r}_1) \cdot (\mathbf{r}_2 - \mathbf{r}_1) = r_2{}^2 + r_1{}^2 - 2\mathbf{r}_2 \cdot \mathbf{r}_1 \tag{6.76}$$

or, since

$$\mathbf{r}_2 \cdot \mathbf{r}_1 = r_2 r_1 \cos (v_2 - v_1), \tag{6.77}$$

it is possible to write

$$c^2 = r_2{}^2 - 2r_2 r_1 + r_1{}^2 + 2r_2 r_1 - 2r_2 r_1 \cos (v_2 - v_1), \tag{6.78}$$

which becomes

$$c^2 = (r_2 - r_1)^2 + 4r_2 r_1 \sin^2 \left( \frac{v_2 - v_1}{2} \right). \tag{6.79}$$

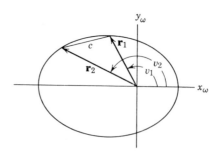

FIGURE 6.2   An elliptical orbit in space.

The immediate problem to be solved is expressing Eq. 6.79 as a function of the eccentric anomaly $E$. Hence, by virtue of

$$r = a(1 - e \cos E), \tag{6.80}$$

the difference $r_2 - r_1$ becomes

$$r_2 - r_1 = ae(\cos E_1 - \cos E_2) \tag{6.81}$$

or, subtracting the cosines,

$$r_2 - r_1 = 2ae \sin \left(\frac{E_2 + E_1}{2}\right) \sin \left(\frac{E_2 - E_1}{2}\right). \tag{6.82}$$

In the same manner, it is possible to verify

$$r_2 + r_1 = 2a\left[1 - e \cos \left(\frac{E_2 + E_1}{2}\right) \cos \left(\frac{E_2 - E_1}{2}\right)\right]. \tag{6.83}$$

Now, since

$$\begin{aligned} r \sin v &= \sqrt{ap} \sin E \\ r \cos v &= a(\cos E - e) \end{aligned} \tag{6.84}$$

and the half-angle identities multiplied by $\sqrt{r}$ are

$$\begin{aligned} \sqrt{r} \sin \frac{v}{2} &= \sqrt{\frac{r(1 - \cos v)}{2}} \\ \sqrt{r} \cos \frac{v}{2} &= \sqrt{\frac{r(1 + \cos v)}{2}}, \end{aligned} \tag{6.85}$$

it is evident that substitution of Eqs. 6.84 and 6.80 into Eq. 6.85 produce

$$\begin{aligned} \sqrt{r} \sin \frac{v}{2} &= \sqrt{a(1 + e)} \sin \frac{E}{2} \\ \sqrt{r} \cos \frac{v}{2} &= \sqrt{a(1 - e)} \cos \frac{E}{2}. \end{aligned} \tag{6.86}$$

Hence the following factor can be formed:

$$\begin{aligned} \sqrt{r_2 r_1} \sin \left(\frac{v_2 - v_1}{2}\right) &= \left[\sqrt{r_2} \sin \frac{v_2}{2}\right]\left[\sqrt{r_1} \cos \frac{v_1}{2}\right] \\ &\quad - \left[\sqrt{r_2} \cos \frac{v_2}{2}\right]\left[\sqrt{r_1} \sin \frac{v_1}{2}\right] \\ &= \sqrt{a^2(1 - e^2)} \left[\sin \frac{E_2}{2} \cos \frac{E_1}{2} - \cos \frac{E_2}{2} \sin \frac{E_1}{2}\right] \\ &= \sqrt{a^2(1 - e^2)} \sin \left(\frac{E_2 - E_1}{2}\right). \end{aligned} \tag{6.87}$$

If Eq. 6.87 is squared and multiplied by 4, the second term on the right side of Eq. 6.79 can be written as

$$4r_2r_1 \sin^2 \left(\frac{v_2 - v_1}{2}\right) = 4a^2(1 - e^2) \sin^2 \left(\frac{E_2 - E_1}{2}\right). \tag{6.88}$$

Substitution of Eqs. 6.82 and 6.88 into the expression for the chord length, that is, Eq. 6.79 develops the relationship

$$c = 2a\sqrt{1 - e^2 \cos^2 \left(\frac{E_2 + E_1}{2}\right)} \sin \left(\frac{E_2 - E_1}{2}\right). \tag{6.89}$$

### 6.3.3 Introduction of transformation of variables

Equation 6.89 possesses a number of unknowns, among them the eccentricity $e$ of the unknown orbit. Suppose then that the transformation

$$e \cos \left(\frac{E_2 + E_1}{2}\right) \equiv \cos v \tag{6.90}$$

is introduced. Then, of course,

$$c = 2a \sin v \sin \left(\frac{E_2 - E_1}{2}\right). \tag{6.91}$$

The sum of the radii, Eq. 6.83 likewise transforms to

$$r_2 + r_1 = 2a\left[1 - \cos v \cos \left(\frac{E_2 - E_1}{2}\right)\right]. \tag{6.92}$$

Two independent relations are therefore obtained by adding and subtracting the chord length from the sum of the radii, that is,

$$r_2 + r_1 + c = 2a\left[1 - \cos v \cos \frac{E_2 - E_1}{2} + \sin v \sin \frac{E_2 - E_1}{2}\right] \tag{6.93}$$

$$r_2 + r_1 - c = 2a\left[1 - \cos v \cos \frac{E_2 - E_1}{2} - \sin v \sin \frac{E_2 - E_1}{2}\right]. \tag{6.94}$$

By introduction of the definitions,

$$\epsilon \equiv v + \left(\frac{E_2 - E_1}{2}\right) \tag{6.95}$$

and

$$\delta \equiv v - \left(\frac{E_2 - E_1}{2}\right), \tag{6.96}$$

it is evident that Eqs. 6.93 and 6.94 become, by the formula for the expansion of the cosine of the sum of two angles,

$$2a[1 - \cos \epsilon] = r_2 + r_1 + c \qquad (6.97)$$

$$2a[1 - \cos \delta] = r_2 + r_1 - c \qquad (6.98)$$

or

$$\cos \epsilon = 1 - \frac{1}{2a}(r_2 + r_1 + c) \qquad (6.99)$$

$$\cos \delta = 1 - \frac{1}{2a}(r_2 + r_1 - c), \qquad (6.100)$$

which can be transformed into the half-angle relationships

$$\sin \tfrac{1}{2}\epsilon = \pm \sqrt{\frac{1}{4a}(r_2 + r_1 + c)} \qquad (6.101)$$

$$\sin \tfrac{1}{2}\delta = \pm \sqrt{\frac{1}{4a}(r_2 + r_1 - c)}. \qquad (6.102)$$

### 6.3.4   Determination of the auxiliary angles

Let a first approximation or guess be made for a value of the semimajor axis $a$. It follows by consequence of Eq. 6.76 that the sine and cosine of $\tfrac{1}{2}\epsilon$ and $\tfrac{1}{2}\delta$, except for the sign of each half-angle, are determinable through Eqs. 6.101 and 6.102. A slight digression must now be made in order to determine uniquely the angle $\tfrac{1}{2}\delta$.

First, consider the trigonometric expansion of

$$\sqrt{r_2 r_1} \cos \left( \frac{v_2 - v_1}{2} \right) = \left[ \sqrt{r_2} \cos \frac{v_2}{2} \right] \left[ \sqrt{r_1} \cos \frac{v_1}{2} \right]$$
$$+ \left[ \sqrt{r_2} \sin \frac{v_2}{2} \right] \left[ \sqrt{r_1} \sin \frac{v_1}{2} \right]. \qquad (6.103)$$

Hence, by utilizing Eqs. 6.84 and 6.85,

$$\sqrt{r_2 r_1} \cos \left( \frac{v_2 - v_1}{2} \right) = a \cos \left( \frac{E_2 - E_1}{2} \right) - ae \cos \left( \frac{E_2 + E_1}{2} \right). \qquad (6.104)$$

But, by transformation (6.90), it is possible to see that

$$\sqrt{r_2 r_1} \cos \left( \frac{v_2 - v_1}{2} \right) = a \left[ \cos \left( \frac{E_2 - E_1}{2} \right) - \cos v \right]. \qquad (6.105)$$

By applying the difference of definitions (6.95) and (6.96), the preceding relation becomes

$$\sqrt{r_2 r_1} \cos\left(\frac{v_2 - v_1}{2}\right) = 2a \sin \tfrac{1}{2}\epsilon \sin \tfrac{1}{2}\delta. \tag{6.106}$$

Equation 6.106 is the key to the unique determination of $\delta$. Consider the various angles

$$\frac{E_2 - E_1}{2}, \quad v, \quad \tfrac{1}{2}\epsilon, \quad \tfrac{1}{2}\delta. \tag{6.107}$$

Obviously, the first of these angles is bounded in the interval

$$0 \leq \frac{E_2 - E_1}{2} \leq \pi, \tag{6.108}$$

so that $\sin\left(\dfrac{E_2 - E_1}{2}\right) \geq 0$. Hence, if the chord length is defined to be a positive length, that is, $c > 0$, then by Eq. 6.91 $\sin v \geq 0$, which implies that

$$0 \leq v \leq \pi. \tag{6.109}$$

Definitions 6.95 and 6.96 then yield the inequalities

$$0 \leq \frac{1}{2}\epsilon \leq \pi \tag{6.110}$$

$$-\frac{\pi}{2} \leq \frac{1}{2}\delta \leq \frac{\pi}{2}, \tag{6.111}$$

which imply

$$\sin \tfrac{1}{2}\epsilon \geq 0 \tag{6.112}$$

$$\cos \tfrac{1}{2}\delta \geq 0. \tag{6.113}$$

Evidently, then, Eq. 6.101 can be revised to read

$$\sin \tfrac{1}{2}\epsilon = +\sqrt{\frac{1}{4a}(r_2 + r_1 + c)}, \tag{6.114}$$

which can be calculated at once. Then, since the difference in true anomalies is known, it is possible to calculate from Eq. 6.106 $\sin \tfrac{1}{2}\delta$, that is,

$$\sin \tfrac{1}{2}\delta = \frac{\sqrt{r_2 r_1} \cos\left(\dfrac{v_2 - v_1}{2}\right)}{2a \sin \tfrac{1}{2}\epsilon}. \tag{6.115}$$

Now, by adding unity to both sides of Eq. 6.100, the cosine of $\frac{1}{2}\delta$ can be obtained as

$$\cos \tfrac{1}{2}\delta = +\sqrt{1 - \frac{1}{4a}(r_2 + r_1 - c)}, \tag{6.116}$$

which uniquely determines $\cos \frac{1}{2}\delta$ and, of course, $\delta$. It is unfortunate that the sign of $\cos \frac{1}{2}\epsilon$ cannot be determined, and so an assumption of this sign must be made, that is, two separate orbits must be carried forward in the calculations.[2]

### 6.3.5   Lambert-Euler equation

Now that $\epsilon$ and $\delta$ have been obtained, the next step is the introduction of Kepler's equation in the differenced form

$$\frac{\sqrt{\mu}\,k(t_2 - t_1)}{a^{3/2}} = E_2 - E_1 + e(\sin E_1 - \sin E_2). \tag{6.117}$$

This equation, by means of definitions (6.95) and (6.96) which yield

$$\epsilon - \delta = E_2 - E_1 \tag{6.118}$$

along with the introduction of the modified time variable $\tau$, can be rewritten as

$$\frac{\sqrt{\mu}\,\tau}{a^{3/2}} = \epsilon - \delta + e(\sin E_1 - \sin E_2) \tag{6.119}$$

or, by subtracting the sines,

$$\frac{\sqrt{\mu}\,\tau}{a^{3/2}} = \epsilon - \delta + 2e \cos \frac{E_2 + E_1}{2} \sin \frac{E_2 - E_1}{2}. \tag{6.120}$$

By transformation (6.90) and introduction of Eq. 6.118, the previous expression becomes

$$\frac{\sqrt{\mu}\,\tau}{a^{3/2}} = \epsilon - \delta + 2 \cos \nu \sin \frac{\epsilon - \delta}{2}. \tag{6.121}$$

But, since addition of definitions (6.95) and (6.96) provides

$$\nu = \frac{\epsilon + \delta}{2}, \tag{6.122}$$

[2] See reference [1], pages 52 and 53, and reference [9], page 147.

it can be seen that

$$\frac{\sqrt{\mu}\,\tau}{a^{3/2}} = \epsilon - \delta + 2\cos\frac{\epsilon+\delta}{2}\sin\frac{\epsilon-\delta}{2}. \tag{6.123}$$

A trigonometric transformation immediately yields the relationship

$$\frac{\sqrt{\mu}\,\tau_c}{a^{3/2}} = (\epsilon - \sin\epsilon) - (\delta - \sin\delta), \tag{6.124}$$

where the subscript $c$ is introduced to denote that the modified time is computed from an assumed value of $a$. The residual from the true time interval is

$$F \equiv \tau - \tau_c. \tag{6.125}$$

The value of $\tau_c$ obtained by means of Eq. 6.124 is, of course, functionally dependent upon the assumed value of the semimajor axis. Therefore, it is evident that the value of the modified time variable $\tau_c$ will not agree with the actual physical value $\tau$ demanded by the orbit to be determined, that is, $F$ will not be zero unless the assumed semimajor axis is the actual semimajor axis of the orbit in question.

Let the value of $F$, obtained by the assumed value of $a$, be denoted by $F(a)$. Saving $F(a)$, it is possible to return to Eq. 6.114 and vary the value of $a$, say by a few per cent, calling it $a + \Delta a$. Therefore, by repeating equatorial loop (6.115) through (6.124) with $a + \Delta a$, as a final step Eq. 6.125 yields

$$F(a + \Delta a). \tag{6.126}$$

Hence, one can form the numerical derivative

$$F'(a) \cong \frac{F(a + \Delta a) - F(a)}{\Delta a}. \tag{6.127}$$

which, by means of the Newton formula, produces a better approximation $a_{j+1}$ as

$$a_{j+1} = a_j - \frac{F(a_j)}{F'(a_j)}, \quad j = 1, 2, \ldots, q. \tag{6.128}$$

This process is repeated $q$ times until

$$|a_{j+1} - a_j| < \Delta, \tag{6.129}$$

where $\Delta$ is a specified tolerance.  Equation 6.118 now yields $E_2 - E_1$ and

$$f = 1 - \frac{a}{r_1} [1 - \cos (E_2 - E_1)], \tag{6.130}$$

$$g = \tau - \frac{a^{3/2}}{\sqrt{\mu}} [E_2 - E_1 - \sin (E_2 - E_1)] \tag{6.131}$$

along with

$$\mathbf{r}_2 = f\mathbf{r}_1 + g\dot{\mathbf{r}}_1,$$

concludes the determination of the velocity vector at $t_1$.  Knowledge of $\mathbf{r}_1$, $\dot{\mathbf{r}}_1$, or the fundamental constants is sufficient to determine the orbit.

### 6.3.6  Computational algorithm

Given $\mathbf{r}_1$ $(x_1, y_1, z_1)$, $\mathbf{r}_2$ $(x_2, y_2, z_2)$ and their corresponding universal times, $t_1$ and $t_2$, along with an indication of whether the orbit is direct or retrograde, proceed as follows:

$$\tau = k(t_2 - t_1) \tag{6.132}$$

$$r_1 = +\sqrt{\mathbf{r}_1 \cdot \mathbf{r}_1} \tag{6.133}$$

$$r_2 = +\sqrt{\mathbf{r}_2 \cdot \mathbf{r}_2} \tag{6.134}$$

$$\mathbf{U}_1 = \frac{\mathbf{r}_1}{r_1} \tag{6.135}$$

$$\mathbf{U}_2 = \frac{\mathbf{r}_2}{r_2} \tag{6.136}$$

$$\cos (v_2 - v_1) = \mathbf{U}_1 \cdot \mathbf{U}_2, \quad v_2 - v_1 \neq \pi. \tag{6.137}$$

For direct motion,[3] that is, $W_z \geq 0$, compute

$$\sin (v_2 - v_1) = \frac{x_1 y_2 - x_2 y_1}{|x_1 y_2 - x_2 y_1|} \sqrt{1 - \cos^2 (v_2 - v_1)}. \tag{6.138}$$

For retrograde motion, that is, $W_z < 0$, compute

$$\sin (v_2 - v_1) = -\frac{x_1 y_2 - x_2 y_1}{|x_1 y_2 - x_2 y_1|} \sqrt{1 - \cos^2 (v_2 - v_1)}. \tag{6.139}$$

As a first approximation, if no better estimate is available, set

$$a = (r_1 + r_2)/2 \tag{6.140}$$

[3] See footnote 1.

and continue calculating with

$$c = [r_2{}^2 + r_1{}^2 - 2(x_1 x_2 + y_1 y_2 + z_1 z_2)]^{1/2} \tag{6.141}$$

$$\sin \tfrac{1}{2}\epsilon = +\sqrt{\frac{1}{4a}(r_2 + r_1 + c)} \tag{6.142}$$

$$\sin \tfrac{1}{2}\delta = +\frac{\sqrt{r_2 r_1}\cos\left(\dfrac{v_2 - v_1}{2}\right)}{2a \sin \tfrac{1}{2}\epsilon} \tag{6.143}$$

$$\cos \tfrac{1}{2}\delta = +\sqrt{1 - \frac{1}{4a}(r_2 + r_1 - c)}. \tag{6.144}$$

Set

$$s = 1. \tag{6.145}$$

Later the analysis will be repeated[4] for

$$s = -1. \tag{6.146}$$

Continue with

$$\cos \tfrac{1}{2}\epsilon = s\sqrt{1 - \sin^2 \tfrac{1}{2}\epsilon}. \tag{6.147}$$

Hence, when one has $\epsilon$, $\delta$, and the sine and cosine of these angles, one can proceed with the iterative solution by solving for $F$ as follows:

$$F = \tau - \tau_c = \tau - \frac{a^{3/2}}{\sqrt{\mu}}[(\epsilon - \sin \epsilon) - (\delta - \sin \delta)]. \tag{6.148}$$

If

$$|F| < \Delta, \tag{6.149}$$

where $\Delta$ is a given tolerance,[5] one may proceed to Eq. 6.154; if it is not, save $F(a)$ and increment $a$, by say 5 per cent, that is, $\Delta a$ to obtain:

$$a + \Delta a. \tag{6.150}$$

Repeat equational loop (6.142) through (6.148) obtaining $F(a + \Delta a)$, and form

$$F'(a) \simeq \frac{F(a + \Delta a) - F(a)}{\Delta a}. \tag{6.151}$$

---

[4] Two valid orbits must be carried along in the analysis since it is not possible to obtain a unique determination of $\epsilon$.

[5] $\Delta \simeq 1 \times 10^{-7}$.

Improve the value of $a$ by

$$a_{j+1} = a_j - \frac{F(a_j)}{F'(a_j)}, \quad j = 1, 2, 3, \ldots, q. \tag{6.152}$$

If

$$|a_{j+1} - a_j| < \Delta, \tag{6.153}$$

proceed to Eq. 6.154; if not, return to Eq. 6.142, replacing $a_j$ by $a_{j+1}$.[6]
Continue calculating with

$$E_2 - E_1 = \epsilon - \delta \tag{6.154}$$

$$f = 1 - \frac{a}{r_1} [1 - \cos (E_2 - E_1)] \tag{6.155}$$

$$g = \tau - \frac{a^{3/2}}{\sqrt{\mu}} [E_2 - E_1 - \sin (E_2 - E_1)] \tag{6.156}$$

$$\dot{\mathbf{r}}_1 = \frac{\mathbf{r}_2 - f\mathbf{r}_1}{g}. \tag{6.157}$$

Hence $\mathbf{r}_1$ and $\dot{\mathbf{r}}_1$ are known and the orbit is considered determined.
Notice that two orbits, corresponding to $s = 1$ and $s = -1$, are obtained.

### 6.4   ORBIT DETERMINATION BY ITERATION ON THE SEMIPARAMETER

A convenient and rather rapid method for determining an elliptical orbit
from two position vectors and the time interval between them is called the
$p$-iteration.   The technique presented herein is a modification of the method
due to Herrick and Liu [5].

### 6.4.1   Obtaining the eccentricity and semimajor axis
with an assumed value of the semiparameter

Consider as given data $\mathbf{r}_2$, $\mathbf{r}_1$ and $t_2$, $t_1$ as illustrated in Figure 6.3.   The
modified time variable is directly related to the universal times $t_2$ and $t_1$,
corresponding to the position vectors $\mathbf{r}_2$ and $\mathbf{r}_1$, by

$$\tau = k(t_2 - t_1). \tag{6.158}$$

---

[6] The use of an iterative process as described above (Newton's method) has no
guarantee of convergence if the initial estimate is very poor.   If the scheme fails to
converge after a certain preset number of iterations, it is advisable to initiate a direct
search on the iterative parameter and watch $F$ until, as must happen, $F = 0$.

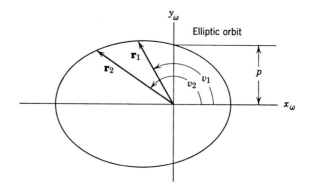

FIGURE 6.3    An elliptic orbit.

It is also possible to compute a set of unit vectors along the corresponding radius vectors as follows:

$$\mathbf{U}_i = \frac{\mathbf{r}_i}{r_i}, \quad i = 1, 2, \tag{6.159}$$

where

$$r_i = \sqrt{\mathbf{r}_i \cdot \mathbf{r}_i}, \quad i = 1, 2. \tag{6.160}$$

Obviously, then, the difference of true anomalies between the two radius vectors is given by

$$\cos (v_2 - v_1) = \mathbf{U}_1 \cdot \mathbf{U}_2. \tag{6.161}$$

The angle $v_2 - v_1$ is completely determined if the direct or retrograde property of the orbit is specified.[7]

The equation of a conic was developed in Section 3.3, as

$$r = \frac{p}{1 + e \cos v}. \tag{6.162}$$

Suppose now that the value of the semiparameter $p$ is guessed. Then from Eq. 6.162, it is possible to write for both times,

$$e \cos v_i = \frac{p}{r_i} - 1, \quad i = 1, 2. \tag{6.163}$$

Expansion of

$$\cos v_2 = \cos (v_2 - v_1 + v_1) \tag{6.164}$$

[7] See Exercise 1.

produces, after multiplying through by $e$ and transposing the equation,

$$e \sin v_1 = \frac{e \cos v_1 \cos (v_2 - v_1) - e \cos v_2}{\sin (v_2 - v_1)},$$ (6.165)

and, in a similar fashion,

$$e \sin v_2 = \frac{-e \cos v_2 \cos (v_2 - v_1) + e \cos v_1}{\sin (v_2 - v_1)}.$$ (6.166)

Therefore, the products of eccentricity and sines of the true anomalies are directly calculable by virtue of Eqs. 6.165 and 6.166. Note the singularity at the point $v_2 - v_1 = \pi$.

The orbital eccentricity is obtained from

$$e^2 = (e \cos v_i)^2 + (e \sin v_i)^2, \quad i = 1, 2$$ (6.167)

and the semimajor axis is then directly obtained as

$$a = \frac{p}{1 - e^2}.$$ (6.168)

### 6.4.2    Utilization of the differenced Keplerian equation

With an incorrectly assumed value of $p$, it should be obvious that the time interval between $\mathbf{r}_1$ and $\mathbf{r}_2$ will not check with the physically given value. Hence a method of calculating the time interval is needed so that the assumed value of $p$ can be corrected.

Since the eccentric and true anomalies are linked through

$$\cos E_i = \frac{r_i}{p} (\cos v_i + e)$$ (6.169)

$$\sin E_i = \frac{r_i}{p} \sqrt{1 - e^2} \sin v_i, \quad i = 1, 2,$$ (6.170)

it follows that $E_2$ and $E_1$ can be readily calculated. These values introduced into a differenced Keplerian equation yield

$$M_2 - M_1 = E_2 - E_1 + e(\sin E_1 - \sin E_2),$$ (6.171)

that is, the difference in mean anomalies. But since the mean anomalies, mean motion, and time are related through

$$M_2 - M_1 = n(t_2 - t_1),$$ (6.172)

where the mean motion is defined as

$$n \equiv k \sqrt{\mu} \, a^{-3/2},$$ (6.173)

the speculative time interval and the iterative function is given by

$$F = \tau - \frac{k}{n}(M_2 - M_1). \tag{6.174}$$

Now, this value of $F$, unless one had been supplied with a crystal ball and picked the correct value of $p$, will surely not be zero. A correction to the assumed value of $p$ can be achieved by a numerical Newton procedure as follows. Remembering the original assumed value of $p$ and the functional value of $F$, that is, $F(p)$ produced by original value, one should return to Eq. 6.163 and increment $p$ by a small amount, say, $\Delta p$. If all the calculations are repeated, then the end product will be $F(p + \Delta p)$; hence it is possible to form the numerical derivative

$$F'(p) \cong \frac{F(p + \Delta p) - F(p)}{\Delta p}. \tag{6.175}$$

The Newton formula will now yield a better value of $p$ as

$$p_{j+1} = p_j - \frac{F(p_j)}{F'(p_j)}, \quad j = 1, 2, \ldots, q, \tag{6.176}$$

where the $j$ subscript stands for the previous values. The procedure can be repeated $q$ times until $p$ no longer varies within some given tolerance, $\epsilon$, that is,

$$|p_{j+1} - p_j| < \epsilon. \tag{6.177}$$

Once the true value of $p$ is known, it can be seen that $a$, $E_2$, and $E_1$ are by-products of the iterative loop, and so the $f$ and $g$ series can be calculated as

$$f = 1 - \frac{a}{r_1}[1 - \cos(E_2 - E_1)] \tag{6.178}$$

$$g = \tau - \frac{a^{3/2}}{\sqrt{\mu}}[E_2 - E_1 - \sin(E_2 - E_1)], \tag{6.179}$$

and thus

$$\dot{\mathbf{r}}_1 = \frac{\mathbf{r}_2 - f\mathbf{r}_1}{g} \tag{6.180}$$

by virtue of the vector relation

$$\mathbf{r}_2 = f\mathbf{r}_1 + g\dot{\mathbf{r}}_1. \tag{6.181}$$

Knowing $\mathbf{r}_1$ and $\dot{\mathbf{r}}_1$ the orbit is considered determined, since it is an easy extension to compute the orbital elements.

### 6.4.3    Computational algorithm

Given $\mathbf{r}_1$ $(x_1, y_1, z_1)$, $\mathbf{r}_2$ $(x_2, y_2, z_2)$ and their corresponding universal times $t_1$ and $t_2$, along with an indication of whether the orbit is direct or retrograde, proceed as follows:

$$\tau = k(t_2 - t_1) \tag{6.182}$$

$$r_1 = +\sqrt{\mathbf{r}_1 \cdot \mathbf{r}_1} \tag{6.183}$$

$$r_2 = +\sqrt{\mathbf{r}_2 \cdot \mathbf{r}_2} \tag{6.184}$$

$$\mathbf{U}_1 = \mathbf{r}_1/r_1 \tag{6.185}$$

$$\mathbf{U}_2 = \mathbf{r}_2/r_2 \tag{6.186}$$

$$\cos(v_2 - v_1) = \mathbf{U}_1 \cdot \mathbf{U}_2, \quad v_2 - v_1 \neq \pi. \tag{6.187}$$

If the motion is direct,[8] that is, $W_z \geq 0$, compute

$$\sin(v_2 - v_1) = \frac{x_1 y_2 - x_2 y_1}{|x_1 y_2 - x_2 y_1|} \sqrt{1 - \cos^2(v_2 - v_1)}. \tag{6.188}$$

If the motion is retrograde, that is, $W_z < 0$, compute

$$\sin(v_2 - v_1) = -\frac{x_1 y_2 - x_2 y_1}{|x_1 y_2 - x_2 y_1|} \sqrt{1 - \cos^2(v_2 - v_1)}. \tag{6.189}$$

As a first approximation, set[9]

$$p = p_g, \tag{6.190}$$

and continue calculating with

$$[e \cos v_1] = p/r_1 - 1 \tag{6.191}$$

$$[e \cos v_2] = p/r_2 - 1 \tag{6.192}$$

$$e \sin v_1 = \frac{\cos(v_2 - v_1)[e \cos v_1] - [e \cos v_2]}{\sin(v_2 - v_1)} \tag{6.193}$$

$$e \sin v_2 = \frac{-\cos(v_2 - v_1)[e \cos v_2] + [e \cos v_1]}{\sin(v_2 - v_1)} \tag{6.194}$$

$$e^2 = (e \cos v_1)^2 + (e \sin v_1)^2 \tag{6.195}$$

$$a = \frac{p}{1 - e^2} \tag{6.196}$$

$$n = k\sqrt{\mu}\, a^{-3/2}. \tag{6.197}$$

[8] See footnote 1.
[9] If no better estimate is available, let $p_g = 0.4(r_1 + r_2)$.

If $e \neq 0$, proceed with Eq. 6.198; if $e = 0$ within a given tolerance, continue with Eq. 6.200

$$\cos E_i = \frac{r_i}{p} (\cos v_i + e), \quad i = 1, 2,$$ (6.198)

$$\sin E_i = \frac{r_i}{p} \sqrt{1 - e^2} \sin v_i, \quad i = 1, 2.$$ (6.199)

Continue calculating with Eq. 6.205

$$e = 0, \quad v_1 = 0$$ (6.200)

$$\cos E_1 = 1$$ (6.201)

$$\cos E_2 = \cos (v_2 - v_1)$$ (6.202)

$$\sin E_1 = 0$$ (6.203)

$$\sin E_2 = \sin (v_2 - v_1)$$ (6.204)

$$M_i = E_i - e \sin E_i, \quad i = 1, 2,$$ (6.205)

$$F = \tau - \left( \frac{M_2 - M_1}{n} \right) k.$$ (6.206)

If $F = 0$, proceed to Eq. 6.209; if not, increment $p$ by say 5 per cent and, by repeating equational loop 6.191 through 6.206, obtain

$$F'(p) \simeq \frac{F(p + \Delta p) - F(p)}{\Delta p}.$$ (6.207)

Hence a better approximation to the semiparameter is

$$p_{j+1} = p_j - \frac{F(p_j)}{F'(p_j)}, \quad j = 1, 2, \ldots, q.$$ (6.208)

Repeat the above loop $q$ times until $p$ is constant within a given tolerance.[10] Finally, continue calculating with Eq. 6.209

$$f = 1 - \frac{a}{r_1} [1 - \cos (E_2 - E_1)]$$ (6.209)

$$g = \tau - \frac{a^{3/2}}{\sqrt{\mu}} [E_2 - E_1 - \sin (E_2 - E_1)]$$ (6.210)

$$\dot{\mathbf{r}}_1 = \frac{\mathbf{r}_2 - f\mathbf{r}_1}{g}.$$ (6.211)

Hence $\mathbf{r}_1$ and $\dot{\mathbf{r}}_1$ are known and the orbit is considered determined.

[10] See footnote 6.

## 6.5  ORBIT DETERMINATION BY ITERATION ON THE TRUE ANOMALY

The $v$-iteration technique is a simple approach to a difficult problem. It was developed by Lascody in 1958 [10].  It has been investigated and appears to be a rather favorable and rapid way of determining an orbit from two position vectors and the time interval between them.  As the reader may have noticed, the previous methods are not valid as the spread of the two position vectors reach the critical value of 180°.  Somewhere in the previous formulations a division by zero will occur at the critical value.  Geometrically, it is obvious that if the two radius vectors are 180° apart, it is impossible to extract information about the orientation of the orbit plane.  This is said in light of the fact that a straight line cannot determine a plane, and at a radius vector spread of 180° this is the unfortunate circumstance.  It is, however, possible to extract information about the dimensional elements and the respective shape and size of the orbit.  The $v$-iteration does not have a mathematical singularity when the radius vectors are colinear and opposed.

### 6.5.1  Obtaining the eccentricity and semimajor axis
### with an assumed value of the true anomaly

Consider the equation of a conic,

$$r = \frac{p}{1 + e \cos v}.$$
(6.212)

If Eq. 6.212 is written for times $t_1$ and $t_2$, it is possible to equate

$$r_1(1 + e \cos v_1) = p = r_2(1 + e \cos v_2),$$
(6.213)

which, upon solution for $e$, yields

$$e = \frac{r_2 - r_1}{r_1 \cos v_1 - r_2 \cos v_2}.$$
(6.214)

Notice that the denominator of Eq. 6.214 will vanish for $r_1 \cos v_1 = r_2 \cos v_2$.  Now, if the angle between the radius vectors, $\Delta v_{21}$, has been determined[11] from the dot and cross products of the $\mathbf{r}_1$ and $\mathbf{r}_2$, it follows that

$$v_2 = v_1 + \Delta v_{21}.$$
(6.215)

[11] See footnote 1.

Hence, upon guessing $v_1$, the eccentricity $e$ becomes calculable from Eq. 6.214. The semiparameter $p$ is given by

$$p = a(1 - e^2),$$  (6.216)

and by consequence of Eqs. 6.213 and 6.216,

$$a = \frac{r_1(1 + e \cos v_1)}{(1 - e^2)}.$$  (6.217)

### 6.5.2    Utilization of the differenced Keplerian equation

For elliptic orbits, by utilizing

$$\sin E_i = \frac{\sqrt{1 - e^2} \sin v_i}{1 + e \cos v_i}, \quad i = 1, 2,$$  (6.218)

$$\cos E_i = \frac{\cos v_i + e}{1 + e \cos v_i}, \quad i = 1, 2,$$  (6.219)

it is evident that $E_1$ and $E_2$ are uniquely known and that the time interval function $F$ for the difference in the actual and speculative modified time between the two radius vectors is given as

$$M_i = E_i - e \sin E_i, \quad i = 1, 2$$  (6.220)

$$n = k \sqrt{\mu} \, a^{-\frac{3}{2}}$$  (6.221)

$$F = \tau - \left(\frac{M_2 - M_1}{n}\right) k.$$  (6.222)

Here again, as in other methods, it follows that by varying $v_1$ in Eq. 6.215 by a small amount, say $\Delta v_1$, it will be possible to obtain $F(v_1 + \Delta v_1)$ and thus the numerical derivative

$$F'(v_1) \cong \frac{F(v_1 + \Delta v_1) - F(v_1)}{\Delta v_1}.$$  (6.223)

A better approximation to $v_1$ is then obtained as

$$(v_1)_{j+1} = (v_1)_j - \frac{F[(v_1)_j]}{F'[(v_1)_j]}, \quad j = 1, 2, \ldots, q,$$  (6.224)

continued $q$ times until

$$|(v_1)_{j+1} - (v_1)_j| < \epsilon,$$  (6.225)

where $\epsilon$ is a specified tolerance.

Once a correct value of $v_1$ has been obtained, it is evident that $E_2 - E_1$ is also known from Eqs. 6.218 and 6.219, so that

$$f = 1 - \frac{a}{r_1} [1 - \cos (E_2 - E_1)] \qquad (6.226)$$

$$g = \tau - \frac{a^{3/2}}{\sqrt{\mu}} [E_2 - E_1 - \sin (E_2 - E_1)]. \qquad (6.227)$$

By virtue of

$$\mathbf{r}_2 = f\mathbf{r}_1 + g\dot{\mathbf{r}}_1 \qquad (6.228)$$

or

$$\dot{\mathbf{r}}_1 = \frac{\mathbf{r}_2 - f\mathbf{r}_1}{g}, \qquad (6.229)$$

the parameter $\dot{\mathbf{r}}_1$ can be calculated directly.  Hence the fundamental set $\mathbf{r}_1$, $\dot{\mathbf{r}}_1$ has been obtained and the orbit can be considered determined.

### 6.5.3   Computational algorithm

Given $\mathbf{r}_1(x_1, y_1, z_1)$, $\mathbf{r}_2(x_2, y_2, z_2)$ and their corresponding universal times, $t_1$ and $t_2$, along with an indication of whether the orbit is direct or retrograde, proceed as follows:

$$\tau = k(t_2 - t_1) \qquad (6.230)$$

$$r_1 = +\sqrt{\mathbf{r}_1 \cdot \mathbf{r}_1} \qquad (6.231)$$

$$r_2 = +\sqrt{\mathbf{r}_2 \cdot \mathbf{r}_2} \qquad (6.232)$$

$$\mathbf{U}_1 = \frac{\mathbf{r}_1}{r_1} \qquad (6.233)$$

$$\mathbf{U}_2 = \frac{\mathbf{r}_2}{r_2} \qquad (6.234)$$

$$\cos (v_2 - v_1) = \mathbf{U}_1 \cdot \mathbf{U}_2, \quad v_2 - v_1 \neq \pi. \qquad (6.235)$$

For a direct orbit,[12] $W_z \geq 0$, compute[13]

$$\sin (v_2 - v_1) = \frac{x_1 y_2 - x_2 y_1}{|x_1 y_2 - x_2 y_1|} \cdot \sqrt{1 - \cos^2 (v_2 - v_1)}. \qquad (6.236)$$

---

[12] See footnote 1.
[13] If $\mathbf{U}_1 \cdot \mathbf{U}_2 \cong -1$, take $\sin (v_2 - v_1) = 0$.

For a retrograde orbit, that is, $W_z < 0$, compute

$$\sin(v_2 - v_1) = -\frac{x_1 y_2 - x_2 y_1}{|x_1 y_2 - x_2 y_1|} \cdot \sqrt{1 - \cos^2(v_2 - v_1)}. \qquad (6.237)$$

As a first approximation, set

$$v_1 = 0° \qquad (6.238)$$

and continue calculating with

$$v_2 = v_1 + (v_2 - v_1) \qquad (6.239)$$

$$e = \frac{(r_2 - r_1)}{r_1 \cos v_1 - r_2 \cos v_2}. \qquad (6.240)$$

If $e < 0$, return to Eq. 6.238 and increment $v_1$ by $\Delta v_1$, say 10 degrees; if $e > 0$, proceed with Eq. 6.241

$$a = \frac{r_1(1 + e \cos v_1)}{(1 - e^2)}. \qquad (6.241)$$

If $e < 1$ but $a < 0$, return to Eq. 6.238 and increment $v_1$ by $\Delta v_1$; if $a > 0$, proceed with Eq. 6.242

$$\sin E_1 = \frac{\sqrt{1 - e^2} \sin v_1}{1 + e \cos v_1} \qquad (6.242)$$

$$\cos E_1 = \frac{\cos v_1 + e}{1 + e \cos v_1} \qquad (6.243)$$

$$\sin E_2 = \frac{\sqrt{1 - e^2} \sin v_2}{1 + e \cos v_2} \qquad (6.244)$$

$$\cos E_2 = \frac{\cos v_2 + e}{1 + e \cos v_2} \qquad (6.245)$$

$$M_2 - M_1 = E_2 - E_1 + e(\sin E_1 - \sin E_2) \qquad (6.246)$$

$$n = k\sqrt{\mu}\, a^{-3/2} \qquad (6.247)$$

$$F = \tau - \left(\frac{M_2 - M_1}{n}\right)k. \qquad (6.248)$$

If the iterative function is less than a specified tolerance $\epsilon_1$, that is,

$$|F| < \epsilon_1, \qquad (6.249)$$

proceed to Eq. 6.254; if not, save the numerical value of $F$ and increment $v_1$ by a small amount, $\Delta v$, to obtain

$$v_1 + \Delta v. \tag{6.250}$$

Repeat equational loop (6.239) to (6.248) obtaining $F(v_1 + \Delta v)$ and form

$$F'(v_1) \simeq \frac{F(v_1 + \Delta v) - F(v_1)}{\Delta v}. \tag{6.251}$$

Improve the value of $v_1$ by

$$(v_1)_{j+1} = (v_1)_j - \frac{F[(v_1)_j]}{F'[(v_1)_j]}, \quad j = 1, 2, 3, \ldots, q. \tag{6.252}$$

If

$$|(v_1)_{j+1} - (v_1)_j| < \epsilon_2, \tag{6.253}$$

where $\epsilon_2$ is another specified tolerance, proceed to Eq. 6.254; if not, return to Eq. 6.239 with the improved value of $v_1$.[14]

Continue calculating with:

$$f = 1 - \frac{a}{r_1} [1 - \cos (E_2 - E_1)] \tag{6.254}$$

$$g = \tau - \frac{a^{3/2}}{\sqrt{\mu}} [E_2 - E_1 - \sin (E_2 - E_1)] \tag{6.255}$$

$$\dot{\mathbf{r}}_1 = \frac{\mathbf{r}_2 - f\mathbf{r}_1}{g}. \tag{6.256}$$

Hence $\mathbf{r}_1$ and $\dot{\mathbf{r}}_1$ are known and the orbit is considered determined.

### 6.6  ORBIT DETERMINATION UTILIZING THE f AND g SERIES

Solution of a two-position vector and time interval orbit determination scheme has been effected by Douglas [11] by use of the $f$ and $g$ time series expansions (Section 3.9) of the fundamental differential equation. In comparison with the methods presented, this technique possesses the advantage of being valid in its formulation for elliptic, hyperbolic, and parabolic motion. It is, in effect, a general method limited only by the amount of terms carried in the $f$ and $g$ series used to effect the solution of the vector equation,

$$\ddot{\mathbf{r}} = -\frac{\mu \mathbf{r}}{r^3}. \tag{6.257}$$

[14] See footnote 6.

### 6.6.1    Preliminary approximations to the position and velocity vectors

Consider the two position vectors $\mathbf{r}_2$ and $\mathbf{r}_1$ of Figure 6.4. Certainly, then, expansion of Eq. 6.257 from a position vector $\mathbf{r}_0$ approximately halfway between $\mathbf{r}_1$ and $\mathbf{r}_2$ yields

$$\mathbf{r}_1 = \mathbf{r}_0 + \tau_1\dot{\mathbf{r}}_0 + \tfrac{1}{2}\tau_1^2\ddot{\mathbf{r}}_0 + \cdots \tag{6.258}$$

$$\mathbf{r}_2 = \mathbf{r}_0 + \tau_2\dot{\mathbf{r}}_0 + \tfrac{1}{2}\tau_2^2\ddot{\mathbf{r}}_0 + \cdots, \tag{6.259}$$

where

$$\tau_1 = k(t_1 - t_0) \tag{6.260}$$

$$\tau_2 = k(t_2 - t_0). \tag{6.261}$$

Time $t_0$ can be arbitrarily picked at, say,

$$t_0 = \frac{t_2 + t_1}{2}. \tag{6.262}$$

Introduce the dynamical constraint, Eq. 6.257, at $t_0$, that is,

$$\ddot{\mathbf{r}}_0 = -\frac{\mu\mathbf{r}_0}{r_0^3} \tag{6.263}$$

into expansions (6.258) and (6.259) as follows:

$$\mathbf{r}_1 = \mathbf{r}_0\left(1 - \frac{\mu\tau_1^2}{2r_0^3}\right) + \tau_1\dot{\mathbf{r}}_0 + \cdots \tag{6.264}$$

$$\mathbf{r}_2 = \mathbf{r}_0\left(1 - \frac{\mu\tau_2^2}{2r_0^3}\right) + \tau_2\dot{\mathbf{r}}_0 + \cdots, \tag{6.265}$$

and truncate after two terms so that

$$\mathbf{r}_1 = A\mathbf{r}_0 + \tau_1\dot{\mathbf{r}}_0 \tag{6.266}$$

$$\mathbf{r}_2 = B\mathbf{r}_0 + \tau_2\dot{\mathbf{r}}_0, \tag{6.267}$$

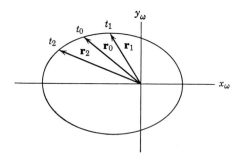

FIGURE 6.4    An elliptic orbit in space.

where

$$A \equiv \left(1 - \frac{\mu \tau_1^2}{2r_0^3}\right) \tag{6.268}$$

$$B \equiv \left(1 - \frac{\mu \tau_2^2}{2r_0^3}\right). \tag{6.269}$$

Elimination of $\dot{r}_0$ from Eqs. 6.266 and 6.267 produces the form

$$\mathbf{r}_0 = \left(\frac{\tau_2}{A\tau_2 - B\tau_1}\right)\mathbf{r}_1 - \left(\frac{\tau_1}{A\tau_2 - B\tau_1}\right)\mathbf{r}_2, \tag{6.270}$$

which upon approximating the magnitude of the radius vector at $t_0$ by

$$r_0 = \frac{r_1 + r_2}{2}, \tag{6.271}$$

allows determination of $A$ and $B$ from Eqs. 6.268 and 6.269.  The starting value of $\mathbf{r}_0$ is therefore known.

By the same procedure, elimination of $\mathbf{r}_0$ from Eqs. 6.266 and 6.267 yields

$$\dot{\mathbf{r}}_0 = \left(\frac{A}{A\tau_2 - B\tau_1}\right)\mathbf{r}_2 - \left(\frac{B}{A\tau_2 - B\tau_1}\right)\mathbf{r}_1. \tag{6.272}$$

Again, by means of approximation (6.271), the $A$ and $B$ coefficients can be calculated.

### 6.6.2   Improvement of the position and velocity vectors

Having first approximations for $\mathbf{r}_0$ and $\dot{\mathbf{r}}_0$ from Eqs. 6.270 and 6.272 it is possible to proceed as follows:

$$r_0 = \sqrt{\mathbf{r}_0 \cdot \mathbf{r}_0} \tag{6.273}$$

$$\dot{r}_0 = (\mathbf{r}_0 \cdot \dot{\mathbf{r}}_0)/r_0 \tag{6.274}$$

$$V_0 = \sqrt{\dot{\mathbf{r}}_0 \cdot \dot{\mathbf{r}}_0} \tag{6.275}$$

and by means of the vis-viva equation (Section 3.6) obtain[15]

$$\frac{1}{a} = \frac{2}{r_0} - \frac{V_0^2}{\mu}. \tag{6.276}$$

[15] This is an indication as to whether the orbit is elliptic, parabolic, or hyperbolic.

Now, in terms of the epoch $t_0$, it is possible to write the following perfectly general expressions:

$$\mathbf{r}_1 = f_1 \mathbf{r}_0 + g_1 \dot{\mathbf{r}}_0 \tag{6.277}$$

$$\mathbf{r}_2 = f_2 \mathbf{r}_0 + g_2 \dot{\mathbf{r}}_0, \tag{6.278}$$

where $f_1, g_1$, and $f_2, g_2$ are the $f$ and $g$ series (Section 3.9) evaluated for $\tau_1$ and $\tau_2$, respectively.

From Eqs. 6.277 and 6.278, eliminate $\dot{\mathbf{r}}_0$ to obtain

$$\mathbf{r}_0 = \left(\frac{g_2}{f_1 g_2 - f_2 g_1}\right)\mathbf{r}_1 - \left(\frac{g_1}{f_1 g_2 - f_2 g_1}\right)\mathbf{r}_2 \tag{6.279}$$

or

$$\mathbf{r}_0 = C_1 \mathbf{r}_1 + C_2 \mathbf{r}_2, \tag{6.280}$$

where

$$C_1 \equiv \frac{g_2}{D}, \tag{6.281}$$

$$C_2 \equiv -\frac{g_1}{D} \tag{6.282}$$

and

$$D = f_1 g_2 - f_2 g_1. \tag{6.283}$$

Similarly, eliminate $\mathbf{r}_0$ from Eqs. 6.277 and 6.278 to yield

$$\dot{\mathbf{r}}_0 = \dot{C}_1 \mathbf{r}_1 + \dot{C}_2 \mathbf{r}_2, \tag{6.284}$$

where

$$\dot{C}_1 \equiv -\frac{f_2}{D}, \tag{6.285}$$

$$\dot{C}_2 \equiv \frac{f_1}{D}. \tag{6.286}$$

Now, using the crude values obtained from Eqs. 6.273, 6.274, and 6.275, evaluate the $f$ and $g$ series (Section 3.9) at $\tau_1$ and $\tau_2$, that is,

$$f_1 = f(V_0, r_0, \dot{r}_0, \tau_1)$$
$$g_1 = g(V_0, r_0, \dot{r}_0, \tau_1)$$
$$f_2 = f(V_0, r_0, \dot{r}_0, \tau_2)$$
$$g_2 = g(V_0, r_0, \dot{r}_0, \tau_2)$$

and compute $C_1, C_2, \dot{C}_1, \dot{C}_2$ from Eqs. 6.281, 6.282, 6.285, and 6.286. Immediately then, Eqs. 6.280 and 6.284 yield improved values of $\mathbf{r}_0$ and $\dot{\mathbf{r}}_0$.

Evidently, by means of Eqs. 6.273, 6.274, and 6.275, it is possible to obtain better values of $r_0$, $\dot{r}_0$, and $V_0$ and re-evaluate the $f$ and $g$ series, etc., each time improving the values of $\mathbf{r}_0$ and $\dot{\mathbf{r}}_0$, that is, obtain a self-perpetuating scheme.

### 6.6.3  Computational algorithm

Given $\mathbf{r}_1(x_1, y_1, z_1)$, $\mathbf{r}_2(x_2, y_2, z_2)$ and their corresponding universal times, $t_1$ and $t_2$, along with an indication of whether the orbit is direct or retrograde, proceed as follows:

$$r_1 = +\sqrt{\mathbf{r}_1 \cdot \mathbf{r}_1} \tag{6.287}$$

$$r_2 = +\sqrt{\mathbf{r}_2 \cdot \mathbf{r}_2} \tag{6.288}$$

$$\mathbf{U}_1 = \frac{\mathbf{r}_1}{r_1} \tag{6.289}$$

$$\mathbf{U}_2 = \frac{\mathbf{r}_2}{r_2} \tag{6.290}$$

$$\cos(v_2 - v_1) = \mathbf{U}_1 \cdot \mathbf{U}_2, \quad v_2 - v_1 \neq \pi. \tag{6.291}$$

If the orbit is direct,[16] that is, if $W_z \geq 0$, compute

$$\sin(v_2 - v_1) = \frac{x_1 y_2 - x_2 y_1}{|x_1 y_2 - x_2 y_1|} \sqrt{1 - \cos^2(v_2 - v_1)}. \tag{6.292}$$

If the orbit is retrograde, that is, if $W_z < 0$, compute

$$\sin(v_2 - v_1) = -\frac{x_1 y_2 - x_2 y_1}{|x_1 y_2 - x_2 y_1|} \sqrt{1 - \cos^2(v_2 - v_1)}. \tag{6.293}$$

If $v_2 - v_1$ is less than 90°, proceed with Eq. 6.294, if it is not, the method will probably not converge.  Continue calculating with

$$t_0 = \frac{t_2 + t_1}{2} \tag{6.294}$$

$$\tau_1 = k(t_1 - t_0) \tag{6.295}$$

$$\tau_2 = k(t_2 - t_0). \tag{6.296}$$

[16] See footnote 1.

As a first approximation, set

$$r_0 = \frac{r_2 + r_1}{2} \tag{6.297}$$

$$A = \left(1 - \frac{\mu \tau_1^2}{2r_0^3}\right) \tag{6.298}$$

$$B = \left(1 - \frac{\mu \tau_2^2}{2r_0^3}\right) \tag{6.299}$$

$$\Delta = A\tau_2 - B\tau_1 \tag{6.300}$$

$$\mathbf{r}_0 = \left(\frac{\tau_2}{\Delta}\right)\mathbf{r}_1 - \left(\frac{\tau_1}{\Delta}\right)\mathbf{r}_2 \tag{6.301}$$

$$\dot{\mathbf{r}}_0 = \left(\frac{A}{\Delta}\right)\mathbf{r}_2 - \left(\frac{B}{\Delta}\right)\mathbf{r}_1, \tag{6.302}$$

so that improved values of the parameters are

$$r_0 = \sqrt{\mathbf{r}_0 \cdot \mathbf{r}_0} \tag{6.303}$$

$$V_0 = \sqrt{\dot{\mathbf{r}}_0 \cdot \dot{\mathbf{r}}_0} \tag{6.304}$$

$$\dot{r}_0 = \mathbf{r}_0 \cdot \dot{\mathbf{r}}_0 / r_0 \tag{6.305}$$

$$\frac{1}{a} = \frac{2}{r_0} - \frac{V_0^2}{\mu}. \tag{6.306}$$

Utilize the $f$ and $g$ functions to compute

$$f_1 = f(V_0, r_0, \dot{r}_0, \tau_1) \tag{6.307}$$

$$f_2 = f(V_0, r_0, \dot{r}_0, \tau_2) \tag{6.308}$$

$$g_1 = g(V_0, r_0, \dot{r}_0, \tau_1) \tag{6.309}$$

$$g_2 = g(V_0, r_0, \dot{r}_0, \tau_2) \tag{6.310}$$

and form

$$D = f_1 g_2 - f_2 g_1. \tag{6.311}$$

Continue calculating with

$$C_1 = g_2/D \tag{6.312}$$

$$C_2 = -g_1/D \tag{6.313}$$

$$\dot{C}_1 = -f_2/D \tag{6.314}$$

$$\dot{C}_2 = f_1/D. \tag{6.315}$$

Hence a better approximation to $\mathbf{r}_0$, $\dot{\mathbf{r}}_0$ is given by

$$\mathbf{r}_0 = C_1\mathbf{r}_1 + C_2\mathbf{r}_2 \tag{6.316}$$

$$\dot{\mathbf{r}}_0 = \dot{C}_1\mathbf{r}_1 + \dot{C}_2\mathbf{r}_2. \tag{6.317}$$

Return to Eq. 6.303 and repeat the equational loop to Eq. 6.317; continue until $r_0$, $\dot{r}_0$, $V_0$ from Eqs. 6.303, 6.304, and 6.305 do not vary, that is,

$$|(r_0)_{n+1} - (r_0)_n| < \epsilon_1 \tag{6.318}$$

$$|(\dot{r}_0)_{n+1} - (\dot{r}_0)_n| < \epsilon_2 \tag{6.319}$$

$$|(V_0)_{n+1} - (V_0)_n| < \epsilon_3, \quad n = 1, 2, \ldots, q, \tag{6.320}$$

where $\epsilon_1$, $\epsilon_2$, $\epsilon_3$ are tolerances. Having $r_0$, $\dot{r}_0$, $V_0$, utilize the derivatives of the $f$ and $g$ functions, that is,

$$\dot{f}_1 = \dot{f}(V_0, r_0, \dot{r}_0, \tau_1) \tag{6.321}$$

$$\dot{g}_1 = \dot{g}(V_0, r_0, \dot{r}_0, \tau_1), \tag{6.322}$$

to obtain

$$\dot{\mathbf{r}}_1 = \dot{f}_1\mathbf{r}_0 + \dot{g}_1\dot{\mathbf{r}}_0. \tag{6.323}$$

The fundamental set $\mathbf{r}_1$, $\dot{\mathbf{r}}_1$ is now complete and the orbit is considered determined.

### 6.7   ORBIT DETERMINATION BY ITERATION ON THE ECCENTRICITY

The last method of this chapter is called the $e$-iteration. It may be new, and was developed by Escobal [13] for the determination of lunar trajectories. The advantage of this technique lies in the fact that, for lunar orbits, the eccentricity of the orbit can be represented well by $e \cong 0.97$. It may be worthwhile to note that by commencing the iteration with a value of $e$, the appropriate formulas for elliptic, parabolic, and hyperbolic motion can be called upon with great convenience. The analysis will be developed in terms of differences of angles from some epoch in order to preserve accuracy. This method has not undergone extensive numerical investigation.

#### 6.7.1   Development of quadratic resolvent

The general equation of a conic section, that is,

$$r = \frac{p}{1 + e \cos v}, \tag{6.324}$$

where

$p$ = the orbital semiparameter = $a(1 - e^2)$,
$a$ = the orbital semimajor axis,
$e$ = the orbital eccentricity,
$v$ = the true anomaly of the point mass in orbit about the dynamical center,
$r$ = the distance or extension between the dynamical center and point mass,

can be modified by introduction of an arbitrary reference true anomaly, $v_0$, as follows:

$$r = \frac{p}{1 + e \cos (v - v_0 + v_0)}. \tag{6.325}$$

By direct trigonometric expansion of Eq. 6.325 it is possible to verify that

$$r = \frac{p}{1 + C_v \cos (v - v_0) - S_v \sin (v - v_0)} \tag{6.326}$$

with the auxiliary elements $C_v$, $S_v$ defined by

$$C_v \equiv e \cos v_0, \quad S_v \equiv e \sin v_0. \tag{6.327}$$

For any two different universal times $t_1$ and $t_2$, since $p$ is invariant,

$$r_2[1 + C_v \cos (v_2 - v_0) - S_v \sin (v_2 - v_0)]$$
$$= r_1[1 + C_v \cos (v_1 - v_0) - S_v \sin (v_1 - v_0)], \tag{6.328}$$

or

$$\frac{(r_2 - r_1) + [r_2 \cos (v_2 - v_0) - r_1 \cos (v_1 - v_0)]C_v}{[r_2 \sin (v_2 - v_0) - r_1 \sin (v_1 - v_0)]} = S_v. \tag{6.329}$$

This equation may be written more concisely by introduction of the following definitions:

$$\beta_r \equiv r_2 - r_1$$
$$\beta_c \equiv r_2 \cos (v_2 - v_0) - r_1 \cos (v_1 - v_0) \tag{6.330}$$
$$\beta_s \equiv r_2 \sin (v_2 - v_0) - r_1 \sin (v_1 - v_0),$$

so that

$$\frac{\beta_r + \beta_c C_v}{\beta_s} = S_v. \tag{6.331}$$

Squaring both sides of Eq. 6.331 results in

$$\frac{\beta_r^2 + 2\beta_r\beta_c C_v + \beta_c^2 C_v^2}{\beta_s^2} = S_v^2 = e^2 - C_v^2$$

or, more compactly,

$$(\beta_{c0}^2 + \beta_{s0}^2)C_{v0}^2 + 2\beta_{r0}\beta_{c0}C_{v0} + \beta_{r0}^2 - \beta_{s0}^2 e^2 = 0. \tag{6.332}$$

The subscript 0 emphasizes the fact that the $\beta$ coefficients and $C_v$ are referred to epoch $v = v_0$. Equation 6.332 is the quadratic resolvent in $C_{v0}$ of the orbit determination problem. Let the quadratic be written for epoch $v_0 = v_1$. Solution of Eq. 6.332 for an assumed value of $e^2 > \beta_r^2/(\beta_c^2 + \beta_s^2)$ will yield $(e \cos v_1)_j$; $j = 1, 2$. The complementary element $(e \sin v_1)_j$ may be found directly from Eq. 6.331, that is,

$$S_{vj} = \frac{\beta_r + \beta_c C_{vj}}{\beta_s}. \tag{6.333}$$

Apparently, as in the Lambert–Euler method, from this point on, two separate orbits must be carried forward in the analysis, that is, for $j = 1, 2$.

### 6.7.2   Computation of time interval

The assumed value of $e^2$ clearly dictates the geometrical properties of the conic to be placed between the terminals $\mathbf{r}_1$ and $\mathbf{r}_2$. Hence if $e^2 < 1$, the orbit is elliptical, and it is possible to compute the mean motion from

$$\begin{aligned} p &= r_1(1 + C_v) \\ a &= p/(1 - e^2) \\ n_e &= k(\mu)^{\frac{1}{2}}a^{-\frac{3}{2}}, \end{aligned} \tag{6.334}$$

with $\mu$ taken as the sum of masses of vehicle and central planet. It should be noticed that

$$\begin{aligned} \cos(v_2 - v_1) &= (\mathbf{r}_1 \cdot \mathbf{r}_2)/r_1 r_2 \\ \sin(v_2 - v_1) &= s[1 - \cos^2(v_2 - v_1)]^{\frac{1}{2}}, \end{aligned}$$

where for a direct orbit $s = \dfrac{x_1 y_2 - x_2 y_1}{|x_1 y_2 - x_2 y_1|}$, while for a retrograde orbit the sign of $s$ is reversed.

The auxiliary elements $S_e$, $C_e$ may be found from

$$S_e = \frac{r_1}{p}[1 - e^2]^{\frac{1}{2}}S_v$$

$$C_e = \frac{r_1}{p}[e^2 + C_v],$$

so that

$$\sin(E_2 - E_1) = \frac{r_2}{[ap]^{\frac{1}{2}}}\sin(v_2 - v_1) - \frac{r_2}{p}[1 - \cos(v_2 - v_1)]S_e \tag{6.335}$$

$$\cos(E_2 - E_1) = 1 - \frac{r_2 r_1}{ap}[1 - \cos(v_2 - v_1)]. \tag{6.336}$$

If $e^2 = 1$, the orbit is parabolic and it is necessary to determine (Section 3.5.3)

$$n_p = k[\mu]^{\frac{1}{2}}$$

$$D_1 = [2q]^{\frac{1}{2}} S_v / (1 + C_v)$$

$$D_2 - D_1 = \frac{r_1 r_2}{(2q)^{\frac{3}{2}}} \{[1 + C_v] \sin (v_2 - v_1) - S_v[1 - \cos (v_2 - v_1)]\}.$$

$$(6.337)$$

For a hyperbolic orbit, that is, $e^2 > 1$, the mean motion (Section 3.5.2) can be found from

$$p = r_1(1 + C_v)$$

$$a = p/(1 - e^2) \tag{6.338}$$

$$n_h = k(\mu)^{\frac{1}{2}}(-a)^{-\frac{3}{2}},$$

and the auxiliary elements $S_h$, $C_h$, defined through

$$S_h = \frac{r_1}{p} [e^2 - 1]^{\frac{1}{2}} S_v$$

$$C_e = C_h = \frac{r_1}{p} [e^2 + C_v]$$

so that

$$\sinh (F_2 - F_1) = \frac{r_2}{[-ap]^{\frac{1}{2}}} \sin (v_2 - v_1) - \frac{r_2}{p} [1 - \cos (v_2 - v_1)] S_h$$

$$(6.339)$$

$$F_2 - F_1 = \log \{\sinh (F_2 - F_1) + [\sinh^2 (F_2 - F_1) + 1]^{\frac{1}{2}}\}.$$

$$(6.340)$$

The differences in mean anomalies are now given for the above three cases as

$$(M_2 - M_1)_e = E_2 - E_1 + 2S_e \sin^2 \left(\frac{E_2 - E_1}{2}\right) - C_e \sin (E_2 - E_1)$$

$$(6.341)$$

$$(M_2 - M_1)_p = \tfrac{1}{6}\{(D_2 - D_1)^3 + 3D_1(D_2 - D_1)^2 + 6r_1(D_2 - D_1)\}$$

$$(6.342)$$

$$(M_2 - M_1)_h = -(F_2 - F_1) + 2S_h \sinh^2 \left(\frac{F_2 - F_1}{2}\right)$$

$$+ C_h \sinh (F_2 - F_1), \quad (6.343)$$

and the corresponding computed times are obtained from

$$\tau_c = k(M_2 - M_1)_e/n_e \tag{6.344}$$

$$\tau_c = k(M_2 - M_1)_p/n_p \tag{6.345}$$

$$\tau_c = k(M_2 - M_1)_h/n_h. \tag{6.346}$$

Evidently, if

$$F = |\tau - \tau_c| < \epsilon, \tag{6.347}$$

where $\epsilon$ is a tolerance, the orbit is accurately determined; if not, save $F(e^2)$ return to Eq. 6.332, vary $e^2$ by a small amount, and repeat the calculations through Eq. 6.347 so that

$$F' = \frac{\partial F}{\partial e^2} \simeq \frac{F(e^2 + \Delta e^2) - F(e^2)}{\Delta e^2}. \tag{6.348}$$

Finally improve the value of $e^2$ by

$$e_{\nu+1}^2 = e_\nu^2 - \frac{F(e_\nu^2)}{F'(e_\nu^2)}, \quad \nu = 1, 2, \ldots, s. \tag{6.349}$$

### 6.7.3 Computation of position and velocity vectors

When the above loop has been satisfied and $e^2$ determined to suitable accuracy, for the elliptical case form

$$
\begin{aligned}
C &= a[1 - \cos(E_2 - E_1)] \\
S &= a^{\frac{1}{2}} \sin(E_2 - E_1), \\
D_1 &= r_1 S_v/p^{\frac{1}{2}};
\end{aligned}
\tag{6.350}
$$

for the parabolic case form

$$
\begin{aligned}
C &= \tfrac{1}{2}(D_2 - D_1)^2 \\
S &= D_2 - D_1;
\end{aligned}
\tag{6.351}
$$

for the hyperbolic case form

$$
\begin{aligned}
C &= -a[\cosh(F_2 - F_1) - 1] \\
S &= [-a]^{\frac{1}{2}} \sinh(F_2 - F_1) \\
D_1 &= r_1 S_v/p^{\frac{1}{2}}
\end{aligned}
\tag{6.352}
$$

and obtain $\mathbf{r}_1$ and $\dot{\mathbf{r}}_1$ through

$$
\begin{aligned}
f &= 1 - \frac{C}{r_1} \\
g &= \frac{1}{\mu^{\frac{1}{2}}} (r_1 S + D_1 C) \\
\dot{\mathbf{r}}_1 &= \frac{\mathbf{r}_2 - f\mathbf{r}_1}{g} \\
\mathbf{r}_1 &= \mathbf{r}_1.
\end{aligned}
\tag{6.353}
$$

The six elements $\mathbf{r}_1$, $\dot{\mathbf{r}}_1$ are known and the orbit is considered determined.

6.8  COMPARISON OF THE FIVE METHODS

### 6.8.1  Results of numerical studies

It is difficult to be specifically precise in a statement of which of the previous methods can be termed "the best." Certainly a method which best decrees the problem at hand should be chosen for the determination of a particular orbit. There are, however, several points of interest that should be known to the analyst before choosing a particular method. For example, which method is fastest from a computational point of view? Which method has the least numerical error propagation? Which method experiences the least convergence difficulties? Numerical studies upon many orbits of varying eccentricity and semimajor axis have provided a very partial answer to these questions.

### 6.8.2  Computing speed

In order to answer the first question, that is, which is the fastest computational method, Table 6.1 is supplied. The computing times shown in Table 6.1 are representative of the actual times to be expected in normal use of the algorithms. As expected from its algorithm, the *True Anomaly Iteration* is generally the fastest. The *Gaussian Iteration* will be even faster for small spread in the radius vectors, but has trouble converging at high spreads, so that the overall computing time is greater.

*Table 6.1   Average Computing Time for Each Method*
(For a nominal orbit with $e = 0.2$ at $E = 0°$, $15°$, $30°$)

| METHOD | ACTUAL COMPUTING TIME sec (IBM 7090) |
| --- | --- |
| Gaussian iteration | 0.0383 |
| Lambert-Euler iteration | 0.0533 |
| Semiparameter iteration | 0.0366 |
| True anomaly iteration | 0.0300 |
| $f$ and $g$ iteration | 0.1550 |

### 6.8.3  Error propagation

The second question, which method has the least numerical error propagation, is difficult to answer, and, as might be expected, indicates that every method is optimum in the computation of a particular element.

A specific orbit scheme will produce a given element with the lowest error residual. It is, however, possible to segregate the overall results of the numerical studies performed in this field into three categories: high, medium, and low accuracy as shown in Table 6.2.

*Table 6.2   Comparative Accuracy Rating*

| HIGH | MEDIUM | LOW |
|------|--------|-----|
| Gaussian iteration | $v$-iteration | $p$-iteration |
| Lambert-Euler iteration | $f$ and $g$ iteration | |

### 6.8.4   Ease of convergence

Before attempting to answer the third question, about ease of convergence, it should be pointed out that the Gaussian and $f$ and $g$ iteration methods are what can be called *self-perpetuating* in their convergence. That is, from an easily estimated first guess an iterative loop is initiated which converges automatically to the desired result. The remaining methods are trial and error types wherein a parameter is guessed, the calculations performed, and a residual obtained. These methods are, of course, coupled with a Newton iteration corrector of the form

$$x_{n+1} = x_n - \frac{f(x_n)}{f'(x_n)}, \tag{6.354}$$

in order to obtain continuously improved values of the iterative parameter $x$.

The results of numerical studies indicate that these methods can be subdivided into small radius vector spread and large radius vector spread categories. That is, some techniques are much more suitable for small differences and others for large differences in true anomaly. Common sense would dictate use as shown in Table 6.3.

For the small radius vector spread, that is, when the two respective radius vectors are less than about 30° apart, the Gaussian and $f$ and $g$ methods converge with the least amount of effort, with a fixed initial guess that is the same for all orbits involved.[17] The Gaussian method suffers from

[17] See the respective algorithms.

instability of convergence for spreads of greater than 90°. Convergence of the given algorithm fails shortly after this point. It is, of course, possible to extend the range of convergence by other devices but the ratio of sector to triangle commences to grow with increasing rapidity in the second quadrant and it is better to turn to another method.

*Table 6.3*

| SMALL RADIUS VECTOR SPREAD | LARGE RADIUS VECTOR SPREAD |
|---|---|
| Gaussian iteration<br>$f$ and $g$ iteration | Lambert–Euler iteration<br>$p$-iteration<br>$v$-iteration |

The $f$ and $g$ iteration is also very stable for small radius vector spreads of about 30°, but fails shortly after about a spread of 60° due to the limitations of the $f$ and $g$ series (Section 3.9) and poor values of the computed initial estimates.[18]

For the remaining methods, the initial estimate into the algorithms is very much a matter of extrasensory perception, unless, of course, other information is available. Elliptical motion does, however, imply the following guess bounds (Table 6.4).

*Table 6.4*

| METHOD | BOUND |
|---|---|
| $p$-iteration | $0 \leq p \leq 2r$ |
| $v$-iteration | $0 \leq v \leq 2\pi$ |
| Lambert–Euler | $0 \leq a \leq \infty$ |

Comparing the three methods listed in Table 6.4, the $v$-iteration and Lambert–Euler method performed very well for small and large radius vector spreads. The Lambert–Euler method functions well into the

[18] See the $f$ and $g$ iteration algorithm.

second quadrant but degenerates at colinear opposed radius vectors[19] with all eccentricities.   The $v$-iteration converged for all spreads, but the method degenerates when the denominator of the eccentricity equation vanishes.[20]   Theoretically, it is the only one of the above methods that is convergent and yields definite results at the difficult 180° radius vector spread condition.   The $p$-iteration was discovered to be troublesome in its convergence.   This is probably due to the nature of the iterative function. It performed well for small radius vector spreads.

In light of the above, it is possible to condense the results into Table 6.5.

*Table 6.5   Ease of Convergence Rating*

|      | SMALL RADIUS VECTOR SPREAD | LARGE RADIUS VECTOR SPREAD |
|------|---------------------------|----------------------------|
| Good | Gaussian iteration $f$ and $g$ iteration | $v$-iteration |
| Fair | Lambert–Euler iteration $v$-iteration $p$-iteration | Lambert–Euler iteration $p$-iteration |
| Poor |                           | Gaussian iteration $f$ and $g$ iteration |

## 6.8.5   Conclusions

It appears that the optimal preliminary orbit determination schemes of the two position vectors and time interval type are representable by the following two cases:

(*a*)  The Gaussian iteration for true anomaly differences of less than 70°.
(*b*)  The $v$-iteration for true anomaly differences greater than 70°.

As backup in case (*a*), the $f$ and $g$ iteration should be used.   The $v$-iteration backup should be the Lambert–Euler iteration.   The above results will yield what seems to be an optimum compromise between the best computing speed, accuracy, and minimum convergence problem. On a computer, the above strategy has the best probability of successfully determining the unknown orbit.

[19] See the Lambert–Euler iteration.
[20] See the $v$-iteration.

#### 6.9  REFERENCE ORBITS

### 6.9.1  Preliminary remarks

For the sake of reference, it will perhaps be beneficial to list sets of elements and corresponding positions of various orbits. These orbits will provide an important check in the machine coding of the previous algorithms. All the listed reference orbits are computed by two-body, inverse square formulations. For radius vectors not too far apart, the Gaussian technique was utilized. The $v$-iteration was utilized for the large radii vector spreads. It should also be noted that

$$k \equiv 0.07436574 \text{ (e.r.)}^{3/2}/\text{min}$$
$$\mu = 1.0 \text{ e.m.}$$
$$a_e = 1.0 \text{ e.r.}$$

In the following orbits the rectangular components are referenced with respect to System 2, Chapter 4, that is, the right ascension-declination coordinate system. The tabulated orbits are geocentric.

### 6.9.2  Reference orbit number I

*Position vectors on January 1, 1964* ($\Delta t = 0.01044412$ Julian days)

| | |
|---|---|
| $x_1 = +2.460809$ e.r. | $x_2 = +1.988041$ e.r. |
| $y_1 = +2.040523$ e.r. | $y_2 = +2.503334$ e.r. |
| $z_1 = +0.143819$ e.r. | $z_2 = +0.314554$ e.r. |

*Corresponding classical elements*

| | |
|---|---|
| $a = 4.0$ e.r. | $i = 15$ degrees |
| $e = 0.2$ | $\Omega = 30$ degrees |
| $T = 1964$ January $1^{\text{day}}, 0^{\text{hr}}, 0^{\text{min}}, 0^{\text{sec}}$ | $\omega = 10$ degrees |

### 6.9.3  Reference orbit number II

*Position vectors on June 1, 1964* ($\Delta t = 0.01527809$ Julian days)

| | |
|---|---|
| $x_1 = -1.75981$ e.r. | $x_2 = -2.23077$ e.r. |
| $y_1 = +1.68113$ e.r. | $y_2 = +0.77454$ e.r. |
| $z_1 = +1.16913$ e.r. | $z_2 = +1.34602$ e.r. |

*Corresponding classical elements*

| | |
|---|---|
| $a = 3.0$ e.r. | $i = 30$ degrees |
| $e = 0.1$ | $\Omega = 80$ degrees |
| $T = 1964$ June 1, $0^{\text{hr}}, 0^{\text{min}}, 0^{\text{sec}}$ | $\omega = 60$ degrees |

### 6.9.4    Reference orbit number III

*Position vectors on December 23, 1963* ($\Delta t$ = 0.01316924 Julian days)

$x_1$ = +0.41136 e.r.          $x_2$ = +0.97757 e.r.

$y_1$ = −1.66250 e.r.          $y_2$ = −1.64428 e.r.

$z_1$ = +0.82272 e.r.          $z_2$ = −0.42363 × $10^{-1}$ e.r.

*Corresponding classical elements*

$a$ = 2.0 e.r.                          $i$ = 60 degrees

$e$ = 0.05                              $\Omega$ = 120 degrees

$T$ = 1963 December 23, $0^{hr}$, $0^{min}$, $0^{sec}$    $\omega$ = 150 degrees

### 6.9.5    Reference orbit number IV

*Position vectors on January 15, 1964* ($\Delta t$ = 0.14971172 Julian days)

$x_1$ = +2.78418 e.r.          $x_2$ = +2.37280 e.r.

$y_1$ = +0.82815 e.r.          $y_2$ = +1.54778 e.r.

$z_1$ = +0.75000 e.r.          $z_2$ = +1.11792 e.r.

*Corresponding classical elements*

$a$ = 6.0 e.r.                          $i$ = 150 degrees

$e$ = 0.5                                $\Omega$ = 170 degrees

$T$ = 1964 January 15, $22^{hr}$, $30^{min}$, $3^{sec}$    $\omega$ = 150 degrees

### 6.9.6    Reference orbit number V

*Position vectors on July 4, 1964* ($\Delta t$ = 0.42710476 Julian days)

$x_1$ = −1.00746 e.r.          $x_2$ = −0.64633 e.r.

$y_1$ = −3.89711 e.r.          $y_2$ = +5.12188 e.r.

$z_1$ = −2.01185 e.r.          $z_2$ = −1.29069 e.r.

*Corresponding classical elements*

$a$ = 5.0 e.r.                          $i$ = 63.4 degrees

$e$ = 0.1                                $\Omega$ = 270 degrees

$T$ = 1964 July 4, $12^{hr}$, $0^{min}$, $0^{sec}$    $\omega$ = 330 degrees

### 6.9.7   Reference orbit number VI

*Position vectors on January 30, 1964* ($\Delta t = 0.21227310$ Julian days)

| | |
|---|---|
| $x_1 = -2.57823$ e.r. | $x_2 = +3.49838$ e.r. |
| $y_1 = +2.13649$ e.r. | $y_2 = -2.94610$ e.r. |
| $z_1 = +0.59004$ e.r. | $z_2 = +0.23276$ e.r. |

*Corresponding classical elements*

| | |
|---|---|
| $a = 4.0$ e.r. | $i = 88$ degrees |
| $e = 0.15$ | $\Omega = 140$ degrees |
| $T = 1964$ January 30, $0^{hr}$, $0^{min}$, $0^{sec}$ | $\omega = 10$ degrees |

### 6.10   FURTHER CONSIDERATIONS

### 6.10.1   Extending the orbit schemes to more than one revolution

As stated previously, it is difficult to single out any one method as best from an overall point of view. For example, the analyst might be interested in determining an orbit from data obtained from successive passes of a satellite over a specific ground station or determining an orbit between one radius vector and another, say on the $n$th revolution of the satellite. In these cases, methods like the $p$-iteration and $v$-iteration can be very easily modified to determine the desired orbit.

To permit such extensions, the only requirement is that a multiplier $2\pi\lambda$ be added to $M_2$, assuming $M_2$ occurs at a later time than $M_1$ in Equation 6.174 of the $p$-iteration and Eq. 6.222 of the $v$-iteration. Hence, by taking $\lambda = 1, 2, \ldots, n$, it is possible to continue until the appropriate orbit is found, that is, one attempts to carry on the solution with an integer value of $\lambda$ until convergence is achieved. These options are important extensions of these methods and may well weigh into the analyst's decision in choosing a method to satisfy the problem requirements.

### 6.11   SUMMARY

Six different methods for the determination of preliminary orbits from two position vectors and the time interval between the respective vectors have been presented in this chapter. It has been seen that the Gaussian and $f$ and $g$ iteration techniques are of the self-perpetuating type and apparently present the best methods for the determination of orbits when the radius vector spread is small. The Gaussian method is preferred because the iterative loop of the scheme is very short.   Of the remaining three methods investigated, the $v$-iteration technique with the Newton corrector appears to emerge as the most practical for large radius vector spreads.   It is to be preferred to the Lambert–Euler iteration due to the simplicity of its iterative loop.   Obviously, all the presented techniques have advantages, depending upon the data peculiar to the orbit about to be determined. For convenience, an algorithm of the first five methods is presented: The last method developed, the $e$-iteration, may find considerable use in the computation and determination of translunar orbits.   A number of reference orbits which might find use in machine coding the above algorithms are recorded.

**EXERCISES**

**1.** Show that if an orbit is direct,

$$s = \frac{x_1 y_2 - x_2 y_1}{|x_1 y_2 - x_2 y_1|}$$

and if an orbit is retrograde,

$$s = -\frac{x_1 y_2 - x_2 y_1}{|x_1 y_2 - x_2 y_1|},$$

so that

$$\sin(v_2 - v_1) = s\sqrt{1 - (\mathbf{U}_1 \cdot \mathbf{U}_2)^2}.$$

**2.** Show that the Gaussian iterative loop reduces to the successive approximation scheme

$$x = m\left\{1 + \frac{2(l+x)\tan^{-1}\left(\frac{\sqrt{4x(1-x)}}{1-2x}\right) - (l+x)\sin\left[2\tan^{-1}\left(\frac{\sqrt{4x(1-x)}}{1-2x}\right)\right]}{[4x(1-x)]^{3/2}}\right\}^{-1} - l,$$

where the correct sign of the arctangents is obtained by examination of the denominator of their arguments.   Differentiate the right-hand side of the above equation with respect to $x$ to obtain $F'(x)$.   Set $F'(x) = \pm 1$, the necessary condition that the successive iterates converge and graphically investigate the domain of convergence of the Gaussian technique for various values of $m$ and $l$.

**3.** Assuming that a zero of the Gaussian procedure is $\hat{x}$, prove that the iterative scheme

$$x_{n+1} = F(x_n),$$

implies that

$$\hat{x} = x_n + ab^n,$$

where $a$ and $b$ are constants independent of $n$. Furthermore, if a set of successive iterates of $x$ are known, show that convergence can be increased by using these iterates in the relation

$$\hat{x} \cong x_{n+2} - \frac{(x_{n+2} - x_{n+1})^2}{x_{n+2} - 2x_{n+1} + x_n}.$$

4. Captain Von Angstrom of the ill-fated spaceship El Relampago has been operating on emergency oxygen ever since a meteorite punctured the main supply tank. The on-board computer displays the geocentric position-velocity coordinates in the right ascension-declination coordinate frame as

$x_1 = + 0.6524196$ e.r.

$y_1 = + 3.8025803$ e.r.

$z_1 = + 2.2274999$ e.r.

$\dot{x}_1 = - 0.5013221$ c.s.u.

$\dot{y}_1 = - 0.7321113$ c.s.u.

$\dot{z}_1 = + 0.3102592$ c.s.u.

$t_1 = 2438030.5$ J.D.

The position coordinates of space station Iota B-3 at time of optimum transfer, initiated at $t_1$, are relayed to Von Angstrom as

$x_2 = - 1.3562699$ e.r.

$y_2 = + 2.9584968$ e.r.

$z_2 = + 3.0510008$ e.r.

$t_2 = 2438030.54622903$ J.D.

Since a great deal of the oxidizer has been lost, the total maximum impulsive velocity increment available to El Relampago has been estimated by Von Angstrom's calculations as 0.145 c.s.u. Can El Relampago successfully reach Iota B-3 if the amount of oxygen needed for survival of the crew reflects itself by a loss of 0.0008 c.s.u./min?

5. The position vectors of a geocentric Earth satellite, when $v_1 = 60°$, are given by

$x_1 = 2.000000 \qquad x_2 = -3.000000$

$y_1 = 0.000000 \qquad y_2 = \phantom{-}0.000000$

$z_1 = 0.000000 \qquad z_2 = \phantom{-}0.000000.$

What is the orbital eccentricity? Semimajor axis? Can more information be extracted about the orbit?

6. Geocentric space station Iota B-3 receives a distress call from the small space freighter, Albatross. The Albatross's computers have short-circuited in the middle of a complicated maneuver. Iota B-1's computers yield the space station's position in the right ascension-declination frame as

$x_{IB1} = 0.1502536$ e.r.
$y_{IB1} = 1.0004317$ e.r.
$z_{IB1} = 0.5023411$ e.r.
$t_{IB1} = 2438030.5$ J.D.,

and a radar strike at the same time of the Albatross relative to Iota B-1 is recorded as

$x_1 = 0.0254823$
$y_1 = 0.0238323$
$z_1 = 0.0976589$

Exactly 0.00360324 days later, a second strike is obtained as

$x_2 = 0.0231132$
$y_2 = 0.0123102$
$z_2 = 0.0135212$,

corresponding to Iota B-1's position

$x_{IB2} = -0.17954105$
$y_{IB2} = +0.91262160$
$z_{IB2} = +0.76463675$.

What is the orbit of the Albatross? Determine the corresponding orbital elements.

7. Derive the Hyperbolic form of the $v$-iteration technique.

8. Intelligence reports that a great amount of vampires are collecting in Transylvania. In the interest of national security determine the necessary ballistic trajectory to impact on the enemy. The attack forces require a launch from Cape Kennedy on 1960 June 15, $4^{hr}$, $10^{min}$, $5^{sec}$ Eastern Standard Time and impact on Transylvania on the same day at $10^{hr}$, $55^{min}$, $20^{sec}$ Transylvania Standard Time. The longitude, geodetic latitude, and elevation above the adopted ellipsoid ($f = 1/298.3$) of Kennedy and Transylvania are respectively given as

| $\lambda_E$ | $\phi$ | $H$ |
|---|---|---|
| 279.42° | 28.45° | 0 ft |
| 5.52° | 15.20° | 2000 ft |

9. At Laredo, Texas, $\lambda_E = 17^{hr}, 22^{min}, 27.744^{sec}, \phi = 27°, 37^{min}, 8.760^{sec}$, $H = 640$ meters, the following coordinates of 1958 Alpha are obtained

| U.T. (1960 JUNE) | $A$ | $h$ | $\rho$ |
|---|---|---|---|
| $11^{day}, 17^{hr} 37^{min} 31.7^{sec}$ | $227° 47^{min} 0.0^{sec}$ | $20° 1^{min} 0.0^{sec}$ | 1477.75 km |
| $11^{day}, 17^{hr} 40^{min} 31.7^{sec}$ | $298° 21^{min} 0.0^{sec}$ | $70° 17^{min} 0.0^{sec}$ | 679.87 km |
| $11^{day}, 17^{hr} 43^{min} 31.7^{sec}$ | $29° 34^{min} 0.0^{sec}$ | $22° 31^{min} 0.0^{sec}$ | 1411.17 km |

Assuming $f = 1/298.3$, $a_e = 1$. What are the classical elements of the orbit?

10. Show that in certain instances a better initial approximation of the ratio of sector to triangle is given by

$$y = 1 + \tfrac{4}{3}l.$$

## REFERENCES

1. M. A. Plummer, *An Introductory Treatise on Dynamical Astronomy*, Dover Publications, New York, 1960.
2. A. D. Dubyago, *The Determination of Orbits*, The Macmillan Company, New York, 1961.
3. F. R. Moulton, *An Introduction to Celestial Mechanics*, The Macmillan Company, New York, 1914.
4. J. Bauschinger and G. Stracke, *Tafeln zur Theoretischen Astronomie*, Verlag Von Wilhelm Engelmann, Leipzig, 1934.
5. S. Herrick, and A. Liu, *Two-Body Orbit Determination From Two Positions and Time of Flight*, Appendix A, Aeronutronic Pub. No. C-365, 1959.
6. R. M. L. Baker, Jr., and M. W. Makemson, *An Introduction to Astrodynamics*, Academic Press, New York, 1960.
7. E. T. Bell, *Men of Mathematics*, Simon Schuster, New York, 1937.
8. P. E. El' Yasberg, "The Determination of an Orbit From Two Positions," *Planetary Space Science*, Vol. II. 1963.
9. C. F. Gauss, *Theoria Motus*, Dover Publications, New York, 1963.
10. R. J. Gunkel, D. N. Lascody, and D. S. Merilees, "Impulsive Mid-Course Correction of an Interplanetary Transfer," Tenth International Congress, London, England, Douglas Aircraft Company Inc., Engineering Paper No. 804, 1959.
11. B. Douglas, Space Technology Laboratories, private communication.
12. K. P. Williams, *The Calculation of the Orbits of Asteroids and Comets*, The Principia Press, Bloomington, Indiana, 1934.
13. P. R. Escobal, *Eccentricity Iteration (A New Method for the Computation of an Orbit between Two Position Vectors with Specified Time Interval)*, TRW Space Technology Laboratories, 9882.3, November 1964.

# 7 Determination of an orbit from angles only

## 7.1 THE ANGLES-ONLY PROBLEM

In this chapter, the problem of determining an orbit only from angular data or observations will be investigated. This problem is actually a true observational one, in which the main participant is the observer. Standing on a given location upon the central planet an observer measures three sets of angular coordinates, say azimuth and elevation, at three different times and asks himself the question "What are the fundamental elements of the orbit?" In essence, the only instruments required by the observer to determine the desired orbit are an accurately calibrated clock and a small graduated scope. With just these rudimentary instruments, it would be possible to obtain the desired fundamental elements. Naturally, to a high degree of sophistication, photographic plates could be measured and angular data extracted to effect the determination with much higher precision.

Two of the methods presented in this chapter are of historical value, since the angles only problem attracted the attention of both Gauss and Laplace. In their day, this was one of the most pressing problems in mathematical astronomy. Today, a century and a half later, these methods are widely utilized and, in short, have stood the test of time. The last method, called herein the "double $r$ iteration," attacks the problem

**239**

of large data spreads, that is, angular measurements that are very far apart, perhaps several revolutions apart.

In this chapter, a preliminary transformation of angles is first discussed and then an entry into the Gaussian technique is initiated. The preliminary transformation may or may not be of interest but is presented here for the sake of completeness.

## 7.2  TRANSFORMATION OF NONINERTIAL OBSERVATIONS TO INERTIAL OBSERVATIONS

### 7.2.1  Azimuth-elevation into topocentric right ascension-declination

Consider an observer on a given meridian of a rotating oblate planet, say Earth (Figure 7.1). From a location on the surface of such a planet, it is possible to directly measure the elevation and azimuth angles of the object in its voyage across space. Consider this observer measuring, through a telescope or other apparatus, the azimuth and elevation angles at three different universal times, that is,

$$[A, h]_{t=t_1}, \qquad [A, h]_{t=t_2}, \qquad [A, h]_{t=t_3}. \qquad (7.1)$$

The central time date or epoch is conveniently taken to be $t_2$. At these separate universal times it is possible for the observer to calculate the sidereal time by means of Eq. 1.26 from the known east longitude $\lambda_E$.

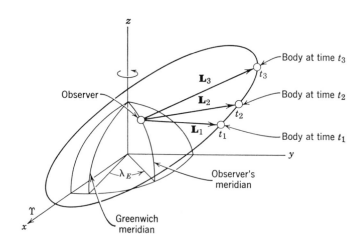

FIGURE 7.1   Observer viewing a satellite.

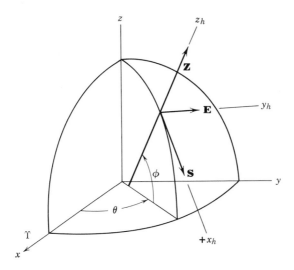

FIGURE 7.2    Introduction of the orthogonal set **S, E, Z**.

Immediately then, the topocentric right ascension-declination[1] of the unknown orbit at the three times, denoted by $\alpha_t$, $\delta_t$ can be obtained as follows.

Introduce a unit vector $\mathbf{L}_h$ along the slant range vector in the azimuth-elevation coordinate system (Chapter 4, System 1) whose components from Figure 4.3 are seen to be

$$\mathbf{L}_{hi} = \begin{bmatrix} L_{xh} \\ L_{yh} \\ L_{zh} \end{bmatrix}_i = \begin{bmatrix} -\cos A \cos h \\ \sin A \cos h \\ \sin h \end{bmatrix}_i, \quad i = 1, 2, 3. \tag{7.2}$$

By means of Figure 7.2, introduce the unit vectors, **S** pointing due south, **E** pointing due east, and **Z** pointing vertically outward along the normal from the observer's meridian (Chapter 4, System 3), and by projective principles, obtain

$$\mathbf{S}_i = \begin{bmatrix} S_x \\ S_y \\ S_z \end{bmatrix}_i = \begin{bmatrix} \sin \phi \cos \theta \\ \sin \phi \sin \theta \\ -\cos \phi \end{bmatrix}_i \tag{7.3}$$

$$\mathbf{E}_i = \begin{bmatrix} E_x \\ E_y \\ E_z \end{bmatrix}_i = \begin{bmatrix} -\sin \theta \\ \cos \theta \\ 0 \end{bmatrix}_i \tag{7.4}$$

[1] The word topocentric refers to the right ascension and declination measured with respect to the observer on the surface of the planet, not the geocenter.

$$\mathbf{Z}_i = \begin{bmatrix} Z_x \\ Z_y \\ Z_z \end{bmatrix}_i = \begin{bmatrix} \cos \theta \cos \phi \\ \sin \theta \cos \phi \\ \sin \phi \end{bmatrix}_i, \quad i = 1, 2, 3. \tag{7.5}$$

These are the direction cosines of a vector in the azimuth-elevation system $(x_h, y_h, z_h)$ with respect to the right ascension-declination system $(x, y, z)$. Hence

$$\mathbf{L}_i = \begin{bmatrix} L_x \\ L_y \\ L_z \end{bmatrix}_i = \begin{bmatrix} S_x & E_x & Z_x \\ S_y & E_y & Z_y \\ S_z & E_z & Z_z \end{bmatrix}_i \begin{bmatrix} L_{xh} \\ L_{yh} \\ L_{zh} \end{bmatrix}_i, \tag{7.6}$$

where $\mathbf{L}$ is a unit vector pointing at body $B$, that is, the object in a topocentric right ascension-declination coordinate frame. The unit vector $\mathbf{L}_h$ has been rotated at the observers position (topocenter) from the azimuth-elevation system (Chapter 4, System 1) to the right ascension-declination system (Chapter 4, System 2). $\mathbf{L}$ is now, owing to utilization of the sidereal time linkage, an inertial unit vector whose components are given by examination of Figure 4.4 as

$$\mathbf{L}_i = \begin{bmatrix} L_x \\ L_y \\ L_z \end{bmatrix}_i = \begin{bmatrix} \cos \delta_t \cos \alpha_t \\ \cos \delta_t \sin \alpha_t \\ \sin \delta_t \end{bmatrix}_i. \tag{7.7}$$

Apparently then,

$$\begin{aligned} \sin \delta_{ti} &= L_{zi} \\ \cos \delta_{ti} &= +\sqrt{1 - L_{zi}^2} \\ \sin \alpha_{ti} &= L_{yi}/\cos \delta_{ti} \\ \cos \alpha_{ti} &= L_{xi}/\cos \delta_{ti}, \end{aligned} \tag{7.8}$$

and the set (7.1) symbolically transforms as

$$\begin{aligned} [A, h]_{t=t_1} &\to \alpha_{t_1}, \delta_{t_1} \\ [A, h]_{t=t_2} &\to \alpha_{t_2}, \delta_{t_2} \\ [A, h]_{t=t_3} &\to \alpha_{t_3}, \delta_{t_3}. \end{aligned} \tag{7.9}$$

The observer is now in possession of three sets of inertial angular observations.[2]

[2] The transformed angles are still referred to as observations even though the angles are computed. Topocentric right ascensions-declinations can also be obtained by direct measurement.

### 7.2.2  Precession of observations

Observed right ascensions and declinations should always be transformed to the mean equinox at some particular epoch, say the beginning of the year, or perhaps some more definite epoch.[3]  Precession transformations, as indicated in Chapter 4, correct for the slow position drift or *precession* of the vernal equinox owing to the attractions of the Moon and Sun on the equatorial bulge of the Earth.

In order to refer an object to the proper frame of reference, convenience in analysis dictates the development of expressions for the direct correction of geocentric right ascensions and declinations. These angles, since referred to a rectangular coordinate frame, are directly affected by perturbative influences.

For example, consider that the right ascension, $\alpha_0$, and declination, $\delta_0$, of a given star are obtained from a star catalog, such as *Tabulae Regiomontanae* for a given year $X < Y$, where $Y$ is the present year. The question to be immediately answered is the determination of $\alpha$ and $\delta$ referred to the start of year $Y$ or perhaps more generally to some other arbitrary epoch within year $Y$.

By rather lengthy but direct analysis it can be shown [14] that the forward precession in right ascension and declination can be obtained with the assistance of the following rigorous trigonometric expressions:

$$\cos \delta \sin \alpha^* = \cos \delta_0 \sin (\alpha_0 + \zeta_0)$$
$$\cos \delta \cos \alpha^* = \cos \theta \cos \delta_0 \cos (\alpha_0 + \zeta_0) - \sin \theta \sin \delta_0 \qquad (7.10)$$
$$\sin \delta = \sin \theta \cos \delta_0 \cos (\alpha_0 + \zeta_0) + \cos \theta \sin \delta_0,$$

where the auxiliary angles $\zeta_0$ and $\theta$ can be deduced from Newcomb's theoretical and observational analysis [15] as

$$\zeta_0 = (2304''.250 + 1''.396T_0)T + 0''.302T^2 + 0''.018T^3$$
$$\theta = (2004''.682 - 0''.853T_0)T - 0''.426T^2 - 0''.042T^3 \qquad (7.11)$$

with $T_0$ defined as the number of tropical centuries measured since 1900.0 to the desired epoch of the coordinate system and $T$ the number of tropical centuries[4] measured since $T_0$, for example, for a coordinate system

---

[3] Appendix I treats the general transformation of rectangular coordinates from one epoch to another with Transformations 32 and 33.

[4] The number of days in a tropical year is rigorously given by $365^d.24219879 - 0^d.00000614\, T_u$. As can be seen the tropical year, measured from equinox to equinox, experiences a slow shift computable in terms of $T_u$, that is, the number of Julian centuries elapsed since 1900.0. In actual practice it suffices to approximate the length of the tropical year by $365^d.24219879$ so that $T \cong \{[\text{J.D.}] - [\text{J.D.}]_{T_0}\}/36524.219879$. A more accurate evaluation of $T$ is rarely needed.

referenced to 1900.0, $T_0 = 0.0$, while for a coordinate system referred to 1970.0, $T_0 = 0.7$.

Computation of $\zeta_0$ and $\theta$ permits the unique determination $\delta$, the sought-for precessed declination and the auxiliary angle $\alpha^*$. From $\alpha^*$ the corresponding precessed geocentric right ascension, $\alpha$ can be found from

$$\alpha = \alpha^* + z, \tag{7.12}$$

where

$$z = \zeta_0 + 0''.791 T^2.$$

When the observational data is to be precessed over a short span and the declination is not too high, say $|\delta| < 80°$, the backward reduction from the mean equinox of date to the desired epoch is approximated by evaluating the annual rates

$$\overline{\left(\frac{d\alpha}{dt}\right)} = m + n \sin \alpha \tan \delta$$

$$\overline{\left(\frac{d\delta}{dt}\right)} = n \cos \alpha, \tag{7.13}$$

where for a given time $\hat{T}$ in tropical centuries since 1900.0

$$m = 3^{\text{sec}}.07234 + 0^{\text{sec}}.00186 \, \hat{T}$$
$$n = 20''.0468 - 0''.0085 \, \hat{T}.$$

Having evaluated these mean or mid-time derivatives, the sought-for $\alpha$, $\delta$, referenced to the earlier epoch, are given by

$$\alpha = \alpha_0 + \overline{\left(\frac{d\alpha}{dt}\right)}(t - t_0), \quad t - t_0 < 0$$

$$\delta = \delta_0 + \overline{\left(\frac{d\delta}{dt}\right)}(t - t_0). \tag{7.14}$$

The inverse problem, of bringing old observations forward to a more recent epoch, that is,

$$\alpha = \alpha_0 + \overline{\left(\frac{d\alpha}{dt}\right)}(t - t_0), \quad t - t_0 > 0$$

$$\delta = \delta_0 + \overline{\left(\frac{d\delta}{dt}\right)}(t - t_0) \tag{7.15}$$

must also be solved by successive approximations, where as a first approximation for evaluation of the mean derivatives it is possible to take $\alpha = \alpha_0$, $\delta = \delta_0$. The previous formulas can be directly derived from Eqs. 7.10 with suitable approximations.

The previous analysis is of particular importance if right ascensions and declinations are determined from measurements of accurate photographic plates wherein the positions of reference stars are obtained from standard star charts, etc. When all the observations are referred to a common standard, the orbit determination process can commence. Once the orbit has been determined, the elements of this orbit, or more directly, the rectangular coordinates at the epoch of the determination, should be precessed backwards to some reference epoch, for example, the beginning of the year 1960.0 or some standard epoch. The standard precession and inverse precession transformations for rectangular coordinates are listed in Appendix I.

### 7.3  THE METHOD OF GAUSS (TRANSFORMATION OF ANGLES INTO POSITION VECTORS)

### 7.3.1  Preliminary approximation of the Gaussian method

A very fundamental and useful transformation from a set of angular data to a set of position vectors in inertial space can be obtained by consideration of three linearly dependent position vectors, $\mathbf{r}_1$, $\mathbf{r}_2$, $\mathbf{r}_3$. Since the orbit in Keplerian mechanics is a plane, and since the three position vectors are dependent, it should be possible to determine a set of scalars $a$, $b$, $c$, not all zero, such that

$$a\mathbf{r}_1 + b\mathbf{r}_2 + c\mathbf{r}_3 = 0, \tag{7.16}$$

or upon solving for the central date corresponding to $\mathbf{r}_2$ and denoting the new coefficients by $c_1$ and $c_3$,

$$\mathbf{r}_2 = c_1\mathbf{r}_1 + c_3\mathbf{r}_3. \tag{7.17}$$

Physically, by crossing $\mathbf{r}_2$ with $\mathbf{r}_1$ and $\mathbf{r}_3$, it is possible to see that

$$\begin{aligned} \mathbf{r}_1 \times \mathbf{r}_2 &= c_3\mathbf{r}_1 \times \mathbf{r}_3 \\ \mathbf{r}_3 \times \mathbf{r}_2 &= c_1\mathbf{r}_3 \times \mathbf{r}_1 \end{aligned} \tag{7.18}$$

or evaluating the cross products (Figure 7.3),

$$\begin{aligned} \mathbf{r}_1 \times \mathbf{r}_2 &= r_1 r_2 \sin \Delta v_{12}\mathbf{W} = 2A_{12}\mathbf{W} \\ \mathbf{r}_2 \times \mathbf{r}_3 &= r_2 r_3 \sin \Delta v_{23}\mathbf{W} = 2A_{23}\mathbf{W} \\ \mathbf{r}_1 \times \mathbf{r}_3 &= r_1 r_3 \sin \Delta v_{13}\mathbf{W} = 2A_{13}\mathbf{W}, \end{aligned} \tag{7.19}$$

where $A_{12}$, $A_{23}$, $A_{13}$ are the areas of the triangles formed between the respective radius vectors. Obviously then, from Eqs. 7.18,

$$\begin{aligned} A_{12}\mathbf{W} &= c_3 A_{13}\mathbf{W} \\ A_{23}\mathbf{W} &= c_1 A_{13}\mathbf{W} \end{aligned} \tag{7.20}$$

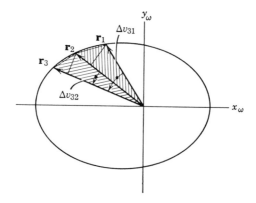

FIGURE 7.3    Physical interpretation of the cross products $\mathbf{r}_1 \times \mathbf{r}_2, \mathbf{r}_2 \times \mathbf{r}_3, \mathbf{r}_1 \times \mathbf{r}_3$.

or, upon dotting with $\mathbf{W}$, a unit vector normal to the orbit plane

$$c_1 = \frac{A_{23}}{A_{13}}, \qquad c_3 = \frac{A_{12}}{A_{13}}, \tag{7.21}$$

which are the coefficients of Eq. 7.17 as a function of the ratios of the areas formed by the respective radius vectors $\mathbf{r}_1$, $\mathbf{r}_2$, and $\mathbf{r}_3$.

It shall now be shown that these area ratios can be approximated as a function of modified time. Consider the expression for $A_{12}$,

$$A_{12} = \tfrac{1}{2}\mathbf{W} \cdot [\mathbf{r}_1 \times \mathbf{r}_2], \tag{7.22}$$

coupled with the solution of the fundamental equation, Section 3.9, at epoch $t = t_2$, that is,

$$\mathbf{r}_1 = f_1 \mathbf{r}_2 + g_1 \dot{\mathbf{r}}_2. \tag{7.23}$$

Substituting Eq. 7.23 into Eq. 7.22 yields

$$A_{12} = \tfrac{1}{2}\mathbf{W} \cdot [(f_1 \mathbf{r}_2 + g_1 \dot{\mathbf{r}}_2) \times \mathbf{r}_2] = -\tfrac{1}{2}hg_1, \tag{7.24}$$

since $\mathbf{W} \cdot (\mathbf{r}_2 \times \dot{\mathbf{r}}_2) = h$. Similarly $A_{23}$ can be expressed as

$$A_{23} = \tfrac{1}{2}\mathbf{W} \cdot [\mathbf{r}_2 \times (f_3 \mathbf{r}_2 + g_3 \dot{\mathbf{r}}_2)] = \tfrac{1}{2}hg_3. \tag{7.25}$$

The common area of the ratios $A_{13}$ can be obtained by noticing that

$$A_{13} = \tfrac{1}{2}\mathbf{W} \cdot [\mathbf{r}_1 \times \mathbf{r}_3] = \tfrac{1}{2}\mathbf{W} \cdot [(f_1 \mathbf{r}_2 + g_1 \dot{\mathbf{r}}_2) \times (f_3 \mathbf{r}_2 + g_3 \dot{\mathbf{r}}_2)] \tag{7.26}$$

or

$$A_{13} = \tfrac{1}{2}h(f_1 g_3 - f_3 g_1). \tag{7.27}$$

In terms of the $f$ and $g$ expansions, Eqs. 3.228 and 3.229, the area ratios are therefore given by

$$c_1 = \frac{g_3}{f_1 g_3 - f_3 g_1} \tag{7.28}$$

$$c_3 = \frac{-g_1}{f_1 g_3 - f_3 g_1}. \tag{7.29}$$

Explicitly expressing the $f$ and $g$ series as functions of $\tau$, with $t_2$ as the epoch time[5] (Section 3.9), that is,

$$f_i = 1 - \tfrac{1}{2} u_2 \tau_i^2 + 0(\tau_i^3) \tag{7.30}$$

$$g_i = \tau_i - \tfrac{1}{6} u_2 \tau_i^3 + 0(\tau_i^4), \quad i = 1, 3, \tag{7.31}$$

it is possible to form

$$f_1 g_3 - f_3 g_1 \cong \tau_3 - \tau_1 - \tfrac{1}{6} u_2 (\tau_3 - \tau_1)^3. \tag{7.32}$$

Introducing the definition $\tau_{13} \equiv \tau_3 - \tau_1$, the reciprocal becomes

$$(f_1 g_3 - f_3 g_1)^{-1} \cong \frac{1}{\tau_{13}} \left[ 1 + \frac{1}{6} u_2 \tau_{13}^2 \right]. \tag{7.33}$$

Hence it is a simple extension to evaluate

$$c_1 \cong \frac{\tau_3}{\tau_{13}} \left[ 1 + \frac{u_2}{6} (\tau_{13}^2 - \tau_3^2) \right] \tag{7.34}$$

$$c_3 \cong -\frac{\tau_1}{\tau_{13}} \left[ 1 + \frac{u_2}{6} (\tau_{13}^2 - \tau_1^2) \right]. \tag{7.35}$$

Equations 7.34 and 7.35 are nothing more than preliminary estimates of the ratios $c_1$ and $c_2$ needed in the iterative procedure to be developed for transforming the given angular measurements into position vectors.

Equation 7.17 can be modified by introduction of the vector triangle relation $\boldsymbol{\rho} = \mathbf{r} + \mathbf{R}$ (Section 3.11) to read

$$c_1(\boldsymbol{\rho}_1 - \mathbf{R}_1) + c_3(\boldsymbol{\rho}_3 - \mathbf{R}_3) - (\boldsymbol{\rho}_2 - \mathbf{R}_2) = \mathbf{0} \tag{7.36}$$

or

$$c_1 \boldsymbol{\rho}_1 + c_2 \boldsymbol{\rho}_2 + c_3 \boldsymbol{\rho}_3 = c_1 \mathbf{R}_1 + c_2 \mathbf{R}_2 + c_3 \mathbf{R}_3, \tag{7.37}$$

where $c_2 = -1$.

Introduction of the known unit vector $\mathbf{L}$, (Eq. 7.7), yields further modification as

$$c_1 \rho_1 \mathbf{L}_1 + c_2 \rho_2 \mathbf{L}_2 + c_3 \rho_3 \mathbf{L}_3 = \mathbf{G}, \tag{7.38}$$

[5] See reference [1], page 207, for a discussion showing that the choice of epoch minimizes calculation effort and certain errors in the method of Laplace, Section 7.4.

since $\mathbf{L}$ is directed along $\boldsymbol{\rho}$, and where, for convenience, the right-hand side of Eq. 7.37 is replaced by $\mathbf{G}$. Considering $c_1\rho_1$, $c_2\rho_2$, $c_3\rho_3$ as unknowns, the three component equations embodied in the vector relation (7.38) can be written in the convenient matrix form

$$\begin{bmatrix} L_{x1} & L_{x2} & L_{x3} \\ L_{y1} & L_{y2} & L_{y3} \\ L_{z1} & L_{z2} & L_{z3} \end{bmatrix} \begin{bmatrix} c_1\rho_1 \\ c_2\rho_2 \\ c_3\rho_3 \end{bmatrix} = \begin{bmatrix} G_x \\ G_y \\ G_z \end{bmatrix}. \tag{7.39}$$

By computing the determinant of the $\mathbf{L}_i$ matrix as

$$D = L_{x1}(L_{y2}L_{z3} - L_{z2}L_{y3}) - L_{x2}(L_{y1}L_{z3} - L_{z1}L_{y3}) \\ + L_{x3}(L_{y1}L_{z2} - L_{z1}L_{y2}), \tag{7.40}$$

it is possible to form the inverse of the $\mathbf{L}_i$ matrix and write

$$\begin{bmatrix} c_1\rho_1 \\ c_2\rho_2 \\ c_3\rho_3 \end{bmatrix} = \begin{bmatrix} a_{11} & a_{12} & a_{13} \\ a_{21} & a_{22} & a_{23} \\ a_{31} & a_{32} & a_{33} \end{bmatrix} \begin{bmatrix} G_x \\ G_y \\ G_z \end{bmatrix}, \tag{7.41}$$

where

$$\begin{aligned} a_{11} &= +(L_{y2}L_{z3} - L_{y3}L_{z2})/D \\ a_{12} &= -(L_{x2}L_{z3} - L_{x3}L_{z2})/D \\ a_{13} &= +(L_{x2}L_{y3} - L_{x3}L_{y2})/D \\ a_{21} &= -(L_{y1}L_{z3} - L_{y3}L_{z1})/D \\ a_{22} &= +(L_{x1}L_{z3} - L_{x3}L_{z1})/D \\ a_{23} &= -(L_{x1}L_{y3} - L_{x3}L_{y1})/D \\ a_{31} &= +(L_{y1}L_{z2} - L_{y2}L_{z1})/D \\ a_{32} &= -(L_{x1}L_{z2} - L_{x2}L_{z1})/D \\ a_{33} &= +(L_{x1}L_{y2} - L_{x2}L_{y1})/D. \end{aligned} \tag{7.42}$$

Evidently, choosing the central date as most convenient, it is possible to perform the matrix multiplication indicated by Eq. 7.41 and obtain

$$c_2\rho_2 = a_{21}G_x + a_{22}G_y + a_{23}G_z. \tag{7.43}$$

Now, for convenience, if the equations

$$c_1 \cong A_1 + B_1 u_2, \qquad c_3 \cong A_3 + B_3 u_2, \tag{7.44}$$

where from Eqs. 7.34 and 7.35,

$$A_1 \equiv \frac{\tau_3}{\tau_{13}}, \qquad B_1 \equiv \frac{1}{6}\frac{\tau_3}{\tau_{13}}(\tau_{13}{}^2 - \tau_3{}^2),$$

$$A_3 \equiv -\frac{\tau_1}{\tau_{13}}, \qquad B_3 \equiv -\frac{1}{6}\frac{\tau_1}{\tau_{13}}(\tau_{13}{}^2 - \tau_1{}^2), \tag{7.45}$$

and vectors **A**, **B**, where

$$\mathbf{A} \equiv [A_1, -1, A_3]$$
$$\mathbf{B} \equiv [B_1, 0, B_3],$$
(7.46)

along with vectors[6] **X**, **Y**, **Z**, that is

$$\mathbf{X} \equiv [X_1, X_2, X_3]$$
$$\mathbf{Y} \equiv [Y_1, Y_2, Y_3]$$
$$\mathbf{Z} \equiv [Z_1, Z_2, Z_3],$$
(7.47)

where **X**, **Y**, **Z** are formed from the components of $\mathbf{R}_i$ are introduced, it is possible to verify by direct expansion of Eq. 7.43 that

$$\rho_2 = A_2{}^* + B_2{}^* u_2,$$
(7.48)

with

$$A_2{}^* \equiv -(a_{21}\mathbf{A} \cdot \mathbf{X} + a_{22}\mathbf{A} \cdot \mathbf{Y} + a_{23}\mathbf{A} \cdot \mathbf{Z})$$
$$B_2{}^* \equiv -(a_{21}\mathbf{B} \cdot \mathbf{X} + a_{22}\mathbf{B} \cdot \mathbf{Y} + a_{23}\mathbf{B} \cdot \mathbf{Z}).$$
(7.49)

Similarly, expressions for $\rho_1$ and $\rho_3$ may be obtained by means of the **A**, **B**, **X**, **Y**, **Z** vectors[7] as:

$$\rho_1 = \frac{A_1{}^* + B_1{}^* u_2}{A_1 + B_1 u_2}$$
(7.50)

$$\rho_3 = \frac{A_3{}^* + B_3{}^* u_2}{A_3 + B_3 u_2},$$
(7.51)

where

$$A_1{}^* \equiv (a_{11}\mathbf{A} \cdot \mathbf{X} + a_{12}\mathbf{A} \cdot \mathbf{Y} + a_{13}\mathbf{A} \cdot \mathbf{Z})$$
$$B_1{}^* \equiv (a_{11}\mathbf{B} \cdot \mathbf{X} + a_{12}\mathbf{B} \cdot \mathbf{Y} + a_{13}\mathbf{B} \cdot \mathbf{Z})$$
$$A_3{}^* \equiv (a_{31}\mathbf{A} \cdot \mathbf{X} + a_{32}\mathbf{A} \cdot \mathbf{Y} + a_{33}\mathbf{A} \cdot \mathbf{Z})$$
$$B_3{}^* \equiv (a_{31}\mathbf{B} \cdot \mathbf{X} + a_{32}\mathbf{B} \cdot \mathbf{Y} + a_{33}\mathbf{B} \cdot \mathbf{Z}).$$
(7.52)

Equations 7.48, 7.50, and 7.51 still contain the unknown parameter $u_2$, which has been previously defined as $u_2 \equiv \mu/r_2{}^3$ (Eq. 3.212). Thus, to satisfy the aim of the analysis, the determination of the magnitude of the radius vector at the central date $r_2$, another equation is needed.

---

[6] In order to save space, the vector components are shown in a row vector instead of the usual column vector.

[7] This formulation is very convenient if a dot product machine function is available.

Consider the fundamental relation, Eq. 3.260,

$$\mathbf{r}_i = \boldsymbol{\rho}_i - \mathbf{R}_i, \quad i = 1, 2, 3, \tag{7.53}$$

or the dot product taken upon itself, that is,

$$r_i^2 = (\boldsymbol{\rho}_i - \mathbf{R}_i) \cdot (\boldsymbol{\rho}_i - \mathbf{R}_i) = \rho_i^2 - 2\boldsymbol{\rho}_i \cdot \mathbf{R}_i + R_i^2. \tag{7.54}$$

Furthermore, utilizing $\boldsymbol{\rho} = \rho\mathbf{L}$, an independent equation reflecting a geometric constraint for simultaneous solution with Eq. 7.48 is

$$r_2^2 = \rho_2^2 - 2\rho_2\mathbf{L}_2 \cdot \mathbf{R}_2 + R_2^2. \tag{7.55}$$

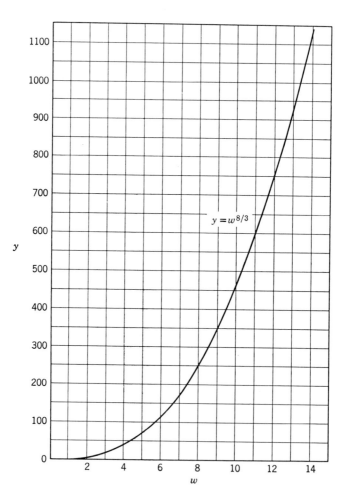

FIGURE 7.4   Graph of $y = w^{8/3}$.

The dot products $L_i \cdot R_i$ are known from the angular observations and the station location.   To be explicit, at the central date, let

$$C_\psi \equiv -2(X_2 L_{x2} + Y_2 L_{y2} + Z_2 L_{z2}), \tag{7.56}$$

and rewrite the system to be solved as

$$\rho_2 = A_2{}^* + \frac{\mu B_2{}^*}{r_2{}^3} \tag{7.57}$$

$$r_2{}^2 = \rho_2{}^2 + \rho_2 C_\psi + R_2{}^2. \tag{7.58}$$

Substitution of Eq. 7.57 into Eq. 7.58 results in

$$f(r_2) \equiv r_2{}^8 - (C_\psi A_2{}^* + A_2{}^{*2} + R_2{}^2)r_2{}^6$$
$$- \mu(C_\psi B_2{}^* + 2A_2{}^* B_2{}^*)r_2{}^3 - \mu^2 B_2{}^{*2} = 0. \tag{7.59}$$

A positive root of this equation will therefore provide an estimate of the magnitude of $r_2$ at the central date.   It is possible to obtain a rather rapid estimate of the root by considering the transformation $r_2 = w^{1/3}$, so that Eq. 7.59 becomes

$$w^{8/3} - (C_\psi A_2{}^* + A_2{}^{*2} + R_2{}^2)w^2 - \mu(C_\psi B_2{}^* + 2A_2{}^* B_2{}^*)w$$
$$- \mu^2 B_2{}^{*2} = 0. \tag{7.60}$$

Certainly, then, if the graph

$$y = w^{8/3} \tag{7.61}$$

is accurately constructed and available, see Figures 7.4 and 7.5, the parabola

$$y = (C_\psi A_2{}^* + A_2{}^{*2} + R_2{}^2)w^2 + \mu(C_\psi B_2{}^* + 2A_2{}^* B_2{}^*)w + \mu^2 B_2{}^{*2} \tag{7.62}$$

may be superimposed by plotting.   The absissa of intersection of Eqs. 7.61 and 7.62 will be the cube of a positive root of the eighth degree equation in $r_2$.[8]

Once an approximate value of the root of Eq. 7.59 is known, a Newton procedure of the form

$$(r_2)_{n+1} = (r_2)_n - \left(\frac{f(r_2)}{f'(r_2)}\right)_n, \quad n = 1, 2, \ldots, q, \tag{7.63}$$

will refine the desired root.

[8] An alternate solution of Eqs. 7.57 and 7.58 is discussed in Section 7.5.

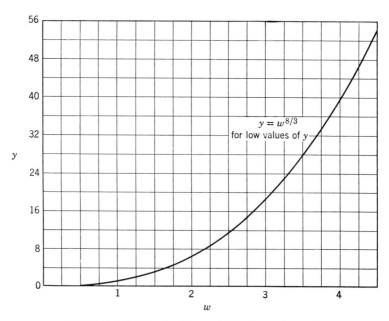

FIGURE 7.5    Graph of $y = w^{8/3}$ for low values of $y$.

Immediately then,

$$u_2 = \frac{\mu}{r_2{}^3},$$    (7.64)

and by Eqs. 7.48, 7.50, and 7.51, the slant ranges $\rho_1$, $\rho_2$, and $\rho_3$ at each date, may be computed. Finally, with the understanding that these are all approximate values due to the truncation of terms in Eqs. 7.30 and 7.31, the vector equation

$$\mathbf{r}_i = \rho_i \mathbf{L}_i - \mathbf{R}_i, \quad i = 1, 2, 3,$$    (7.65)

yields the three components of $\mathbf{r}_i$ at each time.

### 7.3.2    Improving the accuracy

To improve the accuracy of the transformation, let the Lagrange interpolation formula (see reference [8]),

$$\mathbf{r}(\tau) = \sum_{i=0}^{n} \mathbf{r}_i \frac{\displaystyle\prod_{k \neq i}(\tau - \tau_k)}{\displaystyle\prod_{k \neq i}(\tau_i - \tau_k)},$$    (7.66)

be introduced. Hence, for the previous $\mathbf{r}_i$, taking $n = 3$,

$$\mathbf{r}(\tau) = \mathbf{r}_1 \frac{(\tau - \tau_2)(\tau - \tau_3)}{(\tau_1 - \tau_2)(\tau_1 - \tau_3)} + \mathbf{r}_2 \frac{(\tau - \tau_1)(\tau - \tau_3)}{(\tau_2 - \tau_1)(\tau_2 - \tau_3)}$$
$$+ \mathbf{r}_3 \frac{(\tau - \tau_1)(\tau - \tau_2)}{(\tau_3 - \tau_2)(\tau_3 - \tau_1)}. \quad (7.67)$$

This equation yields a modified time curve fit of the sets $[x_1, x_2, x_3]$, $[y_1, y_2, y_3]$, $[z_1, z_2, z_3]$. With this curve fit it will be possible to numerically differentiate and obtain pertinent modified time derivatives. These, as shall be presently shown, will be used to improve the slant ranges $\rho_i$ and in turn recompute the $\mathbf{r}_i$, etc., each time, improving the results.[9]

A simplification of Eq. 7.67 can be effected by noticing that by definition $\tau_2 = 0$, so that

$$\mathbf{r}(\tau) = \frac{\tau(\tau - \tau_3)}{\tau_1(\tau_1 - \tau_3)} \mathbf{r}_1 + \frac{(\tau - \tau_1)(\tau - \tau_3)}{\tau_1\tau_3} \mathbf{r}_2 + \frac{\tau(\tau - \tau_1)}{\tau_3(\tau_3 - \tau_1)} \mathbf{r}_3. \quad (7.68)$$

Furthermore, differentiation yields

$$\dot{\mathbf{r}}(\tau) = \frac{(2\tau - \tau_3)}{\tau_1(\tau_1 - \tau_3)} \mathbf{r}_1 + \frac{(2\tau - \tau_3 - \tau_1)}{\tau_1\tau_3} \mathbf{r}_2 + \frac{(2\tau - \tau_1)}{\tau_3(\tau_3 - \tau_1)} \mathbf{r}_3, \quad (7.69)$$

and evaluation at $\tau_2 = 0$ produces the simple formula for $\dot{\mathbf{r}}(\tau_2)$,

$$\dot{\mathbf{r}}_2 = -\frac{\tau_3}{\tau_1(\tau_1 - \tau_3)} \mathbf{r}_1 - \frac{(\tau_3 + \tau_1)}{\tau_1\tau_3} \mathbf{r}_2 - \frac{\tau_1}{\tau_3(\tau_3 - \tau_1)} \mathbf{r}_3, \quad (7.70)$$

in terms of the known $\tau_i$ and $\mathbf{r}_i$. Evidently then,

$$r_2 = +\sqrt{\mathbf{r}_2 \cdot \mathbf{r}_2} \quad (7.71)$$

$$V_2 = +\sqrt{\dot{\mathbf{r}}_2 \cdot \dot{\mathbf{r}}_2} \quad (7.72)$$

$$\dot{r}_2 = \frac{\mathbf{r}_2 \cdot \dot{\mathbf{r}}_2}{r_2}, \quad (7.73)$$

and use of the $f$ and $g$ functions,

$$f_1 = f(V_2, r_2, \dot{r}_2, \tau_1) \quad (7.74)$$

$$f_3 = f(V_2, r_2, \dot{r}_2, \tau_3) \quad (7.75)$$

$$g_1 = g(V_2, r_2, \dot{r}_2, \tau_1) \quad (7.76)$$

$$g_3 = g(V_2, r_2, \dot{r}_2, \tau_3), \quad (7.77)$$

[9] See reference [1], page 236.

permits the $c_i$ to be directly recomputed from Eqs. 7.28 and 7.29 as

$$c_1 = \frac{g_3}{f_1 g_3 - f_3 g_1}, \qquad c_3 = \frac{-g_1}{f_1 g_3 - f_3 g_1}. \tag{7.78}$$

Better values of $\rho_i$ are obtained by virtue of Eq. 7.41, so that

$$\rho_1 = \frac{1}{c_1}(a_{11}G_x + a_{12}G_y + a_{13}G_z)$$

$$\rho_2 = -(a_{21}G_x + a_{22}G_y + a_{23}G_z) \tag{7.79}$$

$$\rho_3 = \frac{1}{c_3}(a_{31}G_x + a_{32}G_y + a_{33}G_z),$$

where, as before

$$\mathbf{G} \equiv c_1\mathbf{R}_1 + c_2\mathbf{R}_2 + c_3\mathbf{R}_3. \tag{7.80}$$

Eq. 7.65 can now be used to recompute the $\mathbf{r}_i$ and the whole process repeated until the $\rho_i$ stop varying. The convergence of the previous iterative loop has not really undergone much investigation; it is suggested by Moulton [1].

### 7.3.3   Improving the accuracy (Gibbsian transformation)

In the previous section, use of the Lagrange interpolating polynomial permitted the determination of $\dot{\mathbf{r}}$ at the central date in the Gaussian reduction to the order $\tau^3$. This section is concerned with obtaining a transformation from three radius vectors at different times to a velocity vector at the middle time, that is,

$$\mathbf{r}_1(\tau_1), \mathbf{r}_2(\tau_2), \mathbf{r}_3(\tau_3) \rightarrow \dot{\mathbf{r}}_2(\tau_2)$$

with a relatively high degree of accuracy. It should be noticed that this formula will be of direct benefit in the previous section.

Remembering the definition of the modified time variable,

$$\tau_{ij} = k(t_j - t_i), \tag{7.81}$$

where $t_i$ is the epoch time, it is possible to perform a Taylor expansion for $\mathbf{r}_j$ as follows

$$\mathbf{r}_j = \mathbf{r}_2 + \tau_{ij}\dot{\mathbf{r}}_2 + \tau_{ij}{}^2\frac{\ddot{\mathbf{r}}_2}{2} + \tau_{ij}{}^3\frac{\dddot{\mathbf{r}}_2}{6}\ldots, \quad j = 1, 3, \tag{7.82}$$

which, when written for time 1 and 3, yields the system

$$\mathbf{r}_1 - \mathbf{r}_2 = -\tau_{12}\dot{\mathbf{r}}_2 + \tau_{12}{}^2\frac{\ddot{\mathbf{r}}_2}{2} - \tau_{12}{}^3\frac{\dddot{\mathbf{r}}_2}{6} + \tau_{12}{}^4\frac{\overset{IV}{\mathbf{r}_2}}{24} + \cdots \qquad (7.83)$$

$$\mathbf{r}_3 - \mathbf{r}_2 = \tau_{23}\dot{\mathbf{r}}_2 + \tau_{23}{}^2\frac{\ddot{\mathbf{r}}_2}{2} + \tau_{23}{}^3\frac{\dddot{\mathbf{r}}_2}{6} + \tau_{23}{}^4\frac{\overset{IV}{\mathbf{r}_2}}{24} + \cdots \qquad (7.84)$$

Multiplying Eq. 7.83 by $\tau_{23}$, and Eq. 7.84 by $\tau_{12}$, and adding, eliminates $\dot{\mathbf{r}}_2$ so that

$$\tau_{23}\mathbf{r}_1 - \tau_{13}\mathbf{r}_2 + \tau_{12}\mathbf{r}_3 = \tau_{12}\tau_{23}\tau_{13}$$

$$\times \left[\frac{\ddot{\mathbf{r}}_2}{2} + (\tau_{23} - \tau_{12})\frac{\dddot{\mathbf{r}}_2}{6} + (\tau_{12}{}^2 - \tau_{12}\tau_{23} + \tau_{23}{}^2)\frac{\overset{IV}{\mathbf{r}_2}}{24} + \cdots \right].$$
$$(7.85)$$

Multiplying Eq. 7.83 by $-\tau_{23}{}^2$, and Eq. 7.84 by $\tau_{12}{}^2$, and adding, eliminates $\ddot{\mathbf{r}}_2$ so that

$$-\tau_{23}{}^2\mathbf{r}_1 + (\tau_{23}{}^2 - \tau_{12}{}^2)\mathbf{r}_2 + \tau_{12}{}^2\mathbf{r}_3 = \tau_{12}\tau_{23}\tau_{13}$$

$$\times \left[\dot{\mathbf{r}}_2 + \tau_{12}\tau_{23}\frac{\dddot{\mathbf{r}}_2}{6} + \tau_{12}\tau_{23}(\tau_{23} - \tau_{12})\frac{\overset{IV}{\mathbf{r}_2}}{24} + \cdots \right]. \qquad (7.86)$$

Differentiating Eqs. 7.85 and 7.86 yields

$$\tau_{23}\ddot{\mathbf{r}}_1 - \tau_{13}\ddot{\mathbf{r}}_2 + \tau_{12}\ddot{\mathbf{r}}_3 = \tau_{12}\tau_{23}\tau_{13}\frac{\overset{IV}{\mathbf{r}_2}}{2} + 0(\overset{V}{r_2}) \qquad (7.87)$$

$$-\tau_{23}{}^2\ddot{\mathbf{r}}_1 + (\tau_{23}{}^2 - \tau_{12}{}^2)\ddot{\mathbf{r}}_2 + \tau_{12}{}^2\ddot{\mathbf{r}}_3 = \tau_{12}\tau_{23}\tau_{13}\ddot{\mathbf{r}}_2 + 0(\overset{IV}{r_2}). \qquad (7.88)$$

If all derivatives of order greater than $\overset{IV}{\mathbf{r}_2}$ in Eq. 7.87, and $\ddot{\mathbf{r}}_2$ in Eq. 7.88 are neglected, it is possible to solve for $\overset{IV}{\mathbf{r}_2}$ and $\ddot{\mathbf{r}}_2$ and substitute the respective derivatives back into Eq. 7.86

$$-\tau_{23}{}^2\mathbf{r}_1 + (\tau_{23}{}^2 - \tau_{12}{}^2)\mathbf{r}_2 + \tau_{12}{}^2\mathbf{r}_3$$

$$= \tau_{12}\tau_{23}\tau_{13}\left[\dot{\mathbf{r}}_2 - \tau_{23}\frac{\ddot{\mathbf{r}}_1}{12} + (\tau_{23} - \tau_{12})\frac{\ddot{\mathbf{r}}_2}{12} + \tau_{12}\frac{\ddot{\mathbf{r}}}{12}\right]. \qquad (7.89)$$

By rearranging terms, it is possible to write

$$\tau_{12}\tau_{23}\tau_{13}\dot{\mathbf{r}}_2 = -\tau_{23}{}^2\mathbf{r}_1 + (\tau_{23}{}^2 - \tau_{12}{}^2)\mathbf{r}_2 + \tau_{12}{}^2\mathbf{r}_3$$

$$- \frac{\tau_{12}\tau_{23}\tau_{13}}{12}[-\tau_{23}\ddot{\mathbf{r}}_1 + (\tau_{23} - \tau_{12})\ddot{\mathbf{r}}_2 + \tau_{12}\ddot{\mathbf{r}}_3 + \cdots]. \qquad (7.90)$$

The main idea of the Gibbsian approach [4] is to eliminate $\ddot{\mathbf{r}}_1$, $\ddot{\mathbf{r}}_2$, and $\ddot{\mathbf{r}}_3$ in Eq. 7.90 by invoking the inverse square law

$$\ddot{\mathbf{r}}_i = -\mu \frac{\mathbf{r}_i}{r_i^3}. \tag{7.91}$$

Hence

$$\dot{\mathbf{r}}_2 = -\frac{\tau_{23}^2}{\tau_{12}\tau_{23}\tau_{13}} \mathbf{r}_1 + \frac{(\tau_{23}^2 - \tau_{12}^2)}{\tau_{12}\tau_{23}\tau_{13}} \mathbf{r}_2 + \frac{\tau_{12}^2}{\tau_{12}\tau_{23}\tau_{13}} \mathbf{r}_3$$

$$- \frac{\mu}{12} \left[ \tau_{23} \frac{\mathbf{r}_1}{r_1^3} - (\tau_{23} - \tau_{12}) \frac{\mathbf{r}_2}{r_2^3} - \tau_{12} \frac{\mathbf{r}_3}{r_3^3} \right], \tag{7.92}$$

and if

$$\bar{H}_1 \equiv \frac{\mu\tau_3}{12}, \qquad \bar{G}_1 \equiv -\frac{\tau_3}{\tau_1\tau_{13}},$$

$$\bar{H}_3 \equiv -\frac{\mu\tau_1}{12}, \qquad \bar{G}_3 \equiv -\frac{\tau_1}{\tau_3\tau_{13}}, \tag{7.93}$$

$$\bar{H}_2 \equiv \bar{H}_1 - \bar{H}_3, \qquad \bar{G}_2 \equiv \bar{G}_1 - \bar{G}_3,$$

with the understanding that the epoch time is $t_2$, Eq. 7.92 becomes

$$\dot{\mathbf{r}}_2 = -\bar{G}_1\mathbf{r}_1 + \bar{G}_2\mathbf{r}_2 + \bar{G}_3\mathbf{r}_3 - \bar{H}_1 \frac{\mathbf{r}_1}{r_1^3} + \bar{H}_2 \frac{\mathbf{r}_2}{r_2^3} + \bar{H}_3 \frac{\mathbf{r}_3}{r_3^3}. \tag{7.94}$$

Furthermore, if

$$d_i \equiv \bar{G}_i + \frac{\bar{H}_i}{r_i^3}, \quad i = 1, 2, 3,$$

then,

$$\dot{\mathbf{r}}_2 = -d_1\mathbf{r}_1 + d_2\mathbf{r}_2 + d_3\mathbf{r}_3, \tag{7.95}$$

and the sought-for transformation has been effected to the order $(\overset{v}{r})\tau^5/5!$. This equation is known in the literature as the Herrick–Gibbs equation and is a much more exact expression for the velocity vector at the central date than Eq. 7.70.

### 7.3.4  Improving the accuracy (Gaussian equations)

The two previous methods are dependent upon the introduction of some type of approximation, but offer the advantage of a rapid correction technique to the preliminary approximation of the Gaussian reduction. In this section, the Gaussian equations from the sector to triangle theory developed in Chapter 6 will be applied to attain an iterative correction free of approximation and series expansion.

Consider the two radius vectors $\mathbf{r}_1$ and $\mathbf{r}_2$, approximately known from Section 7.3.1. Since the time interval is also known, it is possible to determine the $m$ and $l$ constants of the sector to triangle theory (Section 6.2.7). Evidently then, by writing the first and second equations of Gauss, referenced in Section 6.2.5, as

$$y_{12}{}^2 = \frac{m_{12}}{l_{12} + x} \tag{7.96}$$

$$y_{12}{}^2(y_{12} - 1) = m_{12}X, \tag{7.97}$$

where

$$x = \frac{1}{2}\left[1 - \cos\left(\frac{E_2 - E_1}{2}\right)\right]$$

$$X = \frac{E_2 - E_1 - \sin(E_2 - E_1)}{\sin^3\left(\dfrac{E_2 - E_1}{2}\right)}, \tag{7.98}$$

a system of two equations in two unknowns is obtained, that is, $y_{12}$ and $E_2 - E_1$. Any successive approximation scheme or iterative technique can now be utilized to effect a solution of the above system.[10]    By exactly analogous means, utilization of $\mathbf{r}_1$ and $\mathbf{r}_3$ will result in an approximation for $y_{13}$, and utilization of $\mathbf{r}_2$ and $\mathbf{r}_3$ will yield through the preliminary values of $m_{23}$ and $l_{23}$, the ratio $y_{23}$. But, from the definition of the $c_i$,

$$c_1 = \frac{y_{13}\tau_3}{y_{23}\tau_{13}}, \qquad c_3 = -\frac{y_{13}\tau_1}{y_{12}\tau_{13}}, \tag{7.99}$$

and so the set of Eqs. 7.79 yield better values for $\rho_i$, and again,

$$\mathbf{r}_i = \rho_i \mathbf{L}_i - \mathbf{R}_i \tag{7.100}$$

can be used to improve the $\mathbf{r}_i$. At this point, if further improvement is desired, $m_{ij}$ and $l_{ij}$ may be recalculated and the process from Eq. 7.96 to 7.100 repeated. The convergence of this process is very rapid for small angular spreads. It is also evident that a by-product of the iterative loop is $(E_2 - E_1)$, and so, by Eq. 6.52,

$$\sqrt{a} = \frac{\tau\sqrt{\mu}}{2y_{12}\sqrt{r_2 r_1}\cos\left(\dfrac{v_2 - v_1}{2}\right)\sin\left(\dfrac{E_2 - E_1}{2}\right)}. \tag{7.101}$$

[10] See Exercise 10.

The $f$ and $g$ coefficients, computed by

$$f = 1 - \frac{a}{r_1} [1 - \cos (E_2 - E_1)]$$

$$g = \tau_1 - \frac{a^{3/2}}{\sqrt{\mu}} [E_2 - E_1 - \sin (E_2 - E_1)],$$

$$(7.102)$$

when coupled with

$$\dot{\mathbf{r}}_1 = \frac{\mathbf{r}_2 - f\mathbf{r}_1}{g},$$

$$(7.103)$$

suffices to determine the orbit, since $\mathbf{r}_1$ and $\dot{\mathbf{r}}_1$ have been found.

### 7.3.5  Computational algorithm

Given $\alpha_i$, $\delta_i$, $\phi_i$, $\lambda_{Ei}$, $H_i$, $t_i$ for $i = 1, 2, 3$, and the constants $d\theta/dt$, $f$, $a_e$, $\mu$, $k$, compute the following:

$$\tau_1 = k(t_1 - t_2)$$

$$(7.104)$$

$$\tau_3 = k(t_3 - t_2)$$

$$(7.105)$$

$$\tau_{13} = \tau_3 - \tau_1$$

$$(7.106)$$

$$A_1 = \tau_3/\tau_{13}$$

$$(7.107)$$

$$B_1 = +(\tau_{13}^2 - \tau_3^2)A_1/6$$

$$(7.108)$$

$$A_3 = -\tau_1/\tau_{13}$$

$$(7.109)$$

$$B_3 = +(\tau_{13}^2 - \tau_1^2)A_3/6.$$

$$(7.110)$$

For $i = 1, 2, 3$, compute

$$L_{xi} = \cos \delta_{ti} \cos \alpha_{ti}$$

$$(7.111)$$

$$L_{yi} = \cos \delta_{ti} \sin \alpha_{ti}$$

$$(7.112)$$

$$L_{zi} = \sin \delta_{ti}.$$

$$(7.113)$$

Obtain the Greenwich sidereal time $\theta_{g0}$ from Eq. 1.27, and continue calculating with

$$\theta_i = \theta_{g0} + \frac{d\theta}{dt} (t_i - t_0) + \lambda_{Ei}, \ t_0 = t_2$$

$$(7.114)$$

$$G_{1i} = \frac{a_e}{\sqrt{1 - (2f - f^2) \sin^2 \phi_i}} + H_i$$

$$(7.115)$$

$$G_{2i} = \frac{(1 - f)^2 a_e}{\sqrt{1 - (2f - f^2) \sin^2 \phi_i}} + H_i$$

$$(7.116)$$

$$X_i = -G_{1i} \cos \phi_i \cos \theta_i$$

$$Y_i = -G_{1i} \cos \phi_i \sin \theta_i$$

$$Z_i = -G_{2i} \sin \phi_i.$$

$$(7.117)$$

Compute the following:

$$D = L_{x1}(L_{y2}L_{z3} - L_{z2}L_{y3}) - L_{x2}(L_{y1}L_{z3} - L_{z1}L_{y3})$$
$$+ L_{x3}(L_{y1}L_{z2} - L_{z1}L_{y2}) \tag{7.118}$$

$$a_{11} = +(L_{y2}L_{z3} - L_{y3}L_{z2})/D$$
$$a_{12} = -(L_{x2}L_{z3} - L_{x3}L_{z2})/D$$
$$a_{13} = +(L_{x2}L_{y3} - L_{x3}L_{y2})/D$$
$$a_{21} = -(L_{y1}L_{z3} - L_{y3}L_{z1})/D$$
$$a_{22} = +(L_{x1}L_{z3} - L_{x3}L_{z1})/D \tag{7.119}$$
$$a_{23} = -(L_{x1}L_{y3} - L_{x3}L_{y1})/D$$
$$a_{31} = +(L_{y1}L_{z2} - L_{y2}L_{z1})/D$$
$$a_{32} = -(L_{x1}L_{z2} - L_{x2}L_{z1})/D$$
$$a_{33} = +(L_{x1}L_{y2} - L_{x2}L_{y1})/D,$$

and form the vectors

$$\mathbf{A} = [A_1, -1, A_3] \tag{7.120}$$
$$\mathbf{B} = [B_1, \ 0, \ B_3] \tag{7.121}$$
$$\mathbf{X} = [X_1, X_2, X_3] \tag{7.122}$$
$$\mathbf{Y} = [Y_1, Y_2, Y_3] \tag{7.123}$$
$$\mathbf{Z} = [Z_1, Z_2, Z_3]. \tag{7.124}$$

Evaluate the coefficients

$$A_2{}^* = -(a_{21}\mathbf{A} \cdot \mathbf{X} + a_{22}\mathbf{A} \cdot \mathbf{Y} + a_{23}\mathbf{A} \cdot \mathbf{Z})$$
$$B_2{}^* = -(a_{21}\mathbf{B} \cdot \mathbf{X} + a_{22}\mathbf{B} \cdot \mathbf{Y} + a_{23}\mathbf{B} \cdot \mathbf{Z}) \tag{7.125}$$
$$C_\psi = -2(X_2 L_{x2} + Y_2 L_{y2} + Z_2 L_{z2}) \tag{7.126}$$
$$R_2{}^2 = X_2{}^2 + Y_2{}^2 + Z_2{}^2 \tag{7.127}$$
$$a = -(C_\psi A_2{}^* + A_2{}^{*2} + R_2{}^2) \tag{7.128}$$
$$b = -\mu(C_\psi B_2{}^* + 2A_2{}^* B_2{}^*) \tag{7.129}$$
$$c = -\mu^2 B_2{}^{*2}. \tag{7.130}$$

Solve

$$r_2{}^8 + ar_2{}^6 + br_2{}^3 + c = 0 \tag{7.131}$$

to obtain the applicable real root $r_2$ and continue calculating with

$$u_2 = \mu/r_2{}^3 \tag{7.132}$$
$$D_1 = A_1 + B_1 u_2 \tag{7.133}$$
$$D_3 = A_3 + B_3 u_2 \tag{7.134}$$

$$A_1{}^* = (a_{11}\mathbf{A} \cdot \mathbf{X} + a_{12}\mathbf{A} \cdot \mathbf{Y} + a_{13}\mathbf{A} \cdot \mathbf{Z})$$
$$B_1{}^* = (a_{11}\mathbf{B} \cdot \mathbf{X} + a_{12}\mathbf{B} \cdot \mathbf{Y} + a_{13}\mathbf{B} \cdot \mathbf{Z})$$
(7.135)

$$A_3{}^* = (a_{31}\mathbf{A} \cdot \mathbf{X} + a_{32}\mathbf{A} \cdot \mathbf{Y} + a_{33}\mathbf{A} \cdot \mathbf{Z})$$
$$B_3{}^* = (a_{31}\mathbf{B} \cdot \mathbf{X} + a_{32}\mathbf{B} \cdot \mathbf{Y} + a_{33}\mathbf{B} \cdot \mathbf{Z})$$
(7.136)

$$\rho_1 = \frac{A_1{}^* + B_1{}^* u_2}{D_1}$$
(7.137)

$$\rho_2 = A_2{}^* + B_2{}^* u_2$$
(7.138)

$$\rho_3 = \frac{A_3{}^* + B_3{}^* u_2}{D_3}$$
(7.139)

$$\mathbf{r}_i = \rho_i \mathbf{L}_i - \mathbf{R}_i, \quad i = 1, 2, 3.$$
(7.140)

Then, utilizing the Herrick–Gibbs formulas,[11] calculate

$$d_1 = \tau_3 \left[ \frac{\mu}{12 r_1{}^3} - \frac{1}{\tau_1 \tau_{13}} \right]$$
(7.141)

$$d_2 = (\tau_1 + \tau_3) \left[ \frac{\mu}{12 r_2{}^3} - \frac{1}{\tau_1 \tau_3} \right]$$
(7.142)

$$d_3 = -\tau_1 \left[ \frac{\mu}{12 r_3{}^3} + \frac{1}{\tau_3 \tau_{13}} \right]$$
(7.143)

$$\dot{\mathbf{r}}_2 = -d_1 \mathbf{r}_1 + d_2 \mathbf{r}_2 + d_3 \mathbf{r}_3$$
(7.144)

$$r_2 = \sqrt{\mathbf{r}_2 \cdot \mathbf{r}_2}$$
(7.145)

$$\dot{r}_2 = \dot{\mathbf{r}}_2 \cdot \mathbf{r}_2 / r_2$$
(7.146)

$$V_2 = \sqrt{\dot{\mathbf{r}}_2 \cdot \dot{\mathbf{r}}_2}$$
(7.147)

$$\frac{1}{a} = \frac{2}{r_2} - \frac{V_2{}^2}{\mu}.$$
(7.148)

From the $f$ and $g$ functions, calculate

$$f_1 = f(V_2, r_2, \dot{r}_2, \tau_1)$$
$$f_3 = f(V_2, r_2, \dot{r}_2, \tau_3)$$
$$g_1 = g(V_2, r_2, \dot{r}_2, \tau_1)$$
$$g_3 = g(V_2, r_2, \dot{r}_2, \tau_3).$$
(7.149)

---

[11] The algorithm is stated using the Herrick–Gibbs technique, however, the correction outlined in Section 7.3.4 may be more suitable.   For closely spaced observations the Gaussian scheme can be terminated with Eq. 7.140 (see Chapter 6).

Continue calculating with

$$D^* = f_1 g_3 - f_3 g_1 \qquad (7.150)$$
$$c_1 = g_3/D^* \qquad (7.151)$$
$$c_2 = -1.0 \qquad (7.152)$$
$$c_3 = -g_1/D^* \qquad (7.153)$$
$$\mathbf{G} = c_1 \mathbf{R}_1 + c_2 \mathbf{R}_2 + c_3 \mathbf{R}_3 \qquad (7.154)$$
$$(\rho_1)_n = (1/c_1)(a_{11} G_x + a_{12} G_y + a_{13} G_z) \qquad (7.155)$$
$$(\rho_2)_n = -(a_{21} G_x + a_{22} G_y + a_{23} G_z) \qquad (7.156)$$
$$(\rho_3)_n = (1/c_3)(a_{31} G_x + a_{32} G_y + a_{33} G_z). \qquad (7.157)$$

The first time through, test to see if

$$|(\rho_1)_n - \rho_1| < \epsilon_1$$
$$|(\rho_2)_n - \rho_2| < \epsilon_2 \qquad (7.158)$$
$$|(\rho_3)_n - \rho_3| < \epsilon_3,$$

where $\epsilon_1$, $\epsilon_2$, $\epsilon_3$ are tolerances. If so, proceed to Eq. 7.160; if not, return to Eq. 7.140 using $(\rho_i)_n$ and repeat equational loop 7.141 to 7.157; however from this point on, test to see if

$$|(\rho_1)_{n+1} - (\rho_1)_n| < \epsilon_1$$
$$|(\rho_2)_{n+1} - (\rho_2)_n| < \epsilon_2 \qquad (7.159)$$
$$|(\rho_3)_{n+1} - (\rho_3)_n| < \epsilon_3,$$

and repeat equational loop 7.141 to 7.157 until this test is successful. Continue by calculating

$$\mathbf{r}_2 = \boldsymbol{\rho}_2 - \mathbf{R}_2 \qquad (7.160)$$
$$\dot{\mathbf{r}}_2 = -d_1 \mathbf{r}_1 + d_2 \mathbf{r}_2 + d_3 \mathbf{r}_3. \qquad (7.161)$$

Having $\mathbf{r}_2$ and $\dot{\mathbf{r}}_2$, the orbit is considered determined, and the Gaussian orbit determination scheme is complete.

### 7.4 THE METHOD OF LAPLACE

### 7.4.1 Solution by successive differentiation

Laplace attacked the problem of determining an orbit solely from observations in quite a different manner.[12] Let it be assumed, as in the previous section, that a set of three inertial angular observations $(\alpha_{ti}, \delta_{ti})$

[12] *Mémoires de l'Académie Royale des Sciences de Paris*, 1780.

are available. If not, the transformation of Section 7.2.1 can be conveniently applied. Then the unit vector **L** can be directly determined from Eq. 7.7 as

$$
\mathbf{L}_i = \begin{bmatrix} L_x \\ L_y \\ L_z \end{bmatrix}_i = \begin{bmatrix} \cos \delta_t \ \cos \alpha_t \\ \cos \delta_t \ \sin \alpha_t \\ \sin \delta_t \end{bmatrix}_i, \quad i = 1, 2, 3. \tag{7.162}
$$

Now, since $\mathbf{L}_i$ are unit vectors directed along the slant range vector, Eq. 3.260 permits the following relation to be written.

$$
\rho \mathbf{L} = \mathbf{r} + \mathbf{R}, \tag{7.163}
$$

where, as usual, $\rho$ is the magnitude of the slant range vector, $\mathbf{r}$ is the radius vector from the dynamical center to the satellite, and $\mathbf{R}$ is the station coordinate vector. Let Eq. 7.163 be differentiated twice with respect to modified time, so that

$$
\mathbf{r} = \rho \mathbf{L} - \mathbf{R} \tag{7.164}
$$

$$
\dot{\mathbf{r}} = \dot{\rho} \mathbf{L} + \rho \dot{\mathbf{L}} - \dot{\mathbf{R}} \tag{7.165}
$$

$$
\ddot{\mathbf{r}} = 2\dot{\rho}\dot{\mathbf{L}} + \ddot{\rho}\mathbf{L} + \rho \ddot{\mathbf{L}} - \ddot{\mathbf{R}}. \tag{7.166}
$$

Newton's second law now provides the dynamical relationship

$$
\ddot{\mathbf{r}} = -\mu \frac{\mathbf{r}}{r^3}, \tag{7.167}
$$

which upon substitution into Eq. 7.166 results in

$$
\frac{-\mu(\rho \mathbf{L} - \mathbf{R})}{r^3} = 2\dot{\rho}\dot{\mathbf{L}} + \ddot{\rho}\mathbf{L} + \rho \ddot{\mathbf{L}} - \ddot{\mathbf{R}} \tag{7.168}
$$

by consequence of Eq. 7.164. Multiplying out and collecting terms permits the last equation to be written as

$$
\mathbf{L}\ddot{\rho} + 2\dot{\mathbf{L}}\dot{\rho} + \left(\ddot{\mathbf{L}} + \frac{\mu}{r^3}\mathbf{L}\right)\rho = \ddot{\mathbf{R}} + \mu \frac{\mathbf{R}}{r^3}. \tag{7.169}
$$

For a specified time, the above vector equation represents three component equations in six unknowns. The **L** vectors are known; $\dot{\mathbf{L}}$, $\ddot{\mathbf{L}}$, $\rho$, $\dot{\rho}$, $\ddot{\rho}$ and $r$, however, are not known. Nevertheless, at the central date of the observations, say $t_2$ as depicted in Figure 7.1, the derivatives, $\dot{\mathbf{L}}_2$, $\ddot{\mathbf{L}}_2$, may be evaluated by the following numerical procedure. Assume that the **L** are functions of modified time and apply the numerical differentiation formulas of Section 7.3.2, that is,

$$\mathbf{L}(\tau) = \frac{\tau(\tau - \tau_3)}{\tau_1(\tau_1 - \tau_3)} \mathbf{L}_1 + \frac{(\tau - \tau_1)(\tau - \tau_3)}{\tau_1 \tau_3} \mathbf{L}_2 + \frac{\tau(\tau - \tau_1)}{\tau_3(\tau_3 - \tau_1)} \mathbf{L}_3,$$

(7.170)

so that:

$$\dot{\mathbf{L}} = \frac{(2\tau - \tau_3)}{\tau_1(\tau_1 - \tau_3)} \mathbf{L}_1 + \frac{(2\tau - \tau_3 - \tau_1)}{\tau_1 \tau_3} \mathbf{L}_2 + \frac{(2\tau - \tau_1)}{\tau_3(\tau_3 - \tau_1)} \mathbf{L}_3 \qquad (7.171)$$

and

$$\ddot{\mathbf{L}} = \frac{2}{\tau_1(\tau_1 - \tau_3)} \mathbf{L}_1 + \frac{2}{\tau_1 \tau_3} \mathbf{L}_2 + \frac{2}{\tau_3(\tau_3 - \tau_1)} \mathbf{L}_3. \qquad (7.172)$$

Furthermore, since by definition $\tau_2 = 0$, Eq. 7.171 reduces to

$$\dot{\mathbf{L}}_2 = -\frac{\tau_3}{\tau_1(\tau_1 - \tau_3)} \mathbf{L}_1 - \frac{\tau_3 + \tau_1}{\tau_1 \tau_3} \mathbf{L}_2 - \frac{\tau_1}{\tau_3(\tau_3 - \tau_1)} \mathbf{L}_3. \qquad (7.173)$$

$\dot{\mathbf{L}}_2$ is naturally numerically computable from Eq. 7.172. It should be noted that the above procedure, which yields $\dot{\mathbf{L}}_2$ and $\ddot{\mathbf{L}}_2$, is not limited to the minimum number of observations required to determine the orbit. Certainly, if more than three sets of observations were available, much more accurate derivatives could be obtained by fitting higher order polynomials with the Lagrange interpolation formula, that is, Eq. 7.66. This actually must be done when $\dddot{\mathbf{L}}_2$ and higher order derivatives are not of negligible order [10].

Since the above procedure has produced some information about the derivatives of $\mathbf{L}$ at central date, let Eq. 7.169 be written for $t_2$. Certainly, then, the determinant of this equation, $\Delta$, is given by

$$\Delta = \begin{vmatrix} L_x & 2\dot{L}_x & \ddot{L}_x + \dfrac{\mu}{r^3} L_x \\[2mm] L_y & 2\dot{L}_y & \ddot{L}_y + \dfrac{\mu}{r^3} L_y \\[2mm] L_z & 2\dot{L}_z & \ddot{L}_z + \dfrac{\mu}{r^3} L_z \end{vmatrix}. \qquad (7.174)$$

This determinant can be immediately reduced by subtracting $\mu/r^3$ times the first column from the last column to yield

$$\Delta = 2 \begin{vmatrix} L_x & \dot{L}_x & \ddot{L}_x \\ L_y & \dot{L}_y & \ddot{L}_y \\ L_z & \dot{L}_z & \ddot{L}_z \end{vmatrix}. \qquad (7.175)$$

By applying Cramer's rule to the system defined by Eq. 7.169, it is evident that

$$\Delta\rho = \begin{vmatrix} L_x & 2\dot{L}_x & \ddot{X} + \mu X/r^3 \\ L_y & 2\dot{L}_y & \ddot{Y} + \mu Y/r^3 \\ L_z & 2\dot{L}_z & \ddot{Z} + \mu Z/r^3 \end{vmatrix}. \tag{7.176}$$

The determinant of Eq. 7.176 can be conveniently split to produce

$$\Delta\rho = 2\begin{vmatrix} L_x & \dot{L}_x & \ddot{X} \\ L_y & \dot{L}_y & \ddot{Y} \\ L_z & \dot{L}_z & \ddot{Z} \end{vmatrix} + \frac{2\mu}{r^3}\begin{vmatrix} L_x & \dot{L}_x & X \\ L_y & \dot{L}_y & Y \\ L_z & \dot{L}_z & Z \end{vmatrix}. \tag{7.177}$$

In exactly analogous fashion, one can form

$$\Delta\dot{\rho} = \begin{vmatrix} L_x & \ddot{X} & \dot{L}_x \\ L_y & \ddot{Y} & \dot{L}_y \\ L_z & \ddot{Z} & \dot{L}_z \end{vmatrix} + \frac{\mu}{r^3}\begin{vmatrix} L_x & X & \ddot{L}_x \\ L_y & Y & \ddot{L}_y \\ L_z & Z & \ddot{L}_z \end{vmatrix}. \tag{7.178}$$

If the first determinant of Eq. 7.177 is defined as $D_a$, the second determinant, by $D_b$ and the first determinant of Eq. 7.178 by $D_c$, the second determinant by $D_d$, it is possible to write compactly

$$\rho = \frac{2D_a}{\Delta} + \frac{2\mu D_b}{\Delta r^3}, \quad \Delta \neq 0, \tag{7.179}$$

$$\dot{\rho} = \frac{D_c}{\Delta} + \frac{\mu D_d}{\Delta r^3}, \quad \Delta \neq 0. \tag{7.180}$$

It should be clear that the numerical values of $\Delta$, $D_a$, $D_b$, $D_c$, $D_d$ can be computed directly for the central date. To be more compact and introducing the subscript 2, corresponding to $t_2$ as depicted in Figure 7.1,

$$\rho_2 = A_2{}^* + \frac{\mu B_2{}^*}{r_2{}^3} \tag{7.181}$$

$$\dot{\rho}_2 = C_2{}^* + \frac{\mu D_2{}^*}{r_2{}^3}, \tag{7.182}$$

where

$$\begin{aligned} A_2{}^* &\equiv 2D_a/\Delta & B_2{}^* &\equiv 2D_b/\Delta \\ C_2{}^* &\equiv D_c/\Delta & D_2{}^* &\equiv D_d/\Delta. \end{aligned} \tag{7.183}$$

For the present, let it be assumed that $\Delta \neq 0$. This case will be treated later in Section 7.4.2. It should be noticed that Eqs. 7.181 and 7.182

are relationships derived from dynamic constraints. An independent geometrical relation can be obtained by considering

$$\mathbf{r} = \rho \mathbf{L} - \mathbf{R},  \tag{7.184}$$

which, when dotted into itself, yields

$$r_2{}^2 = \rho_2{}^2 - 2\rho_2 \mathbf{L}_2 \cdot \mathbf{R}_2 + R_2{}^2.  \tag{7.185}$$

The solution of the problem of Laplace now hinges upon the simultaneous solution of Eqs. 7.181 and 7.185. Let the dot product $2\mathbf{L}_2 \cdot \mathbf{R}_2$ be defined by

$$C_\psi \equiv -2(L_{x2} X_2 + L_{y2} Y_2 + L_{z2} Z_2).  \tag{7.186}$$

An eighth-order resultant of the orbit determination scheme is obtained by substituting Eq. 7.181 into Eq. 7.185 as

$$
\begin{aligned}
f(r_2) \equiv{} & r_2{}^8 - (C_\psi A_2{}^* + A_2{}^{*2} + R_2{}^2) r_2{}^6 \\
& - \mu(C_\psi B_2{}^* + 2 A_2{}^* B_2{}^*) r_2{}^2 - \mu^2 B_2{}^{*2} = 0.
\end{aligned} \tag{7.187}
$$

It should be noted that this equation is a resultant of the same form as obtained in the method of Gauss (Eq. 7.59), though it will not give the same answers owing to inherent differences in each method. The procedure proposed in Section 7.3.1 and utilization of Figure 7.4 or 7.5 will greatly expedite the solution of this algebraic equation.

Once a value for the magnitude of $\mathbf{r}_2$ is known, $\rho_2$ and $\dot{\rho}_2$ may be obtained from Eqs. 7.181 and 7.182. Immediately, then,

$$\mathbf{r}_2 = \rho_2 \mathbf{L}_2 - \mathbf{R}_2  \tag{7.188}$$

and

$$\dot{\mathbf{r}}_2 = \dot{\rho}_2 \mathbf{L}_2 + \rho_2 \dot{\mathbf{L}}_2 - \dot{\mathbf{R}}_2,  \tag{7.189}$$

where, if all the observations are from a single station, $\dot{\mathbf{R}}$ is given in analytical form by Eqs. 3.262. If observations are from different stations, then one could again employ the Lagrange interpolating polynomial, Eq. 7.66, to obtain $\mathbf{R}_2$ as a function of modified time. Differentiation will then yield $\dot{\mathbf{R}}_2$ in a straightforth manner. The pertinent equations are included in the Laplacian algorithm (Section 7.4.3).

As indicated previously for near-Earth satellites, the method of Laplace must be modified considerably by the inclusion of higher-order derivatives in $\mathbf{L}_2$. The standard Laplacian technique finds frequent use in the determination of very distant heliocentric planetary orbits. In this case the station coordinate vector $\mathbf{R}$ should be augmented by the coordinates of the Sun relative to the Earth, $\mathbf{R}_\odot$, so that $\mathbf{R}^* = \mathbf{R} + \mathbf{R}_\odot$ replaces $\mathbf{R}$ in the previous analysis. The derivatives of $\mathbf{R}^*$ are obtained in part from numerical differentiation of the coordinates of the Sun.

Further modifications should also include *light time correction.* In essence, once a first approximation of the orbit is obtained and an approximate value of $\rho$, the slant range magnitude, is known the observation times should be corrected for time lag. The correction to the observation times for intervals elapsed from the object to observer is approximated by

$$t = t_{\text{obs}} - \frac{1}{c} \rho, \tag{7.190}$$

where $1/c$ is the reciprocal of the velocity of light, taken herein as 0.005772 days/a.u. It should be evident that since visual observations separated by 1 a.u., for example, the Sun as seen from the Earth, require approximately eight minutes to reach an observer, this correction is an important iterative loop of the orbit determination process.

### 7.4.2   Vanishing of Laplace's determinant

The foregoing analysis has assumed that Eq. 7.175 does not vanish, that is, $\Delta \neq 0$. It will now be shown that $\Delta$ can indeed vanish in a special case. It is an easy exercise to show that $\Delta$ can be written as

$$\Delta \equiv 2 \begin{vmatrix} L_x & \dot{L}_x & \ddot{L}_x \\ L_y & \dot{L}_y & \ddot{L}_y \\ L_z & \dot{L}_z & \ddot{L}_z \end{vmatrix} = 2 \begin{vmatrix} P_1 & \dot{P}_1 & \ddot{P}_1 \\ P_2 & \dot{P}_2 & \ddot{P}_2 \\ P_3 & \dot{P}_3 & \ddot{P}_3 \end{vmatrix} \begin{vmatrix} L_{x1} & L_{x2} & L_{x3} \\ L_{y1} & L_{y2} & L_{y3} \\ L_{z1} & L_{z2} & L_{z3} \end{vmatrix}, \tag{7.191}$$

where

$$P_1 = \frac{\tau(\tau - \tau_3)}{\tau_1(\tau_1 - \tau_3)}$$

$$P_2 = \frac{(\tau - \tau_1)(\tau - \tau_3)}{\tau_1 \tau_3} \tag{7.192}$$

$$P_3 = \frac{\tau(\tau - \tau_1)}{\tau_3(\tau_3 - \tau_1)}.$$

Equation 7.191 is true by virtue of the numerical differentiation process involved in obtaining $\dot{L}_2$ and $\ddot{L}_2$. By direct evaluation, the first determinant on the right side of Eq. 7.191, call it $\Delta_1$, reduces to

$$\Delta_1 = \frac{2}{\tau_1 \tau_3(\tau_1 - \tau_3)}. \tag{7.193}$$

Evidently $\Delta_1$ does not vanish and examination of the second determinant of Eq. 7.191, call it $\Delta_2$, can be undertaken. By direct multiplication of $\Delta_2$

by the product $\rho_1\rho_2\rho_3$, that is, the magnitudes of the slant range vectors, it is possible to see that

$$\rho_1\rho_2\rho_3 \, \Delta_2 = \begin{vmatrix} \rho_{x1} & \rho_{x2} & \rho_{x3} \\ \rho_{y1} & \rho_{y2} & \rho_{y3} \\ \rho_{z1} & \rho_{z2} & \rho_{z3} \end{vmatrix}. \tag{7.194}$$

As indicated by Moulton [1], the preceding determinant is an expression for six times the volume of a tetrahedron formed by the Earth and the three positions of the satellite with respect to the observing station. The volume of this tetrahedron will therefore vanish only if the three positions of the satellite as seen from the observing station lie on the arc of a great circle. Another observation should then be used to remove the indeterminancy. Notice also, that if $\Delta \equiv 0$, Eq. 7.179 yields

$$r_2{}^3 = -\mu D_b / D_a. \tag{7.195}$$

### 7.4.3 Computational algorithm

Given $\alpha_{ti}$, $\delta_{ti}$, $t_i$, $\phi_i$, $\lambda_{Ei}$, $H_i$ for $i = 1, 2, 3$ and the constants $d\theta/dt$, $f$, $a_e$, $\mu$, $k$, compute the following:

$$\tau_1 = k(t_1 - t_2) \tag{7.196}$$
$$\tau_3 = k(t_3 - t_2) \tag{7.197}$$

Then, assuming that derivatives of order $\overset{\cdots}{L}$ are negligible, compute

$$s_1 = -\frac{\tau_3}{\tau_1(\tau_1 - \tau_3)}$$

$$s_2 = -\frac{(\tau_3 + \tau_1)}{\tau_1\tau_3}$$

$$s_3 = -\frac{\tau_1}{\tau_3(\tau_3 - \tau_1)}$$

$$s_4 = \frac{2}{\tau_1(\tau_1 - \tau_3)} \tag{7.198}$$

$$s_5 = \frac{2}{\tau_1\tau_3}$$

$$s_6 = \frac{2}{\tau_3(\tau_3 - \tau_1)}$$

For $i = 1, 2, 3$, calculate

$$L_{xi} = \cos\delta_{ti}\cos\alpha_{ti}$$
$$L_{yi} = \cos\delta_{ti}\sin\alpha_{ti} \tag{7.199}$$
$$L_{zi} = \sin\delta_{ti}$$

and determine

$$\dot{L}_2 = s_1 L_1 + s_2 L_2 + s_3 L_3$$
$$\ddot{L}_2 = s_4 L_1 + s_5 L_2 + s_6 L_3.$$

(7.200)

For $i = 1, 2, 3$, proceed as follows:

$$G_{1i} = \frac{a_e}{\sqrt{1 - (2f - f^2) \sin^2 \phi_i}} + H_i$$

(7.201)

$$G_{2i} = \frac{(1 - f)^2 a_e}{\sqrt{1 - (2f - f^2) \sin^2 \phi_i}} + H_i.$$

Obtain the Greenwich sidereal time $\theta_{g0}$ from Eq. 1.27 and continue calculating with

$$\theta_i = \theta_{g0} + \frac{d\theta}{dt} (t_i - t_0) + \lambda_{Ei}, \quad t_0 = t_2$$

(7.202)

$$X_i = -G_{1i} \cos \phi_i \cos \theta_i$$
$$Y_i = -G_{1i} \cos \phi_i \sin \theta_i$$

(7.203)

$$Z_i = -G_{2i} \sin \phi_i.$$

If the observations are not from a single station, that is, $\phi_1 \neq \phi_2 \neq \phi_3 \neq \phi_1$ and $\lambda_{E1} \neq \lambda_{E2} \neq \lambda_{E3} \neq \lambda_{E1}$, continue with Eq. 7.204; if the observations are from a single station, proceed to Eq. 7.205.

$$\dot{R}_2 = s_1 R_1 + s_2 R_2 + s_3 R_3$$
$$\ddot{R}_2 = s_4 R_1 + s_5 R_2 + s_6 R_3.$$

(7.204)

Proceed to Eq. 7.207.

$$\dot{R}_2 = \begin{bmatrix} -Y_2 \\ X_2 \\ 0 \end{bmatrix} k^{-1} \frac{d\theta}{dt}$$

(7.205)

$$\ddot{R}_2 = \begin{bmatrix} -X_2 \\ -Y_2 \\ 0 \end{bmatrix} k^{-2} \left( \frac{d\theta}{dt} \right)^2.$$

(7.206)

Numerically evaluate the following determinants:

$$\Delta = 2 \begin{vmatrix} L_{x2} & \dot{L}_{x2} & \ddot{L}_{x2} \\ L_{y2} & \dot{L}_{y2} & \ddot{L}_{y2} \\ L_{z2} & \dot{L}_{z2} & \ddot{L}_{z2} \end{vmatrix} \tag{7.207}$$

$$D_a = \begin{vmatrix} L_{x2} & \dot{L}_{x2} & \ddot{X}_2 \\ L_{y2} & \dot{L}_{y2} & \ddot{Y}_2 \\ L_{z2} & \dot{L}_{z2} & \ddot{Z}_2 \end{vmatrix}$$

$$D_b = \begin{vmatrix} L_{x2} & \dot{L}_{x2} & X_2 \\ L_{y2} & \dot{L}_{y2} & Y_2 \\ L_{z2} & \dot{L}_{z2} & Z_2 \end{vmatrix}$$

$$D_c = \begin{vmatrix} L_{x2} & \ddot{X}_2 & \ddot{L}_{x2} \\ L_{y2} & \ddot{Y}_2 & \ddot{L}_{y2} \\ L_{z2} & \ddot{Z}_2 & \ddot{L}_{z2} \end{vmatrix}$$

$$D_d = \begin{vmatrix} L_{x2} & X_2 & \ddot{L}_{x2} \\ L_{y2} & Y_2 & \ddot{L}_{y2} \\ L_{z2} & Z_2 & \ddot{L}_{z2} \end{vmatrix},$$

and form:

$$A_2{}^* = 2D_a/\Delta$$
$$B_2{}^* = 2D_b/\Delta$$
$$C_2{}^* = D_c/\Delta \tag{7.208}$$
$$D_2{}^* = D_d/\Delta$$
$$C_\psi = -2(L_{x2}X_2 + L_{y2}Y_2 + L_{z2}Z_2) \tag{7.209}$$
$$a = -(C_\psi A_2{}^* + A_2{}^{*2} + R_2{}^2)$$
$$b = -\mu(C_\psi B_2{}^* + 2A_2{}^*B_2{}^*) \tag{7.210}$$
$$c = -\mu^2 B_2{}^{*2}.$$

Solve

$$r_2{}^8 + ar_2{}^6 + br_2{}^3 + c = 0 \tag{7.211}$$

to obtain the applicable real root $r_2$, and continue calculating with

$$\rho_2 = A_2{}^* + \frac{\mu B_2{}^*}{r_2{}^3} \tag{7.212}$$

$$\dot{\rho}_2 = C_2{}^* + \frac{\mu D_2{}^*}{r_2{}^3}. \tag{7.213}$$

Finally, the equations,

$$\mathbf{r}_2 = \rho_2 \mathbf{L}_2 - \mathbf{R}_2 \tag{7.214}$$

$$\dot{\mathbf{r}}_2 = \dot{\rho}_2 \mathbf{L}_2 + \rho_2 \dot{\mathbf{L}}_2 - \dot{\mathbf{R}}_2, \tag{7.215}$$

determine the fundamental set $\mathbf{r}_2$, $\dot{\mathbf{r}}_2$, and it is an easy extension to compute the standard orbital elements.

### 7.5  A TRIGONOMETRIC REDUCTION USEFUL IN BOTH THE GAUSSIAN AND LAPLACIAN SCHEMES

### 7.5.1  Simultaneous solution of the two equations

It has been shown that the methods of both Gauss and Laplace reduce to the simultaneous solution of the two equations

$$\rho = A^* + \frac{\mu B^*}{r^3} \tag{7.216}$$

$$r^2 = \rho^2 + \rho C_\psi + R^2. \tag{7.217}$$

These equations, or Eqs. 7.57 and 7.58 and Eqs. 7.181 and 7.185 lead to an eighth-degree polynomial in the variable $r$. Consider, however, Figure 7.6 showing the geometric relation between the dynamical center (DC), observing station (O) and satellite (S). Evidently, from the law of sines,

$$\frac{R}{\sin \xi} = \frac{r}{\sin \psi} \tag{7.218}$$

or

$$r = R \frac{\sin \psi}{\sin \xi}, \tag{7.219}$$

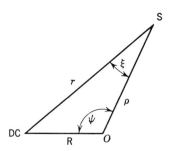

FIGURE 7.6  Geometry of the dynamical center, observer, and satellite.

and also

$$\rho = R\,\frac{\sin(\psi + \xi)}{\sin \xi}. \tag{7.220}$$

The angle $\psi$ is called the *elongation* and is directly determinable from

$$\cos \psi = \mathbf{L} \cdot \mathbf{R}/R. \tag{7.221}$$

By direct substitution of Eqs. 7.219 and 7.220 into Eq. 7.216, it is possible to see that

$$\frac{R \sin(\psi + \xi)}{\sin \xi} = A^* + \frac{\mu B^* \sin^3 \xi}{R^3 \sin^3 \psi} \tag{7.222}$$

or

$$R \sin \psi \cos \xi + (R \cos \psi - A^*) \sin \xi = \frac{\mu B^* \sin^4 \xi}{R^3 \sin^3 \psi}. \tag{7.223}$$

Apparently then, if the following transformation is effected, that is,

$$\begin{aligned} N \sin m &= R \sin \psi \\ N \cos m &= R \cos \psi - A^*, \end{aligned} \tag{7.224}$$

where $N$ and $m$ are defined by and computable from these equations, and the auxiliary parameter $M$ is introduced as

$$M = \frac{N R^3 \sin^3 \psi}{\mu B^*}, \tag{7.225}$$

Eq. 7.223 reduces to

$$\sin^4 \xi - M \sin(\xi + m) = 0. \tag{7.226}$$

A true picture of the solution of this equation may be gleaned from the transformation

$$\begin{aligned} y_1 &= \sin^4 \xi \\ y_2 &= M \sin(\xi + m). \end{aligned} \tag{7.227}$$

Apparently, from Figure 7.7 the absissas of intersection of these curves are the required solutions of Laplace's problem. As can be seen, and is discussed in great detail in Moulton,[13] it is possible to have three positive solutions satisfying Eq. 7.226. To resolve this ambiguity a fourth observation can be used to form a second equation, that is,

$$\sin^4 \xi - M' \sin(\xi + m') = 0, \tag{7.228}$$

[13] See reference [1], page 213.

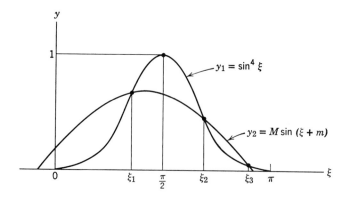

FIGURE 7.7    A graphical construction of the solution of Eq. 7.226.

which along with Eq. 7.226 will now possess a single unique $\xi$ corresponding to the magnitude of the radius vector $r_2$ of the orbit under investigation.[14]

### 7.6    THE DOUBLE $r$-ITERATION

The determination of orbits from angular observations is not a new problem.    Two popular schemes have already stood the test of time: the methods of Gauss and of Laplace.    Both these methods were developed over a century ago primarily for the determination of orbits of minor planets, and they are excellent for that specific purpose.    The method of Gauss can be conveniently modified to the modern problem of the determination of orbits of near-Earth satellites.    For angular observations which are close together, the Gaussian method is second to none.    If, however, the observations are spread out over a considerable time interval, a task this scheme was never designed for, the method of Gauss can still be used, but it becomes complex with no guarantee of convergence. This section proposes an alternative solution to the large spread angles-only orbit determination problem.

A method for the determination of an orbit from angles only is called herein the double $r$-iteration.    It is, unfortunately, an orbit scheme of the type in which two parameters, that is, the magnitudes of the radius vectors at two separate dates, must be guessed in order to effect the solution of the orbit scheme.    This method, however, does possess the advantage of being able to determine an orbit with any interval of time between the

---

[14] See Exercise 2.

given observations.   Indeed, for near-Earth satellites this is an important consideration.   The method presented may be new and is due to Escobal [11].

### 7.6.1   Initialization of the orbit scheme

Let it be assumed that the known data of the problem is the set $\alpha_i$, $\delta_i$, $t_i$, where $\alpha_i$ are the topocentric right ascensions, $\delta_i$ are the topocentric declinations, and $t_i$ are the corresponding universal times of these angular observations for a minimum of three dates, that is, $i = 1, 2, 3$.   Auxiliary data are the location of the observing stations where the preceding topocentric angles are measured.   Usually, adopting an oblate spheroid for the model of the Earth, it is possible to express for $j$, representing a typical station,

$$\mathbf{R}_j = \begin{bmatrix} -G_1 \cos \phi \cos \theta \\ -G_1 \cos \phi \sin \theta \\ -G_2 \sin \phi \end{bmatrix}_j, \tag{7.229}$$

where $\mathbf{R}_j$ are the geocentric rectangular coordinates of the center of the Earth with respect to the station, and

$$G_{1j} \equiv \frac{a_e}{[1 - (2f - f^2) \sin^2 \phi_j]^{\frac{1}{2}}} + H_j$$

$$G_{2j} \equiv \frac{(1 - f)^2 a_e}{[1 - (2f - f^2) \sin^2 \phi_j]^{\frac{1}{2}}} + H_j$$

with

$a_e$ = the Earth's equatorial radius,

$f$ = the Earth's flattening,

$\phi$ = the observing station's geodetic latitude,

$H$ = the observing station's elevation measured normal to the adopted ellipsoid,

$\theta$ = the observing station's local sidereal time corresponding to $t$.

It should be noted that the orbit determination process can have three different stations, or a single station, and so on.

In Figure 7.8, consider the slant range vector $\boldsymbol{\rho}$.   This vector, or a unit vector $\mathbf{L}$, such that $\boldsymbol{\rho} = \rho \mathbf{L}$ can be decomposed into

$$\mathbf{L}_i = \begin{bmatrix} L_x \\ L_y \\ L_z \end{bmatrix}_i = \begin{bmatrix} \cos \delta_t \cos \alpha_t \\ \cos \delta_t \sin \alpha_t \\ \sin \delta_t \end{bmatrix}_i. \tag{7.230}$$

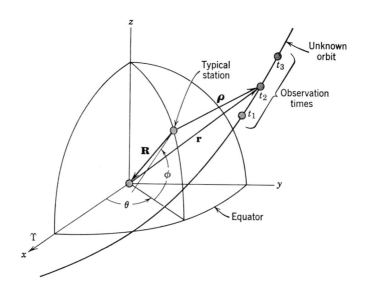

FIGURE 7.8  Orbit geometry.

Hence as a function of the observed data, that is, $\alpha_{ti}$, and $\delta_{ti}$, the slant range unit vectors $\mathbf{L}_i$ are known for $i = 1, 2, 3$.

### 7.6.2  The iterative solution

From the relationship between $\mathbf{r}$, $\boldsymbol{\rho}$, and $\mathbf{R}$, more precisely as evident from Figure 7.8,

$$\boldsymbol{\rho}_i = \mathbf{r}_i + \mathbf{R}_i, \tag{7.231}$$

so that it is possible to obtain, by transposing $\mathbf{R}_i$ and taking the dot product of Eq. 7.231 upon itself, the form

$$\rho_i^2 + \rho_i C_{\psi i} + (R_i^2 - r_i^2) = 0, \tag{7.232}$$

with $C_{\psi i} \equiv -2\mathbf{L}_i \cdot \mathbf{R}_i$. The $C_{\psi i}$ are known from the station position and observational data.

Equation 7.232 can be solved for $\rho_i$ as

$$\rho_i = \tfrac{1}{2}\{-C_{\psi i} + [C_{\psi i}^2 - 4(R_i^2 - r_i^2)]^{1/2}\}, \tag{7.233}$$

where the correct sign of the radical is positive, due to the fact that $R_i^2 - r_i^2 < 0$ and $C_{\psi i} > 0$ as the satellite moves from horizon to horizon.

Let it now be assumed that two estimates for $r_1$ and $r_2$ are known.[15] Immediately Eq. 7.233 yields $\rho_1$ and $\rho_2$, and Eq. 7.230 can be used to obtain $\boldsymbol{\rho}_1$ and $\boldsymbol{\rho}_2$ since $\boldsymbol{\rho}_i = \rho_i \mathbf{L}_i$. Furthermore, Eq. 7.231 or

$$\mathbf{r}_i = \boldsymbol{\rho}_i - \mathbf{R}_i \tag{7.234}$$

can be utilized to compute $\mathbf{r}_1$ and $\mathbf{r}_2$.

For a direct orbit,[16] a vector perpendicular to the orbit plane $\tilde{\mathbf{W}}$ is

$$\tilde{\mathbf{W}} = \frac{\mathbf{r}_1 \times \mathbf{r}_2}{r_1 r_2}, \tag{7.235}$$

which can be used to compute $\mathbf{r}_3$, since the perpendicularity of $\mathbf{r}_3$ and $\tilde{\mathbf{W}}$ in a two-body orbit provide the relationship

$$\mathbf{r}_3 \cdot \tilde{\mathbf{W}} = 0. \tag{7.236}$$

Thus, substituting Eq. 7.234 into Eq. 7.236 yields

$$\rho_3 = \frac{\mathbf{R}_3 \cdot \tilde{\mathbf{W}}}{\mathbf{L}_3 \cdot \tilde{\mathbf{W}}}. \tag{7.237}$$

This equation is used in the scheme proposed in reference [7]. Application of Eq. 7.237 and use of $\mathbf{L}_3$ determines $\mathbf{r}_3$ by virtue of Eq. 7.234. If the slant range vector is in the plane of the unknown orbit, Eq. 7.237 is not defined. A new observation must then be utilized.

In summary, then, the assumption of values for $r_1$ and $r_2$ made possible the computation of $\mathbf{r}_1$, $\mathbf{r}_2$ and $\mathbf{r}_3$ through the known observations and station location.

Further available information is the difference in true anomalies, that is, $v_j - v_k$ for $j = 2, 3$ and $k = 1, 2$, obtained from

$$\cos (v_j - v_k) = \frac{\mathbf{r}_j \cdot \mathbf{r}_k}{r_j r_k}$$
$$\sin (v_j - v_k) = s[1 - \cos^2 (v_j - v_k)]^{1/2} \tag{7.238}$$

with

$$s = \pm \frac{x_k y_j - x_j y_k}{|x_k y_j - x_j y_k|},$$

where the positive sign is taken for a direct orbit and the negative sign is taken for a retrograde orbit.

### 7.6.3 Calculation of time interval

In order to correct the assumed values of $r_1$ and $r_2$, it is necessary to compute the resulting time intervals between $(\mathbf{r}_3, \mathbf{r}_2)$ and $(\mathbf{r}_1, \mathbf{r}_2)$ and obtain

---

[15] For near-Earth orbits let $r_1 = r_2 = 1.1$ Earth radii.
[16] For a retrograde orbit, the sign of $\tilde{\mathbf{W}}$ must be reversed.

residuals from the actual known time differences. To do this, the Gaussian equation,[17] [12], that is,

$$p = \frac{c_1 r_1 + c_3 r_3 - r_2}{c_1 + c_3 - 1} \tag{7.239}$$

is brought into focus. In this equation, $p$ is the semiparameter of the orbit, and $c_1$ and $c_3$ are geometrical ratios, defined as

$$c_1 \equiv \frac{r_2 \sin (v_3 - v_2)}{r_1 \sin (v_3 - v_1)}, \qquad c_3 \equiv \frac{r_2 \sin (v_2 - v_1)}{r_3 \sin (v_3 - v_1)}. \tag{7.240}$$

It should be noted that Gaussian sector to triangle theory is being introduced at the present time (Section 6.2.2). Equation 7.239 was rejected by Gauss in his famous scheme, owing to the fact that, for very short observational arcs, $p$ is poorly determined [13]. For this case, the celebrated Gaussian method completely solves the problem. Actually, by applying a limiting process, another interesting equation for $p$ is

$$p = \frac{r_1 + c_{r3} r_3 - c_{r1} r_2}{1 + c_{r3} - c_{r1}}, \tag{7.241}$$

where

$$c_{r1} \equiv \frac{r_1 \sin (v_3 - v_1)}{r_2 \sin (v_3 - v_2)}, \qquad c_{r3} \equiv \frac{r_1 \sin (v_2 - v_1)}{r_3 \sin (v_3 - v_2)}.$$

This equation is obtained by dividing numerator and denominator of Eq. 7.239 by $c_1$. Hence, singularities inherent in Eq. 7.239 when $v_3 - v_1 = \pi$ are removed by utilizing Eq. 7.241. Actually, Eq. 7.239 should be used if $v_3 - v_1 > \pi$, and Eq. 7.241 if $v_3 - v_1 \leq \pi$. At any rate, either Eq. 7.239 or Eq. 7.241 has yielded the semiparameter by virtue of Eqs. 7.238.

From the equation of a conic, the products of eccentricity and true anomaly, that is, $[e \cos v_i]$ may be readily obtained as

$$[e \cos v_i] = \frac{p}{r_i} - 1, \quad i = 1, 2, 3. \tag{7.242}$$

The next step is the determination of the product $[e \sin v_i]$. By expanding factors of the form $e \sin (v_1 + v_2 - v_2)$, it is possible to verify the following identities,

$$[e \sin v_1] = \frac{\cos (v_2 - v_1)[e \cos v_1] - [e \cos v_2]}{\sin (v_2 - v_1)}$$

$$[e \sin v_2] = \frac{-\cos (v_2 - v_1)[e \cos v_2] + [e \cos v_1]}{\sin (v_2 - v_1)}, \tag{7.243}$$

---

[17] This equation will be derived in Chapter 8.

for $\sin (v_2 - v_1) \neq \pi$, and alternatively,

$$[e \sin v_2] = \frac{\cos (v_3 - v_2)[e \cos v_2] - [e \cos v_3]}{\sin (v_3 - v_1)}$$

$$[e \sin v_3] = \frac{-\cos (v_3 - v_2)[e \cos v_3] + [e \cos v_2]}{\sin (v_3 - v_1)},$$

(7.244)

for $\sin (v_3 - v_1) \neq \pi$. Equations 7.243 and 7.244 uniquely determine the appropriate products of $[e \sin v]$ from the products $[e \cos v]$. Furthermore, the eccentricity $e$ of the assumed orbit is determined from

$$e^2 = [e \cos v_2]^2 + [e \sin v_2]^2$$

(7.245)

and the semimajor axis $a$ is determined by

$$a = \frac{p}{(1 - e^2)}.$$

(7.246)

It should be noted that if $e > 1$, hyperbolic equations must be used from this point on (Section 7.6.5). The elliptical formulation is attacked first.

As an auxiliary calculation, it is possible to determine the mean motion,

$$n = k\mu^{\frac{1}{2}}a^{-3/2},$$

(7.247)

where $k\mu^{\frac{1}{2}}$ is the dynamic gravitational constant of the planet.

The next step is the introduction of Kepler's equation, which will permit calculation of the time interval between observations (as a function of the assumed $r_1$ and $r_2$). Before introducing Kepler's equation, some auxiliary parameters will be introduced. Standard mappings from the true anomaly $v$ to the eccentric anomaly $E$ are given by

$$\sin E = \frac{r}{p} (1 - e^2)^{\frac{1}{2}} \sin v$$

$$\cos E = \frac{r}{p} (e + \cos v),$$

(7.248)

so that in terms of the products of $[e \sin v]$ and $[e \cos v]$ it is possible to obtain the products $[e \sin E]$ and $[e \sin E]$ from

$$S_e \equiv [e \sin E_2] = \frac{r_2}{p} (1 - e^2)^{\frac{1}{2}}[e \sin v_2]$$

$$C_e \equiv [e \cos E_2] = \frac{r_2}{p} (e^2 + [e \cos v_2]).$$

(7.249)

Furthermore, by expanding Eqs. 7.248 in forms such as $\sin(E_3 - E_2 + E_2)$ and regrouping terms, the following transformations from the differences in true anomalies to eccentric anomalies can be verified:

$$\sin(E_3 - E_2) = \frac{r_3}{(ap)^{1/2}} \sin(v_3 - v_2) - \frac{r_3}{p}[1 - \cos(v_3 - v_2)]S_e$$

(7.250)

$$\cos(E_3 - E_2) = 1 - \frac{r_3 r_2}{ap}[1 - \cos(v_3 - v_2)]$$

$$\sin(E_2 - E_1) = \frac{r_1}{(ap)^{1/2}} \sin(v_2 - v_1) + \frac{r_1}{p}[1 - \cos(v_2 - v_1)]S_e$$

(7.251)

$$\cos(E_2 - E_1) = 1 - \frac{r_2 r_1}{ap}[1 - \cos(v_2 - v_1)].$$

Kepler's equation

$$M = E - e \sin E,$$

(7.252)

where $M$ is the mean anomaly and $E$ is the eccentric anomaly, can be modified by referencing with respect to some epoch, say $t_2$, so that

$$M_3 - M_2 = E_3 - E_2 + 2S_e \sin^2\left(\frac{E_3 - E_2}{2}\right) - C_e \sin(E_3 - E_2)$$

$$M_1 - M_2 = -(E_2 - E_1) + 2S_e \sin^2\left(\frac{E_2 - E_1}{2}\right) + C_e \sin(E_2 - E_1).$$

(7.253)

Furthermore, since

$$M_k - M_2 = n(t_k - t_2), \quad k = 1, 3,$$

(7.254)

the time intervals as a function of $r_1$ and $r_2$ are given by

$$\bar{t}_3 - \bar{t}_2 = \frac{M_3 - M_2}{n}, \quad \bar{t}_1 - \bar{t}_2 = \frac{M_1 - M_2}{n},$$

(7.255)

where the overhead bars denote times computed from the assumed $r_1$ and $r_2$. To be concrete, let the following functions be introduced:

$$F_1 \equiv \tau_1 - k\left(\frac{M_1 - M_2}{n}\right)$$

$$F_2 \equiv \tau_3 - k\left(\frac{M_3 - M_2}{n}\right).$$

(7.256)

The functions $F_1$ and $F_2$ must be forced to zero in order to match hypothetical modified times based on incorrectly assumed values of $r_1$ and $r_2$, and true modified times calculable from

$$\begin{aligned}\tau_1 &= k(t_1 - t_2)\\ \tau_3 &= k(t_3 - t_2),\end{aligned} \qquad (7.257)$$

where $t_1$, $t_2$, and $t_3$ are the universal observation times with adopted epoch $t_2$. This forcing process will be attacked by a numerical procedure. Before continuing with the solution, it should be realized that if the observations are obtained on more than one pass, that is, successive revolutions, it is necessary to increment the $F_1$ and $F_2$ functions as follows:

$$F_1 = \tau_1 - k\left(\frac{M_1 - M_2}{n}\right) + k\left(\frac{2\pi}{n}\right)\lambda \qquad (7.258)$$

$$F_2 = \tau_3 - k\left(\frac{M_3 - M_2}{n}\right) - k\left(\frac{2\pi}{n}\right)\lambda, \qquad (7.259)$$

where $\lambda$ is a multiplier. Hence one assumes $a$ $\lambda$, for example, $\lambda = 1, 2, 3, \dots, q$, and for each integer value of $\lambda$ attempts to carry on the solution. Physically, the incrementation of Eqs. 7.256 is nothing more than algebraically adding multiples of the orbital period to the unbounded value of the respective modified time variable.

### 7.6.4 Numerical correction to the assumed magnitude of the radius vectors

In order to effect a numerical solution, it is mandatory to force the $F_i$ functions to zero, that is,

$$F_i(r_1, r_2) = 0, \quad i = 1, 2. \qquad (7.260)$$

Equivalently, by utilizing a two-dimensional Taylor expansion, one can expand $F_i$ and write the linear approximation

$$-F_i = \left(\frac{\partial F_i}{\partial r_1}\right) dr_1 + \left(\frac{\partial F_i}{\partial r_2}\right) dr_2. \qquad (7.261)$$

Furthermore, replacing the differentials by finite differences and solving the system of linear equations provided by Eq. 7.261 for $\Delta r_1$ and $\Delta r_2$, it is possible to write

$$\Delta r_1 = -\frac{\Delta_1}{\Delta}, \qquad \Delta r_2 = -\frac{\Delta_2}{\Delta}, \qquad (7.262)$$

where

$$\Delta \equiv \left(\frac{\partial F_1}{\partial r_1}\right)\left(\frac{\partial F_2}{\partial r_2}\right) - \left(\frac{\partial F_2}{\partial r_1}\right)\left(\frac{\partial F_1}{\partial r_2}\right)$$

$$\Delta_1 \equiv \left(\frac{\partial F_2}{\partial r_2}\right)F_1 - \left(\frac{\partial F_1}{\partial r_2}\right)F_2 \tag{7.263}$$

$$\Delta_2 \equiv \left(\frac{\partial F_1}{\partial r_1}\right)F_2 - \left(\frac{\partial F_2}{\partial r_1}\right)F_1.$$

Evidently, then, if $\partial F/\partial r$ were known, Eqs. 7.262 would provide an increment which, when added to $r_i$, would improve their respective values. It is possible to approximate these partials with the following equations, which in effect are nothing more than the definition of the partials:

$$\frac{\partial F_i}{\partial r_1} \cong \frac{F_i(r_1 + \Delta r_1, r_2) - F_i(r_1, r_2)}{\Delta r_1}$$

$$\frac{\partial F_i}{\partial r_2} \cong \frac{F_i(r_1, r_2 + \Delta r_2) - F_i(r_1, r_2)}{\Delta r_2}. \tag{7.264}$$

These approximate partials may be computed numerically by returning to the original guesses for $r_1$ and $r_2$ and varying $r_1$, by say $r_1 + \Delta r_1$, and holding $r_2$ constant. This will yield, by consequence of Eqs. 7.264 the partials

$$\frac{\partial F_1}{\partial r_1}, \quad \frac{\partial F_2}{\partial r_1}.$$

In a similar fashion, holding $r_1$ to the original guess and varying $r_2$, by say $r_2 + \Delta r_2$, will yield

$$\frac{\partial F_1}{\partial r_2}, \quad \frac{\partial F_2}{\partial r_2}.$$

Thus, every third pass through the orbit scheme provides direct improvement of the estimated $r_i$ through

$$(r_i)_{j+1} = (r_i)_j + (\Delta r_i)_j, \quad j = 1, 2, \ldots, q. \tag{7.265}$$

Once the $r_i$ do not vary, since a side product of the iterative process is $E_3 - E_2$ and $a$, it is possible to form the closed-form $f$ and $g$ coefficients, that is,

$$f = 1 - \frac{a}{r_2}[1 - \cos(E_3 - E_2)]$$

$$g = \tau_3 - \frac{a^{3/2}}{\mu^{1/2}}[E_3 - E_2 - \sin(E_3 - E_2)], \tag{7.266}$$

and solve for $\dot{\mathbf{r}}_2$ as

$$\dot{\mathbf{r}}_2 = \frac{\mathbf{r}_3 - f\mathbf{r}_2}{g}. \tag{7.267}$$

The fundamental set $\mathbf{r}_2$, $\dot{\mathbf{r}}_2$ has been found and the orbit can be considered determined.

### 7.6.5 The hyperbolic case

It may very well happen that in the iteration proposed, the eccentricity $e$, as determined by Eq. 7.245, will be greater than unity. This condition does not present any inherent difficulty and is solved by entering into the regime of hyperbolic calculations [18] so that Eq. 6.247 is replaced by

$$n = k\mu^{1/2}(-a)^{3/2}, \tag{7.268}$$

and Eqs. 6.249 are replaced with

$$S_h \equiv \frac{r_2}{p}(e^2 - 1)^{1/2}[e \sin v_2]$$

$$\tag{7.269}$$

$$C_h \equiv \frac{r_2}{p}(e^2 + [e \cos v_2]).$$

In a similar fashion, hyperbolism can be controlled by using the differenced forms of Chapter 3 so that

$$\sinh(F_3 - F_2) = \frac{r_3}{(-ap)^{1/2}}\sin(v_3 - v_2) - \frac{r_3}{p}[1 - \cos(v_3 - v_2)]S_h$$

$$\tag{7.270}$$

$$\cosh(F_3 - F_2) = 1 - \frac{r_3 r_2}{ap}[1 - \cos(v_3 - v_2)]$$

$$\sinh(F_2 - F_1) = \frac{r_1}{(-ap)^{1/2}}\sin(v_2 - v_1) + \frac{r_1}{p}[1 - \cos(v_2 - v_1)]S_h$$

$$\tag{7.271}$$

$$\cosh(F_2 - F_1) = 1 - \frac{r_2 r_1}{ap}[1 - \cos(v_2 - v_1)]$$

replace Eqs. 7.250 and 7.251.   Furthermore,

$$F_3 - F_2 = \log\{\sinh(F_3 - F_2) + [\sinh^2(F_3 - F_2) + 1]^{1/2}\}$$
$$F_2 - F_1 = \log\{\sinh(F_2 - F_1) + [\sinh^2(F_2 - F_1) + 1]^{1/2}\} \tag{7.272}$$

$$M_3 - M_2 = -(F_3 - F_2) + 2S_h \sinh^2\left(\frac{F_3 - F_2}{2}\right) + C_h \sinh(F_3 - F_2)$$

$$\tag{7.273}$$

$$M_1 - M_2 = (F_2 - F_1) + 2S_h \sinh^2\left(\frac{F_2 - F_1}{2}\right) - C_h \sinh(F_2 - F_1),$$

[18] The iteration may wander into and out of the hyperbolic regime in the process of attaining an elliptic orbit.

and thus having bypassed the elliptic calculations, is possible to continue as outlined previously with Eqs. 7.256.

## 7.6.6  Numerical results

In order to aid in the machine checkout of the above technique, the following sample orbit is presented. The collected data apply to the determination of the geocentric orbit of 1959 Alpha 1.

### Station Location

| STATION | GEODETIC LATITUDE | EAST LONGITUDE | ELEVATION |
|---|---|---|---|
| Tokyo ($T$) | $35° \, 40' \, 23''6$ | $139° \, 32' \, 06''9$ | 58 meters |
| Olifantsfontein ($O$) | $-25° \, 57' \, 34''7$ | $28° \, 14' \, 51''1$ | 1544 meters |

### Observations

| STATION | TIME (U.T.) (MARCH 1959) | RIGHT ASCENSION | DECLINATION |
|---|---|---|---|
| $T$ | $2^{day} \, 18^{hr} \, 4^{min} \, 57.67^{sec}$ | $14^{hr} \, 52^{min} \, 31.01^{sec}$ | $23° \, 59' \, 59''5$ |
| $O$ | $2^{day} \, 19^{hr} \, 19^{min} \, 13.52^{sec}$ | $5^{hr} \, 47^{min} \, 31.36^{sec}$ | $2° \, 8' \, 12''8$ |
| $O$ | $2^{day} \, 19^{hr} \, 21^{min} \, 8.99^{sec}$ | $6^{hr} \, 35^{min} \, 34.41^{sec}$ | $7° \, 55' \, 30''0$ |

### Orbital Elements

| ELEMENT | DOUBLE $r$ ITERATION (two-body) | DIFFERENTIAL CORRECTION (three observations) |
|---|---|---|
| $a$ (e.r.) | $0.13023 \times 10^1$ | $0.13039 \times 10^1$ |
| $e$ | $0.16419 \times 10^0$ | $0.16476 \times 10^0$ |
| $i$ (degrees) | $0.32878 \times 10^2$ | $0.32875 \times 10^2$ |
| $\Omega$ (degrees) | $0.13653 \times 10^3$ | $0.13678 \times 10^3$ |
| $\omega$ (degrees) | $0.20395 \times 10^3$ | $0.20394 \times 10^3$ |

The latest time of perifocal passage $T$ occurs about 36.79 minutes before the middle observation time. This case demonstrates the feasibility of the method for obtaining a preliminary orbit with crude approximations to $r_1$ and $r_2$. For the data, the approximations were $r_1 = 1.10$, $r_2 = 1.11$. Convergence was achieved in about ten iterations. The corrective increments to $r_1$ and $r_2$ were bounded. This prevents overcorrection which may occur sporadically.

Though secular perturbations were not added to this sample orbit, very long spreads between observations will demand that the perturbations in the mean anomaly, argument of perigee, and ascending node be included in the analysis. This does not present any specific obstacle, since these perturbations can be easily included in the iterative loop (Chapter 10).

### 7.6.7  Computational algorithm

Given $\alpha_{ti}$, $\delta_{ti}$, $t_i$, $\phi_i$, $\lambda_{Ei}$, $H_i$, for $i = 1, 2, 3$, and the constants $d\theta/dt$, $f$, $a_e$, $\mu$, $k$, along with an indication as to whether the orbit is direct or retrograde, proceed as follows:

$$\tau_1 = k(t_1 - t_2) \tag{7.274}$$

$$\tau_3 = k(t_3 - t_2). \tag{7.275}$$

For $i = 1, 2, 3$, compute

$$\begin{aligned}
L_{xi} &= \cos \delta_{ti} \cos \alpha_{ti} \\
L_{yi} &= \cos \delta_{ti} \sin \alpha_{ti} \\
L_{zi} &= \sin \delta_{ti}
\end{aligned} \tag{7.276}$$

$$\begin{aligned}
G_{1i} &= \frac{a_e}{\sqrt{1 - (2f - f^2)\sin^2 \phi_i}} + H_i \\
G_{2i} &= \frac{(1 - f)^2 a_e}{\sqrt{1 - (2f - f^2)\sin^2 \phi_i}} + H_i.
\end{aligned} \tag{7.277}$$

Obtain the Greenwich sidereal time $\theta_{g2}$ from Eq. 1.27 and continue calculating with

$$\theta_i = \theta_{g2} + \frac{d\theta}{dt}(t_i - t_2) + \lambda_{Ei} \tag{7.278}$$

$$\begin{aligned}
X_i &= -G_{1i} \cos \phi_i \cos \theta_i \\
Y_i &= -G_{1i} \cos \phi_i \sin \theta_i \\
Z_i &= -G_{2i} \sin \phi_i
\end{aligned} \tag{7.279}$$

$$C_{\psi i} = -2\mathbf{L}_i \cdot \mathbf{R}_i, \quad i = 1, 2, 3. \tag{7.280}$$

As a first approximation,[19] set

$$r_1 = r_{1g}, \; r_2 = r_{2g},$$

and compute $\rho_i$ from

$$\rho_i = \tfrac{1}{2}\{-C_{\psi i} + [C_{\psi i}^2 - 4(R_i^2 - r_i^2)]^{\frac{1}{2}}\}. \tag{7.281}$$

Continue calculating with

$$\mathbf{r}_i = \rho_i \mathbf{L}_i - \mathbf{R}_i, \quad i = 1, 2. \tag{7.282}$$

Compute $\tilde{\mathbf{W}}$ as[20]

$$\begin{aligned}
\tilde{W}_x &= (y_1 z_2 - y_2 z_1)/(r_1 r_2) \\
\tilde{W}_y &= (x_2 z_1 - x_1 z_2)/(r_1 r_2) \\
\tilde{W}_z &= (x_1 y_2 - x_2 y_1)/(r_1 r_2).
\end{aligned} \tag{7.283}$$

Continue calculating with

$$\rho_3 = \frac{\mathbf{R}_3 \cdot \tilde{\mathbf{W}}}{\mathbf{L}_3 \cdot \tilde{\mathbf{W}}} \tag{7.284}$$

$$\mathbf{r}_3 = \rho_3 \mathbf{L}_3 - \mathbf{R}_3 \tag{7.285}$$

$$r_3 = +[\mathbf{r}_3 \cdot \mathbf{r}_3]^{\frac{1}{2}} \tag{7.286}$$

$$\cos (v_j - v_k) = (\mathbf{r}_j \cdot \mathbf{r}_k)/(r_j r_k), \quad j = 2, 3, \; k = 1, 2. \tag{7.287}$$

If $W_z \geq 0$, calculate

$$\sin (v_j - v_k) = \frac{x_k y_j - x_j y_k}{|x_k y_j - x_j y_k|} [1 - \cos^2 (v_j - v_k)]^{\frac{1}{2}}. \tag{7.288}$$

If $W_z < 0$, calculate

$$\sin (v_j - v_k) = -\frac{x_k y_j - x_j y_k}{|x_k y_j - x_j y_k|} [1 - \cos^2 (v_j - v_k)]^{\frac{1}{2}}. \tag{7.289}$$

If $v_3 - v_1 > \pi$, determine $p$ from

$$\begin{aligned}
c_1 &= \frac{r_2 \sin (v_3 - v_2)}{r_1 \sin (v_3 - v_1)} \\[1mm]
c_3 &= \frac{r_2 \sin (v_2 - v_1)}{r_3 \sin (v_3 - v_1)}
\end{aligned} \tag{7.290}$$

$$p = \frac{c_1 r_1 + c_3 r_3 - r_2}{c_1 + c_3 - 1}. \tag{7.291}$$

---

[19] For near-Earth orbits, if no better estimate is available, set $r_{1g} = r_{2g} = 1.1$ e.r.
[20] For retrograde motion, reverse the signs of Eqs. 7.283.

If $v_3 - v_1 \leq \pi$, determine $p$ from

$$c_{r1} = \frac{r_1}{r_2} \frac{\sin (v_3 - v_1)}{\sin (v_3 - v_2)}$$

$$c_{r3} = \frac{r_1}{r_3} \frac{\sin (v_2 - v_1)}{\sin (v_3 - v_2)}$$

(7.292)

$$p = \frac{r_1 + c_{r3}r_3 - c_{r1}r_2}{1 + c_{r3} - c_{r1}}.$$

(7.293)

Continue calculating with

$$[e \cos v_i] = \frac{p}{r_i} - 1, \ i = 1, 2, 3,$$

(7.294)

and for $v_2 - v_1 \neq \pi$, obtain

$$[e \sin v_2] = \frac{-\cos (v_2 - v_1)[e \cos v_2] + [e \cos v_1]}{\sin (v_2 - v_1)}$$

(7.295)

or, if $v_2 - v_1 = \pi$, obtain

$$[e \sin v_2] = \frac{\cos (v_3 - v_2)[e \cos v_2] - [e \cos v_3]}{\sin (v_3 - v_1)}.$$

(7.296)

Evaluate

$$e^2 = [e \cos v_2]^2 + [e \sin v_2]^2$$

(7.297)

$$a = p/(1 - e^2)$$

(7.298)

and if $e^2 < 1$, continue the computations with Eq. 7.299; if $e^2 > 1$, proceed directly to Eq. 7.306.

Continue calculating with

$$n = k\mu^{1/2}a^{-3/2}$$

(7.299)

$$S_e = \frac{r_2}{p} [1 - e^2]^{1/2}[e \sin v_2]$$

(7.300)

$$C_e = \frac{r_2}{p} (e^2 + [e \cos v_2])$$

(7.301)

$$\sin (E_3 - E_2) = \frac{r_3}{[ap]^{1/2}} \sin (v_3 - v_2) - \frac{r_3}{p} [1 - \cos (v_3 - v_2)]S_e$$

(7.302)

$$\cos (E_3 - E_2) = 1 - \frac{r_3 r_2}{ap} [1 - \cos (v_3 - v_2)]$$

$$\sin (E_2 - E_1) = \frac{r_1}{[ap]^{1/2}} \sin (v_2 - v_1) + \frac{r_1}{p} [1 - \cos (v_2 - v_1)]S_e$$

(7.303)

$$\cos (E_2 - E_1) = 1 - \frac{r_2 r_1}{ap} [1 - \cos (v_2 - v_1)]$$

$$M_3 - M_2 = E_3 - E_2 + 2S_e \sin^2 \left(\frac{E_3 - E_2}{2}\right) - C_e \sin (E_3 - E_2)$$

$$(7.304)$$

$$M_1 - M_2 = -(E_2 - E_1) + 2S_e \sin^2 \left(\frac{E_2 - E_1}{2}\right) + C_e \sin (E_2 - E_1)$$

$$F_1 = \tau_1 - k\left(\frac{M_1 - M_2}{n}\right)$$

$$F_2 = \tau_3 - k\left(\frac{M_3 - M_2}{n}\right).$$

$$(7.305)$$

Proceed to Eq. 7.312.

For hyperbolic calculations, continue calculating with

$$n = k\mu^{\frac{1}{2}}(-a)^{-\frac{3}{2}}$$

$$(7.306)$$

$$S_h = \frac{r_2}{p} [e^2 - 1]^{\frac{1}{2}}[e \sin v_2]$$

$$C_h = \frac{r_2}{p} (e^2 + [e \cos v_2])$$

$$(7.307)$$

$$\sinh (F_3 - F_2) = \frac{r_3}{[-ap]^{\frac{1}{2}}} \sin (v_3 - v_2) - \frac{r_3}{p} [1 - \cos (v_3 - v_2)]S_h$$

$$\sinh (F_2 - F_1) = \frac{r_1}{[-ap]^{\frac{1}{2}}} \sin (v_2 - v_1) + \frac{r_1}{p} [1 - \cos (v_2 - v_1)]S_h$$

$$(7.308)$$

$$F_3 - F_2 = \log \{\sinh (F_3 - F_2) + [\sinh^2 (F_3 - F_2) + 1]^{\frac{1}{2}}\}$$

$$(7.309)$$

$$F_2 - F_1 = \log \{\sinh (F_2 - F_1) + [\sinh^2 (F_2 - F_1) + 1]^{\frac{1}{2}}\}$$

$$M_3 - M_2 = -(F_3 - F_2) + 2S_h \sinh^2 \left(\frac{F_3 - F_2}{2}\right)$$
$$+ C_h \sinh (F_3 - F_2)$$

$$(7.310)$$

$$M_1 - M_2 = (F_2 - F_1) + 2S_h \sinh^2 \left(\frac{F_2 - F_1}{2}\right)$$
$$- C_h \sinh (F_2 - F_1)$$

$$F_1 = \tau_1 - k\left(\frac{M_1 - M_2}{n}\right)$$

$$F_2 = \tau_3 - k\left(\frac{M_3 - M_2}{n}\right).$$

$$(7.311)$$

Save $F_1$, $F_2$, $r_1$, increment $r_1$ by $\Delta r_1$ (about 4%) and return to Eq. 7.281; the end result of this calculation will be $F_1(r_1 + \Delta r_1, r_2)$, $F_2(r_1 + \Delta r_1, r_2)$, so that

$$\frac{\partial F_1}{\partial r_1} \simeq \frac{F_1(r_1 + \Delta r_1, r_2) - F_1(r_1, r_2)}{\Delta r_1} \tag{7.312}$$

$$\frac{\partial F_2}{\partial r_1} \simeq \frac{F_2(r_1 + \Delta r_1, r_2) - F_2(r_1, r_2)}{\Delta r_1}. \tag{7.313}$$

Save $\partial F_1/r_1$, $\partial F_2/\partial r_1$, set $r_1$ back to the original value, increment $r_2$ by $\Delta r_2$ (about 4%) and return to Eq. 7.281; the end result of this calculation will be $F_1(r_1, r_2 + \Delta r_2)$, $F_2(r_1, r_2 + \Delta r_2)$, so that

$$\frac{\partial F_1}{\partial r_2} \simeq \frac{F_1(r_1, r_2 + \Delta r_2) - F_1(r_1, r_2)}{\Delta r_2} \tag{7.314}$$

$$\frac{\partial F_2}{\partial r_2} \simeq \frac{F_2(r_1, r_2 + \Delta r_2) - F_2(r_1, r_2)}{\Delta r_2}. \tag{7.315}$$

Continue calculating with

$$\Delta = \left(\frac{\partial F_1}{\partial r_1}\right)\left(\frac{\partial F_2}{\partial r_2}\right) - \left(\frac{\partial F_2}{\partial r_1}\right)\left(\frac{\partial F_1}{\partial r_2}\right) \tag{7.316}$$

$$\Delta_1 = \left(\frac{\partial F_2}{\partial r_2}\right)F_1 - \left(\frac{\partial F_1}{\partial r_2}\right)F_2 \tag{7.317}$$

$$\Delta_2 = \left(\frac{\partial F_1}{\partial r_1}\right)F_2 - \left(\frac{\partial F_2}{\partial r_1}\right)F_1 \tag{7.318}$$

$$\Delta r_1 = -\frac{\Delta_1}{\Delta} \tag{7.319}$$

$$\Delta r_2 = -\frac{\Delta_2}{\Delta}. \tag{7.320}$$

Check to see if

$$\begin{aligned}|\Delta r_1| &< \epsilon \\ |\Delta r_2| &< \epsilon,\end{aligned} \tag{7.321}$$

where $\epsilon$ is a tolerance.[21]    If this test is not satisfied, let

$$\begin{aligned}(r_1)_{n+1} &= (r_1)_n + \Delta r_1 \\ (r_2)_{n+1} &= (r_2)_n + \Delta r_2,\end{aligned} \tag{7.322}$$

[21] For near-Earth orbits $\epsilon < 1.0 \times 10^{-6}$ e.r. has been a satisfactory tolerance.

and return to Eq. 7.281; if it is, continue calculating with

$$f = 1 - \frac{a}{r_2} [1 - \cos (E_3 - E_2)] \tag{7.323}$$

$$g = \tau_3 - \frac{a^{3/2}}{\sqrt{\mu}} [E_3 - E_2 - \sin (E_3 - E_2)] \tag{7.324}$$

$$\dot{\mathbf{r}}_2 = \frac{\mathbf{r}_3 - f\mathbf{r}_2}{g}. \tag{7.325}$$

The fundamental set $\mathbf{r}_2$ and $\dot{\mathbf{r}}_2$ is known and the orbit is considered determined.

### 7.7 REFERENCE ORBITS

#### 7.7.1 Preliminary remarks

For the sake of reference, it will be beneficial to list sets of topocentric angles and the corresponding position and velocity vectors at the central observation or date. All the listed reference orbits have been computed by two-body inverse square formulations. It should be noted that

$k = 0.07436574$ (e.r.)$^{3/2}$/min

$\mu = 1.0$ e.m.

$a_e = 1.0$ e.r.

In the following orbits, the rectangular components are referenced with respect to System 2, Chapter 4, that is, the right ascension-declination coordinate system. The tabulated orbits are geocentric.

#### 7.7.2 Reference orbit number VII

| Date | Topocentric Angles | |
|------|----------------------|--|
| J.D. | RIGHT ASCENSION (degrees) | DECLINATION (degrees) |
| 2438314.7916667 | 153°6949 | + 36°2726 |
| 2438314.8055556 | 186°7296 | + 24°8918 |
| 2438314.8194444 | 202°9475 | + 9°8723 |

*Station Location*

$\phi = +40°00 \qquad \lambda_E = 250°00 \qquad H = 0.78393 \times 10^{-3}$ e.r.

*Corresponding Position and Velocity*
*Vectors at Central Date* (c.u.)

$x = -1.22192$          $\dot{x} = -0.468449$
$y = +3.52894 \times 10^{-2}$     $\dot{y} = -0.513595$
$z = +1.54752$          $\dot{z} = -0.175849$
Iteration estimates $r = 2.0$ e.r., $r_2 = 2.1$ e.r.

### 7.7.3   Reference orbit number VIII

| Date | Topocentric Angles | |
|------|------|------|
| J.D. | RIGHT ASCENSION (degrees) | DECLINATION (degrees) |
| 2438181.9583333 | 96°7675 | 34°1759 |
| 2438182.1666667 | 182°5533 | 35°2127 |
| 2438182.3750000 | 215°0986 | 8°4289 |

*Station Location*

$\phi = 36°4594$      $\lambda_E = 353°7935$      $H = 0.12386 \times 10^{-4}$ e.r.

*Corresponding Position and Velocity*
*Vectors at Central Date* (c.u.)

$x = -6.82944$          $\dot{x} = -0.194685$
$y = +3.88821 \times 10^{-1}$     $\dot{y} = -0.301251$
$z = +5.10408$          $\dot{z} = -0.753532 \times 10^{-1}$
Iteration estimates $r_1 = 10.0$ e.r., $r_2 = 10.1$ e.r.

### 7.8  SUMMARY

Three different methods for the calculation of orbits from angular observations have been developed in this chapter. Each method has particular advantages and will find its appropriate place in the process of
preliminary orbit determination. The method of Gauss is very suitable
for angular data spread over short arcs. It is, however, a true orbit
scheme, in that all three sets of observations satisfy the orbit on the three

required dates.  The Laplacian technique is shorter from a computational standpoint, but only the angular observation on the central date is accurately represented by the computational scheme.  For angular data spread over large arcs, perhaps over a number of revolutions, the double $r$-iteration can be employed to yield the desired orbit.  A number of reference orbits which might find use in machine coding of the angles only techniques were recorded.

**EXERCISES**

1. At Woomera, Australia, with station coordinates $\phi = -31°.1018$, $\lambda_E = 136°.754$, and $H = 162$ meters, the following observation is made on 1959 September $28^{day}$ $19^{hr}$ $39^{min}$ $27.226^{sec}$:

|     | $\alpha_t$ | $\delta_t$ |
|-----|-----------|-----------|
| (1) | $97°.7909$ | $-20°.4979$ |

At this point the satellite is lost due to visibility conditions.  A quick estimate of the direction of the orbit is relayed to northern stations.  On the same day, Organ Pass, New Mexico, U.S.A., with station coordinates $\phi = 32°.4241$, $\lambda_E = 253°.448$, and $H = 1651$ meters, makes the following two sets of angular measurements:

|     | $\alpha_t$ | $\delta_t$ |
|-----|-----------|-----------|
| (2) | $285°.3345$ | $27°.4552$ |
| (3) | $299°.4592$ | $30°.2557$ |

The two measurements at Organ Pass are respectively delayed from the Woomera sighting by $54^{min}$ $56.449^{sec}$ and $57^{min}$ $30.505^{sec}$.  Determine the orbit of 1959 Alpha 2.

2. Obtain a set of equations representing right ascension and declination as functions of modified time to terms of the order $\tau^3$.  Consider these formulas for generating an approximate "fourth observation" in order to resolve ambiguous orbits in the methods of Gauss and Laplace.

3. Is there any advantage in guessing the magnitudes of two radius vectors instead of two slant range vectors in the double $r$-iteration?

4. Devise a computational algorithm for calculating the topocentric right ascension-declination of a geocentric satellite, given the classical orbital elements: $a$, $e$, $T$, $i$, $\Omega$, $\omega$.

5. Show that the $d_i$ coefficients of the Herrick–Gibbs equation can be conveniently rewritten as

$$d_1 = \tau_3 \left[ \frac{\mu}{12 r_1{}^3} - \frac{1}{\tau_1 \tau_{13}} \right]$$

$$d_2 = (\tau_1 + \tau_3) \left[ \frac{\mu}{12 r_2{}^3} - \frac{1}{\tau_1 \tau_3} \right]$$

$$d_3 = - \tau_1 \left[ \frac{\mu}{12 r_3{}^3} + \frac{1}{\tau_3 \tau_{13}} \right].$$

6. The following observations are made from San Fernando, Spain, ($\phi = 36° 27' 49\overset{.}{.}8$, $\lambda_E = 353° 47' 41\overset{..}{.}5$, $H = 24$ meters):

| Universal Time | $\alpha_t$ | $\delta_t$ |
|---|---|---|
| 1959 September | | |
| $26^{\text{day}}, 21^{\text{hr}}, 25^{\text{min}}, 37.403^{\text{sec}}$ | $16^{\text{hr}} 58^{\text{min}} 41.57^{\text{sec}}$ | $13° 5' 33\overset{..}{.}8$ |
| 1959 September | | |
| $26^{\text{day}}, 21^{\text{hr}}, 26^{\text{min}}, 37.862^{\text{sec}}$ | $17^{\text{hr}} 23^{\text{min}} 45.87^{\text{sec}}$ | $13° 17' 8\overset{..}{.}5$ |
| 1959 September | | |
| $26^{\text{day}}, 21^{\text{hr}}, 27^{\text{min}}, 45.919^{\text{sec}}$ | $17^{\text{hr}} 59^{\text{min}} 24.90^{\text{sec}}$ | $13° 0' 15\overset{..}{.}3$ |

Determine the orbit of 1959 Eta and compute the standard orbital elements.

7. Space station Omicron 3 notices an unidentified flying object (U.F.O.) on its radar screen. Assuming that topocentric measurements of right ascension-declination are obtained directly by the on-board computer, how would the orbit of the U.F.O. be determined? Discuss generally.

8. In the method of Gauss, show that

$$c_1 = \frac{y_{13} \tau_3}{y_{23} \tau_{13}}, \qquad c_3 = - \frac{y_{13} \tau_1}{y_{12} \tau_{13}},$$

where $y_{ij}$ are the ratio of the area of the sector to triangle between radius vectors $r_{ij}$.

9. Application of the Gaussian technique yields the eighth-order resolvent

$$r_2{}^8 - 1.000654 r_2{}^6 - 1.077159 r_2{}^3 - 0.320066 = 0.$$

Using the graphical technique of Section 7.3.1, obtain an estimate of the magnitude of the radius vector $r_2$.

10. Show that in the method of Gauss, simultaneous solution for $j = 1$, 2, of

$$F_j \equiv X_j{}^2 (l_j + x_j)^3 + 2 X_j (l_j + x_j) + (l_j + x_j) - m_j = 0$$

will yield eccentric anomaly differences between radius vectors $\mathbf{r}_3$, $\mathbf{r}_2$, and $\mathbf{r}_2$, $\mathbf{r}_1$.

## REFERENCES

1. F. R. Moulton, *An Introduction to Celestial Mechanics*, The Macmillan Company, New York, 1914.

2. H. C. Plummer, *An Introductory Treatise on Dynamical Astronomy*, Dover Publications, New York, 1960.

3. A. D. Dubyago, *The Determination of Orbits*, The Macmillan Company, New York, 1961.

4. P. Herget, *The Computation of Orbits*, privately published by the author, Ann Arbor, Michigan.

5. K. P. Williams, *The Calculation of the Orbits of Asteroids and Comets*, The Principia Press, Bloomington, Indiana, 1934.

6. R. M. L. Baker, Jr., and M. W. Makemson, *An Introduction to Astrodynamics*, Academic Press, New York, 1960.

7. R. E. Briggs, and J. W. Slowey, *An Iterative Method of Orbit Determination from Three Observations of a Nearby Satellite*, Smithsonian Institution Astrophysical Observatory, Special Report No. 27, June 30, 1959.

8. G. Birkhoff and S. MacLane, *A Survey of Modern Algebra*, The Macmillan Company, New York, 1941.

9. E. T. Bell, *Men of Mathematics*, Simon Schuster, New York, 1937.

10. J. Kovalevsky, and F. Barlier, "Determination des Éléments Osculateurs de l'Orbite d'un Satellite Artificiel," Academie Des Sciences, Paris, France, February 27, 1961, p. 1273.

11. P. R. Escobal, *A Solution to the Large Arc Angles-Only Orbit Determination Problem*, Operations Research Incorporated, Technical Report 64-10, April 14, 1964.

12. K. F. Gauss, *Theoria Motus*, Dover Publications, New York, 1963.

13. S. Herrick, *The Laplacian and Gaussian Orbit Methods*, University of California Press, Vol. 1, No. 1, 1940.

14. S. Newcomb, *A Compendium of Spherical Astronomy*, Dover Publications, New York, 1960.

15. *Explanatory Supplement to the Astronomical Ephemeris and the American Ephemeris and Nautical Almanac*, Her Majesty's Stationery Office, London, 1961.

# 8 Mixed data determinations

*What we know is not much; what we do not know is immense.*

LAPLACE [8]

## 8.1 THE MODERN PROBLEM IN ORBIT DETERMINATION

The introduction of radar into the implements of modern science has produced a great variation from established techniques in orbit determination schemes. For the first time, the orbit determiner could measure the distance or extension between the point of observation and the satellite, that is, the *slant range*. Furthermore, modernism provides the orbit determiner with angular data, such as elevation and azimuth. Today, excellent *range rate* or expansion (contraction) rate of the slant range magnitude data is also available for incorporation into the orbit determination problem. This chapter will treat a number of the newer techniques for obtaining an orbit with what is termed herein *mixed data*.

## 8.2 MODIFIED LAPLACIAN DETERMINATION
## (RANGE-RATE AND ANGULAR DATA)

### 8.2.1 A simple modification of Laplace's equation

In Section 7.4, the Laplacian technique for the determination of an orbit from angles only was fully developed. The method of this section is, as the title implies, a slight modification of the Laplacian technique, and allows determination of an orbit from angular data, say $A$, $h$, and range-rate $\dot\rho$. To quickly review the Laplacian method of determining an orbit, consider the fundamental vector relation

$$\mathbf{r} = \rho\mathbf{L} - \mathbf{R}, \tag{8.1}$$

which, upon differentiation twice with respect to modified time, yields

$$\ddot{\mathbf{r}} = \ddot{\rho}\mathbf{L} + 2\dot{\rho}\dot{\mathbf{L}} + \rho\ddot{\mathbf{L}} - \ddot{\mathbf{R}}. \tag{8.2}$$

**293**

It should be remembered that $\mathbf{L}$ is a unit vector along the slant range vector $\boldsymbol{\rho}$. Furthermore, the reader should recall that

$$\mathbf{L} \cdot \mathbf{L} = 1,$$

which implies

$$\mathbf{L} \cdot \dot{\mathbf{L}} = 0$$
$$\mathbf{L} \cdot \ddot{\mathbf{L}} = -\dot{\mathbf{L}} \cdot \dot{\mathbf{L}}, \tag{8.3}$$

as can be proven by direct differentiation with respect to $\tau$. Let the dynamical relationship,

$$\ddot{\mathbf{r}} = -\frac{\mu \mathbf{r}}{r^3} \tag{8.4}$$

be rewritten by virtue of Eq. 8.1 as

$$\ddot{\mathbf{r}} = -\frac{\mu}{r^3} (\rho \mathbf{L} - \mathbf{R}), \tag{8.5}$$

and introduced into Eq. 8.2 to yield

$$-\frac{\mu}{r^3} (\rho \mathbf{L} - \mathbf{R}) = \ddot{\rho} \mathbf{L} + 2\dot{\rho}\dot{\mathbf{L}} + \rho\ddot{\mathbf{L}} - \ddot{\mathbf{R}}. \tag{8.6}$$

It is at this point that a departure from the usual Laplacian technique is initiated by taking the dot product of Eq. 8.6 with $\mathbf{L}$ to produce the equation

$$-\frac{\mu}{r^3} \rho + \frac{\mu}{r^3} \mathbf{L} \cdot \mathbf{R} = \ddot{\rho} + \rho \mathbf{L} \cdot \ddot{\mathbf{L}} - \mathbf{L} \cdot \ddot{\mathbf{R}}. \tag{8.7}$$

Utilization of Eqs. 8.3 provides elimination of $\ddot{\mathbf{L}}$,

$$-\frac{\mu}{r^3} \rho + \frac{\mu}{r^3} \mathbf{L} \cdot \mathbf{R} = \ddot{\rho} - \rho\dot{\mathbf{L}} \cdot \dot{\mathbf{L}} - \mathbf{L} \cdot \ddot{\mathbf{R}} \tag{8.8}$$

or regrouping terms,

$$\left( \dot{\mathbf{L}} \cdot \dot{\mathbf{L}} - \frac{\mu}{r^3} \right) \rho + \frac{\mu}{r^3} \mathbf{L} \cdot \mathbf{R} = \ddot{\rho} - \mathbf{L} \cdot \ddot{\mathbf{R}}. \tag{8.9}$$

It is well to note that if this equation is applied at some specific time, say the central date of the observations, that is, $\dot{\rho}_i$, $A_i$, $h_i$, for $i = 1, 2, 3$, then $\mathbf{L}_i$ are known from Section 7.2, and $\mathbf{R}$ and $\ddot{\mathbf{R}}$ are known from Section 3.11. Thus, Eq. 8.9 represents one equation with the yet unknown parameters $\dot{\mathbf{L}}$, $r$, $\ddot{\rho}$, and $\rho$ at $\tau = \tau_2$.

## 8.2.2 Numerical expansions

In order to obtain numerical expressions for $\ddot{\rho}$, consider the Taylor expansions about some epoch time, say $t_2$, of $\dot{\rho}_1$ and $\dot{\rho}_3$, that is,

$$\dot{\rho}_1 = \dot{\rho}_2 + \tau_1\ddot{\rho}_2 + \frac{\tau_1{}^2\dddot{\rho}_2}{2} + O(\tau_1{}^3)$$

$$\dot{\rho}_3 = \dot{\rho}_2 + \tau_3\ddot{\rho}_2 + \frac{\tau_3{}^2\dddot{\rho}_2}{2} + O(\tau_3{}^3),$$

(8.10)

where, as usual,

$$\tau_1 = k(t_1 - t_2), \qquad \tau_3 = k(t_3 - t_2). \tag{8.11}$$

When the first of Eqs. 8.10 is multiplied by $\tau_3{}^2$ and the second by $\tau_1{}^2$, it is possible to subtract the second equation from the first and obtain

$$\dot{\rho}_1\tau_3{}^2 - \dot{\rho}_3\tau_1{}^2 = \dot{\rho}_2(\tau_3{}^2 - \tau_1{}^2) + \tau_1\tau_3(\tau_3 - \tau_1)\ddot{\rho}_2, \tag{8.12}$$

or,

$$\ddot{\rho}_2 = -\frac{\tau_3}{\tau_1(\tau_1 - \tau_3)}\dot{\rho}_1 - \frac{(\tau_3 + \tau_1)}{\tau_1\tau_3}\dot{\rho}_2 - \frac{\tau_1}{\tau_3(\tau_3 - \tau_1)}\dot{\rho}_3. \tag{8.13}$$

In a similar manner, numerical differentiation can be used to obtain $\dot{\mathbf{L}}_2$ but, for the sake of brevity, from Eq. 7.173,

$$\dot{\mathbf{L}}_2 = -\frac{\tau_3}{\tau_1(\tau_1 - \tau_3)}\mathbf{L}_1 - \frac{(\tau_3 + \tau_1)}{\tau_1\tau_3}\mathbf{L}_2 - \frac{\tau_1}{\tau_3(\tau_3 - \tau_1)}\mathbf{L}_3. \tag{8.14}$$

It is now possible to form the dot product $\dot{\mathbf{L}}_2 \cdot \dot{\mathbf{L}}_2$, so that

$$\dot{\mathbf{L}}_2 \cdot \dot{\mathbf{L}}_2 = s_1{}^2 + s_2{}^2 + s_3{}^2 + 2s_1s_2\mathbf{L}_1 \cdot \mathbf{L}_2$$
$$+ 2s_1s_3\mathbf{L}_1 \cdot \mathbf{L}_3 + 2s_2s_3\mathbf{L}_2 \cdot \mathbf{L}_3, \tag{8.15}$$

where

$$s_1 \equiv -\frac{\tau_3}{\tau_1(\tau_1 - \tau_3)}$$

$$s_2 \equiv -\frac{(\tau_3 + \tau_1)}{\tau_1\tau_3} \tag{8.16}$$

$$s_3 \equiv -\frac{\tau_1}{\tau_3(\tau_3 - \tau_1)}.$$

## 8.2.3 Solution of the equations

In order to effect a solution of the modified Laplacian equations, let Eq. 8.9 be written on the central date as

$$\rho_2 = \frac{A + B/r_2{}^3}{C + D/r_2{}^3}, \tag{8.17}$$

where

$$A \equiv \ddot{\rho}_2 - \mathbf{L}_2 \cdot \ddot{\mathbf{R}}_2$$
$$B \equiv -\mu \mathbf{L}_2 \cdot \mathbf{R}_2$$
$$C \equiv \dot{\mathbf{L}}_2 \cdot \dot{\mathbf{L}}_2 \qquad (8.18)$$
$$D \equiv -\mu.$$

The four constants of Eq. 8.17 are known from observational data and utilization of Eqs. 8.13 and 8.15. This equation represents the dynamical constraint of the orbit determination process. Another independent equation representing geometrical constraints is obtainable from the fundamental vector relationship

$$\mathbf{r}_2 = \boldsymbol{\rho}_2 - \mathbf{R}_2. \qquad (8.19)$$

Therefore,

$$r_2{}^2 = \mathbf{r}_2 \cdot \mathbf{r}_2 = \rho_2{}^2 - 2\boldsymbol{\rho}_2 \cdot \mathbf{R}_2 + R_2{}^2 \qquad (8.20)$$

can be used with the aid of $\boldsymbol{\rho}_2 = \rho_2 \mathbf{L}_2$ as the second equation required for solution of the problem. To be explicit, consider the system

$$\rho = \frac{A + B/r^3}{C + D/r^3} \qquad (8.21)$$

$$F(r) = \rho^2 + \rho C_\psi + R^2 - r^2 = 0, \qquad (8.22)$$

where $C_\psi \equiv -2\mathbf{L} \cdot \mathbf{R}$ and the subscript 2 has been omitted for brevity. Consider $F(r)$ as an iterative function of $r$. By differentiation, it is possible to write

$$F'(r) = (2\rho + C_\psi)\frac{d\rho}{dr} - 2r, \qquad (8.23)$$

where, from Eq. 8.21,

$$\frac{d\rho}{dr} = \frac{3}{r^4}\frac{(D\rho - B)}{(C + D/r^3)}. \qquad (8.24)$$

Hence

$$F'(r) = \frac{3}{r^4}\frac{(2\rho + C_\psi)(D\rho - B)}{(C + D/r^3)} - 2r, \qquad (8.25)$$

and an assumed value of $r$ permits $\rho$ to be obtained from Eq. 8.21, so that $F'(r)$ utilized in the Newton successive approximation formula

$$r_{n+1} = r_n - \frac{F(r_n)}{F'(r_n)}, \quad r = 1, 2, \dots, q, \qquad (8.26)$$

yields an improved value of $r$. The above process can be repeated until an acceptable value of $r$, actually $r_2$, is obtained. The iterative scheme also yields $\rho_2$ by consequence of Eq. 8.21. The position and velocity vectors may then be determined from

$$\mathbf{r}_2 = \rho_2 \mathbf{L}_2 - \mathbf{R}_2$$
$$\dot{\mathbf{r}}_2 = \dot{\rho}_2 \mathbf{L}_2 + \rho_2 \dot{\mathbf{L}}_2 - \dot{\mathbf{R}}_2,$$

(8.27)

and once again the fundamental set has been determined.

It should be pointed out that the method is by no means limited by Eqs. 8.13 and 8.14, since the Lagrange interpolating polynomial (Section 7.3.2) can be advantageously utilized to obtain higher order expressions for $\ddot{\rho}$ and $\dot{\mathbf{L}}$.

### 8.2.4  Computational algorithm

Given the mixed data $\dot{\rho}_i$, $\alpha_{ti}$, $\delta_{ti}$, $t_i$, for $i = 1, 2, 3$, along with $\phi$, $\lambda_E$, $H$ and the constants, $a_e$, $k$, $\mu$, $f$, $d\theta/dt$, proceed as follows:

$$\tau_1 = k(t_1 - t_2)$$
$$\tau_3 = k(t_3 - t_2)$$

(8.28)

$$s_1 = -\frac{\tau_3}{\tau_1(\tau_1 - \tau_3)}$$

$$s_2 = -\frac{(\tau_3 + \tau_1)}{\tau_1 \tau_3}$$

(8.29)

$$s_3 = -\frac{\tau_1}{\tau_3(\tau_3 - \tau_1)}.$$

For $i = 1, 2, 3$, compute

$$L_{xi} = \cos \delta_{ti} \cos \alpha_{ti}$$
$$L_{yi} = \cos \delta_{ti} \sin \alpha_{ti}$$
$$L_{zi} = \sin \delta_{ti}.$$

(8.30)

Continue calculating with

$$\ddot{\rho}_2 = s_1 \dot{\rho}_1 + s_2 \dot{\rho}_2 + s_3 \dot{\rho}_3$$

(8.31)

$$\dot{\mathbf{L}}_2 = s_1 \mathbf{L}_1 + s_2 \mathbf{L}_2 + s_3 \mathbf{L}_3.$$

(8.32)

For observations from a single station, form

$$G_1 = \frac{a_e}{\sqrt{1 - (2f - f^2)\sin^2 \phi}} + H$$

$$G_2 = \frac{(1 - f)^2 a_e}{\sqrt{1 - (2f - f^2)\sin^2 \phi}} + H.$$

(8.33)

Obtain the Greenwich sidereal time $\theta_{g0}$ from Eq. 1.27 and continue calculating with

$$\theta_2 = \theta_{g0} + \frac{d\theta}{dt}(t_2 - t_0) + \lambda_E$$

$$X_2 = -G_1 \cos\phi \cos\theta_2 \tag{8.34}$$
$$Y_2 = -G_1 \cos\phi \sin\theta_2$$
$$Z_2 = -G_2 \sin\phi$$

$$\dot{\mathbf{R}}_2 = \frac{1}{k}\begin{bmatrix} -Y_2 \\ X_2 \\ 0 \end{bmatrix}\frac{d\theta}{dt}$$

$$\tag{8.35}$$

$$\ddot{\mathbf{R}}_2 = \frac{1}{k^2}\begin{bmatrix} -X_2 \\ -Y_2 \\ 0 \end{bmatrix}\left(\frac{d\theta}{dt}\right)^2$$

$$A = \ddot{\rho}_2 - \mathbf{L}_2 \cdot \ddot{\mathbf{R}}_2$$
$$B = -\mu\mathbf{L}_2 \cdot \mathbf{R}_2$$
$$C = \dot{\mathbf{L}}_2 \cdot \dot{\mathbf{L}}_2 \tag{8.36}$$
$$D = -\mu$$
$$C_\psi = -2\mathbf{L}_2 \cdot \mathbf{R}_2.$$

As a first approximation, set $r_2 = r_{2G}$, where $r_{2G}$ is an assumed value of $r_2$, and initiate the following iterative scheme:

$$\rho_2 = \frac{A + B/r_2{}^3}{C + D/r_2{}^3} \tag{8.37}$$

$$F(r_2) = \rho_2{}^2 + \rho_2 C_\psi + R^2 - r_2{}^2 \tag{8.38}$$

$$F'(r_2) = \frac{3}{r_2{}^4}\frac{(2\rho_2 + C_\psi)(D\rho_2 - B)}{(C + D/r_2{}^3)} - 2r_2, \tag{8.39}$$

and obtain a better value of $r_2$, that is,

$$(r_2)_{n+1} = (r_2)_n - \frac{F[(r_2)_n]}{F'[(r_2)_n]}, \quad n = 1, 2, \ldots, q. \tag{8.40}$$

If the improved value of $r_2$ does not vary, that is,

$$|(r_2)_{n+1} - (r_2)_n| < \epsilon, \tag{8.41}$$

where $\epsilon$ is a specified tolerance, proceed to Eq. 8.42; if not, return to Eq. 8.37, and using the latest value of $r_2$, repeat equational loop 8.38 to 8.40.

Continue calculating with

$$\mathbf{r}_2 = \rho_2 \mathbf{L}_2 - \mathbf{R}_2 \tag{8.42}$$

$$\dot{\mathbf{r}}_2 = \dot{\rho}_2 \mathbf{L}_2 + \rho_2 \dot{\mathbf{L}}_2 - \dot{\mathbf{R}}_2. \tag{8.43}$$

Knowing $\mathbf{r}_2$ and $\dot{\mathbf{r}}_2$, it is an easy extension to compute the desired elements and the orbit is considered determined.

### 8.3 THE r-ITERATION (RANGE-RATE AND ANGULAR DATA)

#### 8.3.1 A second method

Another approach to the range-rate and angle determination of an orbit has been devised by Baker. The method possesses the advantage of reducing the relative weight or influence with which the numerically differentiated unit vector $\mathbf{L}$ enters into the calculations. The technique presented here is a slight modification of Baker's approach [2].

#### 8.3.2 f and g series approach

Let is be assumed that $\dot{\rho}_i, \alpha_{ti}, \delta_{ti}$, for $t_i$ and $i = 1, 2, 3$ is the orbital data. Evidently then, as in the previous methods, the $\mathbf{L}_i$ unit vectors may be obtained (Section 7.2), and $\mathbf{R}$ and its time derivatives are also known from Section 3.11.

By forming the respective modified times, that is,

$$\tau_{ij} = k(t_j - t_i), \tag{8.44}$$

where $i$ indicates the arbitrary epoch time, say the second or middle date of observation, Eq. 7.173, permits

$$\dot{\mathbf{L}}_2 = -\frac{\tau_3}{\tau_1(\tau_1 - \tau_3)} \mathbf{L}_1 - \frac{(\tau_3 + \tau_1)}{\tau_1 \tau_3} \mathbf{L}_2 - \frac{\tau_1}{\tau_3(\tau_3 - \tau_1)} \mathbf{L}_3 \tag{8.45}$$

to be computed. This derivative will be used presently.

From Section 3.9, it is possible to write

$$\mathbf{r}_j = f_j \mathbf{r}_2 + g_j \dot{\mathbf{r}}_2, \tag{8.46}$$

where $f$ and $g$ are modified time series expansions of the fundamental form $\ddot{\mathbf{r}} = -\mu \mathbf{r}/r^3$. By differentiation, noting that $\mathbf{r}_2$ and $\dot{\mathbf{r}}_2$ are constants at epoch time $t_2$, it is evident that

$$\dot{\mathbf{r}}_j = \dot{f}_j \mathbf{r}_2 + \dot{g}_j \dot{\mathbf{r}}_2, \tag{8.47}$$

where $\dot{f_j}$ and $\dot{g_j}$ are the derivatives of the $f$ and $g$ series with respect to modified time. For the sake of convenience, a few terms of these series are

$$f_j = 1 - \tfrac{1}{2}u_2\tau_{2j}^2 + \tfrac{1}{2}u_2p_2\tau_{2j}^3 \ldots$$
$$g_j = \tau_{2j} - \tfrac{1}{6}u_2\tau_{2j}^3 + \tfrac{1}{4}u_2p_2\tau_{2j}^4 \ldots$$
$$\dot{f_j} = -u_2\tau_{2j} + \tfrac{3}{2}u_2p_2\tau_{2j}^2 \ldots$$
$$\dot{g_j} = 1 - \tfrac{1}{2}u_2\tau_{2j}^2 + u_2p_2\tau_{2j}^3 \ldots,$$

$$(8.48)$$

with

$$u_2 \equiv \frac{\mu}{r_2^3}$$

$$p_2 \equiv \frac{\mathbf{r}_2 \cdot \dot{\mathbf{r}}_2}{r_2^2}.$$

An alternate expression for $\dot{\mathbf{r}}_j$ may also be obtained by differentiation of the relation between observer, satellite, and dynamical center (Section 3.11), that is,

$$\mathbf{r}_j = \boldsymbol{\rho}_j - \mathbf{R}_j \tag{8.49}$$

or, since $\mathbf{L}_j$ is directed along $\boldsymbol{\rho}_j$,

$$\mathbf{r}_j = \rho_j\mathbf{L}_j - \mathbf{R}_j, \tag{8.50}$$

so that

$$\dot{\mathbf{r}}_j = \dot{\rho}_j\mathbf{L}_j + \rho_j\dot{\mathbf{L}}_j - \dot{\mathbf{R}}_j. \tag{8.51}$$

Hence, for times $t_1$ and $t_2$, it is possible to equate Eqs. 8.47 and 8.51, so that

$$\dot{\mathbf{r}}_j = \dot{f_j}\mathbf{r}_2 + \dot{g_j}\dot{\mathbf{r}}_2 = \dot{\rho}_j\mathbf{L}_j + \rho_j\dot{\mathbf{L}}_j - \dot{\mathbf{R}}_j. \tag{8.52}$$

By dotting Eq. 8.52 with $\mathbf{L}_j$, the following relationship results:

$$\dot{f_j}\mathbf{r}_2 \cdot \mathbf{L}_j + \dot{g_j}\dot{\mathbf{r}}_2 \cdot \mathbf{L}_j = \dot{\rho}_j - \dot{\mathbf{R}}_j \cdot \mathbf{L}_j. \tag{8.53}$$

Substitution of Eqs. 8.50 and 8.51 into Eq. 8.53, yields

$$\dot{f_j}(\rho_2\mathbf{L}_2 - \mathbf{R}_2) \cdot \mathbf{L}_j + \dot{g_j}(\dot{\rho}_2\mathbf{L}_2 + \rho_2\dot{\mathbf{L}}_2 - \dot{\mathbf{R}}_2) \cdot \mathbf{L}_j = \dot{\rho}_j - \dot{\mathbf{R}}_j \cdot \mathbf{L}_j.$$

$$(8.54)$$

Multiplying Eq. 8.54 evaluated at $\tau_1$ by $\dot{g_3}$ and adding it to Eq. 8.54 multiplied by $-\dot{g_1}$ evaluated at $\tau_3$, results in

$$\dot{f_1}\dot{g_3}(\rho_2\mathbf{L}_2 - \mathbf{R}_2) \cdot \mathbf{L}_1 - \dot{f_3}\dot{g_1}(\rho_2\mathbf{L}_2 - \mathbf{R}_2) \cdot \mathbf{L}_3$$
$$+ \dot{g_1}\dot{g_3}[\rho_2\mathbf{L}_2 \cdot (\mathbf{L}_1 - \mathbf{L}_3) + \rho_2\dot{\mathbf{L}}_2 \cdot (\mathbf{L}_1 - \mathbf{L}_3) - \dot{\mathbf{R}}_2 \cdot (\mathbf{L}_1 - \mathbf{L}_3)]$$
$$= \dot{g_3}(\dot{\rho}_1 - \dot{\mathbf{R}}_1 \cdot \mathbf{L}_1) - \dot{g_1}(\dot{\rho}_3 - \dot{\mathbf{R}}_3 \cdot \mathbf{L}_3). \tag{8.55}$$

This equation may be regrouped as follows:

$$\rho_2\{\dot{f}_1\dot{g}_3\mathbf{L}_1 \cdot \mathbf{L}_2 - \dot{f}_3\dot{g}_1\mathbf{L}_2 \cdot \mathbf{L}_3 + \dot{g}_1\dot{g}_3\dot{\mathbf{L}}_2 \cdot (\mathbf{L}_1 - \mathbf{L}_3)\}$$
$$= \{\dot{f}_1\dot{g}_3\mathbf{L}_1 \cdot \mathbf{R}_2 - \dot{f}_3\dot{g}_1\mathbf{L}_3 \cdot \mathbf{R}_2 + \dot{g}_1\dot{g}_3(\mathbf{L}_1 - \mathbf{L}_3) \cdot \dot{\mathbf{R}}_2$$
$$- \dot{g}_3\dot{\mathbf{R}}_1 \cdot \mathbf{L}_1 + \dot{g}_1\dot{\mathbf{R}}_3 \cdot \mathbf{L}_3\}$$
$$- \dot{g}_1\dot{g}_3\dot{\mathbf{L}}_2 \cdot (\mathbf{L}_1 - \mathbf{L}_3)\dot{\rho}_2 + \dot{g}_3\dot{\rho}_1 - \dot{g}_1\dot{\rho}_3, \quad (8.56)$$

and, upon introduction of the definitions,

$$A \equiv \{\dot{f}_1\dot{g}_3\mathbf{L}_1 \cdot \mathbf{R}_2 - \dot{f}_3\dot{g}_1\mathbf{L}_3 \cdot \mathbf{R}_2 + \dot{g}_1\dot{g}_3(\mathbf{L}_1 - \mathbf{L}_3) \cdot \dot{\mathbf{R}}_2$$
$$- \dot{g}_3\mathbf{L}_1 \cdot \dot{\mathbf{R}}_1 + \dot{g}_1\mathbf{L}_3 \cdot \dot{\mathbf{R}}_3\}/E$$

$$B \equiv \dot{g}_3/E$$

$$C \equiv -\dot{g}_1\dot{g}_3\dot{\mathbf{L}}_2 \cdot (\mathbf{L}_1 - \mathbf{L}_3)/E \quad (8.57)$$

$$D \equiv -\dot{g}_1/E$$

$$E \equiv \dot{f}_1\dot{g}_3\mathbf{L}_1 \cdot \mathbf{L}_2 - \dot{f}_3\dot{g}_1\mathbf{L}_3 \cdot \mathbf{L}_2 + \dot{g}_1\dot{g}_3\dot{\mathbf{L}}_2 \cdot (\mathbf{L}_1 - \mathbf{L}_3),$$

it is possible to write compactly

$$\rho_2 = A + \dot{\rho}_1 B + \dot{\rho}_2 C + \dot{\rho}_3 D. \quad (8.58)$$

### 8.3.3 Solution of the equation

Equation 8.58 is an expression for the magnitude of the slant range vector on the central date of observation. The range rates and the $\mathbf{L}_i$ are known from the original data. However, the $A$, $B$, $C$, $D$ coefficients are also functionally dependent upon the derivatives $\dot{f}_i$, $\dot{g}_i$, which are still unknown.

Consider making a guess at the magnitude of the radius vector at the central date, that is, $r_2$. Then, with the help of the auxiliary parameter $C_\psi$ defined through

$$C_\psi \equiv -2\mathbf{L}_2 \cdot \mathbf{R}_2 = -2(L_{x2}X_2 + L_{y2}Y_2 + L_{z2}Z_2), \quad (8.59)$$

it is possible to solve

$$\mathbf{r}_2 \cdot \mathbf{r}_2 = (\rho_2\mathbf{L}_2 - \mathbf{R}_2) \cdot (\rho_2\mathbf{L}_2 - \mathbf{R}_2) = \rho_2{}^2 + \rho_2 C_\psi + R_2{}^2 \quad (8.60)$$

in the form

$$\rho_2{}^2 + C_\psi\rho_2 + (R_2{}^2 - r_2{}^2) = 0, \quad (8.61)$$

to obtain $\rho_2$, the magnitude of the slant range vector. It should be noted that of the two roots obtained in the solution of the quadratic equation for $\rho_2$, the spurious root can be eliminated, since

$$\rho_2 = \tfrac{1}{2}\{-C_\psi + [C_\psi{}^2 - 4(R_2{}^2 - r_2{}^2)]^{1/2}\}, \quad (8.62)$$

where the correct sign of the radical is positive due to the fact that $R_2{}^2 - r_2{}^2 < 0$ and $C_\psi > 0$, as the satellite moves from horizon to horizon. Once $\rho_2$ has been computed, $\mathbf{r}_2$ is obtained directly from

$$\mathbf{r}_2 = \rho_2 \mathbf{L}_2 - \mathbf{R}_2. \tag{8.63}$$

Continuing the process, it is now possible to determine

$$\dot{\mathbf{r}}_2 = \dot{\rho}_2 \mathbf{L}_2 + \rho_2 \dot{\mathbf{L}}_2 - \dot{\mathbf{R}}_2, \tag{8.64}$$

and form

$$\begin{aligned} r_2 &= \mathbf{r}_2 \cdot \mathbf{r}_2 \\ \dot{r}_2 &= \mathbf{r}_2 \cdot \dot{\mathbf{r}}_2 / r_2 \\ V_2 &= +\sqrt{\dot{\mathbf{r}}_2 \cdot \dot{\mathbf{r}}_2}, \end{aligned} \tag{8.65}$$

so that from Eqs. 8.48, or to a higher degree of precision from Section 3.9, one can compute

$$\begin{aligned} \dot{f_i} &= \dot{f}(V_2, r_2, \dot{r}_2, \tau_i) \\ \dot{g_i} &= \dot{g}(V_2, r_2, \dot{r}_2, \tau_i). \end{aligned} \tag{8.66}$$

Equations 8.57 can now be utilized in order to compute $A$, $B$, $C$, $D$, and by virtue of Eq. 8.58, it is possible to recalculate $\rho_2$. Perhaps the simplest technique for solution is to consider this method as belonging to the self-perpetuating type, and once a value of $\rho_2$ is obtained from Eq. 8.58 one can return to Eq. 8.63 and repeat the loop until convergence is achieved. This approach assumes that $F'(\rho_2)$ is bounded in the region $-1 < F'(\rho_2) < 1$ in order that the successive iterates of $\rho_2$ converge [5].

### 8.3.4   Computational algorithm

Given the mixed data $\dot{\rho}_i$, $\alpha_{ti}$, $\delta_{ti}$, $t_i$, for $i = 1, 2, 3$, along with $\phi$, $\lambda_E$, $H$ and the constants $a_e$, $k$, $\mu$, $f$, $d\theta/dt$, proceed as follows:

$$\begin{aligned} \tau_1 &= k(t_1 - t_2) \\ \tau_3 &= k(t_3 - t_2) \end{aligned} \tag{8.67}$$

$$s_1 = -\frac{\tau_3}{\tau_1(\tau_1 - \tau_3)} \tag{8.68}$$

$$s_2 = -\frac{(\tau_3 + \tau_1)}{\tau_1 \tau_3} \tag{8.69}$$

$$s_3 = -\frac{\tau_1}{\tau_3(\tau_3 - \tau_1)}. \tag{8.70}$$

For $i = 1, 2, 3$, compute

$$L_{xi} = \cos \delta_{ti} \cos \alpha_{ti}$$
$$L_{yi} = \cos \delta_{ti} \sin \alpha_{ti} \tag{8.71}$$
$$L_{zi} = \sin \delta_{ti}.$$

Obtain the Greenwich sidereal time $\theta_{g0}$ from Eq. 1.27 and continue calculating with

$$\theta_i = \theta_{g0} + \frac{d\theta}{dt}(t_i - t_0) + \lambda_E \tag{8.72}$$

$$G_1 = \frac{a_e}{\sqrt{1 - (2f - f^2)\sin^2\phi}} + H$$
$$\tag{8.73}$$
$$G_2 = \frac{(1 - f)^2 a_e}{\sqrt{1 - (2f - f^2)\sin^2\phi}} + H$$

$$X_i = -G_1 \cos\phi \cos\theta_i$$
$$Y_i = -G_1 \cos\phi \sin\theta_i \tag{8.74}$$
$$Z_i = -G_2 \sin\phi$$
$$C_\psi = -2(L_{x2}X_2 + L_{y2}Y_2 + L_{z2}Z_2).$$

For observations from a single station, obtain

$$\dot{\mathbf{R}}_i = \frac{1}{k} \begin{bmatrix} -Y_i \\ X_i \\ 0 \end{bmatrix} \frac{d\theta}{dt}. \tag{8.75}$$

As a first approximation, set[1] $r_2 = r_g$ and obtain

$$\rho_2 = \tfrac{1}{2}\{-C_\psi + [C_\psi^2 - 4(R^2 - r^2)]^{1/2}\}. \tag{8.76}$$

Compute the radius vector at the central date from

$$\mathbf{r}_2 = \rho_2 \mathbf{L}_2 - \mathbf{R}_2. \tag{8.77}$$

Obtain the numerical derivative

$$\dot{\mathbf{L}}_2 = s_1 \mathbf{L}_1 + s_2 \mathbf{L}_2 + s_3 \mathbf{L}_3. \tag{8.78}$$

Continue calculating with

$$\mathbf{r}_2 = \rho_2 \mathbf{L}_2 - \mathbf{R}_2$$
$$\dot{\mathbf{r}}_2 = \dot{\rho}_2 \mathbf{L}_2 + \rho_2 \dot{\mathbf{L}}_2 - \dot{\mathbf{R}}_2$$
$$\dot{r}_2 = \mathbf{r}_2 \cdot \dot{\mathbf{r}}_2 / r_2 \tag{8.79}$$
$$V_2 = \sqrt{\dot{\mathbf{r}}_2 \cdot \dot{\mathbf{r}}_2}.$$

[1] For near-Earth orbits, set $r_g = 1.1$ e.r.

Utilize the derivatives of the $f$ and $g$ series to compute

$$\dot{f}_i = \dot{f}(V_2, r_2, \dot{r}_2, \tau_i), \quad i = 1, 3, \tag{8.80}$$

$$\dot{g}_i = \dot{g}(V_2, r_2, \dot{r}_2, \tau_i), \quad i = 1, 3. \tag{8.81}$$

Continue calculating with:

$$E = \dot{f}_1 \dot{g}_3 \mathbf{L}_1 \cdot \mathbf{L}_2 - \dot{f}_3 \dot{g}_1 \mathbf{L}_3 \cdot \mathbf{L}_2 + \dot{g}_1 \dot{g}_3 \dot{\mathbf{L}}_2 \cdot (\mathbf{L}_1 - \mathbf{L}_3)$$

$$A = \{ \dot{f}_1 \dot{g}_3 \mathbf{L}_1 \cdot \mathbf{R}_2 - \dot{f}_3 \dot{g}_1 \mathbf{L}_3 \cdot \mathbf{R}_2$$

$$\qquad + \dot{g}_1 \dot{g}_3 (\mathbf{L}_1 - \mathbf{L}_3) \cdot \dot{\mathbf{R}}_2 - \dot{g}_3 \mathbf{L}_1 \cdot \dot{\mathbf{R}}_1 + \dot{g}_1 \mathbf{L}_3 \cdot \dot{\mathbf{R}}_3 \}/E$$

$$B = \dot{g}_3 / E \tag{8.82}$$

$$C = -\dot{g}_1 \dot{g}_3 \mathbf{L}_2 \cdot (\mathbf{L}_1 - \mathbf{L}_3)/E$$

$$D = -\dot{g}_1 / E$$

$$\rho_2 = A + \dot{\rho}_1 B + \dot{\rho}_2 C + \dot{\rho}_3 D. \tag{8.83}$$

If

$$|(\rho_2)_{n+1} - (\rho_2)_n| < \epsilon, \tag{8.84}$$

where $\epsilon$ is a specified tolerance, proceed to Eq. 8.85; if not, return to Eq. 8.79 with the latest value of $\rho_2$ obtained from Eq. 8.83 and repeat equational loop, Eq. 8.79 to Eq. 8.84.

Continue calculating with

$$\mathbf{r}_2 = \rho_2 \mathbf{L}_2 - \mathbf{R}_2 \tag{8.85}$$

$$\dot{\mathbf{r}}_2 = \dot{\rho}_2 \mathbf{L}_2 + \rho_2 \dot{\mathbf{L}}_2 - \dot{\mathbf{R}}_2. \tag{8.86}$$

Hence the fundamental set $\mathbf{r}_2$ and $\dot{\mathbf{r}}_2$ has been determined, and the orbit is considered determined.

### 8.4    HERRICK–GIBBS TECHNIQUE (RANGE AND ANGULAR DATA)

The Herrick modification of the Gibbs' formulas can be successfully employed to determine an orbit from redundant observations. Even though the assumption is made here that range and angular data are available, this is tantamount to saying that a number of position vectors $\mathbf{r}_i$ are known. The method can be used equally well with either starting point. For the sake of completeness, the range and angular data path is presented.

### 8.4.1 Computation of the radius vectors

Suppose that a number of observations, that is, $\rho_i$, $A_i$, $h_i$, or equivalently, $\rho_i$, $\alpha_{ti}$, $\delta_{ti}$, are known for some $t_i$, with $i = 1, 2, 3$. The $\mathbf{L}_i$ unit vectors, directed along the slant range vector, can be computed from

$$\mathbf{L}_i = \begin{bmatrix} \cos \delta_t \cos \alpha_t \\ \cos \delta_t \sin \alpha_t \\ \sin \alpha_t \end{bmatrix}_i, \qquad (8.87)$$

and, since the positions of given observation stations are known, the $\mathbf{R}_i$ are also known. Hence

$$\mathbf{r}_i = \rho_i \mathbf{L}_i - \mathbf{R}_i \qquad (8.88)$$

immediately yields the three radius vectors. It is evident that, for other applications, the problem could be initiated at this specific point.

### 8.4.2 The Herrick-Gibbs formula

From the observation times, one may compute the respective modified times, that is,

$$\tau_{ij} = k(t_j - t_i), \quad j = 1, 2, 3, \quad i = 2, \qquad (8.89)$$

and, as developed in Section 7.3.3, form

$$\begin{aligned} \bar{G}_1 &\equiv \frac{\tau_{23}}{\tau_{12}\tau_{13}} \\ \bar{G}_3 &\equiv \frac{\tau_{12}}{\tau_{23}\tau_{13}} \\ \bar{G}_2 &\equiv \bar{G}_1 - \bar{G}_3, \end{aligned} \qquad (8.90)$$

with $\tau_{13} \equiv \tau_3 - \tau_1$. Furthermore, by computing

$$\begin{aligned} \bar{H}_1 &\equiv \mu\tau_{23}/12 \\ \bar{H}_3 &\equiv \mu\tau_{12}/12 \\ \bar{H}_2 &\equiv \bar{H}_1 - \bar{H}_3, \end{aligned} \qquad (8.91)$$

and forming the coefficients

$$d_i = \bar{G}_i + \bar{H}_i/r_i^3, \quad i = 1, 2, 3, \qquad (8.92)$$

by Eq. 7.95, that is,

$$\dot{\mathbf{r}}_2 = -d_1\mathbf{r}_1 + d_2\mathbf{r}_2 + d_3\mathbf{r}_3, \qquad (8.93)$$

the velocity vector is determined to the order $(\overset{v}{r}/5!)\tau_{ij}{}^5$. This formula gives excellent results over short observational time spans. In short, since $\mathbf{r}$ and $\dot{\mathbf{r}}$ have been found at the adopted epoch time, the orbit is determined.

### 8.5  THE METHOD OF GIBBS (RANGE AND ANGULAR DATA)

Many modifications of the Gibbsian technique exist in the literature. In the previous section the formulas for direct numerical mapping of three position vectors at times $t_i$ into a velocity vector at the central date have been stated. In this section the same transformation is analyzed without the series approximation. As in the previous section, the method can be initiated at the position vector branch of development rather than the range and angular data stage. The technique to be presented has numerous applications to trajectory analysis.

### 8.5.1  Coplanar condition

Section 8.4.1 developed the relation between range and angular measurements and a minimum of three position vectors. From this point on, the Gibbsian idea is to utilize the condition

$$\mathbf{r}_2 = c_1\mathbf{r}_1 + c_3\mathbf{r}_3, \tag{8.94}$$

as a means of obtaining the desired orbit. This equation expresses the fact that, in a Keplerian orbit, the three radius vectors are coplanar. By taking the cross and dot products of Eq. 8.94 with $\mathbf{r}_1$ and $\mathbf{r}_3$, it is possible to verify that

$$c_1 = \frac{(\mathbf{r}_3 \times \mathbf{r}_2) \cdot (\mathbf{r}_3 \times \mathbf{r}_1)}{(\mathbf{r}_3 \times \mathbf{r}_1) \cdot (\mathbf{r}_3 \times \mathbf{r}_1)}, \qquad c_3 = \frac{(\mathbf{r}_1 \times \mathbf{r}_2) \cdot (\mathbf{r}_1 \times \mathbf{r}_3)}{(\mathbf{r}_1 \times \mathbf{r}_3) \cdot (\mathbf{r}_1 \times \mathbf{r}_3)}. \tag{8.95}$$

Furthermore, by taking the dot product of each radius vector onto itself, the magnitudes $r_1$, $r_2$, $r_3$ are also known. Consider Eq. 8.94 written for the orbit plane coordinate system (Chapter 4, System 8), so that the $x_\omega$ component equation is

$$x_{\omega 2} = c_1 x_{\omega 1} + c_3 x_{\omega 3}. \tag{8.96}$$

Remembering that

$$x_\omega = \frac{p - r}{e},$$

Eq. 8.96 can be written as

$$p - r_2 = c_1(p - r_1) + c_3(p - r_3) \tag{8.97}$$

and solved for $p$, that is,

$$p = \frac{c_1 r_1 + c_3 r_3 - r_2}{c_1 + c_3 - 1}. \tag{8.98}$$

Since the parameter of the orbit is known and the unit vector $\mathbf{W}$, normal to the orbit plane, can be obtained from

$$\mathbf{W} = \frac{\mathbf{r}_1 \times \mathbf{r}_3}{\sqrt{(\mathbf{r}_1 \times \mathbf{r}_3) \cdot (\mathbf{r}_1 \times \mathbf{r}_3)}}, \tag{8.99}$$

the $p$-iteration theory of Section 6.4, can be utilized to determine the orbit. Naturally, an iteration is not required, since the parameter of the orbit $p$, is directly given by Eq. 8.98. It should be noticed that if $\mathbf{r}_1$ and $\mathbf{r}_3$ are $\pi$ radians apart, $\mathbf{W}$ cannot be determined from Eq. 8.99. In this case, the cross product of vectors $\mathbf{r}_1$ and $\mathbf{r}_2$ will yield the desired normal to the orbit plane.

### 8.6 AZIMUTH LACKING TECHNIQUE (RANGE AND ELEVATION ANGLE DATA)

In special space applications it may be better to obtain range and elevation angle data to effect the determination of a given orbit. The following problem has attracted the attention of Douglas [2] and Milstead [3]. The Douglas approach is presented because of its simplicity, even though redundant data are required to determine the orbit.

### 8.6.1 Derivation of a linear system

From a geometrical point of view, consider the fundamental relation

$$\mathbf{r}_i = \boldsymbol{\rho}_i - \mathbf{R}_i, \quad i = 1, 2, \ldots, 6, \tag{8.100}$$

dotted into itself to produce [2]

$$r_i{}^2 = \rho_i{}^2 + R_i{}^2 - 2\rho_i R_i \cos(\pi/2 + h_i). \tag{8.101}$$

The last relation is also evident from examination of Figure 8.1. Notice that the $\mathbf{R}_i$ are known (Section 3.11). Equation 8.101 can be rewritten as

$$r_i = (\rho_i{}^2 + R_i{}^2 + 2\rho_i R_i \sin h_i)^{1/2}, \tag{8.102}$$

which allows immediate determination of the $r_i$. Proceeding along similar lines, it is possible to express Eq. 8.100 as

$$\rho_i{}^2 = r_i{}^2 + R_i{}^2 + 2\mathbf{r}_i \cdot \mathbf{R}_i. \tag{8.103}$$

[2] A spherical Earth is assumed. To correct for the geometrical oblateness of the Earth, $h$ must be augmented by $\zeta$ where $\zeta = \cos^{-1}\left(\dfrac{G_1 \cos^2 \phi + G_2 \sin^2 \phi}{R}\right)$, $0 \leq \zeta \leq \pi/2$. See Section 3.11.

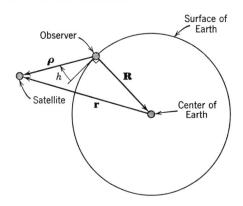

FIGURE 8.1   Orbit geometry.

Selecting arbitrarily the second and fourth observations and introducing the Gibbsian relation 8.94, permits Eq. 8.103 to be formulated as

$$\rho_i^2 = r_i^2 + R_i^2 + 2[c_{2i}\mathbf{r}_2 + c_{4i}\mathbf{r}_4] \cdot \mathbf{R}_i. \tag{8.104}$$

Furthermore, the $c$ coefficients have been developed in Section 7.3 as a function of the $f$ and $g$ series, that is,

$$c_{2i} = \frac{g_{4i}}{(f_{2i}g_{4i} - g_{2i}f_{4i})},$$

$$c_{4i} = \frac{-g_{2i}}{(f_{2i}g_{4i} - g_{2i}f_{4i})}, \tag{8.105}$$

where, from Section 3.9,

$$f_{2i} = 1 - \tfrac{1}{2}u_i\tau_{2i}^2 + \cdots$$
$$f_{4i} = 1 - \tfrac{1}{2}u_i\tau_{4i}^2 + \cdots$$
$$g_{2i} = \tau_{2i} - \tfrac{1}{6}u_i\tau_{2i}^3 + \cdots$$
$$g_{4i} = \tau_{4i} - \tfrac{1}{6}u_i\tau_{4i}^3 + \cdots, \tag{8.106}$$

with $u_i \equiv \mu/r_i^3$.   Hence, if higher-order terms are neglected, and since the $r_i$ are known, an estimate of the $f$ and $g$ series can be obtained through Eq. 8.106.   Then, due to Eqs. 8.105, the $c_{ji}$ coefficients can be numerically obtained.   To obtain a first approximation of the orbit, let Eq. 8.104 be written for $i = 1, 2, \ldots, 6$, that is,

$$c_{2i}\mathbf{r}_2 \cdot \mathbf{R}_i + c_{4i}\mathbf{r}_4 \cdot \mathbf{R}_i = \Delta_i, \tag{8.107}$$

where

$$\Delta_i \equiv (\rho_i^2 - r_i^2 - R_i^2)/2. \tag{8.108}$$

Evidently, this is a system of six linear equations in six unknowns ($x_2$, $y_2$, $z_2$, $x_4$, $y_4$, $z_4$) that can easily be solved by a matrix inversion. The end product will yield approximate values of $\mathbf{r}_2$ and $\mathbf{r}_4$. The velocity vector can be obtained from the vector relation

$$\mathbf{r}_4 = f_{42}\mathbf{r}_2 + g_{42}\dot{\mathbf{r}}_2 \tag{8.109}$$

as

$$\dot{\mathbf{r}}_2 = \frac{\mathbf{r}_4 - f_{42}\mathbf{r}_2}{g_{42}}. \tag{8.110}$$

To increase the accuracy, the $f$ and $g$ functions could be recalculated either by series or in closed form and the process repeated.

Numerical studies seem to indicate that high accuracy must be carried in the matrix inversion of system 8.107.

## 8.7 METHOD OF TRILATERATION (SIMULTANEOUS RANGE AND RANGE-RATE DATA)

### 8.7.1 The problem of simultaneous measurements

A technique which may gain in popularity for the determination of an orbit from simultaneous range and range-rate measurements is termed herein the method of trilateration. This method utilizes as data the range and range-rate ($\rho_i$ and $\dot{\rho}_i$) of a satellite from a minimum of three observation stations, that is, for $i = 1, 2, 3$, that are in contact with each other. The main drawbacks of this system is that three different stations are required instead of the usual one and that the measurements must be obtained at the same time.

Actually, however, if given tracking stations transmit smooth data in the form of polynomials of any arbitrary degree, say, for the sake of discussion, quadratics such as

$$\begin{aligned}
\rho_i &= a_i\tau^2 + b_i\tau + c_i \\
\dot{\rho}_i &= d_i\tau^2 + e_i\tau + f_i,
\end{aligned} \tag{8.111}$$

then, common agreement between the stations on some convenient median time $\tau_0$ will allow computation of $\rho_i$ and $\dot{\rho}_i$ at $\tau_0$ to any degree of simultaneity. The method presented here is exact and yields a precise orbit owing to the fact that only geometric principles are involved.

## 8.7.2    Quadratic resolvent for the position vector

Consider the fundamental relation

$$\boldsymbol{\rho}_i = \mathbf{r}_0 + \mathbf{R}_i, \quad i = 1, 2, 3, \tag{8.112}$$

dotted into itself to yield

$$\rho_i{}^2 = r_0{}^2 + 2\mathbf{r}_0 \cdot \mathbf{R}_i + R_i{}^2, \tag{8.113}$$

where it is noticed that $r_0$ at $\tau_0$ is the same for all three stations. Between Eqs. 8.113 for $i = 1, 2$, eliminate $r_0$, and in the same fashion eliminate $r_0$ for $i = 1, 3$, to yield

$$\begin{aligned}
\rho_3{}^2 - \rho_1{}^2 - (R_3{}^2 - R_1{}^2) &= 2\mathbf{r}_0 \cdot (\mathbf{R}_3 - \mathbf{R}_1) \\
\rho_2{}^2 - \rho_1{}^2 - (R_2{}^2 - R_1{}^2) &= 2\mathbf{r}_0 \cdot (\mathbf{R}_2 - \mathbf{R}_1).
\end{aligned} \tag{8.114}$$

It should be noted that the $\mathbf{R}_i$ are known for the agreed time of determination $\tau_0$ from Section 3.11. Evidently, the system of Eqs. 8.114 can be reformulated as

$$(X_3 - X_1)x_0 + (Y_3 - Y_1)y_0 + (Z_3 - Z_1)z_0 = \zeta_{31} \tag{8.115}$$

$$(X_2 - X_1)x_0 + (Y_2 - Y_1)y_0 + (Z_2 - Z_1)z_0 = \zeta_{21}, \tag{8.116}$$

where

$$\begin{aligned}
\zeta_{31} &\equiv \tfrac{1}{2}[\rho_3{}^2 - \rho_1{}^2 - (R_3{}^2 - R_1{}^2)] \\
\zeta_{21} &\equiv \tfrac{1}{2}[\rho_2{}^2 - \rho_1{}^2 - (R_2{}^2 - R_1{}^2)].
\end{aligned}$$

Multiplication of Eq. 8.115 by $(Y_2 - Y_1)$ and Eq. 8.116 by $-(Y_3 - Y_1)$ yields, upon addition,

$$z_0 = Ax_0 + B, \tag{8.117}$$

where

$$A \equiv \frac{(X_2 - X_1)(Y_3 - Y_1) - (X_3 - X_1)(Y_2 - Y_1)}{(Z_3 - Z_1)(Y_2 - Y_1) - (Z_2 - Z_1)(Y_3 - Y_1)}$$

$$B \equiv \frac{\zeta_{31}(Y_2 - Y_1) - \zeta_{21}(Y_3 - Y_1)}{(Z_3 - Z_1)(Y_2 - Y_1) - (Z_2 - Z_1)(Y_3 - Y_1)}.$$

Similarly, it is possible to obtain

$$y_0 = Cx_0 + D, \tag{8.118}$$

where

$$C \equiv \frac{(X_2 - X_1)(Z_3 - Z_1) - (X_3 - X_1)(Z_2 - Z_1)}{(Y_3 - Y_1)(Z_2 - Z_1) - (Y_2 - Y_1)(Z_3 - Z_1)}$$

$$D \equiv \frac{\zeta_{31}(Z_2 - Z_1) - \zeta_{21}(Z_3 - Z_1)}{(Y_3 - Y_1)(Z_2 - Z_1) - (Y_2 - Y_1)(Z_3 - Z_1)}.$$

Consider the substitution of Eqs. 8.117 and 8.118 along with $r^2 = x^2 + y^2 + z^2$ into Eq. 8.113 for any arbitrary $i$, say $i = 1$, in order to obtain the quadratic resolvent

$$\epsilon_1 x_0^2 + \epsilon_2 x_0 + \epsilon_3 = 0, \tag{8.119}$$

where

$$\epsilon_1 \equiv A^2 + C^2 + 1$$
$$\epsilon_2 \equiv 2(AB + CD + X_1 + CY_1 + AZ_1)$$
$$\epsilon_3 \equiv B^2 + D^2 + 2DY_1 + 2BZ_1 + R_1^2 - \rho_1^2.$$

This quadratic can be solved immediately for $x_{0j}$; and the other two coordinates, $y_{0j}$ and $z_{0j}$, can be obtained from Eqs. 8.117 and 8.118. The spurious root, either $j = 1$ or 2, of the quadratic resolvent can be eliminated by substituting $x_{0j}$, $y_{0j}$, and $z_{0j}$ back into

$$\rho_1^2 = r_{0j}^2 + 2\mathbf{r}_{0j} \cdot \mathbf{R}_1 + R_1^2, \tag{8.120}$$

and rejecting the root that does not produce the acceptable $\rho_1$.

### 8.7.3   Obtaining the velocity vector

Since,

$$\rho_i^2 = \boldsymbol{\rho}_i \cdot \boldsymbol{\rho}_i = (\mathbf{r}_0 + \mathbf{R}_i) \cdot (\mathbf{r}_0 + \mathbf{R}_i), \quad i = 1, 2, 3, \tag{8.121}$$

it follows by differentiation with respect to modified time that

$$\rho_i \dot{\rho}_i = \dot{\mathbf{r}}_0 \cdot (\mathbf{r}_0 + \mathbf{R}_i) + \dot{\mathbf{R}}_i(\mathbf{r}_0 + \mathbf{R}_i), \tag{8.122}$$

where $\rho_i$, $\dot{\rho}_i$, $\mathbf{r}_0$, $\mathbf{R}_i$ and $\dot{\mathbf{R}}_i$ are known respectively from data, Section 8.7.2 and Section 3.11.   Therefore, it is possible to form the coefficients

$$E_i \equiv \rho_i \dot{\rho}_i - \dot{\mathbf{R}}_i \cdot (\mathbf{r}_0 + \mathbf{R}_i) \tag{8.123}$$

so that Eq. 8.122 becomes

$$\dot{\mathbf{r}}_0 \cdot (\mathbf{r}_0 + \mathbf{R}_i) = E_i \tag{8.124}$$

or

$$\dot{\mathbf{r}}_0 \cdot \boldsymbol{\rho}_i = E_i. \tag{8.125}$$

In component form, Eq. 8.125 yields a system of three equations in three unknowns for the components of $\dot{\mathbf{r}}_0$, that is,

$$\begin{bmatrix} \rho_{x1} & \rho_{y1} & \rho_{z1} \\ \rho_{x2} & \rho_{y2} & \rho_{z2} \\ \rho_{x3} & \rho_{y3} & \rho_{z3} \end{bmatrix} \begin{bmatrix} \dot{x}_0 \\ \dot{y}_0 \\ \dot{z}_0 \end{bmatrix} = \begin{bmatrix} E_1 \\ E_2 \\ E_3 \end{bmatrix}, \tag{8.126}$$

where if the slant range matrix is denoted by $[M_s]$, it is possible to write:

$$\begin{bmatrix} \dot{x}_0 \\ \dot{y}_0 \\ \dot{z}_0 \end{bmatrix} = [M_s]^{-1} \begin{bmatrix} E_1 \\ E_2 \\ E_3 \end{bmatrix}. \tag{8.127}$$

Hence the fundamental set $\mathbf{r}_0$, $\dot{\mathbf{r}}_0$ have been determined and the orbit is considered determined.

### 8.7.4    Computational algorithm

Given the mixed data $\rho_j$, $\dot{\rho}_j$, $t_j$, $j = 1, 2, \ldots, q$, for a set of observing stations with coordinates $\phi_i$, $\lambda_{Ei}$, $H_i$, $i = 1, 2, 3$, and constants $a_e$, $f$, $d\theta/dt$, proceed as follows. Reduce the range and range-rate data to a common simultaneous time such that $\rho_i$, $\dot{\rho}_i$, $i = 1, 2, 3$, are available for an arbitrary modified time $\tau_0$ and compute

$$\begin{aligned} G_{1i} &= \frac{a_e}{\sqrt{1 - (2f - f^2) \sin^2 \phi_i}} + H_i \\ G_{2i} &= \frac{a_e(1 - f)^2}{\sqrt{1 - (2f - f^2) \sin^2 \phi_i}} + H_i, \quad i = 1, 2, 3. \end{aligned} \tag{8.128}$$

Obtain the Greenwich sidereal time $\theta_{g0}$ from Eq. 1.27 and compute for $i = 1, 2, 3$:

$$\theta_i = \theta_{g0} + \frac{d\theta}{dt} (t - t_0) + \lambda_{Ei} \tag{8.129}$$

$$\mathbf{R}_i = \begin{bmatrix} X \\ Y \\ Z \end{bmatrix}_i = \begin{bmatrix} -G_1 \cos \phi \cos \theta \\ -G_1 \cos \phi \sin \theta \\ -G_2 \sin \phi \end{bmatrix}_i \tag{8.130}$$

$$R_i^2 = \mathbf{R}_i \cdot \mathbf{R}_i. \tag{8.131}$$

Continue calculating with

$$\zeta_{21} = \tfrac{1}{2}[\rho_2{}^2 - \rho_1{}^2 - (R_2{}^2 - R_1{}^2)]$$
$$\zeta_{31} = \tfrac{1}{2}[\rho_3{}^2 - \rho_1{}^2 - (R_3{}^2 - R_1{}^2)] \tag{8.132}$$

$$\Delta_1 = (Z_3 - Z_1)(Y_2 - Y_1) - (Z_2 - Z_1)(Y_3 - Y_1) \tag{8.133}$$

$$A = [(X_2 - X_1)(Y_3 - Y_1) - (X_3 - X_1)(Y_2 - Y_1)]/\Delta_1$$
$$B = [\zeta_{31}(Y_2 - Y_1) - \zeta_{21}(Y_3 - Y_1)]/\Delta_1$$
$$\Delta_2 = [(Y_3 - Y_1)(Z_2 - Z_1) - (Y_2 - Y_1)(Z_3 - Z_1)]$$
$$C = [(X_2 - X_1)(Z_3 - Z_1) - (X_3 - X_1)(Z_2 - Z_1)]/\Delta_2$$
$$D = [\zeta_{31}(Z_2 - Z_1) - \zeta_{21}(Z_3 - Z_1)]/\Delta_2$$
$$\epsilon_1 = A^2 + C^2 + 1$$
$$\epsilon_2 = 2(AB + CD + X_1 + CY_1 + AZ_1)$$
$$\epsilon_3 = B^2 + D^2 + 2DY_1 + 2BZ_1 + R_1{}^2 - \rho_1{}^2$$

$$x_{0j} = \frac{-\epsilon_2 \pm \sqrt{\epsilon_2{}^2 - 4\epsilon_1\epsilon_3}}{2\epsilon_1} \tag{8.134}$$

$$y_{0j} = Cx_{0j} + D$$
$$z_{0j} = Ax_{0j} + B \tag{8.135}$$
$$r_{0j}{}^2 = \mathbf{r}_{0j} \cdot \mathbf{r}_{0j}.$$

Reject the $\mathbf{r}_{0j}$ that does not satisfy

$$\rho_1{}^2 = r_{0j}{}^2 + 2\mathbf{r}_{0j} \cdot \mathbf{R}_1 + R_1{}^2, \tag{8.136}$$

and continue calculating for $i = 1, 2, 3$, with

$$\dot{\mathbf{R}}_i = \begin{bmatrix} \dot{X} \\ \dot{Y} \\ \dot{Z} \end{bmatrix}_i = \frac{1}{k} \begin{bmatrix} -Y \\ X \\ Z \end{bmatrix}_i \frac{d\theta}{dt} \tag{8.137}$$

$$\boldsymbol{\rho}_i = \mathbf{r}_0 + \mathbf{R}_i \tag{8.138}$$

$$E_i = \rho_i\dot{\rho}_i - \dot{\mathbf{R}}_i \cdot \boldsymbol{\rho}_i. \tag{8.139}$$

Invert the matrix

$$M_s = \begin{bmatrix} \rho_{x1} & \rho_{y1} & \rho_{z1} \\ \rho_{x2} & \rho_{y2} & \rho_{z2} \\ \rho_{x3} & \rho_{y3} & \rho_{z3} \end{bmatrix}, \tag{8.140}$$

and obtain

$$
\begin{bmatrix} \dot{x}_0 \\ \dot{y}_0 \\ \dot{z}_0 \end{bmatrix} = [M_s]^{-1} \begin{bmatrix} E_1 \\ E_2 \\ E_3 \end{bmatrix}. \tag{8.141}
$$

Hence, having obtained $\mathbf{r}_0$, $\dot{\mathbf{r}}_0$, the orbit is determined.

## 8.8  METHOD OF TRILATERATION (SIMULTANEOUS RANGE DATA)

### 8.8.1  Reduction to the two-position vector and time interval problem

If a specified observational station is restricted to measurements of only range data, the method of trilateration, specifically the method of Section 8.7.2, can be successfully employed to determine the unknown orbit when additional data is available. In essence, three values of $\rho_i$ at time $t_0$ allowed the determination of $\mathbf{r}_0$ by means of the quadratic resolvent, Eq. 8.119. Therefore, another three slant range magnitudes at a second date or time, say $t_{00}$, will yield a second position vector $\mathbf{r}_{00}$. The orbit determination process can then be conveniently handled by any of the techniques of Chapter 6, that is, in symbolic notation,

$$
\mathbf{r}_0, \mathbf{r}_{00}, t_0 - t_{00} \rightarrow \mathbf{r}_0, \dot{\mathbf{r}}_0.
$$

It may be feasible to have a third three-dimensional fix; obtain another position vector and employ Eq. 8.93 to yield the velocity vector at the central date. This last attack holds only for closely grouped observations. Both of these attacks involve the assumptions inherent in dynamical relationships used to determine the velocity vector at the epoch time.

## 8.9  SUMMARY

In this chapter a number of different methods for the determination of orbits from mixed data have been presented. The range-rate and angle problem was presented from two different points of view. The range and angle problem was similarly treated. Methods of determining an orbit when one lacks one coordinate (no azimuth), or has simultaneous range and range-rate measurements were included. This last method is an exact geometric six-dimensional trilateration. The numerical stability of these techniques has not been fully investigated.

These problems in orbit determination are frequently of interest today because of the excellent range and range-rate data available to the modern analyst. The range and angle determinations are useful for determining an orbit from observations or for reduction to a three-position vector and time interval problem. The last-mentioned case has many engineering applications.

**EXERCISES**

1. Which expression is correct?

$$\dot{\rho} = (\dot{\boldsymbol{\rho}} \cdot \dot{\boldsymbol{\rho}})^{\frac{1}{2}}$$

or

$$\dot{\rho} = \frac{\dot{\boldsymbol{\rho}} \cdot \boldsymbol{\rho}}{\rho}.$$

2. Explain geometrically why

$$\mathbf{L} \cdot \dot{\mathbf{L}} = 0.$$

3. Develop an algorithm for the computation of range and range-rate, given the orbital elements $a$, $e$, $T$, $i$, $\omega$, $\Omega$, for any specified time $t$.
4. Determine the following geocentric orbit, given the following information:

| Data | $\rho_1$ | $\rho_2$ | $\rho_3$ |
|---|---|---|---|
| | 500 km | 600 km | 700 km |
| | $\dot{\rho}_1$ | $\dot{\rho}_2$ | $\dot{\rho}_3$ |
| | 200 msec | 0 msec | 400 msec |
| Station | 1 | 2 | 3 |
| | | | |
| $\phi$ | 40° | 45° | 50° |
| $\lambda_E$ | 250° | 260° | 270° |
| $H$ | 0 | 0 | 0 |

Assume the measurements were all recorded on January 1, 1964, at midnight. Is the observed object in orbit around the Earth?
5. Solve Exercise 9 of Chapter 6 by means of the Herrick–Gibbs technique.
6. Solve Exercise 9 of Chapter 6 by means of the method of Gibbs.

**7.** A station located on Earth ($\phi = 27°.6191$ $\lambda_W = 99°.3844$, $H = 195$ meters) makes the following measurements on 1 May 1962:

| t | h (degrees) | A (degrees) | $\dot{\rho}$ (km/sec) |
|---|---|---|---|
| 16$^{hr}$ 13$^{min}$ 57.515$^{sec}$ | 36°1 | 6°6 | $-5.834$ |
| 16$^{hr}$ 15$^{min}$ 39.544$^{sec}$ | 30°4 | 35°1 | $-1.960$ |
| 16$^{hr}$ 18$^{min}$ 9.569$^{sec}$ | 15°8 | 62°5 | $+4.509$ |

What is the orbit of 1961 Delta 1?

**8.** Show that in the modified Laplacian technique an eighth-degree resolvent can be written as

$$C^2 r_2{}^8 - (A^2 + ACC_\psi + C^2 R^2) r_2{}^6 + (2CD) r_2{}^5$$
$$- (2AB + \{AD + BC\}C_\psi + 2CDR^2) r_2{}^3 + (D^2) r_2{}^2$$
$$- (B^2 + BDC_\psi + D^2 R^2) = 0.$$

**9.** Where, exactly, in the $r$ iteration method, is the importance of the numerical differentiation of $\dot{L}$ minimized?

**10.** If $r_1$ and $r_3$ are $\pi$ radians apart, the $c$ coefficients of the Gibbsian equation

$$p = \frac{c_1 r_1 + c_3 r_3 - r_2}{c_1 + c_3 - 1}$$

become undefined. How can this situation be eliminated or bypassed?

**11.** In the azimuth lacking technique of Section 8.6, why must $h$ be augmented by

$$\zeta = \cos^{-1}\left(\frac{G_1 \cos^2\phi + G_2 \sin^2\phi}{R}\right), \quad 0 \leq \zeta \leq \pi/2,$$

in order to compensate for geometric oblateness of the central planet?

**REFERENCES**

1. R. M. L. Baker and M. W. Makemson, *An Introduction to Astrodynamics*, Academic Press, New York, 1960, Chapter 6.
2. *Study of Universal Variables and Range and Range-Rate Orbit Determination*, Contract NAS 5-2330, Quarterly Report 2, Lockheed-California Company, Division of Lockheed Aircraft Corporation, Burbank, Calif. August 1, 1962.
3. A. H. Milstead, *Preliminary Orbit Determination from Range and Altitude Measurements*, A-62-1743-664, Aerospace Corp., May 31, 1962.
4. W. G. Gibbs, *On the Determination of Elliptic Orbits*, Memoirs of the National Academy of Sciences, 1888.

5. F. B. Hildebrand, *Introduction to Numerical Analysis*, McGraw-Hill Book Company, 1956, p. 444.

6. C. S. Lorens, *The Doppler Method of Satellite Tracking*, Report 30-2, Jet Propulsion Laboratory, California Institute of Technology, Pasadena, Calif., March 30, 1959.

7. R. B. Patton, Jr., "Orbit Determination from Single Pass Doppler Observations," *IRE Trans. on Military Electronics*, Vol. MIL-4, Nos. 2 and 3, April–July, 1960.

8. E. T. Bell, *Men of Mathematics*, Simon Schuster, New York, 1937.

# 9 Differential correction of orbits

*Observe constantly that all things take place by change.*

MARCUS AURELIUS

## 9.1 DIFFERENTIAL CORRECTION

The preceding chapters dealt with the problem of obtaining a first approximation to a given orbit. Analysis in the previous methods was conveniently restricted to the two-body problem. The effects of perturbing bodies or forces were never even considered. As might be expected, a question comes to mind: Once a first estimate of a particular orbit is known, can a better set of elements be determined? The answer is yes, and the method about to be developed is called the *differential correction* of an approximate orbit leading to the determination of a set of instantaneous elements that are as correct as possible at a given instant of time.

The reader should remember that in the two-body problem a given set of elements, say, $[a, e, i, \Omega, \omega, T]$ are constant in the sense that they do not vary with time. However, if the perturbative effects of the bulge of the central planet about which motion occurs, or the disturbing attraction of a neighboring planet, are taken into account, any set of elements will have a tendency to vary slowly with time. In this chapter, the variation of a given set of elements due to perturbations will not be developed. These variations will be developed in Chapter 10.

In this chapter, the concept of differential correction, a numerical process, is developed with the perturbations treated as a black box whose internal processes will be taken up at a later date.

A brief preview of the method can be stated as follows. Observations are made of a given satellite, call them $O_0$. An orbit is determined, as in the previous chapters, and utilizing this first approximation observations are then computed from the tentative elements at the corresponding observational times, call them $O_c$. Obviously, if the elements

318

of the orbit were correct, then the *residual* $\Delta = O_0 - O_c$ would be zero. But usually this residual is not zero. A little thought would indicate that as the satellite moves from, say, the central or epoch observations, that is, right ascension and declination, the perturbing influence of other bodies deflects the orbit from its basic two-body motion. If it is asked what this residual indicates, one would be correct in assuming that the residual is an index of the perturbative influences acting on the satellite's motion as it moves from, say, the epoch position to the point of the second, or any other position corresponding to the observational data. Hence the purpose of the differential correction procedure is to make use of these obtained residuals $\Delta_i$, which are the difference between the true observations and the computed observations obtained from the best possible prediction of the position of the satellite at the observational times $t_i$. It should be evident that these residuals can always be numerically determined. Furthermore, it is known that the observations are a function of a given set of elements at the adopted epoch time, for example,

$$\alpha = \alpha(\mathbf{r}_0, \dot{\mathbf{r}}_0)$$
$$\delta = \delta(\mathbf{r}_0, \dot{\mathbf{r}}_0). \tag{9.1}$$

Hence, it is possible to form the differential of Eqs. 9.1 and replace $d\alpha$, $d\delta$, by $\Delta\alpha$, $\Delta\delta$, or the observed minus computed values. A set of equations is now available which, if soluble, will yield corrections to the elements $\mathbf{r}_0$, $\dot{\mathbf{r}}_0$, at the adopted epoch time $t_0$.

In this chapter, the differential correction schemes that are adopted are based on correcting the six elements $\mathbf{r}_0$, $\dot{\mathbf{r}}_0$, at the epoch time $t_0$. Other schemes which correct the classical set of elements $(a, e, i, \Omega, \omega, T)$ are fully discussed in references [1] and [2]. Needless to say, at times the classical approach is to be preferred, since in essence the formulations developed are more compact. However, for the computing machine, the method of attack presented herein is straightforward and has the further advantage of letting the modern problems of differential correction based on range and range-rate be formulated in a simple manner.

The basic differential correction scheme utilizing rectangular coordinates is due to Harzer [5]. Modifications by Leuschner [5] have also simplified the analysis.

## 9.2  THE METHOD OF VARIANT ORBITS

### 9.2.1  Computing residuals

Suppose that the two-body set of elements

$$[x_0, y_0, z_0, \dot{x}_0, \dot{y}_0, \dot{z}_0]_{t=t_0} \tag{9.2}$$

is determined by some given scheme. Assume that by analytical or numerical methods a prediction of the satellite's position and velocity vector is obtained at another two times, that is,

$$[x_i, y_i, z_i, \dot{x}_i, \dot{y}_i, \dot{z}_i]_{t=t_i}, \quad i = 1, 2. \tag{9.3}$$

This prediction is made by numerical integration of the equations developed in Chapter 2, or by some other analytical process. Notice that the set of elements $\mathbf{r}_0$, $\dot{\mathbf{r}}_0$, of all the previous preliminary orbit schemes, provides a set of initial constants for the numerical integration of the equations of motion, say, the relative form, developed in Chapter 2. However, assume that the prediction is made by some well-defined process. Hence at all $t_i$, $i = 1, 0, 2$, assuming that the satellite is in coordinate System 1 of Chapter 4, so that available data for the differential correction scheme is the set $[A_i, h_i]$, that is, the azimuth and elevation angles for a minimum of three distinct universal times, the topocentric right ascension and declination are obtained by the rotation

$$\begin{bmatrix} L_x \\ L_y \\ L_z \end{bmatrix} = \begin{bmatrix} S_x & E_x & Z_x \\ S_y & E_y & Z_y \\ S_z & E_z & Z_z \end{bmatrix} \begin{bmatrix} L_{hx} \\ L_{hy} \\ L_{hz} \end{bmatrix}, \tag{9.4}$$

where

$$\begin{bmatrix} L_x \\ L_y \\ L_z \end{bmatrix} = \begin{bmatrix} \cos \alpha_t \cos \delta_t \\ \sin \alpha_t \cos \delta_t \\ \sin \delta_t \end{bmatrix}, \quad \begin{bmatrix} L_{hx} \\ L_{hy} \\ L_{hz} \end{bmatrix} = \begin{bmatrix} -\cos A \cos h \\ \sin A \cos h \\ \sin h \end{bmatrix}$$

with the transformation matrix defined in Appendix I (Transformation 7). Hence, from the observations the $\mathbf{L}_h$ vector is formed, the $\mathbf{L}$ vector obtained, and $\alpha_t$, $\delta_t$ are determined from

$$\sin \delta_t = L_z$$

$$\cos \delta_t = + \sqrt{1 - L_z^2}$$

$$\sin \alpha_t = \frac{L_y}{\cos \delta_t} \tag{9.5}$$

$$\cos \alpha_t = \frac{L_x}{\cos \delta_t}.$$

Needless to say, if the initial data are the topocentric angles $\alpha_t$, $\delta_t$, this initial transformation is not necessary. It should also be realized that $\alpha_t$ and $\delta_t$ are defined as the right ascension and declination measured

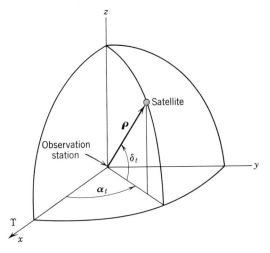

FIGURE 9.1   Topocentric right ascension and declination angles

at the observing station's position.   Hence, as can be seen from Figure 9.1, the following relationships are evident:

$$\sin \alpha_t = \frac{\rho_y}{\sqrt{\rho_x{}^2 + \rho_y{}^2}}, \qquad \cos \alpha_t = \frac{\rho_x}{\sqrt{\rho_x{}^2 + \rho_y{}^2}} \qquad (9.6)$$

$$\sin \delta_t = \frac{\rho_z}{\sqrt{\rho_x{}^2 + \rho_y{}^2 + \rho_z{}^2}}, \qquad \cos \delta_t = \frac{\sqrt{\rho_x{}^2 + \rho_y{}^2}}{\sqrt{\rho_x{}^2 + \rho_y{}^2 + \rho_z{}^2}}. \qquad (9.7)$$

Furthermore, the station, satellite, and dynamical center are related by $\rho = r + R$ (Section 3.11) so that Eqs. 9.6 and 9.7 become functionally dependent on the station and satellite position

$$\sin \alpha_{tc} = \frac{y + Y}{\sqrt{(x + X)^2 + (y + Y)^2}},$$

$$\cos \alpha_{tc} = \frac{x + X}{\sqrt{(x + X)^2 + (y + Y)^2}} \qquad (9.8)$$

$$\sin \delta_{tc} = \frac{z + Z}{\sqrt{(x + X)^2 + (y + Y)^2 + (z + Z)^2}}. \qquad (9.9)$$

Only the first of Eqs. 9.7 is needed to uniquely determine the topocentric declination.   Notice the subscript $c$ has been introduced to denote that these angles are computed from the analytically determined position

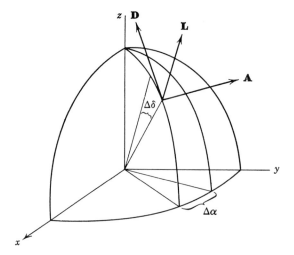

FIGURE 9.2   Orthogonal unit vectors **A, D, L.**

of satellite and station.   These are the computed observations.   Furthermore, the observer on a particular meridian also has the actual topocentric observations corresponding to $t_i$ so that

$$\Delta\alpha_i = (\alpha_{to})_i - (\alpha_{tc})_i$$
$$\Delta\delta_i = (\delta_{to})_i - (\delta_{tc})_i \tag{9.10}$$

yield a set of six residuals.   Naturally, if the orbit were perfect and the position of the station assumed to be error-free, $\Delta\alpha_i$ and $\Delta\delta_i$ would be zero.   These residuals are an index of the perturbations acting on the orbit.

This method of computing residuals is straightforward; there are, however, many different approaches to this problem.   The second method to be presented will be of considerable benefit.

Consider the introduction of an orthogonal set of unit vectors (Figure 9.2) at the observing station's position.   A convenient orientation to adopt is the usual unit vector **L** pointing to the satellite, **A** parallel to the equatorial plane pointing due east, and **D** directed due north along the observing station's meridian.   Furthermore, from Figure 9.2,

$$\Delta \mathbf{L} = (\Delta\alpha \cos \delta)\mathbf{A} + (\Delta\delta)\mathbf{D}, \tag{9.11}$$

since $\Delta \mathbf{L}$ must be at right angles to **L** and is therefore a linear combination of **A** and **D**.   The components of **A** and **D** may be readily evaluated by translating the **A**, **D**, **L** triad to the origin and resolving the components along the respective $x$, $y$, $z$ axes. In brief, it is possible to verify that

$$
\begin{bmatrix} A_x \\ A_y \\ A_z \end{bmatrix} = \begin{bmatrix} -\sin \alpha_t \\ \cos \alpha_t \\ 0 \end{bmatrix}, \qquad \begin{bmatrix} D_x \\ D_y \\ D_z \end{bmatrix} = \begin{bmatrix} -\sin \delta_t \cos \alpha_t \\ -\sin \delta_t \sin \alpha_t \\ \cos \delta_t \end{bmatrix}. \tag{9.12}
$$

The procedure for evaluating residuals by this technique is as follows: evaluate $\mathbf{L}_i$, that is,

$$
\begin{bmatrix} L_x \\ L_y \\ L_z \end{bmatrix} = \begin{bmatrix} \cos \alpha_t \cos \delta_t \\ \sin \alpha_t \cos \delta_t \\ \sin \delta_t \end{bmatrix}_i, \qquad i = 1, 0, 2, \tag{9.13}
$$

along with $\mathbf{A}_i$ and $\mathbf{D}_i$ directly from the topocentric observational data. Next, determine the satellite's position $\mathbf{r}_i$ (Chapter 2) and the station's position $\mathbf{R}_i$ (Section 3.11), and utilize Eqs. 9.8 and 9.9 to obtain the **L** vector as a function of the computed observations; in brief,

$$
L_{xc} = \frac{x + X}{\nabla}, \qquad L_{yc} = \frac{y + Y}{\nabla}, \qquad L_{zc} = \frac{z + Z}{\nabla}, \tag{9.14}
$$

where

$$
\nabla = [(x + X)^2 + (y + Y)^2 + (z + Z)^2]^{1/2}
$$

with the $c$ subscript denoting that these are computed direction cosines. Having $\mathbf{L}_{ci}$, a linear approximation to $\Delta \mathbf{L}_i$ is given by

$$
\Delta \mathbf{L}_i = (\mathbf{L}_0 - \mathbf{L}_c)_i, \tag{9.15}
$$

the observed minus computed direction cosines. Equation 9.11 immediately yields (upon dotting with **A** and **D**)

$$
\begin{aligned}
(\Delta \alpha \cos \delta)_{ti} &= \mathbf{A}_i \cdot \Delta \mathbf{L}_i \\
(\Delta \delta)_{ti} &= \mathbf{D}_i \cdot \Delta \mathbf{L}_i
\end{aligned} \tag{9.16}
$$

for all three observational times. It is seen that this procedure yields the residuals in topocentric right ascension weighted by $\cos \delta_t$. This particular form will be of benefit at a later point in the analysis.

### 9.2.2 The differential correction equations

Since the observed angles are in effect functions, which are usually very complicated, of a set of elements at some arbitrary epoch, it is possible to assume that the functional representation is given by

$$
\begin{aligned}
\alpha_t &= \alpha_t(x_0, y_0, z_0, \dot{x}_0, \dot{y}_0, \dot{z}_0) \\
\delta_t &= \delta_t(x_0, y_0, z_0, \dot{x}_0, \dot{y}_0, \dot{z}_0).
\end{aligned} \tag{9.17}
$$

Furthermore, one can write the linear differential of these functions as

$$d\alpha_t = \frac{\partial \alpha_t}{\partial x_0} dx_0 + \frac{\partial \alpha_t}{\partial y_0} dy_0 + \frac{\partial \alpha_t}{\partial z_0} dz_0 + \frac{\partial \alpha_t}{\partial \dot{x}_0} d\dot{x}_0 + \frac{\partial \alpha_t}{\partial \dot{y}_0} d\dot{y}_0 + \frac{\partial \alpha_t}{\partial \dot{z}_0} d\dot{z}_0$$

(9.18)

$$d\delta_t = \frac{\partial \delta_t}{\partial x_0} dx_0 + \frac{\partial \delta_t}{\partial y_0} dy_0 + \frac{\partial \delta_t}{\partial z_0} dz_0 + \frac{\partial \delta_t}{\partial \dot{x}_0} d\dot{x}_0 + \frac{\partial \delta_t}{\partial \dot{y}_0} d\dot{y}_0 + \frac{\partial \delta_t}{\partial \dot{z}_0} d\dot{z}_0.$$

To be more specific, for all three observational times it is possible to obtain the differential correction matrix $M_D$ so that

$$\begin{bmatrix} \Delta\alpha_1 \\ \Delta\alpha_2 \\ \Delta\alpha_3 \\ \Delta\delta_1 \\ \Delta\delta_2 \\ \Delta\delta_3 \end{bmatrix} = M_D \begin{bmatrix} \Delta x_0 \\ \Delta y_0 \\ \Delta z_0 \\ \Delta \dot{x}_0 \\ \Delta \dot{y}_0 \\ \Delta \dot{z}_0 \end{bmatrix}$$

(9.19)

with approximations $d\alpha_{ti} \cong \Delta\alpha_i$, $d\delta_{ti} \cong \Delta\delta_i$, that is, the differentials are replaced with finite differences. This set of linear equations with the partitioned matrix,[1]

$$M_D \equiv \begin{bmatrix} \begin{bmatrix} \frac{\partial \alpha_1}{\partial x_0} \\ \frac{\partial \alpha_2}{\partial x_0} \\ \frac{\partial \alpha_3}{\partial x_0} \\ \frac{\partial \delta_1}{\partial x_0} \\ \frac{\partial \delta_2}{\partial x_0} \\ \frac{\partial \delta_3}{\partial x_0} \end{bmatrix} \begin{bmatrix} \frac{\partial \alpha_1}{\partial y_0} \\ \frac{\partial \alpha_2}{\partial y_0} \\ \frac{\partial \alpha_3}{\partial y_0} \\ \frac{\partial \delta_1}{\partial y_0} \\ \frac{\partial \delta_2}{\partial y_0} \\ \frac{\partial \delta_3}{\partial y_0} \end{bmatrix} \begin{bmatrix} \frac{\partial \alpha_1}{\partial z_0} \\ \frac{\partial \alpha_2}{\partial z_0} \\ \frac{\partial \alpha_3}{\partial z_0} \\ \frac{\partial \delta_1}{\partial z_0} \\ \frac{\partial \delta_2}{\partial z_0} \\ \frac{\partial \delta_3}{\partial z_0} \end{bmatrix} \begin{bmatrix} \frac{\partial \alpha_1}{\partial \dot{x}_0} \\ \frac{\partial \alpha_2}{\partial \dot{x}_0} \\ \frac{\partial \alpha_3}{\partial \dot{x}_0} \\ \frac{\partial \delta_1}{\partial \dot{x}_0} \\ \frac{\partial \delta_2}{\partial \dot{x}_0} \\ \frac{\partial \delta_3}{\partial \dot{x}_0} \end{bmatrix} \begin{bmatrix} \frac{\partial \alpha_1}{\partial \dot{y}_0} \\ \frac{\partial \alpha_2}{\partial \dot{y}_0} \\ \frac{\partial \alpha_3}{\partial \dot{y}_0} \\ \frac{\partial \delta_1}{\partial \dot{y}_0} \\ \frac{\partial \delta_2}{\partial \dot{y}_0} \\ \frac{\partial \delta_3}{\partial \dot{y}_0} \end{bmatrix} \begin{bmatrix} \frac{\partial \alpha_1}{\partial \dot{z}_0} \\ \frac{\partial \alpha_2}{\partial \dot{z}_0} \\ \frac{\partial \alpha_3}{\partial \dot{z}_0} \\ \frac{\partial \delta_1}{\partial \dot{z}_0} \\ \frac{\partial \delta_2}{\partial \dot{z}_0} \\ \frac{\partial \delta_3}{\partial \dot{z}_0} \end{bmatrix} \end{bmatrix}_t,$$

(9.20)

could be solved rather readily if the column matrices composing $M_D$ were numerically known. Let it be assumed for the present that $M_D$ is

[1] All the partial derivatives of the $M_D$ matrix are of a topocentric nature as denoted by the subscript $t$ external to the matrix.

known; then, by computing the inverse of $M_D$, the corrections to the elements at epoch date are given by

$$
\begin{bmatrix} \Delta x_0 \\ \Delta y_0 \\ \Delta z_0 \\ \Delta \dot{x}_0 \\ \Delta \dot{y}_0 \\ \Delta \dot{z}_0 \end{bmatrix} = M_D^{-1} \begin{bmatrix} \Delta \alpha_1 \\ \Delta \alpha_2 \\ \Delta \alpha_3 \\ \Delta \delta_1 \\ \Delta \delta_2 \\ \Delta \delta_3 \end{bmatrix},
\tag{9.21}
$$

so that

$$
\begin{bmatrix} x_0 \\ y_0 \\ z_0 \\ \dot{x}_0 \\ \dot{y}_0 \\ \dot{z}_0 \end{bmatrix}_{n+1} = \begin{bmatrix} x_0 \\ y_0 \\ z_0 \\ \dot{x}_0 \\ \dot{y}_0 \\ \dot{z}_0 \end{bmatrix}_{n} + \begin{bmatrix} \Delta x_0 \\ \Delta y_0 \\ \Delta z_0 \\ \Delta \dot{x}_0 \\ \Delta \dot{y}_0 \\ \Delta \dot{z}_0 \end{bmatrix}_{n}
\tag{9.22}
$$

with $n = 1, 2, \ldots, q$. Hence the process described above is repeated until the residuals are as small as possible. The reader may recognize this procedure as a six-dimensional Newton iteration.

It should be remembered that each time one seeks to obtain the computed observations at $t_i$, *a rigorous prediction process, including all known perturbations, should be used.* To be repetitive, a numerical integration of the relative equations of motion presented in Chapter 2 should be performed to the $t_i$ times, and the observations recomputed or computed out from the trajectory at these times. Each time this is done, new residuals are obtained and these residuals, by virtue of the recursive relation, Eq. 9.22, will improve the starting values supplied to the general differential equations of motion.

### 9.2.3 Numerical determination of the differential correction matrix

The partitioned matrix $M_D$ can be obtained in several different ways. In this section, the numerical or *variant* approach is adopted. This procedure is very straightforward and finds much use in modern-day machine computational procedures.

If $\xi$ is a typical element of the set (9.2), then remembering that $\alpha = \alpha(x_0, y_0, z_0, \dot{x}_0, \dot{y}_0, \dot{z}_0)$ and $\delta = \delta(x_0, y_0, z_0, \dot{x}_0, \dot{y}_0, \dot{z}_0)$, one can form the partial derivatives from their definition, that is,

$$\frac{\partial \alpha_t}{\partial \xi} = \frac{\alpha_t(x_0, y_0, \ldots, \xi + \Delta\xi, \ldots, \dot{z}_0) - \alpha_t(x_0, y_0, \ldots, \xi, \ldots, \dot{z}_0)}{\Delta\xi}$$

$$(9.23)$$

$$\frac{\partial \delta_t}{\partial \xi} = \frac{\delta_t(x_0, y_0, \ldots, \xi + \Delta\xi, \ldots, \dot{z}_0) - \delta_t(x_0, y_0, \ldots, \xi, \ldots, \dot{z}_0)}{\Delta\xi},$$

by incrementing a typical element $\xi$ at the epoch time and integrating forward or backward as the case may be to $t_i$. This incrementation of a typical element produces the functionally dependent angles $\alpha_t(\xi + \Delta\xi)$, $\delta_t(\xi + \Delta\xi)$, produced by a variation in $\xi$. So that if from these angles the nominal or nonincremented angles $\alpha_t$, $\delta_t$ are subtracted, then a division by $\Delta\xi$ yields a numerical approximation to the desired partial derivatives.

Actually, in practice, a nominal trajectory is computed, and the values of $\alpha_{ti}$, $\delta_{ti}$ are saved. Then, if a trajectory is computed with an initial incrementation of $x_0$, that is, $\Delta x_0$, and the angles $\alpha_t(x_0 + \Delta x_0, y_0, \ldots, \dot{z}_0)$, $\delta_t(x_0 + \Delta x_0, y_0, \ldots, \dot{z}_0)$, analytically formed at $t_1$, $t_2$, $t_3$, it is evident that the first column of the $M_D$ matrix is determined, that is, six partials. In similar fashion an initial incrementation of $y_0$, so that $\alpha_t(x_0, y_0 + \Delta y_0, z_0, \ldots, \dot{z}_0)$, $\delta_t(x_0, y_0 + \Delta y_0, z_0, \ldots, \dot{z}_0)$ are determined, will yield the second column of the differential correction matrix, etc. As can be seen, the nominal orbit and six variant orbits are required in order to fully determine the $M_D$ matrix.

The analyst may wonder how or in what way the $\Delta\xi$ or incrementations should be chosen so as to yield the most accurate approximations to the desired partials. In general, an answer cannot be given, except to say that a change of a few per cent should suffice in most cases. Certainly the effect of the incrementation should be evident in $\alpha_t(\xi + \Delta\xi)$ and $\delta_t(\xi + \Delta\xi)$ to the degree of obtaining a meaningful partial. The partials need not be absolutely accurate due to the fact that convergence can at times be achieved by computing $M_D$ only once! That is, after the first six variant trajectories, the $M_D$ matrix is considered determined and is not recomputed in the second correction of the epoch elements. If a one-dimensional Newton procedure is considered, the above statement can be inferred from Figure 9.3.

In the one-dimensional case, if $f(x) = 0$ is sought, an estimate of $x_1$ is used to compute the derivative $f'(x_1)$, then a better value of $x$ is taken to be

$$x_{n+1} = x_n - \frac{f(x_n)}{f'(x_n)}. \tag{9.24}$$

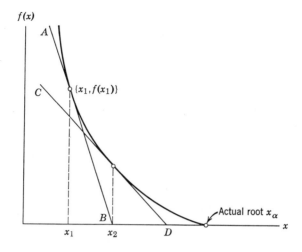

FIGURE 9.3   The geometry of the Newton iterative procedure

Geometrically, a tangent at the point $\{x_1, f(x_1)\}$, that is, tangent $AB$, is used as a linear predictor to produce the next estimate $x_2$.   At the point $\{x_2, f(x_2)\}$ a new tangent $CD$ is used linearly in predicting a closer value to $x_\alpha$, the true zero of the function.   Imagine, however, that once $f'(x_1)$ is computed, it is accepted and the recursive formula

$$x_{n+1} = x_n - \frac{f(x_n)}{f'(x_1)} \tag{9.25}$$

replaces Eq. 9.24.   Geometrically, this is equivalent to always linearly predicting the next value of $x$ with a line parallel to the original tangent $AB$.   Obviously, the predictor will still reach $x_\alpha$, even though it may take longer than if the correct tangent were used every time a correction is made.   This "constant slope" analogy carries over to higher dimensions, even though the whole convergence procedure becomes exceedingly more sensitive (see Section 9.6.2).

### 9.3   ANALYTICAL PARTIAL DERIVATIVES

### 9.3.1   Preliminary remarks

Variant techniques for obtaining the partials of $\alpha_t$, $\delta_t$, with respect to certain elements, that is, the partials of the predicted observations of right ascension and declination with respect to the elements $x_0$, $y_0$, $z_0$,

$\dot{x}_0$, $\dot{y}_0$, $\dot{z}_0$, are not the only methods for obtaining the partial derivative matrix $M_D$. In this section, the $M_D$ matrix will not be discussed from an analytical point of view, because it is better to develop some very important analytical expressions before continuing with the general problem of differential correction.

The next few sections of this chapter will be devoted to the analytical formulation of the partial derivatives of the *state vector* $X$ at time $t$ with respect to the *initial state vector* $X_0$ at time $t_0$. By the state vector is meant an ordered sextuple of parameters $x$, $y$, $z$, $\dot{x}$, $\dot{y}$, $\dot{z}$, whose numerical value is the position and velocity components of a particular body at time $t$ and time $t_0$, that is, $X$ and $X_0$, respectively.

These partial derivatives, namely $\partial X/\partial X_0$, are very useful, not only for the determination of $M_D$ but for the evaluation of guidance equations. Among other things, they can be used to determine velocity corrections for a space vehicle which has deviated slightly from a given reference orbit.

The partial derivatives are obtained by differentiating the two-body expressions for elliptical and hyperbolic orbits. The formulation presented herein as developed by De Bellis and Escobal [3] is also valid for circular orbits. It should be kept in mind that even though the closed expressions for these partials are inherently two-body, this does not detract from their great importance. The $M_D$ matrix, as will be shown at a later stage, can use these expressions and converge very well with only the aid of two-body partials. Furthermore, once the two-body expressions are developed, perturbations can be included.

### 9.3.2   General method

The general method of solution is very simple. From Section 3.7.2, the following set of elements is adopted for the ellipse and circle:

$$a, C_e, S_e, U_0, S_0 \tag{9.26}$$

and

$$a, C_h, S_h, U_0, S_0 \tag{9.27}$$

for the hyperbola. One should recall that, if $X_0$ is known, these elements ($q_i$) are readily computable from the techniques developed in Chapter 3. Furthermore, the following associations should be made:

$$\begin{aligned}
C_e &\equiv e \cos E_0 & C_h &\equiv e \cosh F_0 \\
S_e &\equiv e \sin E_0 & S_h &\equiv e \sinh F_0 \\
S_0 &\equiv \sqrt{\mu p}\, V_0.
\end{aligned} \tag{9.28}$$

The analysis will be carried out for these elements, which are valid for the circle, ellipse, or hyperbola.

For any orbital element, call it $q$ of the set $q_i$, it is possible to assume the functional relationship

$$q = q(\mathbf{X}_0).\tag{9.29}$$

The total differential may then be expressed as

$$dq = \frac{\partial q}{\partial x_0}\, dx_0 + \frac{\partial q}{\partial y_0}\, dy_0 + \cdots + \frac{\partial q}{\partial \dot{z}_0}\, d\dot{z}_0.\tag{9.30}$$

Similarly, for the state vector $\mathbf{X}$, the inverse functional relationship is

$$\mathbf{X} = \mathbf{X}(q_i).\tag{9.31}$$

This equation states that $\mathbf{X}$ or $(\mathbf{r}, \dot{\mathbf{r}})$ at time $t$ depends on the elements $q_i$, that is, either sets 9.26 or 9.27. The total differential of $\mathbf{X}$ is then

$$d\mathbf{X} = \frac{\partial \mathbf{X}}{\partial a}\, da + \frac{\partial \mathbf{X}}{\partial C}\, dC + \frac{\partial \mathbf{X}}{\partial S}\, dS + \cdots + \frac{\partial \mathbf{X}}{\partial S_{z0}}\, dS_{z0},\tag{9.32}$$

where

$$C = C_e \text{ or } C_h$$
$$S = S_e \text{ or } S_h,$$

depending on whether the orbit is an ellipse or hyperbola.

Application of the chain rule of the differential calculus provides

$$\frac{\partial \mathbf{X}}{\partial \mathbf{X}_0} = \sum_{i=1}^{i=9} \frac{\partial \mathbf{X}}{\partial q_i} \cdot \frac{\partial q_i}{\partial \mathbf{X}_0}\tag{9.33}$$

or more explicitly, for example, the partial $\partial x / \partial \dot{x}_0$ is given by

$$\frac{\partial x}{\partial \dot{x}_0} = \frac{\partial x}{\partial a}\frac{\partial a}{\partial \dot{x}_0} + \frac{\partial x}{\partial C}\frac{\partial C}{\partial \dot{x}_0} + \frac{\partial x}{\partial S}\frac{\partial S}{\partial \dot{x}_0} + \cdots + \frac{\partial x}{\partial S_{z0}}\frac{\partial S_{z0}}{\partial \dot{x}_0}.\tag{9.34}$$

The process now reduces to differentiation of the two-body formulas in order to obtain analytical expressions for all the individual partials comprising Eq. 9.34. The analysis is based upon direct utilization of Eqs. 9.30 and 9.32.

The reader may wonder why a future position or velocity vector appears to depend on nine separate elements, Eq. 9.33; the answer is, of course, that it actually does not. In order to preserve clarity of presentation, three redundant orientation elements are carried in the analysis. These redundant components of $\mathbf{U}_0$ and $\mathbf{S}_0$ could be eliminated by means of the relationship between two orthogonal vectors. The method adopted herein has the advantage of yielding the partial derivatives of all the orientation vectors at a small expense in computational efficiency.

### 9.3.3   Elliptic formulation

Partial derivatives of the elements $q$ with respect to $X_0$ may be obtained from two-body formulas by direct differentiation.   For example, selecting the vis-viva equation as a logical candidate for obtaining the partials of semimajor axis with respect to $X_0$, a direct differentiation of

$$\frac{1}{a} = \frac{2}{r_0} - \frac{V_0^2}{\mu},$$    (9.35)

with the understanding that $r_0^2 = x_0^2 + y_0^2 + z_0^2$ and $V_0^2 = \dot{x}_0^2 + \dot{y}_0^2 + \dot{z}_0^2$, yields

$$-\frac{1}{a^2} da = -\frac{2}{r_0^2} dr_0 - \frac{2V_0}{\mu} dV_0$$    (9.36)

or

$$da = \frac{2a^2}{r_0^2} \left( \frac{x_0\, dx_0 + y_0\, dy_0 + z_0 dz_0}{r_0} \right)$$

$$+ \frac{2a^2 V_0}{\mu} \left( \frac{\dot{x}_0\, d\dot{x}_0 + \dot{y}_0\, d\dot{y}_0 + \dot{z}_0\, d\dot{z}_0}{V_0} \right).$$    (9.37)

Therefore, equating coefficients in the a component of Eq. 9.30 yields the partials

$$\begin{bmatrix} \dfrac{\partial a}{\partial x_0} \\[2ex] \dfrac{\partial a}{\partial y_0} \\[2ex] \dfrac{\partial a}{\partial z_0} \end{bmatrix} \begin{bmatrix} \dfrac{2a^2 x_0}{r_0^3} \\[2ex] \dfrac{2a^2 y_0}{r_0^3} \\[2ex] \dfrac{2a^2 z_0}{r_0^3} \end{bmatrix}, \quad \begin{bmatrix} \dfrac{\partial a}{\partial \dot{x}_0} \\[2ex] \dfrac{\partial a}{\partial \dot{y}_0} \\[2ex] \dfrac{\partial a}{\partial \dot{z}_0} \end{bmatrix} = \begin{bmatrix} \dfrac{2a^2 \dot{x}_0}{\mu} \\[2ex] \dfrac{2a^2 \dot{y}_0}{\mu} \\[2ex] \dfrac{2a^2 \dot{z}_0}{\mu} \end{bmatrix}.$$    (9.38)

Proceeding to the next element, $C_e$, the expression to be differentiated is

$$C_e \equiv e \cos E_0 = 1 - \frac{r_0}{a}.$$    (9.39)

Differentiating Eq. 9.39 as a function of $\mathbf{X}_0$ and equating coefficients in the $C_e$ component of Eq. 9.30 yields

$$\begin{bmatrix} \dfrac{\partial C_e}{\partial x_0} \\[2mm] \dfrac{\partial C_e}{\partial y_0} \\[2mm] \dfrac{\partial C_e}{\partial z_0} \end{bmatrix} = \begin{bmatrix} \dfrac{V_0^2 x_0}{\mu r_0} \\[2mm] \dfrac{V_0^2 y_0}{\mu r_0} \\[2mm] \dfrac{V_0^2 z_0}{\mu r_0} \end{bmatrix}, \qquad \begin{bmatrix} \dfrac{\partial C_e}{\partial \dot{x}_0} \\[2mm] \dfrac{\partial C_e}{\partial \dot{y}_0} \\[2mm] \dfrac{\partial C_e}{\partial \dot{z}_0} \end{bmatrix} = \begin{bmatrix} \dfrac{2 r_0 \dot{x}_0}{\mu} \\[2mm] \dfrac{2 r_0 \dot{y}_0}{\mu} \\[2mm] \dfrac{2 r_0 \dot{z}_0}{\mu} \end{bmatrix}. \tag{9.40}$$

Using the relationship

$$S_e \equiv e \sin E_0 = \frac{r_0 \dot{r}_0}{\sqrt{\mu a}} \tag{9.41}$$

and proceeding as before, the partial derivative column vectors are

$$\begin{bmatrix} \dfrac{\partial S_e}{\partial x_0} \\[2mm] \dfrac{\partial S_e}{\partial y_0} \\[2mm] \dfrac{\partial S_e}{\partial z_0} \end{bmatrix} = \begin{bmatrix} \dfrac{\dot{x}_0}{\sqrt{\mu a}} - \dfrac{a S_e x_0}{r_0^3} \\[2mm] \dfrac{\dot{y}_0}{\sqrt{\mu a}} - \dfrac{a S_e y_0}{r_0^3} \\[2mm] \dfrac{\dot{z}_0}{\sqrt{\mu a}} - \dfrac{a S_e z_0}{r_0^3} \end{bmatrix}, \qquad \begin{bmatrix} \dfrac{\partial S_e}{\partial \dot{x}_0} \\[2mm] \dfrac{\partial S_e}{\partial \dot{y}_0} \\[2mm] \dfrac{\partial S_e}{\partial \dot{z}_0} \end{bmatrix} = \begin{bmatrix} \dfrac{x_0}{\sqrt{\mu a}} - \dfrac{a S_e \dot{x}_0}{\mu} \\[2mm] \dfrac{y_0}{\sqrt{\mu a}} - \dfrac{a S_e \dot{y}_0}{\mu} \\[2mm] \dfrac{z_0}{\sqrt{\mu a}} - \dfrac{a S_e \dot{z}_0}{\mu} \end{bmatrix}. \tag{9.42}$$

For the next orbital element, $\mathbf{U}_0$, the expression to be differentiated is

$$\mathbf{U}_0 = \begin{bmatrix} U_{x0} \\[2mm] U_{y0} \\[2mm] U_{z0} \end{bmatrix} = \begin{bmatrix} \dfrac{x_0}{r_0} \\[2mm] \dfrac{y_0}{r_0} \\[2mm] \dfrac{z_0}{r_0} \end{bmatrix}. \tag{9.43}$$

The resulting partial derivatives are

$$\begin{bmatrix} \dfrac{\partial U_{x0}}{\partial x_0} & \dfrac{\partial U_{x0}}{\partial y_0} & \dfrac{\partial U_{x0}}{\partial z_0} \\[3mm] \dfrac{\partial U_{y0}}{\partial x_0} & \dfrac{\partial U_{y0}}{\partial y_0} & \dfrac{\partial U_{y0}}{\partial z_0} \\[3mm] \dfrac{\partial U_{z0}}{\partial x_0} & \dfrac{\partial U_{z0}}{\partial y_0} & \dfrac{\partial U_{z0}}{\partial z_0} \end{bmatrix} = \begin{bmatrix} \left(\dfrac{1}{r_0} - \dfrac{x_0^2}{r_0^3}\right) & \left(-\dfrac{x_0 y_0}{r_0^3}\right) & \left(-\dfrac{x_0 z_0}{r_0^3}\right) \\[3mm] \left(-\dfrac{x_0 y_0}{r_0^3}\right) & \left(\dfrac{1}{r_0} - \dfrac{y_0^2}{r_0^3}\right) & \left(-\dfrac{y_0 z_0}{r_0^3}\right) \\[3mm] \left(-\dfrac{x_0 z_0}{r_0^3}\right) & \left(-\dfrac{y_0 z_0}{r_0^3}\right) & \left(\dfrac{1}{r_0} - \dfrac{z_0^2}{r_0^3}\right) \end{bmatrix} \tag{9.44}$$

and because Eq. 9.43 is independent of velocity components, all the partials of $U_{x0}$, $U_{y0}$, $U_{z0}$, with respect to $\dot{x}_0$, $\dot{y}_0$, $\dot{z}_0$, vanish.

For the element $\mathbf{S}_0$ the expression to be differentiated is

$$\mathbf{S}_0 \equiv \sqrt{\mu p}\, \mathbf{V}_0 = \begin{bmatrix} S_{x0} \\ S_{y0} \\ S_{z0} \end{bmatrix} = \begin{bmatrix} r_0\dot{x}_0 - \dot{r}_0 x_0 \\ r_0\dot{y}_0 - \dot{r}_0 y_0 \\ r_0\dot{z}_0 - \dot{r}_0 z_0 \end{bmatrix}. \tag{9.45}$$

By differentiation, the partial derivatives are obtained as

$$\begin{bmatrix} \dfrac{\partial S_{x0}}{\partial x_0} & \dfrac{\partial S_{x0}}{\partial y_0} & \dfrac{\partial S_{x0}}{\partial z_0} \\[2mm] \dfrac{\partial S_{y0}}{\partial x_0} & \dfrac{\partial S_{y0}}{\partial y_0} & \dfrac{\partial S_{y0}}{\partial z_0} \\[2mm] \dfrac{\partial S_{z0}}{\partial x_0} & \dfrac{\partial S_{z0}}{\partial y_0} & \dfrac{\partial S_{z0}}{\partial z_0} \end{bmatrix}$$

$$= \begin{bmatrix} \left(\dot{r}_0\left\{\dfrac{x_0^2}{r_0^2} - 1\right\}\right) & \left(\dfrac{y_0\dot{x}_0 - x_0\dot{y}_0}{r_0} + \dfrac{x_0 y_0 \dot{r}_0}{r_0^2}\right) \\[3mm] \left(\dfrac{x_0\dot{y}_0 - y_0\dot{x}_0}{r_0} + \dfrac{x_0 y_0 \dot{r}_0}{r_0^2}\right) & \left(\dot{r}_0\left\{\dfrac{y_0^2}{r_0^2} - 1\right\}\right) \\[3mm] \left(\dfrac{x_0\dot{z}_0 - z_0\dot{x}_0}{r_0} + \dfrac{x_0 z_0 \dot{r}_0}{r_0^2}\right)\cdot & \left(\dfrac{y_0\dot{z}_0 - z_0\dot{y}_0}{r_0} + \dfrac{y_0 z_0 \dot{r}_0}{r_0^2}\right) \end{bmatrix}$$

$$\begin{bmatrix} \left(\dfrac{z_0\dot{x}_0 - x_0\dot{z}_0}{r_0} + \dfrac{x_0 z_0 \dot{r}_0}{r_0^2}\right) \\[3mm] \left(\dfrac{z_0\dot{y}_0 - y_0\dot{z}_0}{r_0} + \dfrac{y_0 z_0 \dot{r}_0}{r_0^2}\right) \\[3mm] \left(\dot{r}_0\left\{\dfrac{z_0^2}{r_0} - 1\right\}\right) \end{bmatrix} \tag{9.46}$$

and

$$\begin{bmatrix} \dfrac{\partial S_{x0}}{\partial \dot{x}_0} & \dfrac{\partial S_{x0}}{\partial \dot{y}_0} & \dfrac{\partial S_{x0}}{\partial \dot{z}_0} \\[2mm] \dfrac{\partial S_{y0}}{\partial \dot{x}_0} & \dfrac{\partial S_{y0}}{\partial \dot{y}_0} & \dfrac{\partial S_{y0}}{\partial \dot{z}_0} \\[2mm] \dfrac{\partial S_{z0}}{\partial \dot{x}_0} & \dfrac{\partial S_{z0}}{\partial \dot{y}_0} & \dfrac{\partial S_{z0}}{\partial \dot{z}_0} \end{bmatrix} = \begin{bmatrix} \left(r_0 - \dfrac{x_0^2}{r_0}\right) & \left(-\dfrac{x_0 y_0}{r_0}\right) & \left(-\dfrac{x_0 z_0}{r_0}\right) \\[3mm] \left(-\dfrac{x_0 y_0}{r_0}\right) & \left(r_0 - \dfrac{y_0^2}{r_0}\right) & \left(-\dfrac{y_0 z_0}{r_0}\right) \\[3mm] \left(-\dfrac{x_0 z_0}{r_0}\right) & \left(-\dfrac{y_0 z_0}{r_0}\right) & \left(r_0 - \dfrac{z_0^2}{r_0}\right) \end{bmatrix}. \tag{9.47}$$

It should be remembered that $\dot{r}_0$, the parameter appearing in matrix 9.46, is readily obtainable from

$$\dot{r}_0 = \frac{\mathbf{r}_0 \cdot \dot{\mathbf{r}}_0}{r_0} = \mathbf{U}_0 \cdot \dot{\mathbf{r}}_0. \tag{9.48}$$

In recapitulation, the partial derivatives of the elements $a$, $C_e$, $S_e$, $\mathbf{U}_0$, $\mathbf{S}_0$, with respect to $x_0$, $y_0$, $z_0$, $\dot{x}_0$, $\dot{y}_0$, $\dot{z}_0$, or $\mathbf{X}_0$, have just been found analytically. The next step in the analysis is the determination of the partial derivatives of $\mathbf{X}$ or $x$, $y$, $z$, $\dot{x}$, $\dot{y}$, $\dot{z}$, with respect to the elements. This step is much more complicated, or in truth, more tedious than the previous analytic formulation. In order to commence with the analysis, the reader should bear in mind that the future or past position and velocity vectors are already known, that is, some process, whether the algorithm in Appendix II with the inclusion of perturbative variations or numerical integration of the general equations of motion, has yielded $\mathbf{r}$ and $\dot{\mathbf{r}}$ at time $t$. In essence, the argument of the analytic expressions about to be developed, $v - v_0$, the difference in true anomalies, is also known from

$$\cos (v - v_0) = \frac{\mathbf{r} \cdot \mathbf{r}_0}{r r_0}$$
$$\sin (v - v_0) = s \sqrt{1 - \cos^2 (v - v_0)}, \tag{9.49}$$

with

$$s = \frac{x_0 y - x y_0}{|x_0 y - x y_0|}$$

for a direct orbit, and where the sign of $s$ is reversed for a retrograde orbit.

Before presenting the analysis, the following formulas are presented en masse, as extracted from Chapter 3:[2]

$$\mathbf{r} = x_v \mathbf{U}_0 + y_v \mathbf{V}_0 \tag{9.50}$$

$$r\dot{\mathbf{r}} = \sqrt{\mu a}\, D\mathbf{U} + \sqrt{\mu p}\, \mathbf{V} \tag{9.51}$$

$$\mathbf{V}_0 = \frac{\mathbf{S}_0}{\sqrt{\mu p}} \tag{9.52}$$

$$x_v = r \cos (v - v_0) \tag{9.53}$$

$$y_v = r \sin (v - v_0) \tag{9.54}$$

$$D = \frac{r\dot{r}}{\sqrt{\mu a}} \tag{9.55}$$

$$p = a(1 - C_e^2 - S_e^2) \tag{9.56}$$

[2] The definition of $D$, Eq. 9.55, is slightly modified from the form used in Chapter 3.

$$\mathbf{U} = \mathbf{U}_0 \cos (v - v_0) + \frac{\mathbf{S}_0}{\sqrt{\mu p}} \sin (v - v_0) \tag{9.57}$$

$$\mathbf{S} = \mathbf{S}_0 \cos (v - v_0) - \mathbf{U}_0 \sqrt{\mu p} \sin (v - v_0) \tag{9.58}$$

$$r\dot{r} = \mathbf{r} \cdot \dot{\mathbf{r}} \tag{9.59}$$

$$\cos (v - v_0) = 1 - \frac{ap}{rr_0} [1 - \cos (E - E_0)] \tag{9.60}$$

$$\sin (v - v_0) = \frac{a\sqrt{ap}}{rr_0} [M - M_0 - (E - E_0) + \sin (E - E_0)] \tag{9.61}$$

$$M - M_0 = E - E_0 + S_e[1 - \cos (E - E_0)] - C_e \sin (E - E_0). \tag{9.62}$$

Working first with the position vector $\mathbf{r}$, the analysis is outlined as follows.

Differentiating Eq. 9.50 and equating coefficients so that the form of Eq. 9.32 is maintained, the partial derivative of $\mathbf{r}$ with respect to the elements can be obtained as a function of the elements and $r$, $r_0$, $p$, $\sin (v - v_0)$, $\cos (v - v_0)$, and the difference of mean anomalies, $M - M_0$. Reduction to expressions with arguments of $v - v_0$ will be achieved with the aid of

$$r = a[1 - C_e \cos (E - E_0) + S_e \sin (E - E_0)] \tag{9.63}$$

$$r_0 = a(1 - C_e) \tag{9.64}$$

$$\sin (E - E_0) = \frac{r}{\sqrt{ap}} \sin (v - v_0) - \frac{r}{p} [1 - \cos (v - v_0)]S_e, \tag{9.65}$$

and Eqs. 9.52 to 9.62.

By collecting terms, the partial derivative of $\mathbf{r}$ with respect to the element $a$ (after lengthy reduction) is stated as

$$\frac{\partial \mathbf{r}}{\partial a} = A_1 \mathbf{U}_0 + A_2 \mathbf{S}_0, \tag{9.66}$$

where

$$A_1 \equiv \frac{r}{a} \cos (v - v_0) + \frac{3}{2} a(M - M_0) \left\{ \frac{1}{\sqrt{ap}} \left( \frac{p}{r_0} - C_e \right) \sin (v - v_0) \right.$$
$$\left. + S_e \left( \frac{1}{p} - \frac{1}{r_0} \right) [1 - \cos (v - v_0)] - \frac{S_e}{r} \right\}$$

$$A_2 \equiv \frac{1}{\sqrt{\mu p}} \left\{ \frac{r}{2a} \sin (v - v_0) - \frac{3}{2} \frac{\sqrt{ap}}{r_0} (M - M_0) \right.$$
$$\left. + \frac{3}{2} \sqrt{\frac{a}{p}} (M - M_0)[1 - \cos (v - v_0)] \right\}.$$

The partial derivative of **r** with respect to the element $C_e$ can be verified to be analytically expressible as

$$\frac{\partial \mathbf{r}}{\partial C_e} = C_1 \mathbf{U}_0 + C_2 \mathbf{S}_0, \tag{9.67}$$

where

$$C_1 \equiv -a + \frac{a^2 S_e}{\sqrt{ap}} \sin(v - v_0)$$

$$+ \left( \frac{rr_0 - a^2 S_e^2 + 2arC_e}{p} - \frac{ar}{r_0} \right)[1 - \cos(v - v_0)]$$

$$+ ar\left( \frac{C_e}{p} - \frac{1}{r_0} \right) \sin^2(v - v_0)$$

$$+ \frac{a^2 r S_e}{\sqrt{ap}} \left[ \frac{2}{r_0} - \frac{1}{p}(1 + C_e) \right][1 - \cos(v - v_0)] \sin(v - v_0)$$

$$+ \frac{a^2 S_e^2 r}{p} \left( \frac{1}{p} - \frac{1}{r_0} \right)[1 - \cos(v - v_0)]^2$$

$$C_2 \equiv \frac{ar}{\sqrt{\mu p}} \left\{ \frac{\sin(v - v_0)}{r_0} + \frac{1}{p}\sqrt{\frac{a}{p}} \, S_e[1 - \cos(v - v_0)]^2 \right.$$

$$\left. - \frac{\sin(v - v_0)}{p}[1 - \cos(v - v_0)] \right\}.$$

The partial derivative of **r** with respect to the element $S_e$ is

$$\frac{\partial \mathbf{r}}{\partial S_e} = S_1 \mathbf{U}_0 + S_2 \mathbf{S}_0, \tag{9.68}$$

where

$$S_1 \equiv \frac{ar}{\sqrt{ap}} \sin(v - v_0)\left\{ 1 + [1 - \cos(v - v_0)]\left( 1 - \frac{r_0}{p} C_e \right) \right\}$$

$$+ S_e \frac{ar}{p}[1 - \cos(v - v_0)] \cos(v - v_0)$$

$$+ S_e \frac{ar_0}{p}[1 - \cos(v - v_0)]\left\{ \frac{r}{p}[1 - \cos(v - v_0)] - 1 \right\}$$

$$S_2 \equiv \frac{1}{\sqrt{\mu p}} \left\{ \frac{rr_0\sqrt{ap}}{p^2}[1 - \cos(v - v_0)]^2 \right\}.$$

Continuing with the analysis, the partial derivatives of $x$, $y$, $z$, with respect to the vector element $U_0$, are given by the matrix

$$
\begin{bmatrix}
\dfrac{\partial x}{\partial U_{x0}} & \dfrac{\partial x}{\partial U_{y0}} & \dfrac{\partial x}{\partial U_{z0}} \\[2ex]
\dfrac{\partial y}{\partial U_{x0}} & \dfrac{\partial y}{\partial U_{y0}} & \dfrac{\partial y}{\partial U_{z0}} \\[2ex]
\dfrac{\partial z}{\partial U_{x0}} & \dfrac{\partial z}{\partial U_{y0}} & \dfrac{\partial z}{\partial U_{z0}}
\end{bmatrix}
=
\begin{bmatrix}
x_v & 0 & 0 \\
0 & x_v & 0 \\
0 & 0 & x_v
\end{bmatrix}.
\tag{9.69}
$$

Similarly, the partial derivatives of $x$, $y$, $z$, with respect to the vector element $S_0$ are defined by the matrix

$$
\begin{bmatrix}
\dfrac{\partial x}{\partial S_{x0}} & \dfrac{\partial x}{\partial S_{y0}} & \dfrac{\partial x}{\partial S_{z0}} \\[2ex]
\dfrac{\partial y}{\partial S_{x0}} & \dfrac{\partial y}{\partial S_{y0}} & \dfrac{\partial y}{\partial S_{z0}} \\[2ex]
\dfrac{\partial z}{\partial S_{x0}} & \dfrac{\partial z}{\partial S_{y0}} & \dfrac{\partial z}{\partial S_{z0}}
\end{bmatrix}
=
\begin{bmatrix}
\dfrac{y_v}{\sqrt{\mu p}} & 0 & 0 \\[2ex]
0 & \dfrac{y_v}{\sqrt{\mu p}} & 0 \\[2ex]
0 & 0 & \dfrac{y_v}{\sqrt{\mu p}}
\end{bmatrix}.
\tag{9.70}
$$

This concludes the determination of the partial derivatives of $x$, $y$, $z$, with respect to the elements.

With even lengthier reduction, the partial derivatives of the velocity vector $\dot{\mathbf{r}}$ with respect to the elements will now be attacked with the aid of the auxiliary partial $\partial(r\dot{r})/\partial q$. By direct differentiation of Eq. 9.51, the partial derivatives of $r\dot{r}$ with respect to the elements can be obtained in the same manner as the partial derivatives of $\mathbf{r}$ with respect to the elements. Only results are stated in order to conserve space.

The partial derivative of $r\dot{r}$ with respect to the element $a$ is

$$
\frac{\partial(r\dot{r})}{\partial a} = \tilde{A}_1 U_0 + \tilde{A}_2 S_0,
\tag{9.71}
$$

where

$$
\tilde{A}_1 \equiv \left\{ \frac{3}{2} \frac{(M - M_0)}{r} \sqrt{\mu p}\, aD \left[ \frac{1}{r_0} - \frac{1}{r} \right] - \frac{1}{2} \frac{\sqrt{\mu p}}{a} \right\} \sin(v - v_0)
$$

$$
- \left\{ \frac{3}{2} \frac{(M - M_0)}{r^2} \sqrt{\mu a}\, aD^2 + \frac{3}{2} \frac{(M - M_0)}{r r_0} \sqrt{\mu a}\, aDS_e \right.
$$

$$
\left. + \frac{3}{2} (M - M_0)\sqrt{\frac{\mu}{a}} + \frac{1}{2}\sqrt{\frac{\mu}{a}}\, D \right\} [1 - \cos(v - v_0)]
$$

$$
+ \left\{ \frac{3}{2}(M - M_0)\sqrt{\frac{\mu}{a}} \left( 1 - \frac{a}{r} \right) + \frac{3}{2} \frac{(M - M_0)}{r r_0} p\sqrt{\mu a} + \frac{1}{2}\sqrt{\frac{\mu}{a}}\, D \right\}
$$

$$\tilde{A}_2 \equiv \left\{ \frac{3}{2} \frac{(M - M_0)}{a} \left(1 - \frac{a}{r}\right) \sqrt{\frac{a}{p}} + \frac{3}{2} \frac{(M - M_0)}{r^2} \sqrt{\frac{a}{p}} \, a D^2 \right.$$

$$\left. + \frac{3}{2} \frac{(M - M_0)}{r r_0} \sqrt{ap} \right\} \sin(v - v_0)$$

$$+ \left\{ \frac{3}{2} \frac{(M - M_0)}{r} \frac{aD}{p} - \frac{3}{2} \frac{(M - M_0)}{r r_0} a S_e \right.$$

$$\left. - \frac{3}{2} \frac{(M - M_0)}{r^2} a D \right\} [1 - \cos(v - v_0)]$$

$$- \left\{ \frac{3}{2} \frac{(M - M_0)}{r r_0} a D \right\}.$$

Similarly, the partial derivative of $r\dot{r}$ with respect to the element $C_e$ is

$$\frac{\partial(r\dot{r})}{\partial C_e} = \tilde{C}_1 \mathbf{U}_0 + \tilde{C}_2 \mathbf{S}_0, \tag{9.72}$$

where

$$\tilde{C}_1 \equiv \left\{ a\sqrt{\mu a} \, \beta_1 \cos(v - v_0) + a\sqrt{\frac{\mu}{p}} \, C_e \sin(v - v_0) \right.$$

$$\left. + D\sqrt{\mu a} \, \beta_3 - \sqrt{\mu p} \, \beta_4 \right\}$$

$$\tilde{C}_2 \equiv \left\{ a\sqrt{\frac{a}{p}} \, \beta_1 \sin(v - v_0) + \frac{Da^2}{p\sqrt{ap}} \, C_e \sin(v - v_0) + \beta_3 + D\sqrt{\frac{a}{p}} \, \beta_4 \right\}$$

with the $\beta$ coefficients defined as

$$\beta_1 \equiv \frac{\sin(v - v_0)}{\sqrt{ap}} - \frac{S_e}{p} [1 - \cos(v - v_0)]$$

$$\beta_2 \equiv a\left\{ \frac{Da}{r\sqrt{ap}} \sin(v - v_0) - \left(\frac{1}{r_0} + \frac{1}{r}\right) \right.$$

$$\left. + \frac{1}{p} \left(\frac{r_0}{a} - \frac{DaS_e}{r}\right) [1 - \cos(v - v_0)] \right\}$$

$$\beta_3 \equiv \left\{ \beta_2 + \frac{2aC_e}{p} \right\} [1 - \cos(v - v_0)] - \frac{pa^2\beta_1^2}{r_0}$$

$$\beta_4 \equiv -\left\{ \frac{aC_e}{p} + \beta_2 \right\} \sin(v - v_0) - a\sqrt{\frac{a}{p}} \, \beta_1[1 - \cos(v - v_0)].$$

In the same manner it is possible to find that the partial derivative of $r\dot{r}$ with respect to $S_e$ is

$$\frac{\partial(r\dot{r})}{\partial S_e} = \tilde{S}_1 \mathbf{U}_0 + \tilde{S}_2 \mathbf{S}_0, \tag{9.73}$$

where

$$\tilde{S}_1 \equiv \left\{ \gamma_1 \cos(v - v_0) + a\sqrt{\frac{\mu}{p}} S_e \sin(v - v_0) + \sqrt{\mu a} \, D\gamma_3 - \sqrt{\mu p} \, \gamma_4 \right\}$$

$$\tilde{S}_2 \equiv \left\{ \frac{\gamma_1}{\sqrt{\mu p}} \sin(v - v_0) + \frac{a^2 S_e D}{p\sqrt{ap}} \sin(v - v_0) + \gamma_3 + D\sqrt{\frac{a}{p}} \gamma_4 \right\}$$

with the auxiliary $\gamma$ coefficients defined by

$$\gamma_1 \equiv \sqrt{\mu a} \left\{ 1 - \frac{r_0}{p} [1 - \cos(v - v_0)] \right\}$$

$$\gamma_2 \equiv a \left\{ \beta_1 - \frac{r_0}{rp} D[1 - \cos(v - v_0)] \right\}$$

$$\gamma_3 \equiv \left\{ \frac{2aS_e}{p} + \gamma_2 + a\beta_1 \right\} [1 - \cos(v - v_0)]$$

$$\gamma_4 \equiv -\left\{ \frac{aS_e}{p} + \gamma_2 \right\} \sin(v - v_0) + \frac{r_0\sqrt{ap}}{p^2} [1 - \cos(v - v_0)]^2.$$

The partial derivatives of $r\dot{x}$, $r\dot{y}$, $r\dot{z}$, with respect to the vector element $\mathbf{U}_0$, are defined by the matrix

$$\begin{bmatrix} \dfrac{\partial(r\dot{x})}{\partial U_{x0}} & \dfrac{\partial(r\dot{x})}{\partial U_{y0}} & \dfrac{\partial(r\dot{x})}{\partial U_{z0}} \\[2mm] \dfrac{\partial(r\dot{y})}{\partial U_{x0}} & \dfrac{\partial(r\dot{y})}{\partial U_{y0}} & \dfrac{\partial(r\dot{y})}{\partial U_{z0}} \\[2mm] \dfrac{\partial(r\dot{z})}{\partial U_{x0}} & \dfrac{\partial(r\dot{z})}{\partial U_{y0}} & \dfrac{\partial(r\dot{z})}{\partial U_{z0}} \end{bmatrix} = \begin{bmatrix} \tilde{U} & 0 & 0 \\ 0 & \tilde{U} & 0 \\ 0 & 0 & \tilde{U} \end{bmatrix}, \tag{9.74}$$

where

$$\tilde{U} \equiv \sqrt{\mu a} \, D \cos(v - v_0) - \sqrt{\mu p} \sin(v - v_0).$$

In similar fashion, the derivatives of $r\dot{x}$, $r\dot{y}$, $r\dot{z}$, with respect to the vector element $\mathbf{S}_0$, are defined by

$$\begin{bmatrix} \dfrac{\partial(r\dot{x})}{\partial S_{x0}} & \dfrac{\partial(r\dot{x})}{\partial S_{y0}} & \dfrac{\partial(r\dot{x})}{\partial S_{z0}} \\[2mm] \dfrac{\partial(r\dot{y})}{\partial S_{x0}} & \dfrac{\partial(r\dot{y})}{\partial S_{y0}} & \dfrac{\partial(r\dot{y})}{\partial S_{z0}} \\[2mm] \dfrac{\partial(r\dot{z})}{\partial S_{x0}} & \dfrac{\partial(r\dot{z})}{\partial S_{y0}} & \dfrac{\partial(r\dot{z})}{\partial S_{z0}} \end{bmatrix} = \begin{bmatrix} \tilde{S} & 0 & 0 \\ 0 & \tilde{S} & 0 \\ 0 & 0 & \tilde{S} \end{bmatrix}, \tag{9.75}$$

where

$$\tilde{S} \equiv \cos (v - v_0) + \sqrt{\frac{a}{p}} \, D \sin (v - v_0).$$

Since the above auxiliary partials have been obtained, the sought-for partial derivatives of the components of the velocity vector $\dot{\mathbf{r}}$ with respect to the elements can be obtained by noticing that

$$\frac{\partial (r\dot{\mathbf{r}})}{\partial q} = \dot{\mathbf{r}} \frac{\partial r}{\partial q} + r \frac{\partial \dot{\mathbf{r}}}{\partial q}, \tag{9.76}$$

so that the desired partials are

$$\frac{\partial \dot{\mathbf{r}}}{\partial q} = \frac{1}{r} \left[ \frac{\partial (r\dot{\mathbf{r}})}{\partial q} - \dot{\mathbf{r}} \frac{\partial r}{\partial q} \right], \tag{9.77}$$

where

$$\frac{\partial r}{\partial q} = \frac{1}{r} \left( x \frac{\partial x}{\partial q} + y \frac{\partial y}{\partial q} + z \frac{\partial z}{\partial q} \right)$$

and $q$ is a typical member of the set $[a, C_e, S_e, \mathbf{U}_0, \mathbf{S}_0]$. Determination of the partial $\partial (r\dot{\mathbf{r}})/\partial q$ was merely a device used to avoid tedious algebra in the evaluation of the partial $\partial \dot{\mathbf{r}}/\partial q$. Therefore, in order to determine $\partial \dot{\mathbf{r}}/\partial q$, Eqs. 9.76 and 9.77 are used by letting $q$ equal $a$, $C_e$, $S_e$, $U_{x0}$, $U_{y0}$, $U_{z0}$, $S_{x0}$, $S_{y0}$, $S_{z0}$, respectively. The previous analysis completes the elliptic formulation of the partials of $\mathbf{X}$ with respect to the elements, and the partials of the elements with respect to $\mathbf{X}_0$.

It now remains to combine these partials to yield $\partial \mathbf{X}/\partial \mathbf{X}_0$. This will be done in Section 9.3.5.

### 9.3.4 Hyperbolic formulation

The method of solution for the case of hyperbolic motion is the same as outlined in the previous section. Partial derivatives of $\mathbf{X}$ with respect to the elements, and partial derivatives of the elements with respect to $\mathbf{X}_0$, are obtained in exactly the same manner as the case in which elliptical motion occurs. In fact, owing to the relations between the circular and hyperbolic functions, the formulation of the previous section may be converted directly with the aid of the imaginary $i = \sqrt{-1}$ by means of the following substitutions into the elliptic formulation

$$C_e = C_h \tag{9.78}$$

$$S_e = iS_h \tag{9.79}$$

$$\frac{\partial S_e}{\partial \mathbf{X}_0} = i\,\frac{\partial S_h}{\partial \mathbf{X}_0} \tag{9.80}$$

$$\frac{\partial \mathbf{X}}{\partial S_e} = -i\,\frac{\partial \mathbf{X}}{\partial S_h} \tag{9.81}$$

$$D = iD_h \tag{9.82}$$

$$M - M_0 = -i(M_h - M_{h0}) \tag{9.83}$$

with the understanding that

$$D_h = \frac{r\dot{r}}{\sqrt{-\mu a}} \tag{9.84}$$

$$C_h = e \cosh F_0 \tag{9.85}$$

$$S_h = e \sinh F_0, \tag{9.86}$$

and that the subscript $h$ denotes the hyperbolic form. Furthermore, if these partials were derived in the same manner as the elliptical partials, that is, without making the above-indicated substitutions, the following auxiliary relationships would be necessary. These are presented en masse as:

$$r\dot{r} = \sqrt{-\mu a}\,D_h\mathbf{U} + \sqrt{\mu p}\,\mathbf{V} \tag{9.87}$$

$$p = a(1 - C_h^2 + S_h^2) \tag{9.88}$$

$$\cos(v - v_0) = 1 - \frac{ap}{rr_0}[1 - \cosh(F - F_0)] \tag{9.89}$$

$$\sin(v - v_0) = \frac{a\sqrt{-ap}}{rr_0}[M_h - M_{h0} + (F - F_0) - \sinh(F - F_0)] \tag{9.90}$$

$$M_h - M_{h0} = -(F - F_0) - S_h[1 - \cosh(F - F_0)] + C_h \sinh(F - F_0) \tag{9.91}$$

$$M_h - M_{h0} = n(t - t_0) \tag{9.92}$$

$$n = k\sqrt{\frac{\mu}{-a^3}} \tag{9.93}$$

$$r = a[1 - C_h \cosh(F - F_0) - S_h \sinh(F - F_0)] \tag{9.94}$$

$$r_0 = a(1 - C_h) \tag{9.95}$$

$$\sinh(F - F_0) = \frac{r}{\sqrt{-ap}}\sin(v - v_0) - \frac{r}{p}[1 - \cos(v - v_0)]S_h. \tag{9.96}$$

For the sake of conserving space, statement of these formulas concludes the hyperbolic analysis.

### 9.3.5 The partial derivatives of the state vector X with respect to the state vector $X_0$

Having found the partials of $X$ with respect to $q$, and $q$ with respect to $X_0$ for the circular, elliptic, and hyperbolic cases, the partial derivatives $\partial X/\partial X_0$ can be found from Eq. 9.33. Let $C = C_e$ or $C_h$, and $S = S_e$ or $S_h$, depending on whether the orbit is elliptical or hyperbolic. Then, the following vectors are defined:

$$\tilde{X} \equiv \left[ \frac{\partial x}{\partial a}, \frac{\partial x}{\partial C}, \frac{\partial x}{\partial S}, \frac{\partial x}{\partial U_{x0}}, \quad 0 \quad, \quad 0 \quad, \frac{\partial x}{\partial S_{x0}}, \quad 0 \quad, \quad 0 \quad \right] \tag{9.97}$$

$$\tilde{Y} \equiv \left[ \frac{\partial y}{\partial a}, \frac{\partial y}{\partial C}, \frac{\partial y}{\partial S}, \quad 0 \quad, \frac{\partial y}{\partial U_{y0}}, \quad 0 \quad, \quad 0 \quad, \frac{\partial y}{\partial S_{y0}}, \quad 0 \quad \right] \tag{9.98}$$

$$\tilde{Z} \equiv \left[ \frac{\partial z}{\partial a}, \frac{\partial z}{\partial C}, \frac{\partial z}{\partial S}, \quad 0 \quad, \quad 0 \quad, \frac{\partial z}{\partial U_{z0}}, \quad 0 \quad, \quad 0 \quad, \frac{\partial z}{\partial S_{z0}} \right] \tag{9.99}$$

$$\dot{\tilde{X}} \equiv \left[ \frac{\partial \dot{x}}{\partial a}, \frac{\partial \dot{x}}{\partial C}, \frac{\partial \dot{x}}{\partial S}, \frac{\partial \dot{x}}{\partial U_{x0}}, \frac{\partial \dot{x}}{\partial U_{y0}}, \frac{\partial \dot{x}}{\partial U_{z0}}, \frac{\partial \dot{x}}{\partial S_{x0}}, \frac{\partial \dot{x}}{\partial S_{y0}}, \frac{\partial \dot{x}}{\partial S_{z0}} \right] \tag{9.100}$$

$$\dot{\tilde{Y}} \equiv \left[ \frac{\partial \dot{y}}{\partial a}, \frac{\partial \dot{y}}{\partial C}, \frac{\partial \dot{y}}{\partial S}, \frac{\partial \dot{y}}{\partial U_{x0}}, \frac{\partial \dot{y}}{\partial U_{y0}}, \frac{\partial \dot{y}}{\partial U_{z0}}, \frac{\partial \dot{y}}{\partial S_{x0}}, \frac{\partial \dot{y}}{\partial S_{y0}}, \frac{\partial \dot{y}}{\partial S_{z0}} \right] \tag{9.101}$$

$$\dot{\tilde{Z}} \equiv \left[ \frac{\partial \dot{z}}{\partial a}, \frac{\partial \dot{z}}{\partial C}, \frac{\partial \dot{z}}{\partial S}, \frac{\partial \dot{z}}{\partial U_{x0}}, \frac{\partial \dot{z}}{\partial U_{y0}}, \frac{\partial \dot{z}}{\partial U_{z0}}, \frac{\partial \dot{z}}{\partial S_{x0}}, \frac{\partial \dot{z}}{\partial S_{y0}}, \frac{\partial \dot{z}}{\partial S_{z0}} \right] \tag{9.102}$$

and

$$Q_x \equiv \left[ \frac{\partial a}{\partial x_0}, \frac{\partial C}{\partial x_0}, \frac{\partial S}{\partial x_0}, \frac{\partial U_{x0}}{\partial x_0}, \frac{\partial U_{y0}}{\partial x_0}, \frac{\partial U_{z0}}{\partial x_0}, \frac{\partial S_{x0}}{\partial x_0}, \frac{\partial S_{y0}}{\partial x_0}, \frac{\partial S_{z0}}{\partial x_0} \right] \tag{9.103}$$

$$Q_y \equiv \left[ \frac{\partial a}{\partial y_0}, \frac{\partial C}{\partial y_0}, \frac{\partial S}{\partial y_0}, \frac{\partial U_{x0}}{\partial y_0}, \frac{\partial U_{y0}}{\partial y_0}, \frac{\partial U_{z0}}{\partial y_0}, \frac{\partial S_{x0}}{\partial y_0}, \frac{\partial S_{y0}}{\partial y_0}, \frac{\partial S_{z0}}{\partial y_0} \right] \tag{9.104}$$

$$Q_z \equiv \left[ \frac{\partial a}{\partial z_0}, \frac{\partial C}{\partial z_0}, \frac{\partial S}{\partial z_0}, \frac{\partial U_{x0}}{\partial z_0}, \frac{\partial U_{y0}}{\partial z_0}, \frac{\partial U_{z0}}{\partial z_0}, \frac{\partial S_{x0}}{\partial z_0}, \frac{\partial S_{y0}}{\partial z_0}, \frac{\partial S_{z0}}{\partial z_0} \right] \tag{9.105}$$

$$\dot{Q}_x \equiv \left[ \frac{\partial a}{\partial \dot{x}_0}, \frac{\partial C}{\partial \dot{x}_0}, \frac{\partial S}{\partial \dot{x}_0}, \quad 0 \quad, \quad 0 \quad, \quad 0 \quad, \frac{\partial S_{x0}}{\partial \dot{x}_0}, \frac{\partial S_{y0}}{\partial \dot{x}_0}, \frac{\partial S_{z0}}{\partial \dot{x}_0} \right] \tag{9.106}$$

$$\dot{Q}_y \equiv \left[ \frac{\partial a}{\partial \dot{y}_0}, \frac{\partial C}{\partial \dot{y}_0}, \frac{\partial S}{\partial \dot{y}_0}, \quad 0 \quad, \quad 0 \quad, \quad 0 \quad, \frac{\partial S_{x0}}{\partial \dot{y}_0}, \frac{\partial S_{y0}}{\partial \dot{y}_0}, \frac{\partial S_{z0}}{\partial \dot{y}_0} \right] \tag{9.107}$$

$$\dot{Q}_z \equiv \left[ \frac{\partial a}{\partial \dot{z}_0}, \frac{\partial C}{\partial \dot{z}_0}, \frac{\partial S}{\partial \dot{z}_0}, \quad 0 \quad, \quad 0 \quad, \quad 0 \quad, \frac{\partial S_{x0}}{\partial \dot{z}_0}, \frac{\partial S_{y0}}{\partial \dot{z}_0}, \frac{\partial S_{z0}}{\partial \dot{z}_0} \right]. \tag{9.108}$$

With these definitions, it is possible to write directly the desired partials as

$$
M \equiv
\begin{bmatrix}
\dfrac{\partial x}{\partial x_0} & \dfrac{\partial x}{\partial y_0} & \dfrac{\partial x}{\partial z_0} \\[8pt]
\dfrac{\partial y}{\partial x_0} & \dfrac{\partial y}{\partial y_0} & \dfrac{\partial y}{\partial z_0} \\[8pt]
\dfrac{\partial z}{\partial x_0} & \dfrac{\partial z}{\partial y_0} & \dfrac{\partial z}{\partial z_0}
\end{bmatrix}
=
\begin{bmatrix}
\tilde{\mathbf{X}} \cdot \mathbf{Q}_x & \tilde{\mathbf{X}} \cdot \mathbf{Q}_y & \tilde{\mathbf{X}} \cdot \mathbf{Q}_z \\[6pt]
\tilde{\mathbf{Y}} \cdot \mathbf{Q}_x & \tilde{\mathbf{Y}} \cdot \mathbf{Q}_y & \tilde{\mathbf{Y}} \cdot \mathbf{Q}_z \\[6pt]
\tilde{\mathbf{Z}} \cdot \mathbf{Q}_x & \tilde{\mathbf{Z}} \cdot \mathbf{Q}_y & \tilde{\mathbf{Z}} \cdot \mathbf{Q}_z
\end{bmatrix}
\tag{9.109}
$$

$$
N \equiv
\begin{bmatrix}
\dfrac{\partial x}{\partial \dot{x}_0} & \dfrac{\partial x}{\partial \dot{y}_0} & \dfrac{\partial x}{\partial \dot{z}_0} \\[8pt]
\dfrac{\partial y}{\partial \dot{x}_0} & \dfrac{\partial y}{\partial \dot{y}_0} & \dfrac{\partial y}{\partial \dot{z}_0} \\[8pt]
\dfrac{\partial z}{\partial \dot{x}_0} & \dfrac{\partial z}{\partial \dot{y}_0} & \dfrac{\partial z}{\partial \dot{z}_0}
\end{bmatrix}
=
\begin{bmatrix}
\tilde{\mathbf{X}} \cdot \dot{\mathbf{Q}}_x & \tilde{\mathbf{X}} \cdot \dot{\mathbf{Q}}_y & \tilde{\mathbf{X}} \cdot \dot{\mathbf{Q}}_z \\[6pt]
\tilde{\mathbf{Y}} \cdot \dot{\mathbf{Q}}_x & \tilde{\mathbf{Y}} \cdot \dot{\mathbf{Q}}_y & \tilde{\mathbf{Y}} \cdot \dot{\mathbf{Q}}_z \\[6pt]
\tilde{\mathbf{Z}} \cdot \dot{\mathbf{Q}}_x & \tilde{\mathbf{Z}} \cdot \dot{\mathbf{Q}}_y & \tilde{\mathbf{Z}} \cdot \dot{\mathbf{Q}}_z
\end{bmatrix}
\tag{9.110}
$$

$$
M^* \equiv
\begin{bmatrix}
\dfrac{\partial \dot{x}}{\partial x_0} & \dfrac{\partial \dot{x}}{\partial y_0} & \dfrac{\partial \dot{x}}{\partial z_0} \\[8pt]
\dfrac{\partial \dot{y}}{\partial x_0} & \dfrac{\partial \dot{y}}{\partial y_0} & \dfrac{\partial \dot{y}}{\partial z_0} \\[8pt]
\dfrac{\partial \dot{z}}{\partial x_0} & \dfrac{\partial \dot{z}}{\partial y_0} & \dfrac{\partial \dot{z}}{\partial z_0}
\end{bmatrix}
=
\begin{bmatrix}
\dot{\tilde{\mathbf{X}}} \cdot \mathbf{Q}_x & \dot{\tilde{\mathbf{X}}} \cdot \mathbf{Q}_y & \dot{\tilde{\mathbf{X}}} \cdot \mathbf{Q}_z \\[6pt]
\dot{\tilde{\mathbf{Y}}} \cdot \mathbf{Q}_x & \dot{\tilde{\mathbf{Y}}} \cdot \mathbf{Q}_y & \dot{\tilde{\mathbf{Y}}} \cdot \mathbf{Q}_z \\[6pt]
\dot{\tilde{\mathbf{Z}}} \cdot \mathbf{Q}_x & \dot{\tilde{\mathbf{Z}}} \cdot \mathbf{Q}_y & \dot{\tilde{\mathbf{Z}}} \cdot \mathbf{Q}_z
\end{bmatrix}
\tag{9.111}
$$

$$
N^* \equiv
\begin{bmatrix}
\dfrac{\partial \dot{x}}{\partial \dot{x}_0} & \dfrac{\partial \dot{x}}{\partial \dot{y}_0} & \dfrac{\partial \dot{x}}{\partial \dot{z}_0} \\[8pt]
\dfrac{\partial \dot{y}}{\partial \dot{x}_0} & \dfrac{\partial \dot{y}}{\partial \dot{y}_0} & \dfrac{\partial \dot{y}}{\partial \dot{z}_0} \\[8pt]
\dfrac{\partial \dot{z}}{\partial \dot{x}_0} & \dfrac{\partial \dot{z}}{\partial \dot{y}_0} & \dfrac{\partial \dot{z}}{\partial \dot{z}_0}
\end{bmatrix}
=
\begin{bmatrix}
\dot{\tilde{\mathbf{X}}} \cdot \dot{\mathbf{Q}}_x & \dot{\tilde{\mathbf{X}}} \cdot \dot{\mathbf{Q}}_y & \dot{\tilde{\mathbf{X}}} \cdot \dot{\mathbf{Q}}_z \\[6pt]
\dot{\tilde{\mathbf{Y}}} \cdot \dot{\mathbf{Q}}_x & \dot{\tilde{\mathbf{Y}}} \cdot \dot{\mathbf{Q}}_y & \dot{\tilde{\mathbf{Y}}} \cdot \dot{\mathbf{Q}}_z \\[6pt]
\dot{\tilde{\mathbf{Z}}} \cdot \dot{\mathbf{Q}}_x & \dot{\tilde{\mathbf{Z}}} \cdot \dot{\mathbf{Q}}_y & \dot{\tilde{\mathbf{Z}}} \cdot \dot{\mathbf{Q}}_z
\end{bmatrix}.
\tag{9.112}
$$

In effect, then, the $M$, $N$, $M^*$, $N^*$ matrices completely determine the partials of the state vector $\mathbf{X}$ with respect to $\mathbf{X}_0$ for circular, elliptical, or hyperbolic two-body motion.

### 9.4 ANALYTICAL DETERMINATION OF THE DIFFERENTIAL CORRECTION MATRIX

#### 9.4.1 Computation of the angular observation partials

In the previous section, analytical partials of orbit state with respect to initial orbit state were formulated. In this section, one of the many applications of the state partial derivatives will be presented: the analytical formulation of the $M_D$ matrix. To be precise, a matrix slightly different from the one determined in Section 9.2 will be developed in order to further illustrate the differential correction process.

In the same manner that the functional equations 9.17 were assumed, it is possible to write the following vector relationship:

$$\mathbf{L} = \mathbf{L}(\mathbf{r}_0, \dot{\mathbf{r}}_0, \mathbf{R}), \tag{9.113}$$

where $\mathbf{L}$ is a unit vector pointing towards the satellite along the slant range vector. The differential of Eq. 9.113, in the approximate language of finite differences, is

$$\Delta \mathbf{L} = \frac{\partial \mathbf{L}}{\partial x_0} \Delta x_0 + \frac{\partial \mathbf{L}}{\partial y_0} \Delta y_0 + \frac{\partial \mathbf{L}}{\partial z_0} \Delta z_0$$
$$+ \frac{\partial \mathbf{L}}{\partial \dot{x}_0} \Delta \dot{x}_0 + \frac{\partial \mathbf{L}}{\partial \dot{y}_0} \Delta \dot{y}_0 + \frac{\partial \mathbf{L}}{\partial \dot{z}_0} \Delta \dot{z}_0, \tag{9.114}$$

with the understanding that $\Delta \mathbf{R}$, the differential of the station coordinate vector, is taken to be zero. The assumption under which Eq. 9.114 holds, presumes the position of the observing station or stations is error-free. Usually the simultaneous differential correction of station and satellite coordinates is not attempted. Consider next the transformation of Eq. 9.114 into two scalar equations by dotting $\Delta L$ with the $\mathbf{A}$ and $\mathbf{D}$ vectors of Section 9.2, Eqs. 9.12;

$$\Delta \mathbf{L} \cdot \mathbf{A} = \mathbf{A} \cdot \frac{\partial \mathbf{L}}{\partial x_0} \Delta x_0 + \mathbf{A} \cdot \frac{\partial \mathbf{L}}{\partial y_0} \Delta y_0 + \cdots + \mathbf{A} \cdot \frac{\partial \mathbf{L}}{\partial \dot{z}_0} \Delta \dot{z}_0$$
$$\tag{9.115}$$
$$\Delta \mathbf{L} \cdot \mathbf{D} = \mathbf{D} \cdot \frac{\partial \mathbf{L}}{\partial x_0} \Delta x_0 + \mathbf{D} \cdot \frac{\partial \mathbf{L}}{\partial y_0} \Delta y_0 + \cdots + \mathbf{D} \cdot \frac{\partial \mathbf{L}}{\partial \dot{z}_0} \Delta \dot{z}_0.$$

Furthermore, since the direction cosines of $\mathbf{L}$ are given by Eqs. 9.14, it is possible to verify that

$$\frac{\partial \mathbf{L}}{\partial \xi_0} = -\frac{\mathbf{L}}{\rho} \left[ L_x \frac{\partial x}{\partial \xi_0} + L_y \frac{\partial y}{\partial \xi_0} + L_z \frac{\partial z}{\partial \xi_0} \right] + \frac{1}{\rho} \frac{\partial \mathbf{r}}{\partial \xi_0}, \tag{9.116}$$

where $\xi_0$ is a typical member of the set $(x_0, y_0, z_0, \dot{x}_0, \dot{y}_0, \dot{z}_0)$. The coefficients of Eq. 9.115 can now be readily evaluated by taking the dot product of Eq. 9.116 with $\mathbf{A}$ and $\mathbf{D}$. It is evident that due to the perpendicularity of $\mathbf{A}$, $\mathbf{D}$, $\mathbf{L}$ that the first term of Eq. 9.116 vanishes and

$$\mathbf{A} \cdot \frac{\partial \mathbf{L}}{\partial \xi_0} = \frac{1}{\rho} \mathbf{A} \cdot \frac{\partial \mathbf{r}}{\partial \xi_0}, \quad \mathbf{D} \cdot \frac{\partial \mathbf{L}}{\partial \xi_0} = \frac{1}{\rho} \mathbf{D} \cdot \frac{\partial \mathbf{r}}{\partial \xi_0}. \tag{9.117}$$

Notice that the slant range magnitude is obtained from

$$\rho = [r^2 + 2\mathbf{r} \cdot \mathbf{R} + R^2]^{\frac{1}{2}}. \tag{9.118}$$

### 9.4.2   Using the state partials

The $M_D$ matrix, Eq. 9.20, may be redefined and partitioned as

$$M_D{}^* = \begin{bmatrix} [M_{D1}][M_{D2}] \\ [M_{D3}][M_{D4}] \end{bmatrix}, \tag{9.119}$$

so that with the aid of Eqs. 9.117 the system of Eqs. 9.115 written for three separate universal times becomes defined through the submatrices

$$M_{D1} = \begin{bmatrix} \dfrac{\mathbf{A}_1}{\rho_1} \cdot \dfrac{\partial \mathbf{r}_1}{\partial x_0} & \dfrac{\mathbf{A}_1}{\rho_1} \cdot \dfrac{\partial \mathbf{r}_1}{\partial y_0} & \dfrac{\mathbf{A}_1}{\rho_1} \cdot \dfrac{\partial \mathbf{r}_1}{\partial z_0} \\[2ex] \dfrac{\mathbf{A}_2}{\rho_2} \cdot \dfrac{\partial \mathbf{r}_2}{\partial x_0} & \dfrac{\mathbf{A}_2}{\rho_2} \cdot \dfrac{\partial \mathbf{r}_2}{\partial y_0} & \dfrac{\mathbf{A}_2}{\rho_2} \cdot \dfrac{\partial \mathbf{r}_2}{\partial z_0} \\[2ex] \dfrac{\mathbf{A}_3}{\rho_3} \cdot \dfrac{\partial \mathbf{r}_3}{\partial x_0} & \dfrac{\mathbf{A}_3}{\rho_3} \cdot \dfrac{\partial \mathbf{r}_3}{\partial y_0} & \dfrac{\mathbf{A}_3}{\rho_3} \cdot \dfrac{\partial \mathbf{r}_3}{\partial z_0} \end{bmatrix},$$

$$\tag{9.120}$$

$$M_{D2} = \begin{bmatrix} \dfrac{\mathbf{A}_1}{\rho_1} \cdot \dfrac{\partial \mathbf{r}_1}{\partial \dot{x}_0} & \dfrac{\mathbf{A}_1}{\rho_1} \cdot \dfrac{\partial \mathbf{r}_1}{\partial \dot{y}_0} & \dfrac{\mathbf{A}_1}{\rho_1} \cdot \dfrac{\partial \mathbf{r}_1}{\partial \dot{z}_0} \\[2ex] \dfrac{\mathbf{A}_2}{\rho_2} \cdot \dfrac{\partial \mathbf{r}_2}{\partial \dot{x}_0} & \dfrac{\mathbf{A}_2}{\rho_2} \cdot \dfrac{\partial \mathbf{r}_2}{\partial \dot{y}_0} & \dfrac{\mathbf{A}_2}{\rho_2} \cdot \dfrac{\partial \mathbf{r}_2}{\partial \dot{z}_0} \\[2ex] \dfrac{\mathbf{A}_3}{\rho_3} \cdot \dfrac{\partial \mathbf{r}_3}{\partial \dot{x}_0} & \dfrac{\mathbf{A}_3}{\rho_3} \cdot \dfrac{\partial \mathbf{r}_3}{\partial \dot{y}_0} & \dfrac{\mathbf{A}_3}{\rho_3} \cdot \dfrac{\partial \mathbf{r}_3}{\partial \dot{z}_0} \end{bmatrix}$$

with $M_{D3}$ and $M_{D4}$ the same as $M_{D1}$ and $M_{D2}$, respectively, except that $\mathbf{D}_i$ replaces $\mathbf{A}_i$. $M_D{}^*$ is therefore the six-by-six differerential correction matrix of the system of linear equations defined by Eqs. 9.115 written for $i = 1, 2, 3$. Notice that $t_2 = t_0$ is a convenient choice of epoch.

Furthermore, define the row matrices

$$a_i \equiv \begin{bmatrix} \dfrac{A_{xi}}{\rho_i}, \dfrac{A_{yi}}{\rho_i}, 0 \end{bmatrix}, \qquad d_i \equiv \begin{bmatrix} \dfrac{D_{xi}}{\rho_i}, \dfrac{D_{yi}}{\rho_i}, \dfrac{D_{zi}}{\rho_i} \end{bmatrix}, \tag{9.121}$$

and introduce the notation $[M_i]$, and $[N_i]$, where these three-by-three matrices are respectively defined by Eqs. 9.109 and 9.110, to connote the evaluation of these matrices at time $t_i$. It is now only a matter of bookkeeping to verify that

$$[M_{D1}] = \begin{bmatrix} [a_1][M_1] \\ [a_2][M_2] \\ [a_3][M_3] \end{bmatrix}, \qquad [M_{D2}] = \begin{bmatrix} [a_1][N_1] \\ [a_2][N_2] \\ [a_3][N_3] \end{bmatrix} \tag{9.122}$$

$$[M_{D3}] = \begin{bmatrix} [d_1][M_1] \\ [d_2][M_2] \\ [d_3][M_3] \end{bmatrix}, \qquad [M_{D4}] = \begin{bmatrix} [d_1][N_1] \\ [d_2][N_2] \\ [d_3][N_3] \end{bmatrix}. \tag{9.123}$$

*Illustrative Example:*

Compute the third diagonal element $(a_{33})$ of the $M_D{}^*$ matrix. It is evident from the definition of the partitioned $M_D$ matrix that this element is in $M_{D1}$ and is the dot product of $\mathbf{A}/\rho$ and $\partial\mathbf{r}/\partial z_0$ evaluated at $t = t_3$. Since it is in the bottom row of $M_{D1}$, use of the first equation of 9.122 locates the element as the last one of the product $[a_3][M_3]$. More explicitly, the product of

$$\begin{bmatrix} \dfrac{A_{x3}}{\rho_3}, & \dfrac{A_{y3}}{\rho_3}, & 0 \end{bmatrix} \begin{bmatrix} \dfrac{\partial x_3}{\partial x_0} & \dfrac{\partial x_3}{\partial y_0} & \dfrac{\partial x_3}{\partial z_0} \\[2mm] \dfrac{\partial y_3}{\partial x_0} & \dfrac{\partial y_3}{\partial y_0} & \dfrac{\partial y_3}{\partial z_0} \\[2mm] \dfrac{\partial z_3}{\partial x_0} & \dfrac{\partial z_3}{\partial y_0} & \dfrac{\partial z_3}{\partial z_0} \end{bmatrix}$$

represents the complete bottom row of $M_{D1}$. The last element is computed by taking the inner product of $a_3$ with the last column of $M_3$. Hence

$$\frac{\mathbf{A}_3}{\rho_3} \cdot \frac{\partial \mathbf{r}_3}{\partial z_0} = \frac{A_{x3}}{\rho_3} \cdot \frac{\partial x_3}{\partial z_0} + \frac{A_{y3}}{\rho_3} \cdot \frac{\partial y_3}{\partial z_0} + 0 \cdot \frac{\partial z_3}{\partial z_0},$$

which is the third coefficient of the first of Eqs. 9.115 for $t = t_3$.

The above four matrices comprising $M_D{}^*$ are not expanded, but are left in the compact matrix notation for the sake of saving space. The matrix formulation is very convenient for a machine routine that requires the differential coefficients inherent in Eqs. 9.115.

### 9.4.3 Computational algorithm for differential correction utilizing angular data

In order to crystallize the above analysis, a computational chain is presented which utilizes minimum data, that is, six angular observations.

Before commencing the differential correction, the known data of the problem is therefore the preliminary orbit: $[x_0, y_0, z_0, \dot{x}_0, \dot{y}_0, \dot{z}_0]$, the observational times $t_1$, $t_0$, $t_2$, and corresponding topocentric observations $[\alpha_{t1}, \delta_{t1}]$, $[\alpha_{t0}, \delta_{t0}]$, and $[\alpha_{t2}, \delta_{t2}]$, along with the station location $[\phi, \lambda_E, H]$. The first step of the differential correction process is the accurate determination of the satellite's position and velocity vectors at the universal times $t_1$ and $t_2$. Hence, by direct numerical integration of the relative equations of motion developed in Chapter 2, with initial conditions $\mathbf{r}_0$ and $\dot{\mathbf{r}}_0$, or by application of the algorithm in Appendix II, and with inclusion of additional perturbative corrections to be developed in Chapter 10, a prediction is made to time $t_1$ and $t_2$, so that for $i = 1, 2$ the states

$$[x_i, y_i, z_i, \dot{x}_i, \dot{y}_i, \dot{z}_i]_{t = t_i}$$

are determined.

The second step to be performed in the analysis is the determination of the $M_i$ and $N_i$ three-by-three matrices at the separate times $t_1$, $t_0$, $t_2$. At the central date these matrices are very simple. By application of the previously developed formulas in this chapter, all these matrices may be easily determined.

Third, the locations of the observing station[3] are determined for $t_i$ by

$$\theta_i = \theta_{g0} + \frac{d\theta}{dt}(t_i - t_0) + \lambda_E, \quad i = 1, 0, 2, \tag{9.124}$$

$$G_1 = \frac{a_e}{\sqrt{1 - (2f - f^2)\sin^2\phi}} + H$$
$$G_2 = \frac{(1 - f)^2 a_e}{\sqrt{1 - (2f - f^2)\sin^2\phi}} + H \tag{9.125}$$

$$\mathbf{R}_i = \begin{bmatrix} X \\ Y \\ Z \end{bmatrix} = \begin{bmatrix} -G_1 \cos\phi \cos\theta \\ -G_1 \cos\phi \sin\theta \\ -G_2 \sin\phi \end{bmatrix}_i. \tag{9.126}$$

Compute the following unit vectors from the observational data:

$$\mathbf{L}_i = \begin{bmatrix} L_x \\ L_y \\ L_z \end{bmatrix}_i = \begin{bmatrix} \cos\delta_t \cos\alpha_t \\ \cos\delta_t \sin\alpha_t \\ \sin\delta_t \end{bmatrix}_i$$

[3] The analysis can be extended easily to more than one observational station.

$$\mathbf{D}_i = \begin{bmatrix} D_x \\ D_y \\ D_z \end{bmatrix}_i = \begin{bmatrix} -\sin \delta_t \cos \alpha_t \\ -\sin \delta_t \sin \alpha_t \\ \cos \delta_t \end{bmatrix}_i$$

$$\mathbf{A}_i = \begin{bmatrix} A_x \\ A_y \\ A_z \end{bmatrix}_i = \begin{bmatrix} -\sin \alpha_t \\ \cos \alpha_t \\ 0 \end{bmatrix}_i. \tag{9.127}$$

Determine the magnitude of the slant range vector from

$$\rho_i = [r_i^2 + 2\mathbf{r}_i \cdot \mathbf{R}_i + R_i^2]^{\frac{1}{2}},$$

and form the row matrices

$$a_i = \begin{bmatrix} \dfrac{A_{xi}}{\rho_i}, & \dfrac{A_{yi}}{\rho_i}, & 0 \end{bmatrix}$$

$$d_i = \begin{bmatrix} \dfrac{D_{xi}}{\rho_i}, & \dfrac{D_{yi}}{\rho_i}, & \dfrac{D_{zi}}{\rho_i} \end{bmatrix}. \tag{9.128}$$

Continue calculating with

$$M_{D1} = \begin{bmatrix} [a_1][M_1] \\ [a_0][M_0] \\ [a_2][M_2] \end{bmatrix}$$

$$M_{D2} = \begin{bmatrix} [a_1][N_1] \\ [a_0][N_0] \\ [a_2][N_2] \end{bmatrix}$$

$$\tag{9.129}$$

$$M_{D3} = \begin{bmatrix} [d_1][M_1] \\ [d_0][M_0] \\ [d_2][M_2] \end{bmatrix}$$

$$M_{D4} = \begin{bmatrix} [d_1][N_1] \\ [d_0][N_0] \\ [d_2][N_2] \end{bmatrix}$$

Form the six-by-six matrix

$$M_D{}^* = \begin{bmatrix} [M_{D1}][M_{D2}] \\ [M_{D3}][M_{D4}] \end{bmatrix}. \tag{9.130}$$

Continue calculating with

$$
\mathbf{\rho}_i = \begin{bmatrix} \rho_x \\ \rho_y \\ \rho_z \end{bmatrix}_i = \begin{bmatrix} x + X \\ y + Y \\ z + Z \end{bmatrix}_i \tag{9.131}
$$

$$
\mathbf{L}_{ci} = \begin{bmatrix} L_{xc} \\ L_{yc} \\ L_{zc} \end{bmatrix}_i = \begin{bmatrix} \dfrac{\rho_x}{\rho} \\ \dfrac{\rho_y}{\rho} \\ \dfrac{\rho_z}{\rho} \end{bmatrix}_i \tag{9.132}
$$

$$
\Delta \mathbf{L}_1 = \mathbf{L}_i - \mathbf{L}_{ci}. \tag{9.133}
$$

Invert the $M_D{}^*$ matrix and obtain the corrections

$$
\begin{bmatrix} \Delta x_0 \\ \Delta y_0 \\ \Delta z_0 \\ \Delta \dot{x}_0 \\ \Delta \dot{y}_0 \\ \Delta \dot{z}_0 \end{bmatrix} = [M_D{}^*]^{-1} \begin{bmatrix} \Delta \mathbf{L}_1 \cdot \mathbf{A}_1 \\ \Delta \mathbf{L}_0 \cdot \mathbf{A}_0 \\ \Delta \mathbf{L}_2 \cdot \mathbf{A}_2 \\ \Delta \mathbf{L}_1 \cdot \mathbf{D}_1 \\ \Delta \mathbf{L}_0 \cdot \mathbf{D}_0 \\ \Delta \mathbf{L}_2 \cdot \mathbf{D}_2 \end{bmatrix}. \tag{9.134}
$$

Improve the epoch position and velocity vectors by adding the corrective increments $\Delta x_0$, $\Delta y_0$, $\Delta z_0$, $\Delta \dot{x}_0$, $\Delta \dot{y}_0$, and $\Delta \dot{z}_0$ to the epoch position and velocity vectors; if the magnitude of the corrective increments continues to decrease, return to the first step of the differential correction procedure. If the corrective increments do not decrease, then the orbit is considered to be the best instantaneous representation of the elements at the time $t = t_0$.

## 9.5 DIFFERENTIAL CORRECTION UTILIZING RANGE AND RANGE-RATE DATA

### 9.5.1 Partial derivatives of slant range with respect to initial position

The angles-only differential correction can be supplemented or completely replaced by differential correction schemes based on range data. Indeed, the modern orbit problem where range data is available is an important tool for the differential correction of satellite orbits.

As indicated previously, and as was shown in Section 3.11, the fundamental relation $\rho = \mathbf{r} + \mathbf{R}$, where $\rho$ is the slant range vector, $\mathbf{r}$ is the satellite radius vector, and $\mathbf{R}$ is the station coordinate vector, may be dotted into itself to yield

$$\rho^2 = (\mathbf{r} + \mathbf{R}) \cdot (\mathbf{r} + \mathbf{R}) = r^2 + 2\mathbf{r} \cdot \mathbf{R} + R^2 \tag{9.135}$$

or

$$\rho^2 = x^2 + y^2 + z^2 + 2xX + 2yY + 2zZ + R^2. \tag{9.136}$$

Consider the partial differentiation of $\rho$ with respect to a typical element $\xi$ of the set $x_0, y_0, z_0, \dot{x}_0, \dot{y}_0, \dot{z}_0$, that is, $\partial\rho/\partial\xi$. Evidently, from Eq. 9.136,

$$\rho \frac{\partial\rho}{\partial\xi} = x \frac{\partial x}{\partial\xi} + y \frac{\partial y}{\partial\xi} + z \frac{\partial z}{\partial\xi} + X \frac{\partial x}{\partial\xi} + Y \frac{\partial y}{\partial\xi} + Z \frac{\partial z}{\partial\xi} \tag{9.137}$$

with the understanding that $\partial X/\partial\xi$, $\partial Y/\partial\xi$, $\partial Z/\partial\xi$ vanish. Equation 9.137 may be regrouped as

$$\frac{\partial\rho}{\partial\xi} = \left(\frac{x + X}{\rho}\right) \frac{\partial x}{\partial\xi} + \left(\frac{y + Y}{\rho}\right) \frac{\partial y}{\partial\xi} + \left(\frac{z + Z}{\rho}\right) \frac{\partial z}{\partial\xi}, \tag{9.138}$$

or, by introduction of the definitions

$$L_x \equiv \frac{x + X}{\rho}, \qquad L_y \equiv \frac{y + Y}{\rho}, \qquad L_z \equiv \frac{z + Z}{\rho}, \tag{9.139}$$

the partial of slant range magnitude with respect to initial rectangular components becomes

$$\frac{\partial\rho}{\partial\xi} = L_x \frac{\partial x}{\partial\xi} + L_y \frac{\partial y}{\partial\xi} + L_z \frac{\partial z}{\partial\xi}. \tag{9.140}$$

It should be noticed that if the position of satellite $\mathbf{r}$ and the particular time corresponding to this position is known, the state partials $\partial x/\partial\xi$, $\partial y/\partial\xi$, and $\partial z/\partial\xi$ are known from Section 9.3, and $\partial\rho/\partial\xi$ is determined by virtue of Eqs. 9.140 and definitions 9.139.

### 9.5.2 Differential correction equations for range data

Equation 9.136 enables the following functional relationship to be written:

$$\rho = f(x, y, z, X, Y, Z), \tag{9.141}$$

but $x, y, z$ are functions of some initial set of elements, say $\mathbf{r}_0, \dot{\mathbf{r}}_0$, so that

$$\rho = \rho(x_0, y_0, z_0, \dot{x}_0, \dot{y}_0, \dot{z}_0, X, Y, Z). \tag{9.142}$$

The differential of Eq. 9.142 is then expressible as

$$\Delta \rho = \frac{\partial \rho}{\partial x_0} \Delta x_0 + \frac{\partial \rho}{\partial y_0} \Delta y_0 + \frac{\partial \rho}{\partial z_0} \Delta z_0$$

$$+ \frac{\partial \rho}{\partial \dot{x}_0} \Delta \dot{x}_0 + \frac{\partial \rho}{\partial \dot{y}_0} \Delta \dot{y}_0 + \frac{\partial \rho}{\partial \dot{z}_0} \Delta \dot{z}_0 \quad (9.143)$$

with the finite difference approximation $\Delta \xi = d\xi$, and the understanding that $\Delta X$, $\Delta Y$, $\Delta Z$ are zero. The differentials of the station coordinate vector components are taken to be zero because the position of the station is assumed to be absolutely correct, that is, in the relation

$$\boldsymbol{\rho} = \mathbf{r} + \mathbf{R},$$

or by differentiation and replacement of differentials by finite differences

$$\Delta \boldsymbol{\rho} = \Delta \mathbf{r} + \Delta \mathbf{R},$$

$\Delta \mathbf{R}$ is taken to be zero.  This would not be true if one wished to differentially correct the position of the observing station using an orbit whose elements are assumed to be known exactly [4].

Evidently, if Eq. 9.143 is written for six distinct range residuals, $\Delta \rho_j$, $j = 1, 2, \ldots, 6$, a system of six equations in six unknowns, that is, the appropriate corrections to the adopted elements $\mathbf{r}_0$, $\dot{\mathbf{r}}_0$, is determined. The residuals are determined as the difference between the observed or measured slant range magnitude (from radar data), and the computed value of $\rho$ determined analytically from the best possible prediction of that satellite at time $t_j$, that is,

$$\Delta \rho_j = \rho_{0j} - \rho_{cj}. \quad (9.144)$$

If angular and range data are available, a combination of $q$ equations of the form (9.18) and $p$ equations of the form (9.143), where $p + q = 6$, will be an available variation or option for the analyst to apply in order to effect a given differential correction scheme.

### 9.5.3   Partial derivatives of range-rate with respect to initial position and velocity

Consider that the previous differential correction schemes are to be extended due to the availability of range-rate data $\dot{\rho}$.

Differentiation of Eq. 9.136 with respect to modified time $\tau$ yields

$$\rho\dot{\rho} = x\dot{x} + y\dot{y} + z\dot{z} + x\dot{X} + \dot{x}X + y\dot{Y} + \dot{y}Y + z\dot{Z} + \dot{z}Z. \quad (9.145)$$

Partial differentiation of $\rho\dot{\rho}$ with respect to a typical epoch element $\xi$ reduces Eq. 9.145 to

$$\frac{\partial\dot{\rho}}{\partial\xi} = L_x \frac{\partial\dot{x}}{\partial\xi} + L_y \frac{\partial\dot{y}}{\partial\xi} + L_z \frac{\partial\dot{z}}{\partial\xi}$$

$$+ L_x' \frac{\partial x}{\partial\xi} + L_y' \frac{\partial y}{\partial\xi} + L_z' \frac{\partial z}{\partial\xi} - \frac{\dot{\rho}}{\rho} \frac{\partial\rho}{\partial\xi}, \quad (9.146)$$

where

$$L_x \equiv \frac{x + X}{\rho}, \qquad L_y \equiv \frac{y + Y}{\rho}, \qquad L_z \equiv \frac{z + Z}{\rho}$$

$$L_x' \equiv \frac{\dot{x} + \dot{X}}{\rho}, \qquad L_y' \equiv \frac{\dot{y} + \dot{Y}}{\rho}, \qquad L_z' \equiv \frac{\dot{z} + \dot{Z}}{\rho}$$

with $\rho$ obtained from $\rho = [r^2 + 2\mathbf{r} \cdot \mathbf{R} + R^2]^{1/2}$.

Furthermore, by consequence of Eq. 9.140,

$$\frac{\partial\dot{\rho}}{\partial\xi} = L_x \frac{\partial\dot{x}}{\partial\xi} + L_y \frac{\partial\dot{y}}{\partial\xi} + L_z \frac{\partial\dot{z}}{\partial\xi} + \left(L_x' - \frac{\dot{\rho}}{\rho}L_x\right)\frac{\partial x}{\partial\xi}$$

$$+ \left(L_y' - \frac{\dot{\rho}}{\rho}L_y\right)\frac{\partial y}{\partial\xi} + \left(L_z' - \frac{\dot{\rho}}{\rho}L_z\right)\frac{\partial z}{\partial\xi}. \quad (9.147)$$

Evidently, having a prediction of the trajectory state, that is, $\mathbf{r}, \dot{\mathbf{r}}$ enables the determination of the appropriate coefficients of Eq. 9.147. It should be noted that $\dot{\rho}$, as it appears in Eq. 9.147, may be obtained directly from Eq. 9.145. The derivatives of the station coordinate vector have been tabulated previously, Eqs. 3.262. The state partials may be obtained directly from Section 9.3.

### 9.5.4 Differential correction equations for range-rate data

Proceeding as in Section 9.5.2, by virtue of Eq. 9.145, it is possible to express the following functional relationship:

$$\dot{\rho} = \dot{\rho}(x_0, y_0, z_0, \dot{x}_0, \dot{y}_0, \dot{z}_0, X, Y, Z, \dot{X}, \dot{Y}, \dot{Z}), \quad (9.148)$$

whose differential, written in terms of finite differences, is

$$\Delta\dot{\rho} = \frac{\partial\dot{\rho}}{\partial x_0}\Delta x_0 + \frac{\partial\dot{\rho}}{\partial y_0}\Delta y_0 + \frac{\partial\dot{\rho}}{\partial z_0}\Delta z_0$$

$$+ \frac{\partial\dot{\rho}}{\partial\dot{x}_0}\Delta\dot{x}_0 + \frac{\partial\dot{\rho}}{\partial\dot{y}_0}\Delta\dot{y}_0 + \frac{\partial\dot{\rho}}{\partial\dot{z}_0}\Delta\dot{z}_0. \quad (9.149)$$

Here again, the differentials of station position and velocity are taken to be zero.

If Eq. 9.149 is written for six different times, that is, $\Delta\dot{\rho}_j = \dot{\rho}_{0j} - \dot{\rho}_{cj}$ with $\dot{\rho}_{0j}$ being the radar measured values of range rate and $\dot{\rho}_{cj}$ obtained from Eq. 9.145, a system of six linear equations in six unknowns is obtained. Simultaneous solution of this system for the corrective increments to the epoch position and velocity components will now yield the first differential correction of the orbit. If angular, range, and range-rate data are available, a combination of $q$ equations of the form (9.18), $p$ equations of the form (9.143), and $w$ equations of the form (9.149), where $p + q + w = 6$ will be sufficient to differentially correct the given orbit.

## 9.6  NUMERICAL EXAMPLE

### 9.6.1  Differential correction of 1959 ALPHA 1

The purpose of this section is to provide some numerical results to aid in the code checking of (a) two-body prediction routines, (b) the state partial matrices $M$, $N$, $M^*$, $N^*$, and (c) the analytical $M_D$ matrix. In the process of stating these results, it will also be of interest to watch the numerical differential correction of 1959 Alpha 1 using the proposed algorithm in Section 9.4.3.

To initiate the differential correction process, the observational data of the problem are given as

*Station Location*

| STATION | GEODETIC LATITUDE $\phi$ (degrees) | EAST LONGITUDE $\lambda_E$ (degrees) | ELEVATION $H$ (meters) |
|---|---|---|---|
| Organ Pass (O) | 32° 25′ 26″7 | 253° 26′ 51″8 | 1651.0 |
| Jupiter (J) | 27° 01′ 16″6 | 279° 53′ 11″8 | 12.0 |

*Observations*

| STATION | TIME (1959 March 2) U.T. | RIGHT ASCENSION $\alpha_t$ (degrees) | DECLINATION $\delta_t$ (degrees) |
|---|---|---|---|
| O | $9^{hr}$ $38^{min}$ $54.865^{sec}$ | 224°1417 | 26°1675 |
| J | $9^{hr}$ $43^{min}$ $54.271^{sec}$ | 204°6274 | 45°9345 |
| J | $9^{hr}$ $45^{min}$ $9.612^{sec}$ | 219°1732 | 48°2733 |

## 9.6.2    Numerical results

Utilization of any of the angles-only schemes of Chapter 7 provides the first approximation of rectangular geocentric coordinates at the central date of the orbit in Section 9.6.1 as

$$
\begin{aligned}
x_0 &= -0.885 & \dot{x}_0 &= +0.632 \\
y_0 &= -0.751 & \dot{y}_0 &= -0.530 \\
z_0 &= +0.743 & \dot{z}_0 &= -0.016.
\end{aligned}
$$

Using the algorithm of Appendix II with $k = 0.07437$ and $\mu = 1$, the position and velocity vectors at $t - t_0 = -4.990032$ min are obtainable as

$$
\begin{aligned}
x_1 &= -0.109512 \times 10^1 & \dot{x}_1 &= +0.497810 \times 10^0 \\
y_1 &= -0.536914 \times 10^0 & \dot{y}_1 &= -0.617649 \times 10^0 \\
z_1 &= +0.730041 \times 10^0 & \dot{z}_1 &= +0.840039 \times 10^{-1}.
\end{aligned}
$$

The corresponding state partial matrices are

$$
M_1 = \begin{bmatrix}
0.101099 \times 10^1 & 0.258468 \times 10^{-1} & -0.281062 \times 10^{-1} \\
0.257783 \times 10^{-1} & 0.993242 \times 10^0 & -0.200654 \times 10^{-1} \\
-0.280732 \times 10^{-1} & -0.200948 \times 10^{-1} & 0.996404 \times 10^0
\end{bmatrix}
$$

$$
N_1 = \begin{bmatrix}
-0.372610 \times 10^0 & -0.305822 \times 10^{-2} & 0.349945 \times 10^{-2} \\
-0.305398 \times 10^2 & -0.370008 \times 10^0 & 0.228522 \times 10^{-2} \\
0.349740 \times 10^2 & 0.228706 \times 10^{-2} & -0.370601 \times 10^0
\end{bmatrix}
$$

$$
M_1^* = \begin{bmatrix}
-0.718238 \times 10^{-1} & -0.134065 \times 10^0 & 0.153236 \times 10^0 \\
-0.133164 \times 10^0 & 0.453002 \times 10^{-1} & 0.100101 \times 10^0 \\
0.152801 \times 10^0 & 0.100489 \times 10^0 & 0.198617 \times 10^{-1}
\end{bmatrix}
$$

$$
N_1^* = \begin{bmatrix}
0.101515 \times 10^1 & 0.235936 \times 10^{-1} & -0.284770 \times 10^{-1} \\
0.235279 \times 10^{-1} & 0.989615 \times 10^0 & -0.169741 \times 10^{-1} \\
-0.284454 \times 10^{-1} & -0.170024 \times 10^{-1} & 0.995844 \times 10^0
\end{bmatrix}
$$

The $M_1^*$ and $N_1^*$ matrices are not used in the differential correction process, but are included for reference.

Using the algorithm of Appendix II with $t - t_0 = 1.255680$ min, the position and velocity vectors at the future or second date are obtained as

$$x_2 = -0.824531 \times 10^0 \qquad \dot{x}_2 = +0.662896 \times 10^0$$
$$y_2 = -0.799202 \times 10^0 \qquad \dot{y}_2 = -0.501975 \times 10^0$$
$$z_2 = +0.740259 \times 10^0 \qquad \dot{z}_2 = -0.428108 \times 10^{-1}.$$

The corresponding state partial matrices are

$$M_2 = \begin{bmatrix} 0.100032 \times 10^1 & 0.177151 \times 10^{-2} & -0.171399 \times 10^{-2} \\ 0.177194 \times 10^{-2} & 0.999893 \times 10^0 & -0.152101 \times 10^{-2} \\ -0.171419 \times 10^{-2} & -0.152082 \times 10^{-2} & 0.999791 \times 10^0 \end{bmatrix}$$

$$N_2 = \begin{bmatrix} 0.933889 \times 10^{-1} & 0.551315 \times 10^{-4} & -0.530942 \times 10^{-4} \\ 0.551534 \times 10^{-4} & 0.933779 \times 10^{-1} & -0.481419 \times 10^{-4} \\ -0.531049 \times 10^{-4} & -0.481245 \times 10^{-4} & 0.933734 \times 10^{-1} \end{bmatrix}$$

$$M_2{}^* = \begin{bmatrix} 0.599495 \times 10^{-2} & 0.381772 \times 10^{-1} & -0.365351 \times 10^{-1} \\ 0.381816 \times 10^{-1} & -0.145962 \times 10^{-2} & -0.331465 \times 10^{-1} \\ -0.365372 \times 10^{-1} & -0.331446 \times 10^{-1} & -0.441387 \times 10^{-2} \end{bmatrix}$$

$$N_2{}^* = \begin{bmatrix} 0.100024 \times 10^1 & 0.179230 \times 10^{-2} & -0.169662 \times 10^{-2} \\ 0.179260 \times 10^{-2} & 0.999969 \times 10^0 & -0.157336 \times 10^{-2} \\ -0.169676 \times 10^{-2} & -0.157322 \times 10^{-2} & 0.999795 \times 10^0 \end{bmatrix}.$$

For $t - t_0 = 0$, the above matrices are very simple, that is,

$$M_0 = \begin{bmatrix} 1 & 0 & 0 \\ 0 & 1 & 0 \\ 0 & 0 & 1 \end{bmatrix}, \qquad N_0 = \begin{bmatrix} 0 & 0 & 0 \\ 0 & 0 & 0 \\ 0 & 0 & 0 \end{bmatrix}$$

$$M_0{}^* = \begin{bmatrix} 0 & 0 & 0 \\ 0 & 0 & 0 \\ 0 & 0 & 0 \end{bmatrix}, \qquad N_0{}^* = \begin{bmatrix} 1 & 0 & 0 \\ 0 & 1 & 0 \\ 0 & 0 & 1 \end{bmatrix}.$$

As the next step, the $M_D$ differential correction matrix is formed as[4]

[4] The matrix elements have been rounded to six significant figures.

$$M_D{}^* = \begin{bmatrix}
0.152661 \times 10^1 & -0.154705 \times 10^1 & -0.115229 \times 10^{-1} & -0.573087 \times 10^0 & 0.586504 \times 10^0 & 0.177517 \times 10^{-2} \\
0.102517 \times 10^1 & -0.223634 \times 10^1 & 0.0 & 0.0 & 0.0 & 0.0 \\
0.162792 \times 10^1 & -0.199855 \times 10^1 & 0.249100 \times 10^{-3} & 0.152202 \times 10^0 & -0.186820 \times 10^0 & 0.976939 \times 10^{-5} \\
0.673950 \times 10^0 & 0.657313 \times 10^0 & 0.195778 \times 10^1 & -0.257734 \times 10^0 & -0.250625 \times 10^0 & -0.736615 \times 10^0 \\
0.160691 \times 10^1 & 0.736632 \times 10^0 & 0.171097 \times 10^1 & 0.0 & 0.0 & 0.0 \\
0.149357 \times 10^1 & 0.121712 \times 10^1 & 0.171373 \times 10^1 & 0.139488 \times 10^0 & 0.113661 \times 10^0 & 0.160325 \times 10^0
\end{bmatrix}$$

Finally, the residuals $\Delta L \cdot A$ and $\Delta L \cdot D$ are determined from

$$
\begin{bmatrix}
\Delta L_1 \cdot A_1 \\
\Delta L_0 \cdot A_0 \\
\Delta L_2 \cdot A_2 \\
\Delta L_1 \cdot D_1 \\
\Delta L_0 \cdot D_0 \\
\Delta L_2 \cdot D_2
\end{bmatrix}
=
\begin{bmatrix}
-0.302908 \times 10^{-3} \\
0.198940 \times 10^{-2} \\
0.325664 \times 10^{-2} \\
0.310452 \times 10^{-2} \\
0.236647 \times 10^{-2} \\
0.149792 \times 10^{-2}
\end{bmatrix}.
$$

Simultaneous solution of the linear system of equations defined by the $M_D{}^*$ matrix and the residuals yields the corrected position and velocity vectors at the central date as

$$x_0 = -0.884022 \times 10^0 \qquad \dot{x}_0 = +0.632126 \times 10^0$$
$$y_0 = -0.751441 \times 10^0 \qquad \dot{y}_0 = -0.534088 \times 10^0$$
$$z_0 = +0.743655 \times 10^0 \qquad \dot{z}_0 = -0.166264 \times 10^{-1}.$$

By repeating the above loop and completely recomputing the $M_D$ matrix, it is possible to find the differential correction matrix displayed on p. 357 along with the associated residuals

$$
\begin{bmatrix}
\Delta L_1 \cdot A_1 \\
\Delta L_0 \cdot A_0 \\
\Delta L_2 \cdot A_2 \\
\Delta L_1 \cdot D_1 \\
\Delta L_0 \cdot D_0 \\
\Delta L_2 \cdot D_2
\end{bmatrix}
=
\begin{bmatrix}
0.103777 \times 10^{-7} \\
0.104409 \times 10^{-7} \\
0.354045 \times 10^{-7} \\
0.180897 \times 10^{-7} \\
-0.145102 \times 10^{-7} \\
-0.121433 \times 10^{-7}
\end{bmatrix}.
$$

Solution of the above system of equations yields the new position and velocity vectors at the epoch time, that is,

$$x_0 = -0.884022 \times 10^0 \qquad \dot{x}_0 = +0.632126 \times 10^0$$
$$y_0 = -0.751441 \times 10^0 \qquad \dot{y}_0 = -0.534088 \times 10^0$$
$$z_0 = +0.743655 \times 10^0 \qquad \dot{z}_0 = -0.166266 \times 10^{-1}.$$

Because of the small magnitude of each residual, the orbit can be considered as fairly accurate and the differential correction process halted. The second time the $M_D{}^*$ matrix is computed, it should be noticed that little change occurs in its elements. In this case, it would have sufficed to have used the $M_D{}^*$ matrix obtained the very first time to carry on the correction process. The reader should bear in mind that only a two-body prediction was used in the above example.

$$M_D^* = \begin{bmatrix}
0.152959 \times 10^1 & -0.155015 \times 10^1 & -0.115308 \times 10^{-1} & -0.574226 \times 10^0 & 0.587674 \times 10^0 & 0.177994 \times 10^{-2} \\
0.102523 \times 10^1 & -0.223646 \times 10^1 & 0.0 & 0.0 & 0.0 & 0.0 \\
0.162675 \times 10^1 & -0.199712 \times 10^1 & 0.253850 \times 10^{-3} & 0.152091 \times 10^0 & -0.186684 \times 10^0 & 0.998333 \times 10^{-5} \\
0.675202 \times 10^0 & 0.658549 \times 10^0 & 0.196174 \times 10^1 & -0.258235 \times 10^0 & -0.251116 \times 10^0 & -0.738093 \times 10^0 \\
0.160700 \times 10^1 & 0.736670 \times 10^0 & 0.171106 \times 10^1 & 0.0 & 0.0 & 0.0 \\
0.149249 \times 10^1 & 0.121625 \times 10^1 & 0.171251 \times 10^1 & 0.139387 \times 10^0 & 0.113579 \times 10^0 & 0.160209 \times 10^0
\end{bmatrix}$$

## 9.7 SUMMARY

This chapter has introduced a new concept, the concept of differential correction. Use of the equations developed enables the analyst to gradually bring the first two-body estimate of the orbit into full agreement with observations or measurements originally used to determine the orbit. Naturally the orbit will only reflect the accuracy of the observations or measurements.

Two techniques were developed. The method of variant orbits, a strictly numerical method, and a semi-analytical method, wherein analytical partial derivatives are used instead of finite difference approximations. Analytic two-body partial derivatives of trajectory state with respect to initial trajectory state were developed. By means of these partials, even though the most compact formulation of a given differential correction scheme may not be achieved, it was possible to obtain very easy derivations of the angles only, range and range-rate orbit improvement equations. Convergence of these differential correction schemes can be accomplished by means of two-body partial derivatives, if observation points are not separated by very large arcs.

**EXERCISES**

1. Show that by elimination of the two equations at the central date of the $M_D$ matrix, a fully rigorous, differential correction scheme using a four-by-four matrix $M_L$ can be conveniently formulated. This is basically the modification of Leuschner.

2. Derive the $M_L$ matrix of Problem 1.

3. Clearly explain the implications of moving the satellite from an adopted epoch to the two other states required by the differential correction process by means of only the two-body equation of motion.

4. Given the following initial position and velocity vectors at the central date

$$x = +0.40 \qquad \dot{x} = +0.60$$
$$y = -1.20 \qquad \dot{y} = +0.30$$
$$z = +0.80 \qquad \dot{z} = +0.14,$$

differentially correct the geocentric orbit of 1959 Alpha 2. The observational data are listed as

### Station Location

| STATION | GEODETIC LATITUDE (degrees) | EAST LONGITUDE (degrees) | ELEVATION (meters) |
|---|---|---|---|
| Woomera (W) | $-31°\ 06'\ 06\rlap{.}''7$ | $136°\ 46'\ 54\rlap{.}''9$ | 162.0 |
| Organ Pass (O) | $32°\ 25'\ 26\rlap{.}''7$ | $253°\ 26'\ 51\rlap{.}''8$ | 1651.0 |

*Observations*

| STATION | TIME (1959 MAY 25)<br>(U.T.) | RIGHT ASCENSION<br>$\alpha_t$ (degrees) | DECLINATION<br>$\delta_t$ (degrees) |
|---|---|---|---|
| (W) | $9^{hr}\ 38^{min}\ 56.126^{sec}$ | $97°7909$ | $-20°4976$ |
| (O) | $10^{hr}\ 33^{min}\ 52.575^{sec}$ | $285°3345$ | $27°4552$ |
| (O) | $10^{hr}\ 36^{min}\ 26.631^{sec}$ | $299°4592$ | $30°2557$ |

Assume a two-body prediction scheme is used to obtain residuals at the three dates. Assume $\mu = 1$.

5. Verify that

$$\frac{\partial L}{\partial \xi_0} = -\frac{L}{\rho}\left[L_x \frac{\partial x}{\partial \xi_0} + L_y \frac{\partial y}{\partial \xi_0} + L_z \frac{\partial z}{\partial \xi_0}\right] + \frac{1}{\rho}\frac{\partial r}{\partial \xi_0},$$

where $\xi_0$ is a typical member of the set $(x_0, y_0, z_0, \dot{x}_0, \dot{y}_0, \dot{z}_0)$. See Eq. 9.116.

6. Suppose that residuals in position of an enemy interceptor are obtained, that is, miss distances $\Delta x$, $\Delta y$, $\Delta z$, which are the differences between the enemy satellite's position and the interceptor's position at time $t$. Imagine that the intercepting missile has the position and velocity vectors $(x_0, y_0, z_0, \dot{x}_0, \dot{y}_0, \dot{z}_0)$ at time $t_0$ with $t_0 < t$. Discuss generally and obtain equations for the differential correction process to correct the required epoch elements in order to intercept the target.

**REFERENCES**

1. D. Brouwer and G. M. Clemence, *Methods of Celestial Mechanics*, Academic Press, New York and London, 1961, Chapter 9.
2. A. D. Dubyago, *The Determination of Orbits*, The Macmillan Company, New York, 1961, Chapter 11.
3. P. R. Escobal and R. DeBellis, *State to Initial State Analytic Partial Derivatives*, Technical Note 64-11, Operations Research Incorporated, Santa Monica, Calif., April 15, 1964.
4. P. E. Koskela, L. Nicola, and L. G. Walters, "Station Coordinates from Satellite Observations," *ARS Journal*, February 1962.
5. F. R. Moulton, *An Introduction to Celestial Mechanics*, The Macmillan Company, New York, 1914, p. 232.

# 10 Secular perturbations

*The Great Architect of the Universe now begins to appear as a pure mathematician.*

J. H. JEANS [12]

## 10.1 PERTURBATIVE EFFECTS

A satellite under the influence of an inverse square gravitational law has truly constant orbital elements, that is, the set $[a, e, T, i, \Omega, \omega]$ is composed of constants[1] devoid of explicit time dependency. For many practical problems, the approximation of two-body motion is sufficient, especially if two closely neighboring points on a trajectory are under investigation. There are, however, situations in which the cumulative effect of the gradual shift or variation of elements from true epoch values cannot be ignored. Specifically, for long time intervals, ignoring a small gradual shift in a given element due to a perturbative force, can bring about a totally erroneous prediction of a satellite's position and velocity. The perturbative effects causing deviations from basic two-body motion are many: for example, the force field of the primary body about which motion occurs is not truly of an inverse square variety, the effect of atmospheric drag enters into the equations of motion, radiation pressure of the Sun produces accelerations, the closeness of a neighboring celestial body attracts the object in question, etc. Symbolically, then, a given element $q$ is functionally dependent upon the perturbing forces as

$$q = q(F_1, F_2, F_3, \ldots, F_k), \tag{10.1}$$

where $F_i$ are the perturbing forces discussed above. The $F_i$ are actually functions of the position and velocity vectors of the satellite whose motion is under study. In turn, the position and velocity vectors are functions

---

[1] See Chapter 3.

of universal or, more exactly, ephemeris time. Evidently, the expansion of a set of elements $[a, e, M_0, i, \Omega, \omega]$ about some epoch $t_0$ can be attempted[2] by the Taylor expansions

$$a = a_0 + \dot{a}_0(t - t_0) + \ddot{a}_0(t - t_0)^2/2! + \cdots$$
$$e = e_0 + \dot{e}_0(t - t_0) + \ddot{e}_0(t - t_0)^2/2! + \cdots \qquad (10.2)$$
$$\vdots$$
$$\omega = \omega_0 + \dot{\omega}_0(t - t_0) + \ddot{\omega}_0(t - t_0)^2/2! + \cdots,$$

where the time derivatives of the elements depend upon the perturbing $F_i$.

A little thought will make the reader wonder whether the series expansions (10.2) are all encompassing in the sense of describing the physical situation at hand in a convenient manner. For example, a drag-free geocentric planetary body moves in an orbit with an approximately constant semimajor axis; perturbations do, however, cause the value of $a$ to vary or fluctuate about some mean value. Perhaps, then, a Fourier expansion containing trigonometric terms to account for periodic changes might be a more suitable representation.

In essence, then, the aim of *general perturbation* schemes is the development of infinite series or, at times, closed expressions in a suitably chosen variable in order to arrive at an analytical prediction of the satellite's future (past) position and velocity or, equivalently, elements. These developments are contrasted to special perturbation schemes or direct numerical methods (Chapter 2) to accomplish the same end result. Each method has distinct advantages and disadvantages that will become evident as the analysis progresses.

Analytical investigation of the *oblateness effects* of a central body on a satellite has shown that certain elements, such as $\omega$, $\Omega$, $M_0$, experience *secular variations* or ever-increasing or decreasing changes from the adopted epoch values and *periodic variations* or fluctuations about these epoch values. Other elements such as $a$, $i$, and $e$ are possessed of only periodic variations and, hence, vary only about their mean values. Moreover, among periodic variations, a further distinction is made between *short period variations* and *long period variations*. To visualize these effects, consider Figure 10.1. Elements that experience secular changes can be depicted by the straight line defined by the points $(t_0, q_0)$ and $(t, q)$. The long period variations, denoted by curve $AB$, are bounded fluctuations of these elements about the secular variation line. These oblateness variations are caused by the continuous variance of $\omega$, owing to the fact

---

[2] For large values of $t$, an inordinate amount of terms may be required to bound the truncation error within tolerable limits.

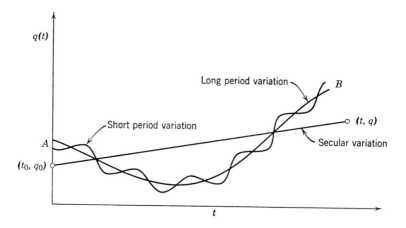

FIGURE 10.1   Typical elements $A$ such as $\omega$, $\Omega$, $M_0$ as a function of ephemeris time over a single revolution.

that the trigonometric functions of $\omega$ have secular variations with period $2\pi$. Fluctuations superimposed on the long period variation line are called short period variations and are caused by the trigonometric functions of linear combinations of $M$ or $v$ and $\omega$. These short wiggles (Figure 10.1) are caused by the variations in true anomaly which are much more rapid than the slow secular variations in the argument of perigee.[3]   The reader should not be confused with these definitions. To reiterate, secular variations are associated with a steady nonoscillatory, continuous drift of an element from the adopted epoch value, short period variations with the trigonometric functions of linear combinations of $v$ and $\omega$, and long period variations with trigonometric functions of $\omega$ and multiples of $\omega$.   With these definitions, the total variance of an element $q$, that is,

$$q = q_0 + \dot{q}_0(t - t_0) + K_1 \cos (2\omega) + K_2 \sin (2v + 2\omega), \qquad (10.3)$$

could be represented by the hypothetical relation (10.3), where the first term is the adopted epoch mean element, the second term is the secular variation, the third term the long period variation, and the last term the short period variation.   In this chapter, only the equations for secular

[3] The fleas we know have other fleas
   Upon their backs to bite 'em,
   And these in turn have other fleas,
   And so *ad infinitum*.

variations in the orbital elements will be developed, that is, a secular theory will be presented.   Furthermore, to introduce the subject of general perturbations, the effects of aspherical central planets will be treated by the direct method of Kozai [1].

It may be helpful to point out that the following convention is adopted in this chapter: any quantity that is a true constant in two-body motion is referred to as an *element*, for example, $a$, $e$, $\omega$, $M_0$, $v_0$, $E_0$, etc.; any combination of variables that are shifting with time, including two-body variations, are referred to as *parameters*, for example, $a$, $e$, $\omega$, $M$, $v$, $E$, etc.

The principal effects of *drag* on the orbits of near-Earth satellites will be shown to manifest themselves as secular variations in the eccentricity, semimajor axis, and, to a lesser degree, inclination.   These effects will be treated by the techniques developed by Sterne [2] later on in the chapter.

In essence, this chapter is restricted to a treatment of only the extremely important secular variations of the orbital elements of a near-Earth satellite.   The complete field of general perturbations is immense; the interested reader is directed to the developments and methods of Gauss [3], Brouwer [4], Petty and Breakwell [5], Vinti [6], and Garfinkel [7], to mention a few.   Further information is available from an excellent bibliography on this subject by Gabbard and Levin [8].

## 10.2   SECULAR PERTURBATIONS

### 10.2.1   The method of Kozai

Kozai derives the secular perturbations on a close-Earth satellite due to an aspherical central body in a very clear and direct fashion.   The next section will deal with the development of analytical expressions for the slow drift of the elements $M_0$, $\Omega$, and $\omega$, from their adopted epoch values at $t_0$, that is, the elements obtained from the differential correction process (Chapter 9) at the central date.   It is emphasized that only the perturbations due to an aspherical central planet are taken into account, and thus inclusion of other forces such as drag, etc., are not presently implied.

### 10.2.2   Introduction of the perturbative function

Equation 2.74 provides an analytical model for the potential $\Phi$ of an aspherical Earth, while Eq. 2.72 provides an analytical representation of the potential $V$ of a purely spherical Earth.   Let the *perturbative function* $\bar{R}$ be defined by

$$\bar{R} \equiv \Phi - V. \tag{10.4}$$

In essence, the part of the potential causing two-body motion is removed from $\Phi$.   The perturbative function is very important and will be used presently.   To have the perturbative function in a useable form, a transformation of $\bar{R} = \bar{R}(r, \sin \delta)$ into the composite function $R$ will be introduced by means of the equation of a conic, that is,

$$r = \frac{a(1 - e^2)}{1 + e \cos v}, \tag{10.5}$$

where $a$ is the semimajor axis of the orbit, $e$ is the orbital eccentricity, and $v$ is the true anomaly; and the relation,

$$U_z = \sin \delta = \sin i \sin (v + \omega) \tag{10.6}$$

with $i$ being the orbital inclination and $\omega$ the argument of perigee.   The transformation is accomplished as [4]

$$\bar{R}(r, \sin \delta) = R\left(\frac{a(1 - e^2)}{1 + e \cos v}, \sin i \sin (v + \omega)\right),$$

or, explicitly substituting into Eq. 10.4 and recovering $r$, it is possible to verify that to the order of $J_4$

$$
\begin{aligned}
R = k^2 m \Bigg[ \frac{3}{2} \frac{J_2}{a^3} &\left(\frac{a}{r}\right)^3 \left\{\frac{1}{3} - \frac{1}{2} \sin^2 i + \frac{1}{2} \sin^2 i \cos 2(v + \omega)\right\} \\
&- \frac{J_3}{a^4} \left(\frac{a}{r}\right)^4 \left\{\left(\frac{15}{8} \sin^2 i - \frac{3}{2}\right) \sin (v + \omega)\right. \\
&\qquad\qquad \left. - \frac{5}{8} \sin^2 i \sin 3(v + \omega)\right\} \sin i \\
&- \frac{35}{8} \frac{J_4}{a^5} \left(\frac{a}{r}\right)^5 \left\{\frac{3}{35} - \frac{3}{7} \sin^2 i + \frac{3}{8} \sin^4 i\right. \\
&\qquad\qquad + \sin^2 i \left(\frac{3}{7} - \frac{1}{2} \sin^2 i\right) \cos 2(v + \omega) \\
&\qquad\qquad \left. + \frac{1}{8} \sin^4 i \cos 4(v + \omega)\right\}\Bigg]. \tag{10.7}
\end{aligned}
$$

---

[4] The development of the perturbative function for the lunar potential is explicitly developed in Section 10.5.

### 10.2.3  Rate of change of the classical elements

By lengthy analysis, it is possible to verify that the perturbative function, the elements, and time are related by the following system of differential equations:

$$\frac{da}{dt} = \frac{2}{na} \frac{\partial R}{\partial M},$$

$$\frac{de}{dt} = \frac{1 - e^2}{na^2 e} \frac{\partial R}{\partial M} - \frac{\sqrt{1 - e^2}}{na^2 e} \frac{\partial R}{\partial \omega},$$

$$\frac{d\omega}{dt} = -\frac{\cos i}{na^2 \sqrt{1 - e^2} \sin i} \frac{\partial R}{\partial i} + \frac{\sqrt{1 - e^2}}{na^2 e} \frac{\partial R}{\partial e},$$

$$\frac{di}{dt} = \frac{\cos i}{na^2 \sqrt{1 - e^2} \sin i} \frac{\partial R}{\partial \omega}, \tag{10.8}$$

$$\frac{d\Omega}{dt} = \frac{1}{na^2 \sqrt{1 - e^2} \sin i} \frac{\partial R}{\partial i},$$

$$\frac{dM}{dt} = n - \frac{1 - e^2}{na^2 e} \frac{\partial R}{\partial e} - \frac{2}{na} \frac{\partial R}{\partial a},$$

where $n$, the mean motion, is defined by $n = k\sqrt{\mu}\, a^{-3/2}$. Derivation of these equations is presented in references [2], [3], [9], and [10], to mention a few. By accepting these equations as known, it is possible to continue with the derivation of the secular rates. It should be noticed that if $R$ is free from the explicit appearance of $\omega$, then $i$ is constant and does not vary. Other inferences can be drawn from Eqs. 10.8. In passing, it is also worthwhile to note that, in secular theory, the divisors $e$ and $\sin i$, as they approach zero, do not cause any trouble, since, as will be presently seen, $e$ and $\sin i$ are also presented in the numerators of the partials of $R$ with respect to the elements.

### 10.2.4  Partitioning the perturbative function

Examination of $R$ enables those terms, which will contribute to secular variations in the elements to be segregated as indicated in Section 10.1, that is, short and long period terms are omitted so that

$$R_1 = k^2 m \left[ \frac{3}{2} \frac{J_2}{a^3} \left(\frac{a}{r}\right)^3 \left\{ \frac{1}{3} - \frac{1}{2} \sin^2 i \right\} \right]$$

$$R_2 = k^2 m \left[ -\frac{35}{8} \frac{J_4}{a^5} \left(\frac{a}{r}\right)^5 \left\{ \frac{3}{35} - \frac{3}{7} \sin^2 i + \frac{3}{8} \sin^4 i \right\} \right], \tag{10.9}$$

where $i$ does not experience any secular variations since $\partial R / \partial \omega = 0$.

The perturbative function $R_1$ represents the first-order $(J_2)$ part of the disturbing function, while $R_2$ is of the second order $(J_4)$. Since the main interest of the discussion deals with the nonperiodic variation of the elements undergoing perturbations, Eqs. 10.9 may be averaged over a given revolution. To do this, it is necessary to find

$$\overline{\left(\frac{a}{r}\right)^3} \equiv \frac{1}{2\pi} \int_0^{2\pi} \left(\frac{a}{r}\right)^3 dM, \qquad \overline{\left(\frac{a}{r}\right)^5} \equiv \frac{1}{2\pi} \int_0^{2\pi} \left(\frac{a}{r}\right)^5 dM. \tag{10.10}$$

Note that the overhead bar denotes the average value of $(a/r)^n$. To compute these values, the transformation of variables $dv/dM = (dE/dM) \cdot (dv/dE)$, or, more explicitly,

$$\frac{dM}{dv} = \left(\frac{r}{a}\right)^2 \frac{1}{\sqrt{1 - e^2}} \tag{10.11}$$

reduces the first of Eqs. 10.10 to

$$\overline{\left(\frac{a}{r}\right)^3} = \frac{1}{2\pi} \int_0^{2\pi} \left(\frac{a}{r}\right)^3 \left(\frac{r}{a}\right)^2 \frac{1}{\sqrt{1 - e^2}} \, dv = \int_0^{2\pi} \frac{1 + e \cos v}{(1 + e)^{3/2}} \, dv$$

$$= \frac{1}{2\pi} \int_0^{2\pi} (1 - e^2)^{-3/2} \, dv + \frac{1}{2\pi} \int_0^{2\pi} \frac{e \cos v}{(1 - e^2)^{3/2}} \, dv$$

$$= (1 - e^2)^{-3/2}. \tag{10.12}$$

In a similar fashion,

$$\overline{\left(\frac{a}{r}\right)^5} = (1 - e^2)^{-7/2} \left(1 + \frac{3}{2} e^2\right), \tag{10.13}$$

where $e$ has been assumed constant over the interval of integration.

Substitution of Eqs. 10.12 and 10.13 for the ratios $a/r$ in Eqs. 10.9 yields

$$R_1 = k^2 m \left[ \frac{3}{2} \frac{J_2}{a^3} (1 - e^2)^{-3/2} \left\{ \frac{1}{3} - \frac{1}{2} \sin^2 i \right\} \right]$$

$$\tag{10.14}$$

$$R_2 = k^2 m \left[ -\frac{35}{8} \frac{J_4}{a^5} (1 - e^2)^{-7/2} \left(1 + \frac{3}{2} e^2\right) \left\{ \frac{3}{35} - \frac{3}{7} \sin^2 i + \frac{3}{8} \sin^4 i \right\} \right].$$

### 10.2.5   Derivation of the secular perturbations of the first order

Consider that $R_1$ is accepted as the perturbing function, that is, all other parts of $R$ are neglected. Then, from Eqs. 10.8, the rate of change of the mean motion is

$$\frac{dM}{dt} = n - \frac{1 - e^2}{na^2 e} \frac{\partial R_1}{\partial e} - \frac{2}{na} \frac{\partial R_1}{\partial a}, \tag{10.15}$$

and since

$$\frac{\partial R_1}{\partial e} = k^2 m \left[ +2 \left(\frac{3}{2}\right)^2 \frac{J_2}{a^3} e(1 - e^2)^{-5/2} \left\{ \frac{1}{3} - \frac{1}{2} \sin^2 i \right\} \right]$$

$$\frac{\partial R_1}{\partial a} = k^2 m \left[ -2 \left(\frac{3}{2}\right)^2 \frac{J_2}{a^4} (1 - e^2)^{-3/2} \left\{ \frac{1}{3} - \frac{1}{2} \sin^2 i \right\} \right], \tag{10.16}$$

it is possible to verify with the aid of $k^2 m = n^2 a^3$ and $p = a(1 - e^2)$ that

$$\bar{n} \equiv \frac{dM}{dt} = n \left[ 1 + \frac{3}{2} J_2 \frac{\sqrt{1 - e^2}}{p^2} \left( 1 - \frac{3}{2} \sin^2 i \right) \right], \tag{10.17}$$

where $n$ is the unperturbed or two-body mean motion, and $p$ is the semiparameter of the orbit. Some interesting inferences may be drawn from Eq. 10.17.

Mathematically, the mean anomaly $M$ is defined as

$$M \equiv n(t - T), \tag{10.18}$$

where $T$ is the time of perifocal passage. In two-body motion, $dM/dt = n = $ constant. The equation for $dM/dt$ in the first-order secular theory is also a constant, since $da/dt$, $de/dt$, and $di/dt$ experience no secular variations. As a matter of fact, if $J_2$ is taken to be zero, the familiar two-body expression for the rate of change of $M$ is obtained from Eq. 10.17. Hence, the unperturbed mean motion is increased or decreased by the coefficient of $J_2$ according to the relative inclination of the orbit. Adopting some convenient epoch time $t = t_0$, where $M = M_0$, the integral of Eq. 10.17 can be written as

$$M = M_0 + \bar{n}(t - t_0). \tag{10.19}$$

Once the secular variation in the mean anomaly has been developed, secular rates in the longitude of the ascending node and argument of perigee are obtained easily with the aid of Eqs. 10.8. Working with the expression for $d\Omega/dt$,

$$\int d\Omega = \int \left( \frac{1}{na^2 \sqrt{1 - e^2} \sin i} \right) \left( -\frac{3}{2} k^2 m \frac{J_2}{a^3} (1 - e^2)^{-3/2} \right) \sin i \cos i \, dt, \tag{10.20}$$

where $n$ is related to $a$ by $n^2 a^3 = k^2 m$, the following relation is evident:

$$\int d\Omega = -\frac{3}{2} \frac{J_2}{p^2} \cos i \int n \, dt. \tag{10.21}$$

However, since

$$\int n \, dt = M - M_0,$$     (10.22)

by utilizing Eq. 10.19 and integrating Eq. 10.21,

$$\Omega = \Omega_0 - \left(\frac{3}{2}\frac{J_2}{p^2}\cos i\right)\bar{n}(t - t_0).$$     (10.23)

In exactly analogous fashion, use of the expression for $d\omega/dt$ from Eqs. 10.8 results in the secular expression for $\omega$, that is,

$$\omega = \omega_0 + \frac{3}{2}\frac{J_2}{p^2}\left(2 - \frac{5}{2}\sin^2 i\right)\bar{n}(t - t_0).$$     (10.24)

The reader may be a little puzzled by the form of Eq. 10.19.   Actually, to make the mean anomaly equation consistent with Eqs. 10.23 and 10.24, it is possible to write

$$M = M_0 + \left(\frac{3}{2}J_2\frac{\sqrt{1 - e^2}}{p^2}\left(1 - \frac{3}{2}\sin^2 i\right)\right)n_0(t - t_0) + n_0(t - t_0)$$     (10.25)

or

$$M = M_0 + \dot{M}_0(t - t_0) + n_0(t - t_0),$$     (10.26)

with $\dot{M}_0$ defined by coefficient of $(t - t_0)$ in middle term of Eq. 10.25. In similar fashion, the variance in $\Omega$ and $\omega$ can be written as

$$\Omega = \Omega_0 + \dot{\Omega}_0(t - t_0)$$     (10.27)

$$\omega = \omega_0 + \dot{\omega}_0(t - t_0)$$     (10.28)

with $\dot{\Omega}_0$ and $\dot{\omega}_0$ defined by the coefficients of $(t - t_0)$ in Eqs. 10.23 and 10.24.   Examination and comparison of the last three equations shows that Eq. 10.26 has an extra term on the right side, namely, $n_0(t - t_0)$. This is to be expected since $M$ is a two-body parameter which varies with time, while $\Omega$ and $\omega$ are two-body elements which, in opposite fashion, do not vary with time for Keplerian motion.   In essence then, the perturbation in $M_0$ due to oblateness forces is $\dot{M}_0(t - t_0)$.   In passing, it is well to note that for convenience, in the last few expressions, an overhead dot represents differentiation with respect to universal or, more correctly, ephemeris time.[5]

---

[5] It should be remembered that an overhead dot usually denotes differentiation with respect to $\tau$, modified time.

## 10.2.6 Compendium of the first-order $J_2$ secular variation equations

As developed in the previous sections, the first-order theory for the secular perturbations has resulted in the following equations.

*Anomalistic mean motion and period*

$$\bar{n} = n_0 \left[ 1 + \frac{3}{2} J_2 \frac{\sqrt{1 - e^2}}{p^2} \left( 1 - \frac{3}{2} \sin^2 i \right) \right] \tag{10.29}$$

$$\bar{P} = \frac{2\pi}{\bar{n}} \tag{10.30}$$

*Mean anomaly*

$$M = M_0 + \bar{n}(t - t_0) \tag{10.31}$$

*Longitude of the ascending node*

$$\Omega = \Omega_0 - \left( \frac{3}{2} \frac{J_2}{p^2} \cos i \right) \bar{n}(t - t_0) = \Omega_0 + \dot{\Omega}(t - t_0) \tag{10.32}$$

*Argument of perigee*

$$\omega = \omega_0 + \left( \frac{3}{2} \frac{J_2}{p^2} \left[ 2 - \frac{5}{2} \sin^2 i \right] \right) \bar{n}(t - t_0) = \omega_0 + \dot{\omega}(t - t_0) \tag{10.33}$$

These equations represent the gradual drift of the classical elements $[a, e, M, i, \Omega, \omega]$ from their adopted epoch values at $t = t_0$. In a secular first-order theory, with the influence of only the first coefficient of the Earth's harmonic taken into account, only $\Omega$, $\omega$ and $M_0$ are possessed of drift tendencies, and $a$, $e$, $i$ are taken as constant by virtue of the model adopted for $R$ and Eqs. 10.8.

## 10.2.7 Outline of the procedure for obtaining secular terms of the second order

By adopting for the perturbing function $R$ Eqs. 10.14, that is, $R_1 + R_2$, the second-order secular effects upon the parameters $M$, $\omega$, and $\Omega$ may be determined as in the previous sections. Actually, if $q_i$ is one of the parameters of the set $[a, e, M, i, \Omega, \omega]$, Eqs. 10.8, that is,

$$\frac{dq_i}{dt} = f_i \tag{10.34}$$

may be expanded into a power series of deviations from the mean orbital elements as

$$\frac{dq_i}{dt} = (f_i) + \sum_j \left( \frac{\partial f_i}{\partial q_j} \right) dq_j + \cdots . \tag{10.35}$$

Secular perturbations of the second order will then be obtained from second-order terms on the right side of Eq. 10.35, [1]. Integration of Eq. 10.35 may be accomplished in a straightforward manner by parts, that is,

$$q - q_0 = \int (f_i)\, dt + \sum_j [F_{ij}\, dq_j] - \sum_j \int F_{ij} \frac{dq_j}{dt}\, dt, \tag{10.36}$$

where

$$F_{ij} \equiv \int \left( \frac{\partial f_i}{\partial q_j} \right) dt.$$

Use of this equation entails considerable manipulation in collecting terms, etc., but it is straightforward. The results are collected in the next section.

### 10.2.8   Compendium of the second-order $J_2$ and $J_4$ secular variation equations

In accordance with the discussion of the previous section, the second-order theory for the secular perturbations will yield the following equations:

*Anomalistic mean motion and period*[6]

$$
\begin{aligned}
\bar{n} = n_0 \Bigg[ 1 &+ \frac{3}{2} J_2 \frac{\sqrt{1 - e^2}}{p^2} \left( 1 - \frac{3}{2} \sin^2 i \right) \\
&+ \frac{3}{128} J_2^2 \frac{\sqrt{1 - e^2}}{p^4} \Bigg( 16\sqrt{1 - e^2} + 25(1 - e^2) - 15 \\
&+ [30 - 96\sqrt{1 - e^2} - 90(1 - e^2)] \cos^2 i \\
&+ [105 + 144\sqrt{1 - e^2} + 25(1 - e^2)] \cos^4 i \Bigg) \\
&- \frac{45}{128} J_4 \frac{\sqrt{1 - e^2}}{p^4} e^2 \Big( 3 - 30 \cos^2 i + 35 \cos^4 i \Big) \Bigg]
\end{aligned}
\tag{10.37}
$$

$$\bar{P} = \frac{2\pi}{\bar{n}} \tag{10.38}$$

*Mean anomaly*

$$M = M_0 + \bar{n}(t - t_0) \tag{10.39}$$

[6] This expression for $\bar{n}$ is developed in reference [4].

*Longitude of the ascending node*

$$\Omega = \Omega_0 - \left\{ \frac{3}{2} \frac{J_2}{p^2} \bar{n} \cos i \left[ 1 + \frac{3}{2} \frac{J_2}{p^2} \left\{ \frac{3}{2} + \frac{e^2}{6} - 2\sqrt{1 - e^2} \right. \right.\right.$$

$$\left. - \left( \frac{5}{3} - \frac{5}{24} e^2 - 3\sqrt{1 - e^2} \right) \sin^2 i \right\} \right]$$

$$\left. + \frac{35}{8} \frac{J_4}{p^4} n_0 \left( 1 + \frac{3}{2} e^2 \right) \left( \frac{12 - 21 \sin^2 i}{14} \right) \cos i \right\} (t - t_0)$$

$$(10.40)$$

*Argument of perigee*

$$\omega = \omega_0 + \left\{ \frac{3}{2} \frac{J_2}{p^2} \bar{n} \left( 2 - \frac{5}{2} \sin^2 i \right) \left[ 1 + \frac{3}{2} \frac{J_2}{p^2} \left\{ 2 + \frac{e^2}{2} - 2\sqrt{1 - e^2} \right. \right.\right.$$

$$\left. - \left( \frac{43}{24} - \frac{e^2}{48} - 3\sqrt{1 - e^2} \right) \sin^2 i \right\}\right]$$

$$- \frac{45}{36} \frac{J_2^2}{p^4} e^2 n_0 \cos^4 i - \frac{35}{8} \frac{J_4}{p^4} n_0 \left[ \frac{12}{7} - \frac{93}{14} \sin^2 i \right.$$

$$\left. + \frac{21}{4} \sin^4 i + e^2 \left\{ \frac{27}{14} - \frac{189}{28} \sin^2 i + \frac{81}{16} \sin^4 i \right\} \right] \right\} (t - t_0).$$

$$(10.41)$$

## 10.3   NULLIFICATION OF THE TWO-BODY APPROXIMATION

### 10.3.1   Step function approach

Assuming that a given physical process can be represented by a two-body or Keplerian model will in many instances permit the analyst to achieve a closed solution (Chapter 5).   The solution will then depend on the orbital elements $a$, $e$, $M_0$, $i$, $\Omega$, $\omega$, some of which, as demonstrated in this chapter, experience drift from their epoch value.   Consider, however, that for any single revolution the wandering parameters $\omega$, $\Omega$, $M$ are assumed to be strictly dominated by an inverse square law and are true Keplerian parameters.   Consider further that some convenient epoch is adopted, say, perifocus.   It certainly appears feasible to solve the desired problem, for example: eclipse times, rise-and-set times from a particular ground station, nodal crossing times, etc., as a two-body problem for the *next revolution.*   The next time that perifocus is reached, the elements are updated and the time slippage is corrected by

$$\Omega = \Omega_0 + \Delta\Omega$$
$$\omega = \omega_0 + \Delta\omega \qquad\qquad (10.42)$$
$$T = T_0 + \bar{P},$$

where the zero subscript refers to the value of $\Omega$, $\omega$, $T$ at the latest time of perifocal passage.   Note that $\bar{P}$ is the anomalistic period, Sections 10.2.6 and 10.2.8.   This process of *step incrementation* is repeated at every future perifocal crossing.

Some conclusions relating to the step incrementation process can be reached immediately, for example, element updating can be at any specified time, it need not be perifocal crossing, and updating can be performed as many times as desired per orbital revolution.   Furthermore, deviation of the satellite from its unperturbed path is always a bounded process in the sense that the satellite never wanders very far from its true position over a single revolution, owing to the definition of the secular rates of change.   Graphically, the updating process is approximately depicted in Figure 10.2.

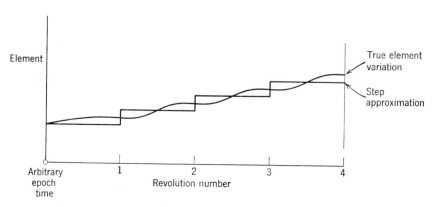

FIGURE 10.2   Step incrementation process.

It is perhaps easy to visualize the incrementation of $\Omega$ and $\omega$, but a little harder to grasp how time is obtained as consistently as possible over a given step interval.   This will be evident if Kepler's equation (Chapter 3)

$$M = n(t - T) = E - e\sin E \qquad\qquad (10.43)$$

is rewritten as

$$M = \bar{n}(t - T) = E - e\sin E, \qquad\qquad (10.44)$$

with $\bar{n}$ obtained from Eq. 10.29 or Eq. 10.37, depending on the accuracy desired. Evidently, then, the true mean universal time is obtained from

$$t = \frac{E - e \sin E}{\bar{n}} + T. \qquad (10.45)$$

Notice that as $E$ varies from 0 to $2\pi$, the anomalistic period is added to $T$.

### 10.3.2   Application: The ground trace of a satellite about an oblate planet

A problem of frequent interest is the determination of the *ground trace* of a particular satellite. To be definitive, the ground trace of a satellite is the path traced by the pierce point of a ray dropped from a given satellite in such a direction that it intersects normally the surface of the planet about which motion occurs. Geometrically, this is illustrated in Figure 10.3.

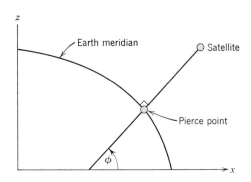

FIGURE 10.3   Vehicle sublatitude point.

In essence, as the satellite moves through a complete period or a variation in eccentric anomaly $E$ of $2\pi$, a continuous mapping is produced from $E$ to $\phi$ and $\lambda_E$, that is, the vehicle geodetic sublatitude and east sublongitude. The eccentric anomaly is chosen as the independent variable in order to avoid the iterative solution of Kepler's equation each time a ground point is desired.

The purpose of this section is to illustrate how two-body formulations can be recast or amended to incorporate the secular influences of the oblate field of a central planet. Geometrical flattening of the Earth's surface is also included in the analysis. The reader should bear in mind the difference between *geometrical flattening*, caused by the geometry of oblate spheroid, and *dynamical flattening*, occasioned by variations in the internal constitution of the central planet. The analysis is presented in the following algorithmic form.

Given the following common data,

$$k, \ \mu, \ f, \ J_2, \ a_e, \ \frac{d\theta}{dt}, \ \Delta E, \ t_s, \ t_{sp},$$

where

$k$ = gravitational constant $\equiv 0.07436574$ (e.r.)$^{3/2}$/min,

$\mu$ = sum of the masses of satellite and Earth = 1 c.m.,

$f$ = flattening of Earth $\simeq 1/298.3$,

$J_2$ = second harmonic coefficient $\fallingdotseq 1082.28 \times 10^{-6}$,

$a_e$ = equatorial radius of Earth = 1 e.r.,

$\dfrac{d\theta}{dt}$ = rate of change of sideral time $\simeq 0.00437526950$ rad/min,

$t_s$ = universal time at start of ground trace generation,

$t_{sp}$ = universal stop time of ground trace generation,

$\Delta E$ = increment in eccentric anomaly,

along with

$$a, \ e, \ i, \ \Omega, \ \omega, \ T,$$

the standard classical orbital elements (Chapter 3), proceed as follows.

By the techniques of Chapter 1, obtain the Julian dates corresponding to $t_s$, $t_{sp}$, and $T$. Notice that if a set of elements are given at time $T$, it may be desired to start the generation of the ground trace a number of days later, say at $t_s$. Symbolically, then, the following correspondence is made:

$$T \rightarrow (\text{J.D.})_1$$

$$t_s \rightarrow (\text{J.D.})_2 \tag{10.46}$$

$$t_{sp} \rightarrow (\text{J.D.})_3.$$

Before commencing the actual ground trace generation, since $t_s$ has not been taken equal to $T$, an updating of the elements to the latest time of perifocal passage, perhaps several revolutions later, is necessary.

The starting revolution number $N$, or the number of revolutions elapsed since perigee crossing at time $T$, can be obtained from the first order model as

$$\bar{n} = k\sqrt{\mu}\, a^{-\frac{3}{2}}\left[1 + \frac{3}{2}J_2\frac{\sqrt{1-e^2}}{p^2}\left(1 - \frac{3}{2}\sin^2 i\right)\right] \qquad (10.47)$$

$$\bar{P} = \frac{2\pi}{\bar{n}} \quad \text{(in minutes)} \qquad (10.48)$$

$$\Delta t = (\text{J.D.})_2 - (\text{J.D.})_1 \quad \text{(in days)} \qquad (10.49)$$

$$N = \text{int}\left(\frac{1440\,\Delta t}{\bar{P}}\right), \text{(in revolutions).}[7] \qquad (10.50)$$

Notice that the number of revolutions from $T$ have been computed using the anomalistic period $\bar{P}$, Eq. 10.30. This accounts for the actual shift in $\omega$ from revolution to revolution.

At this point, the orbital elements $\omega$, $\Omega$, $T$ can be updated to their local values at the latest time of perifocal passage $T_N$, by

$$\omega_N = \omega + \left(\frac{3}{2}J_2\left\{\frac{a_e}{p}\right\}^2\left[2 - \frac{5}{2}\sin^2 i\right]\bar{n}\right)N\cdot\bar{P}$$

$$\Omega_N = \Omega - \left(\frac{3}{2}J_2\left\{\frac{a_e}{p}\right\}^2[\cos i]\bar{n}\right)N\cdot\bar{P} \qquad (10.51)$$

$$T_N = T + N \times \bar{P},$$

where the subscript $N$ refers to the elements updated to the start of revolution $N$. Notice that $N \times \bar{P} = (T_N - T)$. The reader may wonder why $N \times \bar{P}$ is used in place of the difference $T_N - T$; the answer lies in the fact that in a given machine program, the Julian dates corresponding to $T_N$ and $T$ would have to be determined and then the subtraction performed. The revolution-times-period concept is therefore more convenient. Furthermore, if canonical units are utilized, $a_e = 1$ and Eqs. 10.51 reduce to Eqs. 10.32 and 10.33.

Since generation of the desired ground trace is to be initiated at time $t_s$, it will be convenient to determine the starting value of the eccentric anomaly $E$ corresponding to $t_s$. This will enable the incrementation of $E$ to be started at the correct point in the orbit.

[7] The integer function is defined as taking the argument $x$ of int($x$) and reducing the argument to the nearest whole integer $< x$.

Restricting the analysis to elliptic motion, it is necessary to solve the perturbed Keplerian equation (Chapter 3) as

$$E - e \sin E = \bar{n}(t_s - T) = M,$$

or, in more convenient form,[8]

$$E - e \sin E = \text{mod}\,(1440\bar{n}\,\Delta t,\, 2\pi). \tag{10.52}$$

Notice that $M$ has been reduced to an angle between 0 and $2\pi$ without affecting the value of $E$. The eccentric anomaly at the start time $E_{ts}$ is directly obtained by iteration from $\Delta t$ as defined by Eq. 10.49.

The reader should notice that initialization is complete, that is, in symbolic form,

$$\begin{bmatrix} a \\ e \\ T \\ i \\ \Omega \\ \omega \end{bmatrix}_{t=T} + \begin{bmatrix} 0 \\ 0 \\ \Delta T \\ 0 \\ \Delta\Omega \\ \Delta\omega \end{bmatrix}_{\Delta t = (T_N - T)} \rightarrow \begin{bmatrix} a \\ e \\ T_N \\ i \\ \Omega_N \\ \omega_N \end{bmatrix}_{t=T_N}. \tag{10.53}$$

Since the value of $E_{ts}$ has also been determined, the ground trace generation can be commenced. To repeat, the correct elements at $T_N$, for a first-order theory, have been determined. This was necessary because, for the purpose of illustration, the starting time $t_s$ was selected so that it did not correspond to $T$, the time of perifocal passage. Therefore, $\Omega$ and $\omega$ had drifted from their initial values at $T$ for a length of time equal to $T_N - T$ and a correction was necessary.

The orientation vectors, Section 3.4, are computed as

$$\begin{aligned}
P_{xN} &= \cos\omega_N \cos\Omega_N - \sin\omega_N \sin\Omega_N \cos i \\
P_{yN} &= \cos\omega_N \sin\Omega_N + \sin\omega_N \cos\Omega_N \cos i \\
P_{zN} &= \sin\omega_N \sin i \\
Q_{xN} &= -\sin\omega_N \cos\Omega_N - \cos\omega_N \sin\Omega_N \cos i \\
Q_{yN} &= -\sin\omega_N \sin\Omega_N + \cos\omega_N \cos\Omega_N \cos i \\
Q_{zN} &= \cos\omega_N \sin i,
\end{aligned} \tag{10.54}$$

---

[8] The modulo function is defined as taking the first argument $x$ of mod $(x, y)$ and reducing it modulo $y$.

and the following chain of calculations is performed:[9]

$$x_\omega = a(\cos E - e)$$
$$y_\omega = a\sqrt{1 - e^2}\sin E \tag{10.55}$$

$$\begin{bmatrix} x \\ y \\ z \end{bmatrix} = \begin{bmatrix} P_x & Q_x & 0 \\ P_y & Q_y & 0 \\ P_z & Q_z & 0 \end{bmatrix}_N \begin{bmatrix} x_\omega \\ y_\omega \\ 0 \end{bmatrix} \tag{10.56}$$

$$r = (x^2 + y^2 + z^2)^{1/2} \tag{10.57}$$

$$\bar{\imath} = \frac{E - e\sin E}{\bar{n}} \tag{10.58}$$

$$\sin\delta = \frac{z}{r}, \quad -\frac{\pi}{2} \le \delta \le \frac{\pi}{2}, \tag{10.59}$$

$$\sin\alpha = \frac{y}{\sqrt{x^2 + y^2}}, \quad \cos\alpha = \frac{x}{\sqrt{x^2 + y^2}}, \quad 0 \le \alpha \le 2\pi. \tag{10.60}$$

The above equations have determined the position **r**, right ascension and declination $\alpha$, $\delta$, and the number of minutes $\bar{\imath}$ after $T_N$ of the satellite whose ground trace is desired. By the procedures of Section 1.3, the local sidereal time at Greenwich $\theta_g$ corresponding to (J.D.)$_2$ is utilized to obtain

$$\lambda_E' = \alpha - \theta_g - \frac{d\theta}{dt}t, \tag{10.61}$$

where $t$ is the total number of minutes elapsed since the year, month, and day of $t_s$. Notice that $\theta_g$, the Greenwich sidereal time, is evaluated at time $t_s$. Then,

$$\lambda_E = \mathrm{mod}(\lambda_E', 2\pi), \quad 0 \le \lambda_E \le 2\pi, \tag{10.62}$$

yields the east longitude of the ground trace. Using the equations of Transformation 3, Appendix I, the following iterative procedure is initiated in order to determine the subvehicle geodetic latitude. As a first approximation, set $\phi_s' = \delta$, where $\delta$ has already been determined, and continue calculating with

$$r_c = a_e\left[\frac{1 - (2f - f^2)}{1 - (2f - f^2)\cos^2\phi_s'}\right]^{1/2} \tag{10.63}$$

$$\phi_s = \tan^{-1}\left[\frac{\tan\phi_s'}{(1-f)^2}\right], \quad -\frac{\pi}{2} \le \phi_s \le \frac{\pi}{2}, \tag{10.64}$$

$$H_s = [r^2 - r_c^2\sin^2(\phi_s - \phi_s')]^{1/2} - r_c\cos(\phi_s - \phi_s') \tag{10.65}$$

$$\Delta\phi_s' = \sin^{-1}\left[\frac{H_s}{r}\sin(\phi_s - \phi_s')\right], \quad -\frac{\pi}{2} \le \Delta\phi_s' \le \frac{\pi}{2}. \tag{10.66}$$

[9] The first time through this loop $E = E_{ts}$.

Recalculate $\phi_s' = \delta - \Delta\phi_s'$ and return to Eq. 10.63. Repeat this loop until $\phi_s'$ no longer varies. This process is exact and rapidly convergent, and at the same time yields the ground trace geodetic latitude, $\phi$. In recapitulation, a value of $E$ has yielded the corresponding ground trace coordinates $\phi$ and $\lambda_E$.

The ground trace generation is continued by checking to see if

$$\nabla \equiv (\text{J.D.})_t - (\text{J.D.})_3 > 0, \tag{10.67}$$

where $(\text{J.D.})_3$ is the stop time.[10] If $\nabla > 0$, the calculations are finished and the trace has been completed; if not, check to see if $E = 2\pi$, if so,

$$\omega_{N+1} = \omega_N + \left(\frac{3}{2}J_2\left\{\frac{a_e}{p}\right\}^2\left[2 - \frac{5}{2}\sin^2 i\right]\bar{n}\right)\bar{\iota}$$

$$\Omega_{N+1} = \Omega_N - \left(\frac{3}{2}J_2\left\{\frac{a_e}{p}\right\}^2[\cos i]\bar{n}\right)\bar{\iota} \tag{10.68}$$

$$T_{N+1} = T_N + \bar{P},$$

where at $E = 2\pi$, $\bar{\iota} = \bar{P}$, the anomalistic period of the orbit. Recalculate $\mathbf{P}_N$, $\mathbf{Q}_N$ from Eqs. 10.54. If $E \neq 2\pi$, increment $E$, that is, $E_{i+1} = E_i + \Delta E$, and return to Eqs. 10.55 in order to obtain the next point of the ground trace.

### 10.3.3  Application: Oblateness effects
### in the differential correction process

Chapter 9 was devoted to the differential correction process. This section will indicate how it will be possible to include the perturbative effects of oblateness. Figure 10.4 indicates graphically the adopted epoch time $t_0$ and associated other times $t_1$ and $t_2$.

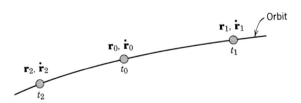

FIGURE 10.4  The three common points of a minimal differential correction process.

[10] Revolution numbers may be checked instead of Julian dates.

As formulated in Chapter 9, the differential correction process depends upon the adopted epoch time $t_0$ and the associated epoch position and velocity vectors $\mathbf{r}_0$, $\dot{\mathbf{r}}_0$ and the predicted position and velocity vectors at two other times, previously referred to as $\mathbf{r}_i$, $\dot{\mathbf{r}}_i$ for $i = 1, 2$. In essence, an accurate prediction of $\mathbf{r}_i$ and $\dot{\mathbf{r}}_i$ is required as input to the differential correction process, both for the computation of residuals and for better determination of the analytical partial derivatives developed in Chapter 9.

A rather simple procedure to follow involves the calculation of the classical elements $a$, $e$, $T$, $i$, $\omega$, $\Omega$ from the given elements $\mathbf{r}_0$, $\dot{\mathbf{r}}_0$ by the standard techniques of Chapter 3. Furthermore, since the time arguments $t_i - t_0$ are known, use of Eqs. 10.32 and 10.33, or to higher accuracy, Eqs. 10.40 and 10.41, will yield $\omega_i$ and $\Omega_i$ corrected for drift. From $\omega_i$ and $\Omega_i$ the rectangular coordinates can be obtained with the aid of $M = \bar{n}(t - T)$ as

$$\mathbf{r}_i = x_{\omega i}\mathbf{P}_i + y_{\omega i}\mathbf{Q}_i \tag{10.69}$$

$$\dot{\mathbf{r}}_i = \dot{x}_{\omega i}\mathbf{P}_i + \dot{y}_{\omega i}\mathbf{Q}_i, \tag{10.70}$$

where $\mathbf{P}$, $\mathbf{Q}$, $x_\omega$, $y_\omega$, $\dot{x}_\omega$, $\dot{y}_\omega$ are defined in Sections 3.4 and 3.5. Naturally the corrected values of $\omega$ and $\Omega$ are used in the computation of $\mathbf{P}$ and $\mathbf{Q}$. Once the correct rectangular coordinates are known at $t_2$ and $t_1$, the differential correction process can be initiated.

As can be seen, the perturbative effects enter into the differential correction process through the prediction equations used to locate the satellite at $t_2$ and $t_1$ and at the epoch if the time origin is not chosen coincident with central observations.

### 10.3.4 Application: Solution of the intercept problem

A problem of current interest today is called the intercept problem. In this section a special case of the intercept problem is solved by direct application of the principles developed in Chapters 6 and 9. In essence, the intercept problem is what can be called an initial value problem. The aim of the intercept problem is the determination of an initial set of elements, say $[a, e, i, \Omega, \omega, M_0]$, which will place a missile at the location of an enemy missile in a specified amount of time. For example, in Figure 10.5, consider the orbit of an enemy satellite denoted by $s_i$ whose orbital elements $[a, e, i, \Omega, \omega, M_0]_{s_i}$ have been determined, for instance, from the angular observations of a ground station (Chapter 7). Let it be

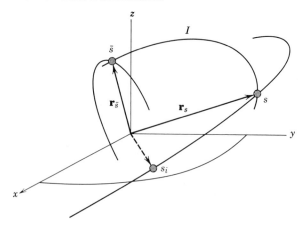

FIGURE 10.5    Interception process.

assumed that $s_i$ will not change its orbit in the immediate future. Evidently then, the trajectory of $s_i$ is well known as a function of time. Suppose that a satellite $\bar{s}$ with elements $[a, e, i, \Omega, \omega, M_0]_{\bar{s}}$ desires to intercept $s_i$ within a time span of duration $\Delta t$ at $s$.

The general solution of this problem can be handled as follows.    In time $\Delta t$, $s_i$ with elements $[a, e, i, \Omega, \omega, M_0]$ will have advanced to position $s$ with parameters $[a, e, i, \Omega + \dot{\Omega} \Delta t, \omega + \dot{\omega} \Delta t, M_0 + \bar{n} \Delta t]$.    The reader is directed to Sections 10.2.6 and 10.2.8 for analytical expressions of $\dot{\Omega}$, $\dot{\omega}$ and $\bar{n}$.    Hence, at time corresponding to position $s$, the elements of the enemy satellite are completely known and, by the standard techniques of Chapter 3, the position vector of $s$ can be directly computed.    Symbolically, this process is outlined as

$$[a, e, i, \Omega + \dot{\Omega} \Delta t, \omega + \dot{\omega} \Delta t, M_0 + \bar{n} \Delta t] \rightarrow \mathbf{r}_s.$$

Furthermore, when $\Delta t = 0$, the position of $\bar{s}$ is also known, that is,

$$[a, e, i, \Omega, \omega, M_0]_{\bar{s}} \rightarrow \mathbf{r}_{\bar{s}}.$$

The analysis is now reduced to the two-position vector and time interval problem, that is, the placement of an orbit between $\mathbf{r}_{\bar{s}}$ and $\mathbf{r}_s$ with time interval $\Delta t$.    However, since the techniques of Chapter 6 were derived with two-body assumptions, a slight modification is necessary. Consider a two-body orbit placed between the terminals of $\mathbf{r}_{\bar{s}}$ and $\mathbf{r}_s$. Any of the techniques of Chapter 6 enables the determination of the position and velocity vectors at the intercept time.    Symbolically, this is represented as

$$\mathbf{r}_s, \mathbf{r}_{\bar{s}}, \Delta t \rightarrow \mathbf{r}_s, \dot{\mathbf{r}}_s.$$

Evidently $\mathbf{r}_s$ is the exact value of the radius vector at the intercept point; but $\dot{\mathbf{r}}_s$ is a two-body approximation to the velocity vector. In this problem, since velocity matching is not important, the two-body value of $\dot{\mathbf{r}}_s$ is adopted and assumed to be correct. Equipped with $\mathbf{r}_s$ and $\dot{\mathbf{r}}_s$, the standard techniques of Chapter 3 enable the computation of a set of correct instantaneous elements at the intercept time. Symbolically, then,

$$\mathbf{r}_s, \dot{\mathbf{r}}_s \rightarrow [a, e, i, \Omega, \omega, M_0]_I,$$

where the subscript $I$ denotes that these are the elements of the intercept trajectory at point $s$ (Figure 10.5). The next step of the intercept problem is the determination of these elements $\Delta t$ time units earlier. Hence, reversing the earlier process,

$$[a, e, i, \Omega, \omega, M_0]_I \rightarrow [a, e, i, \Omega - \dot{\Omega} \Delta t, \omega - \dot{\omega} \Delta t, M_0 - \bar{n} \Delta t]_{I0},$$

where the subscript $I0$ denotes the initial values of the intercept trajectory.

If the interception analysis were restricted to Keplerian mechanics, the problem would be solved with the elements $I0$. However, computation of the radius vector at time $\Delta t = 0$ with elements $I0$ will, in general, produce a perturbed value of $\mathbf{r}_{\bar{s}}$, which is clearly not permitted. In brief, residuals will be present in the radius vector determined from subscripted elements $\bar{s}$ and $I0$. To remedy this situation, the adopted two-body value of $\dot{\mathbf{r}}_s$ must be slightly adjusted.

Differential correction of $\dot{\mathbf{r}}_s$ will be used to force the residuals at the initial terminal to zero. Certainly it is possible to assume that $\mathbf{r}_{\bar{s}}$ is a function of $\dot{\mathbf{r}}_s$, that is,

$$\mathbf{r}_{\bar{s}} = \mathbf{r}_{\bar{s}}(\dot{x}_s, \dot{y}_s, \dot{z}_s),$$

with the position vector $\mathbf{r}_s$ held fixed. By direct differentiation, the differential correction equations are given by

$$\Delta \mathbf{r}_s = \frac{\partial \mathbf{r}_{\bar{s}}}{\partial \dot{x}_s} \Delta \dot{x}_s + \frac{\partial \mathbf{r}_{\bar{s}}}{\partial \dot{y}_s} \Delta \dot{y}_s + \frac{\partial \mathbf{r}_{\bar{s}}}{\partial \dot{z}_s} \Delta \dot{z}_s.$$

Hence, knowing the residuals at the first terminal, simultaneous solution of the three by three system of equations with the partials obtained by variant calculations or the analytical expressions of Chapter 9 will yield velocity corrections to $\dot{\mathbf{r}}_s$. Usually, for short arc interception, one correction will suffice for most purposes.

## 10.4  DRAG PERTURBATIONS

The secular rates of changes derived in the previous section considered only the effects due to an aspherical central planet. When the motion of a near satellite is under consideration, it may well be that the drag perturbation is dominant, and that its omission in the general equations of motion would involve serious errors.

It is unfortunate that no drag theory exists, and probably will never exist, which will yield parallelism between the elegant formulations of the previous aspherical analysis and the numerical techniques of drag analysis. This is true because of the intrinsic empirical nature of the problem, that is, the variation of atmospheric density and accurate prediction of drag coefficients[11] (Section 2.8).

Drag perturbation expressions stated in this section will be of a hybrid nature, in essence a mixture of general and special perturbation procedures. The formulas presented are due to Sterne [2] and will be very useful to the analyst dealing with near-Earth satellite orbits.

### 10.4.1    Drag perturbation equations

For a planet and atmosphere rotating about the positive $z$ axis of System 2, Chapter 4, Sterne clearly shows that

$$\left(\frac{da}{dE}\right)_D = -2b\rho a^2 \frac{(1 + e\cos E)^{3/2}}{(1 - e\cos E)^{1/2}} \left[1 - d\frac{(1 - e\cos E)}{(1 + e\cos E)}\right]^2 \tag{10.71}$$

$$\left(\frac{de}{dE}\right)_D = -2b\rho a(1 - e^2)\left[\frac{1 + e\cos E}{1 - e\cos E}\right]^{1/2}\left[1 - d\frac{(1 - e\cos E)}{(1 + e\cos E)}\right]$$

$$\times \left\{\cos E - \frac{d}{2}(1 - e^2)^{-1}(1 - e\cos E)\right.$$

$$\left. \times (2\cos E - e - e\cos^2 E)\right\} \tag{10.72}$$

$$\left(\frac{di}{dE}\right)_D = -\frac{1}{2}b\rho a\omega_s \frac{\sin i}{n}(1 - e^2)^{-1/2}(1 - \cos 2u)(1 - e\cos E)^{5/2}$$

$$\times \left\{(1 + e\cos E)^{1/2}\left[1 - d\frac{(1 - e\cos E)}{(1 + e\cos E)}\right]\right\}, \tag{10.73}$$

where

$$b = \frac{C_D A}{2m}$$

$$d = \left(\frac{\omega_s}{n}\right)(1 - e^2)^{1/2}\cos i$$

[11] For satellites of small diameter compared to the mean free path of air molecules, a drag coefficient of 2 can be assumed, that is, $C_D = 2$.

and

$\rho$ = the atmospheric density,

$E$ = the perturbed eccentric anomaly,

$u$ = the perturbed argument of latitude,

$\omega_s$ = the planetary rotation rate,

$m$ = satellite mass,

$A$ = satellite area consistent with $C_D$.

In evaluating rates of change of $a$, $e$, $i$, with respect to $E$, the perturbed eccentric anomaly or the eccentric anomaly computed from Eq. 10.44 should be used, that is, the secular variations due to gravitational anomalies should be incorporated. Atmospheric density $\rho$ is naturally a function of altitude because the argument of interpolation in tables is usually the satellite altitude above the reference ellipsoid (see Transformation 3, Appendix I). Actually, $\rho = \rho(E)$, since the altitude is functionally dependent upon the angular position of the satellite $E$. It should also be noted that $1 + \cos 2u$ may be obtained from

$$1 + \cos 2\omega \cos 2v - \sin 2\omega \sin 2v,$$

with the true anomaly obtained by the standard mapping of $v$ to $E$ (Chapter 3).

The general analysis of Sterne indicates that secular rates of change due to drag, as denoted by the subscript $D$ in Eqs. 10.71, 10.72, and 10.73 are mainly predominant in $a$ and $e$. To a lesser degree, a small secular shift in $i$ is also present.

Use of the drag perturbation equations is handled in the following semianalytical manner. A nominal or reference orbit is adopted. This reference orbit is a two-body orbit, which accounts for the secular drift in $\Omega$, $\omega$, due to an aspherical potential, and utilizes the "mean" mean motion $\bar{n}$. The reference orbit assumes that $a$, $e$, and $i$ variations due to drag perturbations are negligible. By stepping around the orbit from some adopted point, say perifocus, at $p$ intervals of $E$, it will be possible to determine

$$\left(\frac{da}{dE}\right)_{Di}, \quad \left(\frac{de}{dE}\right)_{Di}, \quad \left(\frac{di}{dE}\right)_{Di}, \quad i = 1, 2, \ldots, p.$$

Immediately, a numerical integration by means of a trapezoidal or Simpson rule [11] will yield

$$\Delta a_n = \int_0^{2\pi} \left(\frac{da}{dE}\right)_D dE, \tag{10.74}$$

$$\Delta e_n = \int_0^{2\pi} \left(\frac{de}{dE}\right)_D dE, \tag{10.75}$$

$$\Delta i_n = \int_0^{2\pi} \left(\frac{di}{dE}\right)_D dE, \tag{10.76}$$

the appropriate nominal changes in $a$, $e$, and $i$ as denoted by the subscript $n$. At this point the reference orbit is abandoned and the elements are considered as experiencing mean rates of change defined by

$$\overline{\left(\frac{da}{dE}\right)}_D = \frac{\Delta a_n}{2\pi} \tag{10.77}$$

$$\overline{\left(\frac{de}{dE}\right)}_D = \frac{\Delta e_n}{2\pi} \tag{10.78}$$

$$\overline{\left(\frac{di}{dE}\right)}_D = \frac{\Delta i_n}{2\pi}, \tag{10.79}$$

so that

$$a_{n+1} = a_n + \overline{\left(\frac{da}{dE}\right)}_D (E - E_n) \tag{10.80}$$

$$e_{n+1} = e_n + \overline{\left(\frac{de}{dE}\right)}_D (E - E_n) \tag{10.81}$$

$$i_{n+1} = i_n + \overline{\left(\frac{di}{dE}\right)}_D (E - E_n). \tag{10.82}$$

In essence, every time the eccentric anomaly varies through $2\pi$ or a period, the elements $a$, $e$, and $i$ are corrected by Eqs. 10.80, 10.81, and 10.82. It should be noticed that since

$$a^3 n^2 = k^2 \mu = \text{constant},$$

$$\Delta n = -\frac{3}{2} \frac{n}{a} \Delta a$$

and it follows that the mean variation in the mean motion is

$$\overline{\left(\frac{dn}{dE}\right)}_D = \frac{\Delta n}{2\pi},$$

so that

$$n_{n+1} = n_n + \overline{\left(\frac{dn}{dE}\right)}_D (E - E_n). \tag{10.83}$$

The reader should realize that the nominal orbit has enabled by quadrature of Eqs. 10.74, 10.75, and 10.76 certain mean rates to be determined. These mean rates are used to predict the variance of $a$, $e$, and $i$ over a number of $N$ revolutions, say, from ten to one hundred. After $N$ revolutions, a new nominal orbit is adopted and the mean rates revaluated. The advantage and power of such a solution is obvious.

### 10.4.2  Combined inclusion of gravitation and drag anomalies

To conclude the complete problem, it should be mentioned that if $a$, $e$, and $i$ are perturbed due to drag forces, coefficients of the derivatives $\dot{\Omega}$, $\dot{\omega}$ and $\bar{n}$ of Sections 10.2.6 and 10.2.8 are varying.   Hence the parameters $p$, $\bar{n}$, and $i$ of Eqs. 10.32 and 10.33 or, more accurately, Eqs. 10.40 and 10.41, should be revaluated per revolution.

In brief, if corrections are applied at perifocus, the total secular variance of an orbit about an oblate planet, with due consideration given to first-order gravitation and drag effects, is

$$a_{n+1} = a_n + \overline{\left(\frac{da}{dE}\right)}_D 2\pi \tag{10.84}$$

$$e_{n+1} = e_n + \overline{\left(\frac{de}{dE}\right)}_D 2\pi \tag{10.85}$$

$$i_{n+1} = i_n + \overline{\left(\frac{di}{dE}\right)}_D 2\pi \tag{10.86}$$

$$\Omega_{n+1} = \Omega_n - \left(\frac{3}{2}\frac{J_2}{p_n^2}\cos i_n\right)2\pi \tag{10.87}$$

$$\omega_{n+1} = \omega_n + \left(\frac{3}{2}\frac{J_2}{p_n^2}\left[2 - \frac{5}{2}\sin^2 i_n\right]\right)2\pi \tag{10.88}$$

$$(M_0)_{n+1} = (M_0)_n + n_n\left(\frac{3}{2}J_2\frac{\sqrt{1-(e_n)^2}}{p_n^2}\left[1 - \frac{3}{2}\sin^2 i_n\right]\right)\bar{P}. \tag{10.89}$$

Hence for every revolution of a satellite, the above incrementation should be performed in order to correct for the drift of all elements used in a particular analytical process.

## 10.5  SECULAR RATES OF CHANGE OF THE ELEMENTS OF A LUNAR SATELLITE

As a satellite moves about the Moon, it will experience certain perturbations due to the triaxiallity of the Moon. The purpose of this section is to develop closed expressions for predicting the secular rates of change of the fundamental elements of a lunar satellite. The basic theorem of MacCullagh [13] is used to develop the lunar potential, and then the technique of Kozai [1] is applied in order to find analytical expressions for the rates of change of:

$a$ = the semimajor axis of the selenocentered orbit,

$e$ = the eccentricity of the selenocentered orbit,

$i$ = inclination of the selenocentered orbit to the Moon's equatorial plane,

$\Omega$ = the argument of the ascending node of the selenocentered orbit,

$\omega$ = the argument of perigee of the selenocentered orbit,

$M$ = the mean anomaly of the selenocentered orbit.

It will be seen that $a$, $e$, and $i$ do not vary, owing to the secular potential of a triaxial Moon. The basic technique of this section is similar to the technique utilized to compute the secular rates of change of the elements of an Earth satellite. However, since the expression for the lunar potential is much shorter than the Earth potential, it will be possible to examine the analysis in greater detail, and thereby gain a better understanding of the technique employed in the determination of the secular variances.

### 10.5.1   Partitioning the lunar perturbative function

MacCullagh's theorem [13],

$$\Phi_m = \frac{k_m^2 m}{r_m} \left[ 1 + \frac{A + B + C - 3I}{2mr_m^2} + \epsilon \right], \qquad (10.90)$$

where

$k_m^2$ = gravitational constant of the Moon,

$m$ = mass of the Moon,

$A$ = moment of inertia about the Moon's polar axis in the seleno-graphic coordinate system,

$B$ = moment of inertia about the principal axis contained in the Moon's equatorial plane,

$C$ = moment of inertia about the remaining orthogonal axis,

$r_m$ = radius vector magnitude from the selenocenter to the space vehicle,

$\epsilon$ = higher order terms, $0(r^{-3})$,

can be directly utilized to determine the lunar potential as a function of the rectangular coordinates $x_m$, $y_m$, $z_m$, of a space vehicle. In brief, since the moment of inertia $I$ about the radius vector $\mathbf{r}_m$ to the vehicle is given by

$$I = AU_{xm}^2 + BU_{ym}^2 + CU_{zm}^2, \tag{10.91}$$

where $\mathbf{U}_m \equiv \mathbf{r}_m/r_m$, it is possible with the aid of the unit vector relationship

$$U_{xm}^2 = 1 - U_{ym}^2 - U_{zm}^2 \tag{10.92}$$

to obtain $\Phi_m$ with the help of these equations as

$$\Phi_m = \frac{k_m^2 m}{r_m}\left\{1 + \frac{C}{2mr_m^2}\left[\frac{B-A}{C}(1-3U_{ym}^2)\right.\right.$$
$$\left.\left. + \frac{C-A}{C}(1-3U_{zm}^2)\right]\right\}. \tag{10.93}$$

It should be noted that $r_m$ in the above equation is in mean lunar radii. The remaining auxiliary constants may be taken as

$m = 1/81.3015$ earth masses, $a_m = 1738.09$ km,

$$\tilde{\omega}_1 \equiv \frac{C}{2m} \simeq 0.200066,$$

$$\tilde{\omega}_2 \equiv \frac{B-A}{C} \simeq 0.0002026,$$

$$\tilde{\omega}_3 \equiv \frac{C-A}{C} \simeq 0.0006191.$$

With these definitions the lunar potential, that is, the potential of a triaxial ellipsoid, reduces to

$$\Phi_m = \frac{k_m{}^2 m}{r_m} \left\{ 1 + \frac{\tilde{\omega}_1}{r_m{}^2} [\tilde{\omega}_2(1 - 3U_{ym}{}^2) + \tilde{\omega}_3(1 - 3U_{zm}{}^2)] \right\}. \quad (10.94)$$

The perturbative function, $\bar{R}_m$, is found by subtracting out the effect of the pure two-body lunar potential so that

$$\bar{R}_m \equiv \Phi_m - \frac{k_m{}^2 m}{r_m} = \frac{k_m{}^2 m}{r_m{}^3} \{\tilde{\omega}_1[\tilde{\omega}_2(1 - 3U_{ym}{}^2) + \tilde{\omega}_3(1 - 3U_{zm}{}^2)]\}. $$

$$(10.95)$$

In order to apply Kozai's theory, the potential must be transformed with the aid of

$$r_m = \frac{a(1 - e^2)}{1 + e \cos v} \quad (10.96)$$

$$U_{zm} = \sin i \sin (v + \omega) \quad (10.97)$$

$$U_{ym} = \cos (v + \omega) \sin \Omega + \sin (v + \omega) \cos \Omega \cos i, \quad (10.98)$$

where all the variables, that is, $a$, $e$, $v$, $\omega$, $\Omega$, and $i$, refer to a lunicentered orbit in a selenographic coordinate system. Notice that $\mathbf{U}_m$ is a unit vector pointing to the vehicle in orbit about the Moon.

Since the expansions are short, the transformation of $\bar{R}_m$ into $R$, the composite perturbative function, will be explicitly performed. The components of $\mathbf{U}_m$ are attacked first by the direct expansions

$$3U_{zm}{}^2 = 3 \sin^2 i \sin^2 (v + \omega) = \tfrac{3}{2} \sin^2 i - \tfrac{3}{2} \cos 2 (v + \omega) \sin^2 i$$

$$(10.99)$$

$$3U_{ym}{}^2 = 3\left( \cos^2 (v + \omega) \sin^2 \Omega + \tfrac{1}{2} \sin 2(v + \omega) \sin 2\Omega \cos i \right.$$

$$\left. + \sin^2 (v + \omega) \cos^2 \Omega \cos^2 i \right)$$

$$= 3\left( \tfrac{1}{4} + \tfrac{1}{4} \cos 2(v + \omega) + \tfrac{1}{2} \sin 2 (v + \omega) \sin 2\Omega \cos i \right.$$

$$+ \tfrac{1}{4} \cos^2 i - \tfrac{1}{4} \cos 2(v + \omega) \cos 2\Omega$$

$$- \tfrac{1}{4} \cos 2\Omega + \tfrac{1}{4} \cos 2\Omega \cos^2 i - \tfrac{1}{4} \cos 2(v + \omega) \cos^2 i$$

$$\left. - \tfrac{1}{4} \cos 2(v + \omega) \cos 2\Omega \cos^2 i \right) \quad (10.100)$$

which, upon substitution into Eq. 10.95 and collection of terms, yields

$$
\begin{aligned}
R_m = \frac{k_m{}^2 m}{r_m{}^3} \Big[ & \tilde{\omega}_1 \tilde{\omega}_2 + \tilde{\omega}_1 \tilde{\omega}_3 - \tilde{\omega}_1 \tilde{\omega}_2 \left( \tfrac{3}{4} + \tfrac{3}{4} \cos^2 i + \tfrac{3}{4} \cos 2(v + \omega) \right. \\
& - \tfrac{3}{4} \cos 2(v + \omega) \cos^2 i - \tfrac{3}{4} \cos 2\Omega \\
& - \tfrac{3}{4} \cos 2(v + \omega) \cos 2\Omega \\
& + \tfrac{3}{2} \sin 2(v + \omega) \sin 2\Omega \cos i + \tfrac{3}{4} \cos 2\Omega \cos^2 i \\
& \left. - \tfrac{3}{4} \cos 2(v + \omega) \cos 2\Omega \cos^2 i \right) \\
& - \tilde{\omega}_1 \tilde{\omega}_3 \left( \tfrac{3}{2} \sin^2 i - \tfrac{3}{2} \cos 2(v + \omega) \sin^2 i \right) \Big] .
\end{aligned}
$$

$$(10.101)$$

The potential of the Moon as expressed by Eq. 10.101 is completely rigorous within the accuracy of MacCullagh's theorem and is in a suitable form for observing the short- and long-period terms, that is, trigonometric multiples of $v + \omega$ and $\Omega$, respectively. The partitioned potential is obtained by deleting short- and long-period effects, so that

$$
R_m{}' = \frac{k_m{}^2 m}{r_m{}^3} \left[ \frac{\beta_1}{3} + \beta_2 \cos^2 i \right], \tag{10.102}
$$

where

$$
\beta_1 \equiv \tfrac{3}{4} \omega_1 \omega_2 - \tfrac{3}{2} \omega_1 \omega_3
$$
$$
\beta_2 \equiv \tfrac{3}{2} \omega_1 \omega_3 - \tfrac{3}{4} \omega_1 \omega_2 .
$$

Equation 10.96 is next utilized to yield

$$
R_m{}' = \frac{k_m{}^2 m}{a^3} \left( \frac{a}{r_m} \right)^3 \left[ \frac{\beta_1}{3} + \beta_2 \cos^2 i \right], \tag{10.103}
$$

and since, by Eq. 10.12, the average value of $(a/r)^3$ over one orbital revolution is $(1 - e^2)^{-3/2}$, the complete partitioned potential $R_{1m}$ is given by

$$
R_{1m} = \frac{k_m{}^2 m}{a^3 (1 - e^2)^{3/2}} \left[ \frac{\beta_1}{3} + \beta_2 \cos^2 i \right]. \tag{10.104}
$$

### 10.5.2 Determination of the secular rates of change

Adopting $R_{1m}$ as the perturbing function, and utilizing the standard expressions for the rates of change of the classical elements, that is, the time derivatives $da/dt$, $de/dt$, $d\omega/dt$, $di/dt$, $d\Omega/dt$, $dM/dt$ of Section 10.2.3, it may be directly verified that

$$
da/dt = 0, \qquad de/dt = 0, \qquad di/dt = 0. \tag{10.105}
$$

Furthermore, by evaluating

$$\frac{\partial R_{1m}}{\partial i} = -\frac{2k_m{}^2 m}{a^3(1 - e^2)^{3/2}} \left[\beta_2 \cos i \sin i\right] \tag{10.106}$$

$$\frac{\partial R_{1m}}{\partial a} = -\frac{3k_m{}^2 m}{a^4(1 - e^2)^{3/2}} \left[\frac{\beta_1}{3} + \beta_2 \cos^2 i\right] \tag{10.107}$$

$$\frac{\partial R_{1m}}{\partial e} = +\frac{3k_m{}^2 m}{a^3(1 - e^2)^{5/2}} \left[\frac{\beta_1}{3} + \beta_2 \cos^2 i\right] e \tag{10.108}$$

and noting that $n^2 a^3 = k_m{}^2 m$, the time derivatives yield

$$\frac{dM}{dt} \equiv \bar{n} = n\left[1 + \frac{\sqrt{1 - e^2}}{p^2} (\beta_1 + 3\beta_2 \cos^2 i)\right], \tag{10.109}$$

with $p = a(1 - e^2)$.

Having determined the mean "mean" motion, the nodal regression is computed from

$$\int d\Omega = -\int \left(\frac{1}{na^2 \sqrt{1 - e^2} \sin i}\right) \left(\frac{2k_m{}^2 m\beta_2}{a^3(1 - e^2)^{3/2}}\right) \beta_2 \cos i \sin i \, dt$$

or, more conveniently,

$$\int d\Omega = -2\frac{\beta_2}{p^2} \cos i \int n \, dt. \tag{10.110}$$

Hence, since

$$\int n \, dt = M - M_0$$

$$\Omega = \Omega_0 - \left(\frac{2\beta_2 \cos i}{p^2}\right) \bar{n}(t - t_0) \tag{10.111}$$

and, by a similar analysis,

$$\omega = \omega_0 + \left(\frac{\beta_1 + 5\beta_2 \cos^2 i}{p^2}\right) \bar{n}(t - t_0). \tag{10.112}$$

The previous secular prediction equations may be simplified by noticing that $\beta_1 = -\beta_2$. For convenience, the simplified equations are listed in Section 10.2.6 with the understanding that $J_2$ is replaced with $J_{2m}$, where

$$J_{2m} = \tilde{\omega}_1(2\tilde{\omega}_3 - \tilde{\omega}_2) \simeq 0.0002072, \tag{10.113}$$

and that the respective satellite elements refer to a selenocentered satellite.

**10.6 SUMMARY**

This chapter has shown that, owing to perturbative influences of oblateness and drag, the classical orbital elements undergo secular variations or drift from a set of instantaneously correct values. Equations were developed for the secular drift of the argument of perigee, longitude of the ascending node, and mean anomaly at the epoch caused by gravitational anomalies.

The variance equations were applied to solution of the ground trace, differential correction and intercept problems.

Drag perturbation equations were stated, and a discussion of their general use outlined. Simultaneous effects of gravitational and drag analysis were outlined. Use of this technique will result in a nullification of the two-body assumption and result in general orbital analysis corrected for element drift. Finally, the secular perturbations upon a satellite in orbit about a triaxial ellipsoid, the Moon, were developed. Periodic variations of short and long periods were not discussed in analytical terms.

**EXERCISES**

1. Discuss in general terms what the effect of omission of periodic variations implies.
2. Show that

$$\frac{dM}{dv} = \left(\frac{r}{a}\right)^2 \frac{1}{\sqrt{1 - e^2}}.$$

3. What is the time average of $a/r$ over a given revolution of a geocentric satellite?
4. Where do the maximum and minimum first order rates of change of $\Omega$ and $\omega$ occur for an orbit with constant $a$ and $e$?
5. Find an orbit for which $\bar{n} = n$ to the first order.
6. A geocentric orbit with elements:

$$a = 1.5 \text{ e.r.,} \qquad e = 0.2, \qquad M_0 = 0°$$
$$i = 30°, \qquad \Omega = 45°, \qquad \omega = 60°$$

is to be subjected to a first order perturbative analysis due to gravitational anomalies. What are the values of the elements 1000 revolutions after epoch?
7. Is there an orbit for which the first order drift rates of $\Omega$ and $\omega$ are equal?

## REFERENCES

1. Y. Kozai, "The Motion of a Close Earth Satellite," *The Astronomical Journal*, Vol. 64, No. 9, November 1959.
2. T. E. Sterne, *An Introduction to Celestial Mechanics*, Interscience Publishers, New York, 1960.
3. D. Brouwer, and G. M. Clemence, *Methods of Celestial Mechanics*, Academic Press, New York, 1961, p. 302.
4. D. Brouwer, "Solution of the Problem of Artificial Satellite Theory Without Drag," *The Astronomical Journal*, Vol. 64, No. 9, November 1959.
5. C. M. Petty and J. V. Breakwell, "Satellite Orbits About a Planet with Rotational Symmetry," *J. Franklin Inst.*, Vol. 270, 1960.
6. J. P. Vinti, "New Method of Solution for Unretarded Satellite Orbits," *J. Res. Nat. Bur. Stand. B.*, Vol. 65, 1961.
7. B. Garfinkel, "The Orbit of a Satellite of an Oblate Planet," *The Astronomical Journal*, Vol. 64, No. 9, 1959.
8. T. Gabbard, Jr., and E. Levin, "A Bibliography of General Perturbation Solutions of Earth-Satellite Motion," *Astronautics and Aerospace Engineering*, November 1963.
9. H. C. Plummer, *An Introductory Treatise on Dynamical Astronomy*, Dover Publications, New York, 1960.
10. F. R. Moulton, *An Introduction to Celestial Mechanics*, The Macmillan Co., New York, 1914.
11. F. B. Hildebrand, *Introduction to Numerical Analysis*, McGraw-Hill Book Co., 1956.
12. E. T. Bell, *Men of Mathematics*, Simon Schuster, New York, 1937.
13. A. S. Ramsey, *An Introduction to the Theory of Newtonian Attraction*, Cambridge University Press, 1961.

# APPENDIX I

# A compendium of thirty-six basic coordinate transformations

Analytical transformations from one coordinate system to another are very often used in the fields of astrodynamics and trajectory analysis. The purpose of this appendix is to list the most frequently used transformations in a convenient manner. To utilize the appendix, the reader is directed to the symbolic outline of transformations and their inverses, that is, the Table of Transformations. Full utilization of this appendix assumes a knowledge of the notation adapted in this book. It is hoped that this appendix will provide the much needed amalgamation of the various routes from one system to another. It should be noted that all these transformations, with the exception of the selenographic, Martian, and precession transformations, are derivable from the material presented in Chapters 1, 3, and 4. The other three transformations are developed in reference [5] of Chapter 4.

**TABLE OF TRANSFORMATIONS**

TRANSFORMATION 1 (*Spherical to rectangular equatorial*)

Object
$V, r, \gamma, A, \delta, \lambda_E, t \rightarrow x, y, z, \dot{x}, \dot{y}, \dot{z}$

TRANSFORMATION 2 (*Inverse Transformation 1*)

Object
$x, y, z, \dot{x}, \dot{y}, \dot{z}, t \rightarrow V, r, \gamma, A, \delta, \lambda_E$

TRANSFORMATION 3 (*Equatorial rectangular position to geographic subvehicle position*)

Object
$x, y, z, t \rightarrow \phi_s', \phi_s, \lambda_E, H_s$

TRANSFORMATION 4 (*Inverse Transformation* 3)

Object
$\phi_s{}'$, $H_s$, $\lambda_E$, $t \rightarrow x$, $y$, $z$

TRANSFORMATION 5 (*Spherical subvehicle to rectangular equatorial*)

Object
$V$, $H_s$, $\gamma$, $A$, $\phi_s{}'$, $\lambda_E$, $t \rightarrow x$, $y$, $z$, $\dot{x}$, $\dot{y}$, $\dot{z}$

TRANSFORMATION 6 (*Inverse Transformation* 5)

Object
$x$, $y$, $z$, $\dot{x}$, $\dot{y}$, $\dot{z}$, $t \rightarrow V$, $H_s$, $\gamma$, $A$, $\phi_s{}'$, $\lambda_E$

TRANSFORMATION 7 (*Position polar topocentric to position polar equatorial*)

Object                    Observer
$A$, $h$, $\rho_h$            $\phi'$, $\lambda_E$, $H$, $t \rightarrow \alpha$, $\delta$, $r$

TRANSFORMATION 8 (*Inverse Transformation* 7)

Object                    Observer
$\alpha$, $\delta$, $r$             $\phi'$, $\lambda_E$, $H$, $t \rightarrow A$, $h$, $\rho_h$

TRANSFORMATION 9 (*Position polar topocentric to position polar equatorial*)

Object                    Observer
$A'$, $h$, $\rho_h$           $\phi'$, $\lambda_E$, $H$, $t \rightarrow \alpha$, $\delta$, $r$

TRANSFORMATION 10 (*Inverse Transformation* 9)

Object                    Observer
$\alpha$, $\delta$, $r$             $\phi'$, $\lambda_E$, $H$, $t \rightarrow A'$, $h$, $\rho_h$

TRANSFORMATION 11 (*Angular topocentric to rectangular topocentric*)

Object
$\rho_h$, $\dot{\rho}_h$, $A$, $h$, $\dot{A} \cos h$, $\dot{h} \rightarrow x_h$, $y_h$, $z_h$, $\dot{x}_h$, $\dot{y}_h$, $\dot{z}_h$

TRANSFORMATION 12 (*Inverse Transformation* 11)

Object
$x_h$, $y_h$, $z_h$, $\dot{x}_h$, $\dot{y}_h$, $\dot{z}_h \rightarrow \rho_h$, $\dot{\rho}_h$, $A$, $h$, $\dot{A} \cos h$, $\dot{h}$

TRANSFORMATION 13 (*Rectangular topocentric to rectangular equatorial*)

Object                              Observer
$x_h$, $y_h$, $z_h$, $\dot{x}_h$, $\dot{y}_h$, $\dot{z}_h$        $\phi'$, $\lambda_E$, $H$, $t \rightarrow x$, $y$, $z$, $\dot{x}$, $\dot{y}$, $\dot{z}$

TRANSFORMATION 14 (*Inverse Transformation* 13)

Object                    Observer
$x$, $y$, $z$, $\dot{x}$, $\dot{y}$, $\dot{z}$        $\phi'$, $\lambda_E$, $H$, $t \rightarrow x_h$, $y_h$, $z_h$, $\dot{x}_h$, $\dot{y}_h$, $\dot{z}_h$

TRANSFORMATION 15 (*Rectangular topocentric to angular equatorial*)

Object

Observer

$x_h, y_h, z_h, \dot{x}_h, \dot{y}_h, \dot{z}_h$    $\phi', \lambda_E, H, t \rightarrow \dot{\alpha} \cos \delta, \dot{\delta}, \alpha, \delta, \rho_h, \dot{\rho}_h$

TRANSFORMATION 16 (*Rectangular equatorial to rectangular ecliptic*)

Object

$x, y, z, \dot{x}, \dot{y}, \dot{z}, t \rightarrow x_\epsilon, y_\epsilon, z_\epsilon, \dot{x}_\epsilon, \dot{y}_\epsilon, \dot{z}_\epsilon$

TRANSFORMATION 17 (*Inverse Transformation* 16)

Object

$x_\epsilon, y_\epsilon, z_\epsilon, \dot{x}_\epsilon, \dot{y}_\epsilon, \dot{z}_\epsilon, t \rightarrow x, y, z, \dot{x}, \dot{y}, \dot{z}$

TRANSFORMATION 18 (*Position rectangular ecliptic to position polar ecliptic*)

Object

$x_\epsilon, y_\epsilon, z_\epsilon \rightarrow \beta, \lambda, r_\epsilon$

TRANSFORMATION 19 (*Inverse Transformation* 18)

Object

$\beta, \lambda, r_\epsilon \rightarrow x_\epsilon, y_\epsilon, z_\epsilon$

TRANSFORMATION 20 (*Rectangular of the hour angle-declination system to rectangular equatorial*)

Object

Observer

$x_\delta, y_\delta, z_\delta, \dot{x}_\delta, \dot{y}_\delta, \dot{z}_\delta$    $\lambda_E, t \rightarrow x, y, z, \dot{x}, \dot{y}, \dot{z}$

TRANSFORMATION 21 (*Inverse Transformation* 20)

Object

Observer

$x, y, z, \dot{x}, \dot{y}, \dot{z}$    $\lambda_E, t \rightarrow x_\delta, y_\delta, z_\delta, \dot{x}_\delta, \dot{y}_\delta, \dot{z}_\delta$

TRANSFORMATION 22 (*Polar position of the hour angle-declination system to rectangular position of the same system*)

Object

$HA, \delta, r \rightarrow x_\delta, y_\delta, z_\delta$

TRANSFORMATION 23 (*Inverse Transformation* 22)

Object

$x_\delta, y_\delta, z_\delta \rightarrow HA, \delta, r$

TRANSFORMATION 24 (*Oblate spheroidal to rectangular equatorial*)

Object

$\xi, \eta, \alpha, \dot{\xi}, \dot{\eta}, \dot{\alpha} \rightarrow x, y, z, \dot{x}, \dot{y}, \dot{z}$

TRANSFORMATION 25 (*Inverse Transformation* 24)

Object

$x, y, z, \dot{x}, \dot{y}, \dot{z} \rightarrow \xi, \eta, \alpha, \dot{\xi}, \dot{\eta}, \dot{\alpha}$

TRANSFORMATION 26 (*Mean rectangular equatorial position to mean seleno-graphic rectangular position*)

Object

$x, y, z, x_{\oplus m}, y_{\oplus m}, z_{\oplus m}, t \rightarrow x_m, y_m, z_m$

TRANSFORMATION 27 (*Inverse Transformation* 26)

Object

$x_m, y_m, z_m, x_{\oplus m}, y_{\oplus m}, z_{\oplus m}, t \rightarrow x, y, z$

TRANSFORMATION 28 (*Mean rectangular equatorial position to true seleno-graphic rectangular position*)

Object

$x, y, z, x_{\oplus m}, y_{\oplus m}, z_{\oplus m}, t \rightarrow x_m, y_m, z_m$

TRANSFORMATION 29 (*Inverse Transformation* 28)

Object

$x_m, y_m, z_m, x_{\oplus m}, y_{\oplus m}, z_{\oplus m}, t \rightarrow x, y, z$

TRANSFORMATION 30 (*Rectangular equatorial to orbit plane*)

Object

$x, y, z, \dot{x}, \dot{y}, \dot{z}, \Omega, \omega, i \rightarrow x_\omega, y_\omega, z_\omega, \dot{x}_\omega, \dot{y}_\omega, \dot{z}_\omega$

TRANSFORMATION 31 (*Inverse Transformation* 30)

Object

$x_\omega, y_\omega, z_\omega, \dot{x}_\omega, \dot{y}_\omega, \dot{z}_\omega, \Omega, \omega, i \rightarrow x, y, z, \dot{x}, \dot{y}, \dot{z}$

TRANSFORMATION 32 (*Precession Transformation*)

Object

$x, y, z, t \rightarrow x, y, z, t_0$

TRANSFORMATION 33 (*Inverse Precession Transformation*)

Object

$x, y, z, t_0 \rightarrow x, y, z, t$

TRANSFORMATION 34 (*Martian Transformation*)

Object

$x, y, z, \dot{x}, \dot{y}, \dot{z}, t \rightarrow x_\delta, y_\delta, z_\delta, \dot{x}_\delta, \dot{y}_\delta, \dot{z}_\delta$

TRANSFORMATION 35 (*Inverse Martian Transformation*)

Object

$$x_{\delta}, y_{\delta}, z_{\delta}, \dot{x}_{\delta}, \dot{y}_{\delta}, \dot{z}_{\delta}, t \rightarrow x, y, z, \dot{x}, \dot{y}, \dot{z}$$

TRANSFORMATION 36 (*Martian geographic to Martian rectangular*)

Object

$$\phi', H_s, \lambda_E, t \rightarrow x_{\delta}, y_{\delta}, z_{\delta}$$

---

TRANSFORMATION 1.    *Transformation from the vehicle-centered coordinate system to the right ascension-declination coordinate system.*

Symbolically, the following transformation is accomplished:

$$V, r, \gamma, A, \delta, \lambda_E, t \rightarrow x, y, z, \dot{x}, \dot{y}, \dot{z}.$$

The transformation is accomplished by means of the following equations:[1]

$$\theta = \theta_g + \dot{\theta}(t - t_g) - (360° - \lambda_E), \quad 0° \le \theta \le 360°, \qquad (1A.1)$$
$$x = r \cos \delta \cos \theta \qquad (1A.2)$$
$$y = r \cos \delta \sin \theta \qquad (1A.3)$$
$$z = r \sin \delta \qquad (1A.4)$$
$$V_S = - V \cos \gamma \cos A \qquad (1A.5)$$
$$V_E = V \cos \gamma \sin A \qquad (1A.6)$$
$$V_R = V \sin \gamma \qquad (1A.7)$$
$$\dot{x} = V_S \sin \delta \cos \theta - V_E \sin \theta + V_R \cos \delta \cos \theta \qquad (1A.8)$$
$$\dot{y} = V_S \sin \delta \sin \theta + V_E \cos \theta + V_R \cos \delta \sin \theta \qquad (1A.9)$$
$$\dot{z} = - V_S \cos \delta + V_R \sin \delta. \qquad (1A.10)$$

The subscripts $S$, $E$, and $R$ refer to South, East, and radial directions, respectively.

TRANSFORMATION 2.    *Transformation from the right ascension-declination coordinate system to the vehicle-centered coordinate system.*

Symbolically, the following transformation is accomplished:

$$x, y, z, \dot{x}, \dot{y}, \dot{z}, t \rightarrow V, r, \gamma, A, \delta, \lambda_E.$$

---

[1] In the transformations presented in this appendix, $360° - \lambda_E$ will be written in the sidereal time equation because some analysts prefer to use $\lambda_W$, the west longitude, and $360° - \lambda_E = \lambda_W$.

The transformation is accomplished by means of the following equations:

$$r = (x^2 + y^2 + z^2)^{\frac{1}{2}} \tag{1A.11}$$

$$\alpha = \tan^{-1}\left(\frac{y}{x}\right), \quad 0° \le \alpha \le 360°, \tag{1A.12}$$

$$\delta = \tan^{-1}\left(\frac{z}{\sqrt{x^2 + y^2}}\right), \quad -90° \le \delta \le 90°, \tag{1A.13}$$

$$\lambda_E = \alpha - [\theta_g + \dot{\theta}(t - t_g)], \quad 0° \le \lambda_E \le 360°, \tag{1A.14}$$

$$V = (\dot{x}^2 + \dot{y}^2 + \dot{z}^2)^{\frac{1}{2}} \tag{1A.15}$$

$$\beta = \cos^{-1}\left[\frac{x\dot{x} + y\dot{y} + z\dot{z}}{rV}\right], \quad 0° \le \beta \le 180°, \tag{1A.16}$$

$$\gamma = 90° - \beta, \quad -90° \le \gamma \le 90°, \tag{1A.17}$$

$$A = \tan^{-1}\left[\frac{r(x\dot{y} - \dot{x}y)}{y(\dot{z}y - z\dot{y}) - x(\dot{x}z - x\dot{z})}\right], \quad 0° \le A \le 360°. \tag{1A.18}$$

It should be noted that Eqs. (1A.12) and (1A.18) require examination of the numerator and denominator in order to determine the correct quadrant of the angle.

TRANSFORMATION 3. *Transformation from position in the right ascension-declination coordinate system to position in the latitude-longitude coordinate system.*

Symbolically, the following transformation is accomplished:

$$x, y, z, t \to \phi_s', \phi_s, \lambda_E, H_s.$$

It should be stated that the subscript $s$ refers to the vehicle sublatitude point. This, in effect, assumes that height above the reference ellipsoid is measured normal to the ellipsoidal surface (Figure 1A. 1).

The following equations are used:

$$r = \sqrt{x^2 + y^2 + z^2} \tag{1A.19}$$

$$\alpha = \tan^{-1}\left(\frac{y}{x}\right) \tag{1A.20}$$

$$\lambda_E = \alpha - [\theta_g + \dot{\theta}(t - t_g)], \quad 0° \le \lambda_E \le 360°, \tag{1A.21}$$

$$\delta = \tan^{-1}\left(\frac{z}{\sqrt{x^2 + y^2}}\right), \quad -90° \le \delta \le 90°. \tag{1A.22}$$

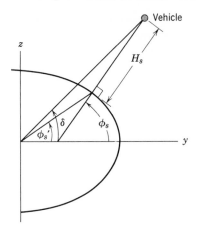

FIGURE 1A. 1    The vehicle above the reference ellipsoid

At this point, unless $f$ the flattening is zero, assume that $\phi_s' = \delta$, and continue calculating as follows:

$$r_c = a_e\sqrt{\frac{1 - (2f - f^2)}{1 - (2f - f^2)\cos^2\phi_s'}} \tag{1A.23}$$

$$\phi_s = \tan^{-1}\left[\frac{1}{(1-f)^2}\tan\phi_s'\right], \quad -90° \le \phi_s \le 90°, \tag{1A.24}$$

$$H_s = \sqrt{r^2 - r_c^2\sin^2(\phi_s - \phi_s')} - r_c\cos(\phi_s - \phi_s') \tag{1A.25}$$

$$\Delta\phi_s' = \sin^{-1}\left[\frac{H_s}{r}\sin(\phi_s - \phi_s')\right]. \tag{1A.26}$$

Now, recalculate

$$\phi_s' = \delta - \Delta\phi_s', \tag{1A.27}$$

and return to Eq. 1A.23, repeating this loop until $\phi_s'$ is within the desired tolerance.

TRANSFORMATION 4.    *Transformation from position in the latitude-longitude coordinate system to position in the right ascension-declination coordinate system.*

Symbolically, the following transformation is accomplished:

$$\phi_s', H_s, \lambda_E, t \to x, y, z.$$

It should be stated that the subscript $s$ refers to the vehicle sublatitude point. This, in effect, assumes that height above the reference ellipsoid is measured normal to the ellipsoidal surface.

The following equations are used:

$$r_c{}^2 = \frac{a_e{}^2[1 - (2f - f^2)]}{1 - (2f - f^2) \cos^2 \phi_s{}'} \tag{1A.28}$$

$$\phi_s = \tan^{-1}\left[\frac{1}{(1 - f)^2} \tan \phi_s{}'\right], \quad -90° \le \phi_s \le 90°, \tag{1A.29}$$

$$r = \sqrt{r_c{}^2 + H_s{}^2 + 2r_c H_s \cos (\phi_s - \phi_s{}')} \tag{1A.30}$$

$$\theta = \theta_g + \dot{\theta}(t - t_g) - (360° - \lambda_E), \quad 0° \le \theta \le 360°, \tag{1A.31}$$

$$\Delta\phi_s{}' = \sin^{-1}\left[\frac{H_s}{r} \sin (\phi_s - \phi_s{}')\right], \quad -90° \le \Delta\phi_s{}' \le 90°, \tag{1A.32}$$

$$\delta = \phi_s{}' + \Delta\phi_s{}' \tag{1A.33}$$

$$x = r \cos \delta \cos \theta \tag{1A.34}$$

$$y = r \cos \delta \sin \theta \tag{1A.35}$$

$$z = r \sin \delta. \tag{1A.36}$$

TRANSFORMATION 5.    *Transformation from the vehicle-centered coordinate system to the right ascension-declination coordinate system.*

Symbolically, the following transformation is accomplished:

$$V, H_s, \gamma, A, \phi_s{}', \lambda_E, t \rightarrow x, y, z, \dot{x}, \dot{y}, \dot{z}.$$

The transformation is accomplished by means of the following procedure:

    (*a*) Apply Transformation 4 to obtain $\delta$, $r$ (internal to the fourth transformation),

    (*b*) Apply Transformation 1.

TRANSFORMATION 6.    *Transformation from the right ascension-declination coordinate system to the vehicle-centered coordinate system.*

Symbolically, the following transformation is accomplished:

$$x, y, z, \dot{x}, \dot{y}, \dot{z}, t \rightarrow V, H_s, \gamma, A, \phi_s{}', \lambda_E.$$

The transformation is accomplished by means of the following procedure:

    (*a*) Apply Transformation 3 to obtain $H_s$, $\phi_s{}'$,

    (*b*) Apply Transformation 2 omitting the calculation of $r$, $\delta$.

TRANSFORMATION 7.    *Transformation from position in the azimuth-elevation coordinate system to position in the right ascension-declination coordinate system.*

Symbolically, the following transformation is accomplished:

$A, h, \rho_h, \phi', \lambda_E, H, t \rightarrow \alpha, \delta, r.$

The following equations are used to effect the transformation:

$$\theta = \theta_g + \dot{\theta}(t - t_g) - (360° - \lambda_E), \quad 0° \leq \theta \leq 360°, \quad (1A.37)$$

$$L_{xh} = -\cos A \cos h$$
$$L_{yh} = \sin A \cos h \qquad\qquad (1A.38)$$
$$L_{zh} = \sin h$$

$$\phi = \tan^{-1}\left[\frac{1}{(1-f)^2}\tan\phi'\right], \quad -90° \leq \phi \leq 90°, \quad (1A.39)$$

$$G_1 = \frac{a_e}{\sqrt{1 - (2f - f^2)\sin^2\phi}} + H \qquad\qquad (1A.40)$$

$$G_2 = \frac{a_e(1-f)^2}{\sqrt{1 - (2f - f^2)\sin^2\phi}} + H \qquad\qquad (1A.41)$$

$$X = -G_1 \cos\phi \cos\theta \qquad\qquad (1A.42)$$
$$Y = -G_1 \cos\phi \sin\theta \qquad\qquad (1A.43)$$
$$Z = -G_2 \sin\phi \qquad\qquad (1A.44)$$
$$S_x = \sin\phi \cos\theta \text{ (see footnote}^2)$$
$$S_y = \sin\phi \sin\theta \qquad\qquad (1A.45)$$
$$S_z = -\cos\phi$$
$$E_x = -\sin\theta$$
$$E_y = \cos\theta \qquad\qquad (1A.46)$$
$$E_z = 0$$
$$Z_x = \cos\theta \cos\phi$$
$$Z_y = \sin\theta \cos\phi \qquad\qquad (1A.47)$$
$$Z_z = \sin\phi.$$

[2] It is assumed that the fundamental plane is the horizon.    If the fundamental plane were taken as being a plane normal to the radial distance, then the angle $\phi$ in Eqs. 1A.45 and 1A.47 should be replaced by $\phi'' = \tan^{-1}\left[\frac{G_2}{G_1}\tan\phi\right], \quad -90° \leq \phi'' \leq 90°.$

$$
\begin{bmatrix} L_x \\ L_y \\ L_z \end{bmatrix} = \begin{bmatrix} S_x & E_x & Z_x \\ S_y & E_y & Z_y \\ S_z & E_z & Z_z \end{bmatrix} \begin{bmatrix} L_{xh} \\ L_{yh} \\ L_{zh} \end{bmatrix}
\tag{1A.48}
$$

$\sin \delta_t = L_z$ (see footnote[3])

$$\to \delta_t, \quad -90° \le \delta \le 90°, \tag{1A.49}$$

$\cos \delta_t = \sqrt{1 - L_z^2}$

$\sin \alpha_t = \dfrac{L_y}{\cos \delta}$

$$\to \alpha_t, \quad 0° \le \alpha \le 360°, \tag{1A.50}$$

$\cos \alpha_t = \dfrac{L_x}{\cos \delta}$

$$\rho_x = \rho_h L_x \tag{1A.51}$$
$$\rho_y = \rho_h L_y \tag{1A.52}$$
$$\rho_z = \rho_h L_z \tag{1A.53}$$
$$x = \rho_x - X \tag{1A.54}$$
$$y = \rho_y - Y \tag{1A.55}$$
$$z = \rho_z - Z \tag{1A.56}$$
$$r = \sqrt{x^2 + y^2 + z^2}. \tag{1A.57}$$

TRANSFORMATION 8.   *Transformation from position in the right ascension-declination coordinate system to position in the azimuth-elevation coordinate system.*

Symbolically, the following transformation is accomplished:

$$\alpha, \ \delta, \ r, \ \phi', \ \lambda_E, \ H, \ t \to A, \ h, \ \rho_h.$$

The following equations are used to effect the transformation:

$$\theta = \theta_g + \dot\theta(t - t_g) - (360° - \lambda_E), \quad 0° \le \theta \le 360°, \tag{1A.58}$$

$$\phi = \tan^{-1}\left[\frac{1}{(1-f)^2} \tan \phi'\right], \quad -90° \le \phi \le 90°, \tag{1A.59}$$

---

[3] Greater accuracy can be achieved if the right ascension and declination are calculated directly from Eqs. 1A.54, 1A.55, and 1A.56, especially for nearby objects. Hence, after calculating the rotation by means of Eq. 1A.48, proceed to Eq. 1A.51. Equations 1A.49 and 1A.50 yield *topocentric* angles. The right ascension and declination derivable from Eqs. 1A.54, 1A.55, and 1A.56, yield *geocentric* angles.

$$G_1 = \frac{a_e}{\sqrt{1 - (2f - f^2)\sin^2 \phi}} + H \tag{1A.60}$$

$$G_2 = \frac{a_e(1 - f)^2}{\sqrt{1 - (2f - f^2)\sin^2 \phi}} + H \tag{1A.61}$$

$$X = -G_1 \cos \phi \cos \theta \tag{1A.62}$$
$$Y = -G_1 \cos \phi \sin \theta \tag{1A.63}$$
$$Z = -G_2 \sin \phi \tag{1A.64}$$
$$U_x = \cos \delta \cos \alpha \quad \text{(see footnote}^4) \tag{1A.65}$$
$$U_y = \cos \delta \sin \alpha \tag{1A.66}$$
$$U_z = \sin \delta \tag{1A.67}$$
$$\rho_x = rU_x + X \tag{1A.68}$$
$$\rho_y = rU_y + Y \tag{1A.69}$$
$$\rho_z = rU_z + Z \tag{1A.70}$$
$$\rho_h = \sqrt{\rho_x{}^2 + \rho_y{}^2 + \rho_z{}^2} \tag{1A.71}$$

$$L_x = \frac{\rho_x}{\rho_h} \tag{1A.72}$$

$$L_y = \frac{\rho_y}{\rho_h} \tag{1A.73}$$

$$L_z = \frac{\rho_z}{\rho_h} \tag{1A.74}$$

$$\begin{bmatrix} L_{xh} \\ L_{yh} \\ L_{zh} \end{bmatrix} = \begin{bmatrix} S_x & S_y & S_z \\ E_x & E_y & E_z \\ Z_x & Z_y & Z_z \end{bmatrix} \begin{bmatrix} L_x \\ L_y \\ L_z \end{bmatrix} \quad \text{(see footnote}^5) \tag{1A.75}$$

$$\sin h = L_{zh}$$
$$\rightarrow h, \quad -90° \le h \le 90°, \tag{1A.76}$$
$$\cos h = \sqrt{1 - L_{zh}{}^2}$$

$$\cos A = -\frac{L_{xh}}{\cos h}$$
$$\rightarrow A, \quad 0° \le A \le 360°, \tag{1A.77}$$
$$\sin A = \frac{L_{yh}}{\cos h}$$

[4] These are geocentric angles ($\delta$, $\alpha$). If topocentric angles are available, then bypass Eqs. 1A.68 through 1A.71 and set $L_x = U_x$, $L_y = U_y$ and $L_z = U_z$.
[5] The elements of the transformation matrix are identical to those of Transformation 7.

TRANSFORMATION 9.    *Transformation from position in the azimuth-elevation coordinate system (observation station not exactly aligned with North) to position in the right ascension-declination coordinate system.*

Symbolically, the following transformation is accomplished:

$$A', h, \rho_h, \phi', \lambda_E, H, t \rightarrow \alpha, \delta, r,$$

where $A'$ is the pseudo azimuth defined by $A \equiv A' + S$ and $S$ is the station skew azimuth from the true North.

The following procedure is employed to effect the transformation:

(a) $A = A' + S$,
(b) Apply Transformation 7.

TRANSFORMATION 10.    *Transformation from position in the right ascension-declination coordinate system (observation station not aligned with North) to position in the azimuth-elevation coordinate system.*

Symbolically, the following transformation is accomplished:

$$\alpha, \delta, r, \phi', \lambda_E, H, t \rightarrow A', h, \rho_h,$$

where $A'$ is the pseudo azimuth defined by $A \equiv A' + S$ and $S$ is the station skew azimuth from the true North.

The following procedure is used to effect the transformation.

(a) Apply Transformation 8,
(b) $A' = A - S$.

TRANSFORMATION 11.    *Transformation from polar coordinates in the azimuth-elevation coordinate system to rectangular coordinates of the same system.*

Symbolically, the following transformation is accomplished:

$$\rho_h, \dot{\rho}_h, A, h, \dot{A} \cos h, \dot{h} \rightarrow x_h, y_h, z_h, \dot{x}_h, \dot{y}_h, \dot{z}_h.$$

The following equations are employed:

$$x_h = -\rho_h \cos h \cos A \tag{1A.78}$$

$$y_h = \rho_h \cos h \sin A \tag{1A.79}$$

$$z_h = \rho_h \sin h \tag{1A.80}$$

$$\dot{x}_h = -\dot{\rho}_h \cos h \cos A + \rho_h \dot{h} \sin h \cos A + \rho_h \dot{A} \cos h \sin A \tag{1A.81}$$

$$\dot{y}_h = \dot{\rho}_h \cos h \sin A - \rho_h \dot{h} \sin h \sin A + \rho_h \dot{A} \cos h \cos A \tag{1A.82}$$

$$\dot{z}_h = \dot{\rho}_h \sin h + \rho_h \dot{h} \cos h. \tag{1A.83}$$

Note that $(x_h, y_h, z_h) \cdot (\dot{x}_h, \dot{y}_h, \dot{z}_h) = \rho_h \dot{\rho}_h$, where the subscript refers to topocentric conditions. The subscript $h$ is not actually required on $\rho$ and $\dot{\rho}$; usually, however, these parameters are measured in the horizon system.

TRANSFORMATION 12.   *Transformation from rectangular coordinates of the azimuth-elevation system to polar coordinates of the same system.*

Symbolically, the following transformation is accomplished:

$$x_h, \ y_h, \ z_h, \ \dot{x}_h, \ \dot{y}_h, \ \dot{z}_h \rightarrow \rho_h, \ \dot{\rho}_h, \ A, \ h, \ \dot{A} \cos h, \ \dot{h}.$$

The following equations are employed to effect the transformation:

$$\rho_h = \sqrt{x_h{}^2 + y_h{}^2 + z_h{}^2} \tag{1A.84}$$

$$\sin h = \frac{z_h}{\rho_h} \tag{1A.85}$$

$$\cos h = +\sqrt{1 - \sin^2 h} \tag{1A.86}$$

$$\cos A = -\frac{x_h}{\sqrt{x_h{}^2 + y_h{}^2}} \tag{1A.87}$$

$$\sin A = \frac{y_h}{\sqrt{x_h{}^2 + y_h{}^2}} \tag{1A.88}$$

$$\dot{\rho}_h = \frac{\mathbf{r}_h \cdot \dot{\mathbf{r}}_h}{\rho_h} \tag{1A.89}$$

$$\dot{A} \cos h = \frac{\dot{x}_h y_h - \dot{y}_h x_h}{x_h{}^2 + y_h{}^2} \cos h \tag{1A.90}$$

$$\dot{h} = \frac{\dot{z}_h - \dot{\rho}_h \sin h}{\sqrt{x_h{}^2 + y_h{}^2}}. \tag{1A.91}$$

TRANSFORMATION 13.   *Transformation of Rectangular Coordinates from the azimuth-elevation coordinate system to the right ascension-declination coordinate system.*

Symbolically, the following transformation is accomplished:

$$x_h, \ y_h, \ z_h, \ \dot{x}_h, \ \dot{y}_h, \ \dot{z}_h, \ \phi', \ \lambda_E, \ H, \ t \rightarrow x, \ y, \ z, \ \dot{x}, \ \dot{y}, \ \dot{z}.$$

Transformation is achieved by means of the following equations:

$$\theta = \theta_g + \dot{\theta}(t - t_g) - (360° - \lambda_E), \quad 0° \le \theta \le 360°, \tag{1A.92}$$

$$\phi = \tan^{-1}\left[\frac{1}{(1-f)^2} \tan \phi'\right], \quad 0° \le \phi \le 90°, \tag{1A.93}$$

$$G_1 = \frac{a_e}{\sqrt{1 - (2f - f^2) \sin^2 \phi}} + H \tag{1A.94}$$

$$G_2 = \frac{a_e(1 - f)^2}{\sqrt{1 - (2f - f^2) \sin^2 \phi}} + H \tag{1A.95}$$

$$X = -G_1 \cos \phi \cos \theta \qquad (1\text{A}.96)$$

$$Y = -G_1 \cos \phi \sin \theta \qquad (1\text{A}.97)$$

$$Z = -G_2 \sin \phi \qquad (1\text{A}.98)$$

$$\dot{X} = -\dot{\theta} Y \qquad (1\text{A}.99)$$

$$\dot{Y} = \dot{\theta} X \qquad (1\text{A}.100)$$

$$\dot{Z} = 0 \qquad (1\text{A}.101)$$

$$S_x = \sin \phi \cos \theta \text{ (see footnote}[6]) \qquad (1\text{A}.102)$$

$$S_y = \sin \phi \sin \theta$$

$$S_z = -\cos \phi$$

$$E_x = -\sin \theta$$

$$E_y = \cos \theta \qquad (1\text{A}.103)$$

$$E_z = 0$$

$$Z_x = \cos \theta \cos \phi$$

$$Z_y = \sin \theta \cos \phi \qquad (1\text{A}.104)$$

$$Z_z = \sin \phi$$

$$\begin{bmatrix} \rho_x \\ \rho_y \\ \rho_z \end{bmatrix} = \begin{bmatrix} S_x & E_x & Z_x \\ S_y & E_y & Z_y \\ S_z & E_z & Z_z \end{bmatrix} \begin{bmatrix} x_h \\ y_h \\ z_h \end{bmatrix}$$

$$(1\text{A}.105)$$

$$\begin{bmatrix} \dot{\rho}_x' \\ \dot{\rho}_y' \\ \dot{\rho}_z' \end{bmatrix} = \begin{bmatrix} S_x & E_x & Z_x \\ S_y & E_y & Z_y \\ S_z & E_z & Z_z \end{bmatrix} \begin{bmatrix} \dot{x}_h \\ \dot{y}_h \\ \dot{z}_h \end{bmatrix}$$

$$\dot{\rho}_x = \dot{\rho}_x' - \dot{\theta} \rho_y \qquad (1\text{A}.106)$$

$$\dot{\rho}_y = \dot{\rho}_y' + \dot{\theta} \rho_x \qquad (1\text{A}.107)$$

$$\dot{\rho}_z = \dot{\rho}_z' \qquad (1\text{A}.108)$$

$$x = \rho_x - X$$

$$y = \rho_y - Y \qquad (1\text{A}.109)$$

$$z = \rho_z - Z$$

$$\dot{x} = \dot{\rho}_x - \dot{X}$$

$$\dot{y} = \dot{\rho}_y - \dot{Y} \qquad (1\text{A}.110)$$

$$\dot{z} = \dot{\rho}_z - \dot{Z}.$$

[6] See footnote of Transformation 7.

TRANSFORMATION 14.    *Transformation of rectangular coordinates from the right ascension-declination coordinate system to the azimuth-elevation coordinate system.*

Symbolically, the following transformation is accomplished:

$$x, y, z, \dot{x}, \dot{y}, \dot{z}, \phi', \lambda_E, H, t \rightarrow x_h, y_h, z_h, \dot{x}_h, \dot{y}_h, \dot{z}_h.$$

Transformation is effected by the following equations:

$$\theta = \theta_g + \dot{\theta}(t - t_g) - (360° - \lambda_E), \quad 0° \leq \theta \leq 360°, \qquad (1A.111)$$

$$\phi = \tan^{-1}\left[\frac{1}{(1-f)^2} \tan \phi'\right], \quad -90° \leq \phi \leq 90°, \qquad (1A.112)$$

$$G_1 = \frac{a_e}{\sqrt{1 - (2f - f^2)\sin^2 \phi}} + H \qquad (1A.113)$$

$$G_2 = \frac{a_e(1 - f)^2}{\sqrt{1 - (2f - f^2)\sin^2 \phi}} + H \qquad (1A.114)$$

$$X = -G_1 \cos \phi \cos \theta \qquad (1A.115)$$
$$Y = -G_1 \cos \phi \sin \theta \qquad (1A.116)$$
$$Z = -G_2 \sin \phi \qquad (1A.117)$$
$$\dot{X} = -\dot{\theta}Y \qquad (1A.118)$$
$$\dot{Y} = \dot{\theta}X \qquad (1A.119)$$
$$\dot{Z} = 0 \qquad (1A.120)$$
$$\rho_x = x + X \qquad (1A.121)$$
$$\rho_y = y + Y \qquad (1A.122)$$
$$\rho_z = z + Z \qquad (1A.123)$$
$$\dot{\rho}_x = \dot{x} + \dot{X} \qquad (1A.124)$$
$$\dot{\rho}_y = \dot{y} + \dot{Y} \qquad (1A.125)$$
$$\dot{\rho}_z = \dot{z} + \dot{Z} \qquad (1A.126)$$
$$S_x = \sin \phi \cos \theta \quad (\text{see footnote}[7])$$
$$S_y = \sin \phi \sin \theta \qquad (1A.127)$$
$$S_z = -\cos \phi$$
$$E_x = -\sin \theta$$
$$E_y = \cos \theta \qquad (1A.128)$$
$$E_z = 0$$
$$Z_x = \cos \theta \cos \phi$$
$$Z_y = \sin \theta \cos \phi \qquad (1A.129)$$
$$Z_z = \sin \phi$$

[7] See footnote of Transformation 7.

$$
\begin{bmatrix} x_h \\ y_h \\ z_h \end{bmatrix} = \begin{bmatrix} S_x & S_y & S_z \\ E_x & E_y & E_z \\ Z_x & Z_y & Z_z \end{bmatrix} \begin{bmatrix} \rho_x \\ \rho_y \\ \rho_z \end{bmatrix}
$$
(1A.130)

$$
\dot{\rho}_x' = \dot{\rho}_x + \dot{\theta}\rho_y
$$
(1A.131)

$$
\dot{\rho}_y' = \dot{\rho}_y - \dot{\theta}\rho_x
$$
(1A.132)

$$
\dot{\rho}_z' = \dot{\rho}_z
$$
(1A.133)

$$
\begin{bmatrix} \dot{x}_h \\ \dot{y}_h \\ \dot{z}_h \end{bmatrix} = \begin{bmatrix} S_x & S_y & S_z \\ E_x & E_y & E_z \\ Z_x & Z_y & Z_z \end{bmatrix} \begin{bmatrix} \dot{\rho}_x' \\ \dot{\rho}_y' \\ \dot{\rho}_z' \end{bmatrix}.
$$
(1A.134)

TRANSFORMATION 15.   *Transformation from rectangular coordinates of the azimuth-elevation system to polar coordinates of the right ascension-declination system.*

Symbolically, the following transformation is accomplished:

$$
x_h, y_h, z_h, \dot{x}_h, \dot{y}_h, \dot{z}_h, \phi', \lambda_E, H, t \to \dot{\alpha}\cos\delta, \dot{\delta}, \alpha, \delta, \rho_h, \dot{\rho}_h.
$$

The transformation can be effected by the following procedure.
Apply Transformation 13 and continue the calculations as follows:

$$
\dot{\rho}_h = \frac{\rho_x\dot{\rho}_x + \rho_y\dot{\rho}_y + \rho_z\dot{\rho}_z}{\sqrt{\rho_x^2 + \rho_y^2 + \rho_z^2}}
$$
(1A.135)

$$
r_p = \sqrt{x^2 + y^2}
$$
(1A.136)

$$
r = \sqrt{x^2 + y^2 + z^2}
$$
(1A.137)

$$
\cos\delta = \frac{r_p}{r}
$$
(1A.138)

$$
\to \delta
$$

$$
\sin\delta = \frac{z}{r}
$$
(1A.139)

$$
\cos\alpha = \frac{x}{r_p}
$$
(1A.140)

$$
\to \alpha
$$

$$
\sin\alpha = \frac{y}{r_p}
$$
(1A.141)

$$
A_x = -\sin\alpha
$$

$$
A_y = \cos\alpha
$$
(1A.142)

$$
A_z = 0
$$

$$
D_x = -\cos\alpha\sin\delta
$$

$$
D_y = -\sin\alpha\sin\delta
$$
(1A.143)

$$
D_z = \cos\delta
$$

$$\dot{\alpha} \cos \delta = (\dot{\rho}_x A_x + \dot{\rho}_y A_y + \dot{\rho}_z A_z)/\rho_h \qquad (1A.144)$$

$$\dot{\delta} = (\dot{\rho}_x D_x + \dot{\rho}_y D_y + \dot{\rho}_z D_z)/\rho_h. \qquad (1A.145)$$

TRANSFORMATION 16.   *Transformation of rectangular coordinates from the right ascension-declination coordinate system to the celestial latitude-longitude coordinate system.*

Symbolically, the following transformation is accomplished:

$$x, y, z, \dot{x}, \dot{y}, \dot{z}, t \to x_\epsilon, y_\epsilon, z_\epsilon, \dot{x}_\epsilon, \dot{y}_\epsilon, \dot{z}_\epsilon.$$

The transformation can be effected by using the following equations:

$$x_\epsilon = x \qquad (1A.146)$$
$$y_\epsilon = y \cos \epsilon + z \sin \epsilon \qquad (1A.147)$$
$$z_\epsilon = -y \sin \epsilon + z \cos \epsilon \qquad (1A.148)$$
$$\dot{x}_\epsilon = \dot{x} \qquad (1A.149)$$
$$\dot{y}_\epsilon = \dot{y} \cos \epsilon + \dot{z} \sin \epsilon \qquad (1A.150)$$
$$\dot{z}_\epsilon = -\dot{y} \sin \epsilon + \dot{z} \cos \epsilon. \qquad (1A.151)$$

The obliquity of the ecliptic, $\epsilon$, can be obtained from Eq. 1A.207 of Transformation 26.

TRANSFORMATION 17.   *Transformation of rectangular coordinates from the celestial latitude-longitude coordinate system to the right ascension-declination coordinate system.*

Symbolically, the following transformation is accomplished:

$$x_\epsilon, y_\epsilon, z_\epsilon, \dot{x}_\epsilon, \dot{y}_\epsilon, \dot{z}_\epsilon, t \to x, y, z, \dot{x}, \dot{y}, \dot{z}.$$

The transformation can be effected by using the following equations:

$$x = x_\epsilon \qquad (1A.152)$$
$$y = y_\epsilon \cos \epsilon - z_\epsilon \sin \epsilon \qquad (1A.153)$$
$$z = y_\epsilon \sin \epsilon + z_\epsilon \cos \epsilon \qquad (1A.154)$$
$$\dot{x} = \dot{x}_\epsilon \qquad (1A.155)$$
$$\dot{y} = \dot{y}_\epsilon \cos \epsilon - \dot{z}_\epsilon \sin \epsilon \qquad (1A.156)$$
$$\dot{z} = \dot{y}_\epsilon \sin \epsilon + \dot{z}_\epsilon \cos \epsilon. \qquad (1A.157)$$

The obliquity of the ecliptic, $\epsilon$, can be obtained from Eq. 1A.207 of Transformation 26.

TRANSFORMATION 18.    *Transformation of position from rectangular coordinates of the celestial latitude-longitude coordinate system to polar coordinates of the same system.*

Symbolically, the following transformation is accomplished:

$$x_\epsilon, y_\epsilon, z_\epsilon \rightarrow \beta, \lambda, r_\epsilon.$$

The transformation can be effected by using the following equations:

$$r_p = \sqrt{x_\epsilon^2 + y_\epsilon^2} \tag{1A.158}$$

$$r_\epsilon = \sqrt{x_\epsilon^2 + y_\epsilon^2 + z_\epsilon^2} \tag{1A.159}$$

$$\cos \beta = \frac{r_p}{r_\epsilon} \tag{1A.160}$$

$$\rightarrow \beta$$

$$\sin \beta = \frac{z_\epsilon}{r_\epsilon} \tag{1A.161}$$

$$\cos \lambda = \frac{x_\epsilon}{r_p}$$

$$\rightarrow \lambda \tag{1A.162}$$

$$\sin \lambda = \frac{y_\epsilon}{r_p}.$$

TRANSFORMATION 19.    *Transformation of position from the celestial latitude-longitude coordinate system to rectangular coordinates of the same system.*

Symbolically, the following transformation is accomplished:

$$\beta, \lambda, r_\epsilon \rightarrow x_\epsilon, y_\epsilon, z_\epsilon.$$

The transformation can be effected by using the following equations:

$$x_\epsilon = r_\epsilon \cos \beta \cos \lambda \tag{1A.163}$$
$$y_\epsilon = r_\epsilon \cos \beta \sin \lambda \tag{1A.164}$$
$$z_\epsilon = r_\epsilon \sin \beta. \tag{1A.165}$$

TRANSFORMATION 20.    *Transformation of rectangular coordinates from the hour angle-declination coordinate system to the right ascension-declination coordinate system.*

Symbolically, the following transformation is accomplished:

$$x_\delta, y_\delta, z_\delta, \dot{x}_\delta, \dot{y}_\delta, \dot{z}_\delta, \lambda_E, t \rightarrow x, y, z, \dot{x}, \dot{y}, \dot{z}.$$

Transformation can be effected by use of the following equations:

$$\theta = \theta_g + \dot{\theta}(t - t_g) - (360° - \lambda_E), \quad 0° \le \theta \le 360°, \quad \text{(1A.166)}$$
$$x = x_\delta \cos \theta - y_\delta \sin \theta \quad \text{(1A.167)}$$
$$y = x_\delta \sin \theta + y_\delta \cos \theta \quad \text{(1A.168)}$$
$$z = z_\delta \quad \text{(1A.169)}$$
$$\dot{x} = \dot{x}_\delta \cos \theta - \dot{y}_\delta \sin \theta - y\dot{\theta} \quad \text{(1A.170)}$$
$$\dot{y} = \dot{x}_\delta \sin \theta + \dot{y}_\delta \cos \theta + x\dot{\theta} \quad \text{(1A.171)}$$
$$\dot{z} = \dot{z}_\delta. \quad \text{(1A.172)}$$

TRANSFORMATION 21. *Transformation of rectangular coordinates from the right ascension-declination coordinate system to the hour angle-declination coordinate system.*

Symbolically, the following transformation is accomplished:

$$x, y, z, \dot{x}, \dot{y}, \dot{z}, \lambda_E, t \rightarrow x_\delta, y_\delta, z_\delta, \dot{x}_\delta, \dot{y}_\delta, \dot{z}_\delta.$$

Transformation can be effected by the use of the following equations:

$$\theta = \theta_g + \dot{\theta}(t - t_g) - (360° - \lambda_E), \quad 0° \le \theta \le 360°, \quad \text{(1A.173)}$$
$$x_\delta = x \cos \theta + y \sin \theta \quad \text{(1A.174)}$$
$$y_\delta = -x \sin \theta + y \cos \theta \quad \text{(1A.175)}$$
$$z_\delta = z \quad \text{(1A.176)}$$
$$\dot{x}_\delta = \dot{x} \cos \theta + \dot{y} \sin \theta + y_\delta\dot{\theta} \quad \text{(1A.177)}$$
$$\dot{y}_\delta = -\dot{x} \sin \theta + \dot{y} \cos \theta - x_\delta\dot{\theta}. \quad \text{(1A.178)}$$
$$\dot{z}_\delta = \dot{z}. \quad \text{(1A.179)}$$

TRANSFORMATION 22. *Transformation of position from the hour angle-declination coordinate system to rectangular coordinates of the same system.*

Symbolically, the following transformation is accomplished:

$$HA, \delta, r \rightarrow x_\delta, y_\delta, z_\delta.$$

Transformation is effected by the following equations:

$$x_\delta = r \cos HA \cos \delta \quad \text{(1A.180)}$$
$$y_\delta = r \sin HA \cos \delta \quad \text{(1A.181)}$$
$$z_\delta = r \sin \delta. \quad \text{(1A.182)}$$

TRANSFORMATION 23. *Transformation of position from rectangular coordinates of the hour angle-declination coordinate system to polar coordinates of the same system.*

Symbolically, the following transformation is accomplished:

$$x_\delta, y_\delta, z_\delta \to HA, \delta, r.$$

Transformation is effected by the following equations:

$$r = \sqrt{x_\delta{}^2 + y_\delta{}^2 + z_\delta{}^2} \tag{1A.183}$$

$$r_p = \sqrt{x_\delta{}^2 + y_\delta{}^2} \tag{1A.184}$$

$$\left.\begin{aligned} \sin \delta &= \frac{z_\delta}{r} \\[4pt] &\quad\to \delta \\[4pt] \cos \delta &= \frac{r_p}{r} \end{aligned}\right. \tag{1A.185}$$

$$\left.\begin{aligned} \sin HA &= \frac{y_\delta}{r_p} \\[4pt] &\quad\to HA \\[4pt] \cos HA &= \frac{x_\delta}{r_p}. \end{aligned}\right. \tag{1A.186}$$

TRANSFORMATION 24.   *Transformation from oblate spheroidal coordinates to rectangular coordinates of the right ascension-declination coordinate system.*

Symbolically, the following transformation is accomplished:

$$\xi, \eta, \alpha, \dot\xi, \dot\eta, \dot\alpha \to x, y, z, \dot x, \dot y, \dot z.$$

The transformation is accomplished by means of the following equations:

$$x = c\sqrt{(1 + \xi^2)(1 - \eta^2)} \cos \alpha \tag{1A.187}$$

$$y = c\sqrt{(1 + \xi^2)(1 - \eta^2)} \sin \alpha \tag{1A.188}$$

$$z = c\xi\eta \tag{1A.189}$$

$$\dot x = c\,\frac{(1 - \eta^2)\xi\dot\xi - (1 + \xi^2)\eta\dot\eta}{\sqrt{(1 + \xi^2)(1 - \eta^2)}} \cos \alpha \tag{1A.190}$$

$$\quad - c\sqrt{(1 + \xi^2)(1 - \eta^2)}\, \dot\alpha \sin \alpha$$

$$\dot y = c\,\frac{(1 - \eta^2)\xi\dot\xi - (1 + \xi^2)\eta\dot\eta}{\sqrt{(1 + \xi^2)(1 - \eta^2)}} \sin \alpha \tag{1A.191}$$

$$\quad + c\sqrt{(1 + \xi^2)(1 - \eta^2)}\, \dot\alpha \cos \alpha$$

$$\dot z = c(\xi\dot\eta + \eta\dot\xi). \tag{1A.192}$$

The constant $c$ is included in the transformation for generality.

TRANSFORMATION 25. *Transformation from rectangular coordinates of the right ascension-declination coordinate system to oblate spheroidal coordinates.*

Symbolically, the following transformation is accomplished:

$$x, y, z, \dot{x}, \dot{y}, \dot{z} \rightarrow \xi, \eta, \alpha, \dot{\xi}, \dot{\eta}, \dot{\alpha}.$$

The following equations are used to effect the transformation:

$$r^2 = x^2 + y^2 + z^2 \tag{1A.193}$$

$$\xi = \sqrt{\frac{r^2 - c^2}{2c^2} + \frac{1}{2}\sqrt{\left(\frac{r^2 - c^2}{c^2}\right)^2 + \frac{4z^2}{c^2}}}, \quad 0 < \xi < \infty, \tag{1A.194}$$

$$\eta = \frac{z}{c\xi}, \quad -1 \leq \eta \leq 1, \tag{1A.195}$$

$$\begin{aligned}
\cos \alpha &= \frac{x}{c\sqrt{(1 + \xi^2)(1 - \eta^2)}} \\
& \qquad\qquad\qquad\qquad 0° \leq \alpha \leq 360°, \\
\sin \alpha &= \frac{y}{c\sqrt{(1 + \xi^2)(1 - \eta^2)}}
\end{aligned} \tag{1A.196}$$

$$\dot{r} = \frac{x\dot{x} + y\dot{y} + z\dot{z}}{r} \tag{1A.197}$$

$$\dot{\xi} = \frac{1}{2c^2\xi}\left[ r\dot{r} + \frac{\left(\dfrac{r^2 - c^2}{c^2}\right)r\dot{r} + 2z\dot{z}}{\sqrt{\left(\dfrac{r^2 - c^2}{c^2}\right)^2 + \dfrac{4z^2}{c^2}}} \right] \tag{1A.198}$$

$$\dot{\eta} = \left(\frac{\dot{z}}{\xi} - \frac{z\dot{\xi}}{\xi^2}\right)\frac{1}{c} \tag{1A.199}$$

$$\dot{\alpha} = \frac{x\dot{y} - y\dot{x}}{c^2(1 + \xi^2)(1 - \eta^2)}. \tag{1A.200}$$

TRANSFORMATION 26. *Transformation of rectangular position from the right ascension-declination coordinate system to the selenographic coordinate system (Mean equator to mean selenographic).*

Symbolically, the following transformation is accomplished:

$$x, y, z, t \rightarrow x_m, y_m, z_m.$$

The transformation is accomplished by means of the following equations:

$$t \to \text{J.D.} \tag{1A.201}$$

$$T_e = \frac{\text{J.D.} - 2415020.0}{36525.0}. \tag{1A.202}$$

Compute the mean longitude of the Sun's perigee

$$\Gamma = 281°2208333 + 1°7191750T_e + 0°45277778$$
$$\times 10^{-3}T_e^2 + 0°33333333 \times 10^{-5}T_e^3. \tag{1A.203}$$

Compute the mean longitude of the Moon's perigee

$$\Gamma' = 334°3295556 + 4069°0340333T_e - 0°10325000$$
$$\times 10^{-1}T_e^2 - 0°12500000 \times 10^{-4}T_e^3. \tag{1A.204}$$

Compute the mean longitude of the Sun

$$L = 279°6966778 + 36000°768925T_e + 0°30250000 \times 10^{-3}T_e^2. \tag{1A.205}$$

Compute the longitude (referenced to the mean equinox) of the mean ascending node of the lunar orbit

$$\Omega = 259°1832750 - 1934°1420083T_e + 0°20777778$$
$$\times 10^{-2}T_e^2 + 0°22222222 \times 10^{-5}T_e^3. \tag{1A.206}$$

Compute the mean obliquity of the ecliptic

$$\epsilon = 23°45229444 - 0°13012500 \times 10^{-1}T_e - 0°16388889$$
$$\times 10^{-5}T_e^2 + 0°50277778 \times 10^{-6}T_e^3. \tag{1A.207}$$

Compute the geocentric mean longitude of the Moon

$$\mathbb{C} = 270°4341639 + 481267°8831417T_e - 0°11333$$
$$\times 10^{-2}T_e^2 + 0°1888889 \times 10^{-5}T_e^3, \tag{1A.208}$$

and select

$$\begin{aligned}
I &= 1° 32'1 \\
g &= L - \Gamma \\
g' &= \mathbb{C} - \Gamma' \\
\omega' &= \Gamma' - \Omega.
\end{aligned} \tag{1A.209}$$

Compute Hayn's physical librations
(*Inclination*)

$$\rho = -107'' \cos g' + 37'' \cos(g' + 2\omega') - 11'' \cos(2g' + 2\omega'), \tag{1A.210}$$

(*Node*)

$$\sigma = [-109'' \sin g' + 37'' \sin (g' + 2\omega')$$
$$- 11'' \sin (2g' + 2\omega')]/\sin I, \quad (1A.211)$$

(*Longitude*)

$$\tau = -12'' \sin g' + 59'' \sin g + 18'' \sin 2\omega'. \qquad (1A.212)$$

For mean equator to mean selenographic, select

$$a = I$$
$$b = \epsilon \qquad (1A.213)$$
$$c = \Omega.$$

For mean equator to true selenographic, select

$$a = I + \rho$$
$$b = \epsilon \qquad (1A.214)$$
$$c = \Omega + \sigma.$$

Compute the rotation angles $\theta$, $\phi$, and the auxiliary angle $\Delta$ from

$$\cos \theta = \cos a \cos b + \sin a \sin b \cos c \qquad (1A.215)$$
$$\sin \theta = +\sqrt{1 - \cos^2 \theta}$$
$$\cos \phi = [\cos a \sin b - \sin a \cos b \cos c]/\sin \theta \qquad (1A.216)$$
$$\sin \phi = [-\sin a \sin c]/\sin \theta$$
$$\cos \Delta = [\sin a \cos b - \cos a \sin b \cos c]/\sin \theta \qquad (1A.217)$$
$$\sin \Delta = [-\sin b \sin c]/\sin \theta.$$

For mean equator to mean selenographic, select

$$\psi = \Delta + \mathbb{C} - \Omega. \qquad (1A.218)$$

For mean equator to true selenographic, select

$$\psi = \Delta + (\mathbb{C} + \tau) - (\Omega + \sigma). \qquad (1A.219)$$

Compute the rotation elements

$$A_{11} = \cos \phi \cos \psi - \cos \theta \sin \phi \sin \psi$$
$$A_{12} = \sin \phi \cos \psi + \cos \theta \cos \phi \sin \psi$$
$$A_{13} = \sin \psi \sin \theta$$
$$A_{21} = -\sin \psi \cos \phi - \cos \theta \sin \phi \cos \psi$$
$$A_{22} = -\sin \phi \sin \psi + \cos \theta \cos \phi \cos \psi \qquad (1A.220)$$
$$A_{23} = \sin \theta \cos \psi$$
$$A_{31} = \sin \phi \sin \theta$$
$$A_{32} = -\cos \phi \sin \theta$$
$$A_{33} = \cos \theta,$$

so that if the coordinates of the Moon relative to the Earth are $x_{\oplus m}$, $y_{\oplus m}$, $z_{\oplus m}$, then

$$\bar{x} = x - x_{\oplus m}$$
$$\bar{y} = y - y_{\oplus m} \qquad\qquad (1A.221)$$
$$\bar{z} = z - z_{\oplus m},$$

and, finally, a rotation about the Moon's center yields

$$\begin{bmatrix} x_m \\ y_m \\ z_m \end{bmatrix} = \begin{bmatrix} A_{11} & A_{12} & A_{13} \\ A_{21} & A_{22} & A_{23} \\ A_{31} & A_{32} & A_{33} \end{bmatrix} \begin{bmatrix} \bar{x} \\ \bar{y} \\ \bar{z} \end{bmatrix}. \qquad (1A.222)$$

TRANSFORMATION 27. *Transformation of rectangular position from the selenographic coordinate system to the right ascension-declination coordinate system (Mean selenographic to mean equator).*

Symbolically, the following transformation is accomplished:

$$x_m, y_m, z_m, t \rightarrow x, y, z.$$

The transformation is accomplished by applying Transformation 26 and replacing the last four equations by

$$\begin{bmatrix} \bar{x} \\ \bar{y} \\ \bar{z} \end{bmatrix} = \begin{bmatrix} A_{11} & A_{21} & A_{31} \\ A_{12} & A_{22} & A_{32} \\ A_{13} & A_{23} & A_{33} \end{bmatrix} \begin{bmatrix} x_m \\ y_m \\ z_m \end{bmatrix}, \text{ (see footnote[8])} \qquad (1A.223)$$

$$x = \bar{x} + x_{\oplus m}$$
$$y = \bar{y} + y_{\oplus m} \qquad\qquad (1A.224)$$
$$z = \bar{z} + z_{\oplus m},$$

where $x_{\oplus m}$, $y_{\oplus m}$, and $z_{\oplus m}$ are the coordinates of the center of the Moon with respect to the Earth.

TRANSFORMATION 28. *Transformation of rectangular position from the right ascension-declination coordinate system to the selenographic coordinate system (Mean equator to true selenographic).*

Symbolically, the following transformation is accomplished:

$$x, y, z, x_{\oplus m}, y_{\oplus m}, z_{\oplus m}, t \rightarrow x_m, y_m, z_m.$$

The transformation is effected by applying Transformation 26 and making the indicated substitutions.

---

[8] The coefficients of the transformation matrix are identical to those in Transformation 26.

TRANSFORMATION 29. *Transformation of rectangular position from the selenographic coordinate system to the right ascension-declination coordinate system* (*True selenographic to mean equator*).

Symbolically, the following transformation is accomplished:

$$x_m, y_m, z_m, x_{\oplus m}, y_{\oplus m}, z_{\oplus m}, t \rightarrow x, y, z.$$

The transformation is effected by applying Transformation 27 and making the indicated substitutions.

TRANSFORMATION 30. *Transformation of rectangular coordinates of the right ascension-declination coordinate system to rectangular coordinates of the orbit plane coordinate system.*

Symbolically, the following transformation is accomplished:

$$x, y, z, \dot{x}, \dot{y}, \dot{z}, \Omega, \omega, i \rightarrow x_\omega, y_\omega, z_\omega, \dot{x}_\omega, \dot{y}_\omega, \dot{z}_\omega.$$

The transformation is effected by use of the equations:

$$
\begin{aligned}
P_x &= \cos \omega \cos \Omega - \sin \omega \sin \Omega \cos i \\
P_y &= \cos \omega \sin \Omega + \sin \omega \cos \Omega \cos i \\
P_z &= \sin \omega \sin i
\end{aligned}
\tag{1A.225}
$$

$$
\begin{aligned}
Q_x &= -\sin \omega \cos \Omega - \cos \omega \sin \Omega \cos i \\
Q_y &= -\sin \omega \sin \Omega + \cos \omega \cos \Omega \cos i \\
Q_z &= \cos \omega \sin i
\end{aligned}
\tag{1A.226}
$$

$$
\begin{aligned}
W_x &= \sin \Omega \sin i \\
W_y &= -\cos \Omega \sin i \\
W_z &= \cos i
\end{aligned}
\tag{1A.227}
$$

$$
\begin{bmatrix} x_\omega \\ y_\omega \\ z_\omega \end{bmatrix} =
\begin{bmatrix} P_x & P_y & P_z \\ Q_x & Q_y & Q_z \\ W_x & W_y & W_z \end{bmatrix}
\begin{bmatrix} x \\ y \\ z \end{bmatrix}
\tag{1A.228}
$$

$$
\begin{bmatrix} \dot{x}_\omega \\ \dot{y}_\omega \\ \dot{z}_\omega \end{bmatrix} =
\begin{bmatrix} P_x & P_y & P_z \\ Q_x & Q_y & Q_z \\ W_x & W_y & W_z \end{bmatrix}
\begin{bmatrix} \dot{x} \\ \dot{y} \\ \dot{z} \end{bmatrix}.
\tag{1A.229}
$$

It should be noted that $\Omega$, $\omega$, and $i$ are the standard orientation elements, that is,

$\Omega \equiv$ longitude of the ascending node,

$\omega \equiv$ argument of perifocus,

$i \equiv$ orbit inclination.

TRANSFORMATION 31.    *Transformation of rectangular coordinates from the orbit plane coordinate system to rectangular coordinates of the right ascension-declination coordinate system.*

Symbolically, the following transformation is accomplished:

$$x_\omega, \; y_\omega, \; z_\omega, \; \dot{x}_\omega, \; \dot{y}_\omega, \; \dot{z}_\omega, \; \Omega, \; \omega, \; i \to x, \; y, \; z, \; \dot{x}, \; \dot{y}, \; \dot{z}.$$

The transformation is effected by use of the equations of Transformation 30 except that the last two equations are replaced by

$$\begin{bmatrix} x \\ y \\ z \end{bmatrix} = \begin{bmatrix} P_x & Q_x & W_x \\ P_y & Q_y & W_y \\ P_z & Q_z & W_z \end{bmatrix} \begin{bmatrix} x_\omega \\ y_\omega \\ z_\omega \end{bmatrix} \tag{1A.230}$$

$$\begin{bmatrix} \dot{x} \\ \dot{y} \\ \dot{z} \end{bmatrix} = \begin{bmatrix} P_x & Q_x & W_x \\ P_y & Q_y & W_y \\ P_z & Q_z & W_z \end{bmatrix} \begin{bmatrix} \dot{x}_\omega \\ \dot{y}_\omega \\ \dot{z}_\omega \end{bmatrix}. \tag{1A.231}$$

It should be noted that $\Omega$, $\omega$, and $i$ are the standard orientation elements defined in Transformation 30.

TRANSFORMATION 32.    *Transformation of rectangular coordinates from a specific epoch to rectangular coordinates at the initial epoch* (*The precession transformation*).

Symbolically, the following transformation is accomplished:

$$(x, \; y, \; z)_t \to (x, \; y, \; z)_0.$$

The transformation is effected by use of the following equations:

$$t \to \text{J.D.} \tag{1A.232}$$

$$T = \frac{\text{J.D.} - [\text{J.D.}]_{1950}}{36524.219879} \; (\text{see footnote}[9]) \tag{1A.233}$$

$$T_0 = 0.5$$

$$\zeta_0 = [0°64006944 + 0°38777778 \times 10^{-3}T_0]T$$
$$+ \; 0°83888889 \times 10^{-4}T^2$$
$$+ \; 0°50000000 \times 10^{-5}T^3 \tag{1A.234}$$

$$Z = \zeta_0 + 0°21972222 \times 10^{-3}T^2 \tag{1A.235}$$

$$\theta = [0°55685611 - 0°2369444 \times 10^{-3}T_0]T$$
$$- \; 0°11833333 \times 10^{-3}T^2 - 0°11666667 \times 10^{-4}T^3 \tag{1A.236}$$

[9] $T$ is the time in tropical centuries which has elapsed between the reference epoch (1950.0) and a particular given instant ($t$). $T_0$ is the time in tropical centuries from the year 1900 to the reference epoch. The transformation is formulated for 1950.0.

$a_{11} = \cos \zeta_0 \cos \theta \cos Z - \sin \zeta_0 \sin Z$

$a_{12} = -\sin \zeta_0 \cos \theta \cos Z - \cos \zeta_0 \sin Z$

$a_{13} = -\sin \theta \cos Z$

$a_{21} = \cos \zeta_0 \cos \theta \sin Z + \sin \zeta_0 \cos Z$

$a_{22} = -\sin \zeta_0 \cos \theta \sin Z + \cos \zeta_0 \cos Z$         (1A.237)

$a_{23} = -\sin \theta \sin Z$

$a_{31} = \cos \zeta_0 \sin \theta$

$a_{32} = -\sin \zeta_0 \sin \theta$

$a_{33} = \cos \theta$

$$\begin{bmatrix} x \\ y \\ z \end{bmatrix}_0 = \begin{bmatrix} a_{11} & a_{21} & a_{31} \\ a_{12} & a_{22} & a_{32} \\ a_{13} & a_{23} & a_{33} \end{bmatrix} \begin{bmatrix} x \\ y \\ z \end{bmatrix}_t . \tag{1A.238}$$

TRANSFORMATION 33. *Transformation of rectangular coordinates from an initial epoch to rectangular coordinates at a specific epoch (The inverse precession transformation).*

Symbolically, the following transformation is effected:

$(x, y, z)_0 \rightarrow (x, y, z)_t.$

The transformation is effected by replacing the last equation of Transformation 32 by

$$\begin{bmatrix} x \\ y \\ z \end{bmatrix}_t = \begin{bmatrix} a_{11} & a_{12} & a_{13} \\ a_{21} & a_{22} & a_{23} \\ a_{31} & a_{32} & a_{33} \end{bmatrix} \begin{bmatrix} x \\ y \\ z \end{bmatrix}_0 , \tag{1A.239}$$

where the elements of the inverse precession matrix are given in Transformation 32.

TRANSFORMATION 34. *Transformation of rectangular coordinates from the geocentric right ascension-declination coordinate system to the areocentric coordinate system (Martian transformation).*

Symbolically, the following transformation is effected:

$x, y, z, \dot{x}, \dot{y}, \dot{z}, t \rightarrow x_\delta, y_\delta, z_\delta, \dot{x}_\delta, \dot{y}_\delta, \dot{z}_\delta.$

The transformation is accomplished by the following equations.

Compute the position of the Martian north pole at the beginning of year $t'$

$\alpha_0' = 317°793416667 + 0°6520833 \times 10^{-2}(t' - 1950.0)$

$\delta_0' = 54°657500000 + 0°3500000 \times 10^{-2}(t' - 1950.0).$     (1A.240)

If desired, add the secular variation in $\alpha_0'$, $\delta_0'$

$$\tau = \frac{(\text{J.D.})_t - (\text{J.D.})_{t'}}{365.25}$$

$$\alpha_0 = \alpha_0' - 0\overset{s}{.}001013\tau$$
$$\delta_0 = \delta_0' - 0\overset{s}{.}000631\tau. \tag{1A.241}$$

Determine $\Omega$, the distance along the ecliptic from the vernal equinox to the ascending node of the Martian orbit,

$$T_e = \frac{(\text{J.D.})_t - 2415020.0}{36525.0}, \tag{1A.242}$$

$$\Omega = 48\overset{\circ}{.}78644167 + 0\overset{\circ}{.}77099167T_e - 0\overset{\circ}{.}13888889 \times 10^{-5}T_e{}^2. \tag{1A.243}$$

Determine the inclination of the Martian orbit plane to the ecliptic plane

$$i = 1\overset{\circ}{.}850333333 - 0\overset{\circ}{.}67500000 \times 10^{-3}T_e$$
$$+ 0.12611111 \times 10^{-4}T_e{}^2. \tag{1A.244}$$

Compute the obliquity of the ecliptic and the auxiliary angles $\tilde{x}$, $\tilde{y}$, $\tilde{z}$

$$\epsilon = 23\overset{\circ}{.}45229444 - 0\overset{\circ}{.}13012500 \times 10^{-1}T_e$$
$$- 0\overset{\circ}{.}16388889 \times 10^{-5}T_e{}^2 + 0\overset{\circ}{.}50277778 \times 10^{-6}T_e{}^3, \tag{1A.245}$$

$$\cos \tilde{z} = \cos \epsilon \sin \Omega \cos \alpha_0 - \cos \Omega \sin \alpha_0$$
$$\sin \tilde{z} = +\sqrt{1 - \cos^2 \tilde{z}}, \tag{1A.246}$$

$$\sin \tilde{x} = \sin \epsilon \cos \alpha_0 / \sin \tilde{z}$$
$$\cos \tilde{x} = [-\cos \epsilon \cos \Omega \cos \alpha_0 - \sin \Omega \sin \alpha_0]/\sin \tilde{z}, \tag{1A.247}$$

$$\sin \tilde{y} = \sin \epsilon \sin \Omega / \sin \tilde{z}$$
$$\cos \tilde{y} = [\cos \epsilon \sin \Omega \sin \alpha_0 + \cos \Omega \cos \alpha_0]/\sin \tilde{z}. \tag{1A.248}$$

Compute the inclination of the Martian orbit with respect to the Martian equator

$$\cos I = \cos (\tilde{x} - i) \sin (\tilde{y} - \delta_0) + \sin (\tilde{x} - i) \cos (\tilde{y} - \delta_0) \cos \tilde{z}, \tag{1A.249}$$

$$\sin I = +\sqrt{1 - \cos^2 I}.$$

Calculate $\omega_{\vec{\delta}}$, the argument of perigee of the Martian principal axis with respect to the Earth's equator plane

$$\sin \omega_{\vec{\delta}} = \sin \tilde{z} \sin (x - i)/\sin I,$$

$$\cos \omega_{\vec{\delta}} = [-\cos (\tilde{x} - i) \cos (\tilde{y} - \delta_0) \tag{1A.250}$$
$$+ \sin (\tilde{x} - i) \sin (\tilde{y} - \delta_0) \cos \tilde{z}]/\sin I.$$

Calculate $\Omega_\delta$, the longitude of the ascending node of the Martian principal axis with respect to the Earth's vernal equinox

$$\Omega_\delta = \alpha_0 + \pi/2. \tag{1A.251}$$

Calculate $i_\delta$, the inclination of the Martian equator plane with respect to the Earth's equator plane

$$i_\delta = \pi/2 - \delta_0. \tag{1A.252}$$

Continue calculating with

$$
\begin{aligned}
\bar{P}_x &= \cos \omega_\delta \cos \Omega_\delta - \sin \omega_\delta \sin \Omega_\delta \cos i_\delta \\
\bar{P}_y &= \cos \omega_\delta \sin \Omega_\delta + \sin \omega_\delta \cos \Omega_\delta \cos i_\delta \\
\bar{P}_z &= \sin \omega_\delta \sin i_\delta, \\
\bar{Q}_x &= -\sin \omega_\delta \cos \Omega_\delta - \cos \omega_\delta \sin \Omega_\delta \cos i_\delta \\
\bar{Q}_y &= -\sin \omega_\delta \sin \Omega_\delta + \cos \omega_\delta \cos \Omega_\delta \cos i_\delta \\
\bar{Q}_z &= \cos \omega_\delta \sin i_\delta, \\
\bar{W}_x &= \sin \Omega_\delta \sin i_\delta \\
\bar{W}_y &= -\cos \Omega_\delta \sin i_\delta \\
\bar{W}_z &= \cos i_\delta.
\end{aligned}
\tag{1A.253}
$$

If the radius vector from the Earth to Mars is $\mathbf{r}_{\oplus\delta}$, translate by means of the equations

$$\bar{\mathbf{r}} = \mathbf{r} - \mathbf{r}_{\oplus\delta}, \tag{1A.254}$$

$$\dot{\bar{\mathbf{r}}} = \dot{\mathbf{r}} - \dot{\mathbf{r}}_{\oplus\delta}.$$

Perform the rotations

$$
\begin{bmatrix} x_\delta \\ y_\delta \\ z_\delta \end{bmatrix} =
\begin{bmatrix} \bar{P}_x & \bar{P}_y & \bar{P}_z \\ \bar{Q}_x & \bar{Q}_y & \bar{Q}_z \\ \bar{W}_x & \bar{W}_y & \bar{W}_z \end{bmatrix}
\begin{bmatrix} \bar{x} \\ \bar{y} \\ \bar{z} \end{bmatrix},
\tag{1A.255}
$$

$$
\begin{bmatrix} \dot{x}_\delta \\ \dot{y}_\delta \\ \dot{z}_\delta \end{bmatrix} =
\begin{bmatrix} \bar{P}_x & \bar{P}_y & \bar{P}_z \\ \bar{Q}_x & \bar{Q}_y & \bar{Q}_z \\ \bar{W}_x & \bar{W}_y & \bar{W}_z \end{bmatrix}
\begin{bmatrix} \dot{\bar{x}} \\ \dot{\bar{y}} \\ \dot{\bar{z}} \end{bmatrix}.
\tag{1A.256}
$$

TRANSFORMATION 35.  *Transformation of rectangular coordinates from the rectangular areocentric coordinate system to the geocentric right ascension-declination coordinate system (Inverse Martian transformation).*

Symbolically, the following transformation is effected:

$$x_\delta, \, y_\delta, \, z_\delta, \, \dot{x}_\delta, \, \dot{y}_\delta, \, \dot{z}_\delta, \, t \rightarrow x, \, y, \, z, \, \dot{x}, \, \dot{y}, \, \dot{z}.$$

The transformation is accomplished by the following procedure. Utilize Transformation 34 with the last equations replaced by

$$
\begin{bmatrix} \bar{x} \\ \bar{y} \\ \bar{z} \end{bmatrix} = \begin{bmatrix} \bar{P}_x & \bar{Q}_x & \bar{W}_x \\ \bar{P}_y & \bar{Q}_y & \bar{W}_y \\ \bar{P}_z & \bar{Q}_z & \bar{W}_z \end{bmatrix} \begin{bmatrix} x_\delta \\ y_\delta \\ z_\delta \end{bmatrix},
\tag{1A.257}
$$

$$
\begin{bmatrix} \dot{\bar{x}} \\ \dot{\bar{y}} \\ \dot{\bar{z}} \end{bmatrix} = \begin{bmatrix} \bar{P}_x & \bar{Q}_x & \bar{W}_x \\ \bar{P}_y & \bar{Q}_y & \bar{W}_y \\ \bar{P}_z & \bar{Q}_z & \bar{W}_z \end{bmatrix} \begin{bmatrix} \dot{x}_\delta \\ \dot{y}_\delta \\ \dot{z}_\delta \end{bmatrix},
\tag{1A.258}
$$

$$
\mathbf{r} = \bar{\mathbf{r}} + \mathbf{r}_{\oplus\delta}
$$
$$
\dot{\mathbf{r}} = \dot{\bar{\mathbf{r}}} + \dot{\mathbf{r}}_{\oplus\delta}.
\tag{1A.259}
$$

TRANSFORMATION 36. *Transformation of areocentric latitude-longitude coordinates into rectangular coordinates in an areocentric right ascension-declination coordinate system.*

Symbolically, the following transformation is effected:

$$\phi', H_s, \lambda_E, t \rightarrow x_\delta, y_\delta, z_\delta.$$

The transformation is accomplished by the following equations:

$$t \rightarrow \text{J.D.} \tag{1A.260}$$

Compute the hour angle of the Martian vernal equinox measured from the zero meridian

$$HA = 145.845 + 350°891962(\text{J.D.} - 2418322.0). \tag{1A.261}$$

Compute the sidereal time of the Martian zero meridian

$$\theta_{g\delta} = -HA \tag{1A.262}$$

$$\frac{d\theta_{g\delta}}{dt} = 369.34445375 \text{ deg/day} \tag{1A.263}$$

$$\theta = \theta_{g\delta} + \frac{d\theta_\delta}{dt}(t - t_0) + \lambda_E. \tag{1A.264}$$

Apply Transformation 4, bypassing Eq. 1A.31 with $a_e, f$, referring to the planet Mars and obtain

$$x_\delta, y_\delta, z_\delta.$$

# APPENDIX II

# A complete algorithm for two-body motion in space

Within the scope of two-body mechanics, an algorithm for movement from one position and velocity vector $(\mathbf{r}_0, \dot{\mathbf{r}}_0)$ to another position and velocity vector $(\mathbf{r}, \dot{\mathbf{r}})$, at some time $t$, is a very important analytical tool. The computational algorithm is a slight modification of the form developed by Samuel Herrick.

The function of this algorithm can be symbolically represented as follows:

$$[x, y, z, \dot{x}, \dot{y}, \dot{z}]_{t=t_0} \rightarrow [x, y, z, \dot{x}, \dot{y}, \dot{z}]_{t=t}.$$

In the process of moving from state 1, that is, $t = t_0$, to state 2 at the desired time $t$, where the position and velocity vectors are to be calculated, great care has been taken to insure that the algorithm can be used for all types of motion, including rectilinear trajectories. The algorithm will in effect force a nearly parabolic orbit into a true parabolic orbit, etc.

To use the equations presented, the reader should start at subheading (a) and continue reading, without skipping either equations or text; the computational path will be clearly indicated.

## COMPUTATIONAL SCHEME

### a.   The common calculations

Given the position and velocity components of a point mass in space, at some time $t_0$, along with $\mu$, $k$, and $t$, it is possible to convert these elements into characteristic units (Section 1.2) and proceed with the following group of calculations valid for all orbits:

$$r_0^2 = \mathbf{r}_0 \cdot \mathbf{r}_0 \tag{2A.1}$$

$$D_0 = \frac{\mathbf{r}_0 \cdot \dot{\mathbf{r}}_0}{\sqrt{\mu}} \tag{2A.2}$$

$$\left[\frac{V_0{}^2}{\mu}\right] = \frac{\dot{\mathbf{r}}_0 \cdot \dot{\mathbf{r}}_0}{\mu} \text{ (see footnote}^1) \tag{2A.3}$$

$$\frac{1}{a} = \frac{2}{r_0} - \left[\frac{V_0{}^2}{\mu}\right] \tag{2A.4}$$

$$e^2 = \left(1 - \frac{r_0}{a}\right)^2 + \frac{1}{a} D_0{}^2 \tag{2A.5}$$

$$p = r_0\left(2 - \frac{r_0}{a}\right) - D_0{}^2 \tag{2A.6}$$

$$2q = 2r_0 - D_0{}^2. \tag{2A.7}$$

### b.   Rectilinear orbits

If the following conditions are existent, within a specific tolerance $\epsilon$,[2] that is, where

$$e = 1 \pm \epsilon \tag{2A.8}$$

$$p = 0 \pm \epsilon, \tag{2A.9}$$

then the orbit is nearly rectilinear and, for convenience, formulas specialized to such rectilinear orbits are utilized,[3] that is, start with Eq. 2A.10; if conditions 2A.8 and 2A.9 are not fulfilled, then proceed to subheading (f).
   Recalculate

$$\dot{\mathbf{r}}_0 = V_0 \frac{\mathbf{r}_0}{r_0}, \tag{2A.10}$$

where $V_0$ is obtained from Eq. 2A.3.   Hence $\dot{\mathbf{r}}_0$ and the following parameters are recalculated in order to force a true rectilinear orbit.

$$D_0 = \frac{\mathbf{r}_0 \cdot \dot{\mathbf{r}}_0}{\sqrt{\mu}} \tag{2A.11}$$

$$\left[\frac{V_0{}^2}{\mu}\right] = \frac{\dot{\mathbf{r}}_0 \cdot \dot{\mathbf{r}}_0}{\mu} \tag{2A.12}$$

$$\frac{1}{a} = \frac{2}{r_0} - \left[\frac{V_0{}^2}{\mu}\right]. \tag{2A.13}$$

---

[1] The square brackets indicate that the quantity is calculated as a whole.
[2] $\epsilon \cong 0.1 \times 10^{-6}$.
[3] The formulas in subheading (f) are, however, still perfectly general and apply if $e = 1$ and $p = 0$.   The computation is, nevertheless, simplified if one branches into Eq. 2A.10.

## c. A rectilinear elliptical orbit

If $1/a > 0$, the orbit is a rectilinear ellipse ($e = 1, p = 0$) and it is possible to continue with Eq. 2A.14; if not, proceed to subheading (d).
Start calculating with

$$a = 1/(1/a) \tag{2A.14}$$

$$\sin E_0 = \frac{D_0}{\sqrt{a}} \tag{2A.15}$$

$$\left.\begin{array}{l} \\ \cos E_0 = \left(1 - \frac{r_0}{a}\right) \end{array}\right\} \rightarrow E_0 \tag{2A.16}$$

$$M_0 = E_0 - \sin E_0 \tag{2A.17}$$

$$\mathbf{U}_0 = \mathbf{r}_0/r_0$$

$$n = k\sqrt{\mu}/a^{3/2}.$$

At the future (past) time, compute

$$M = M_0 + n(t - t_0) \tag{2A.18}$$

$$M = E - \sin E \xrightarrow{\text{Iteration}} E \tag{2A.19}$$

$$r = a(1 - \cos E) \tag{2A.20}$$

$$\dot{r} = \frac{\sqrt{\mu a}}{r} \sin E \tag{2A.21}$$

$$\mathbf{r} = r\mathbf{U}_0 \tag{2A.22}$$

$$\dot{\mathbf{r}} = \dot{r}\mathbf{U}_0. \tag{2A.23}$$

This is the end of the rectilinear ellipse calculations.   Proceed to subheading (i).

## d. A rectilinear hyperbolic orbit

If $1/a < 0$, the orbit is a rectilinear hyperbola ($e = 1, p = 0$) and it is possible to continue with Eq. 2A.24; if not, proceed to subheading (e). Start calculating with

$$a = 1/(1/a) \tag{2A.24}$$

$$\sinh F_0 = D_0/\sqrt{-a} \tag{2A.25}$$

$$F_0 = \log_e[\sinh F_0 + \sqrt{\sinh^2 F_0 + 1}] \tag{2A.26}$$

$$M_0 = \sinh F_0 - F_0 \tag{2A.27}$$

$$\mathbf{U}_0 = \frac{\mathbf{r}_0}{r_0} \tag{2A.28}$$

$$n = k\sqrt{\mu}/(-a)^{3/2}. \tag{2A.29}$$

At the future (past) time, compute

$$M = M_0 + n(t - t_0) \tag{2A.30}$$

$$M = \sinh F - F \xrightarrow{\text{Iteration}} F \tag{2A.31}$$

$$r = -a(\cosh F - 1) \tag{2A.32}$$

$$\dot{r} = \frac{\sqrt{-\mu a}}{r} \sinh F \tag{2A.33}$$

$$\mathbf{r} = r\mathbf{U}_0 \tag{2A.34}$$

$$\dot{\mathbf{r}} = \dot{r}\mathbf{U}_0. \tag{2A.35}$$

This is the end of the rectilinear hyperbola calculations. Proceed to subheading (i).

### e. A rectilinear parabolic orbit

If $1/a = 0 \pm \epsilon$, the orbit is a nearly rectilinear parabola and it is possible to force a true parabola by continuing with Eq. 2A.36; if not, proceed to subheading (f).
Start calculating with

$$V_0 = \sqrt{2\mu/r_0} \tag{2A.36}$$

$$D_0 = \sqrt{2r_0} \tag{2A.37}$$

$$M_0 = \tfrac{1}{6}D_0{}^3 \tag{2A.38}$$

$$n = k\sqrt{\mu}. \tag{2A.39}$$

At the future (past) time, compute

$$M = M_0 + n(t - t_0) \tag{2A.40}$$

$$D = \sqrt[3]{6M} \tag{2A.41}$$

$$r = \tfrac{1}{2}D^2 \tag{2A.42}$$

$$\dot{r} = \frac{\sqrt{\mu}}{r} D \tag{2A.43}$$

$$\mathbf{r} = r\frac{\mathbf{r}_0}{r_0} \tag{2A.44}$$

$$\dot{\mathbf{r}} = \dot{r}\frac{\mathbf{r}_0}{r_0}. \tag{2A.45}$$

This is the end of the rectilinear parabola calculations. Proceed to subheading (i).

## f. An elliptic or circular orbit

If $e \neq 1, p \neq 0$ but $1/a > 0$, the orbit is either an ellipse or circle and it is possible to continue with Eq. 2A.46; if not, proceed to subheading (g). Start calculating with

$$C_e \equiv [e \cos E]_0 = 1 - \frac{r_0}{a} \tag{2A.46}$$

$$S_e \equiv [e \sin E]_0 = D_0/\sqrt{a}. \tag{2A.47}$$

At the future (past) time, compute

$$M - M_0 = (t - t_0)k\sqrt{\mu}/a^{3/2}, \tag{2A.48}$$

and solve Kepler's equation for $g$ by the Newton procedure in the form

$$g_{n+1} = g_n - \frac{g_n + S_e \sin^2 g_n - C_e \sin g_n \cos g_n - \frac{1}{2}(M - M_0)}{1 + 2S_e \sin g_n \cos g_n - C_e(1 - 2\sin^2 g_n)}, \tag{2A.49}$$

for $n = 1, 2, 3 \ldots q$ until $|g_{n+1} - g_n| < \epsilon$.   Continue calculating with

$$E - E_0 = 2g \tag{2A.50}$$

$$C = a[1 - \cos(E - E_0)] \tag{2A.51}$$

$$S = \sqrt{a}\sin(E - E_0) \tag{2A.52}$$

$$f = 1 - \frac{C}{r_0} \tag{2A.53}$$

$$g = \frac{1}{\sqrt{\mu}}(r_0 S + D_0 C) \tag{2A.54}$$

$$r = r_0 + \left(1 - \frac{r_0}{a}\right)C + D_0 S \tag{2A.55}$$

$$\dot{f} = -\frac{\sqrt{\mu}}{r r_0}S \tag{2A.56}$$

$$\dot{g} = 1 - \frac{C}{r} \tag{2A.57}$$

$$\mathbf{r} = f\mathbf{r}_0 + g\dot{\mathbf{r}}_0 \tag{2A.58}$$

$$\dot{\mathbf{r}} = \dot{f}\mathbf{r}_0 + \dot{g}\dot{\mathbf{r}}_0. \tag{2A.59}$$

This is the end of the elliptic and circular calculations.   Proceed to subheading (i).

## g.  A hyperbolic orbit

If $e \neq 1$ and $p \neq 0$, but $1/a < 0$, the orbit is a hyperbola and it is possible to continue with Eq. 2A.60; if not, proceed to subheading (h).  Start calculating with

$$C_h \equiv [e \cosh F]_0 = 1 - \frac{r_0}{a} \qquad (2A.60)$$

$$S_h \equiv [e \sinh F]_0 = D_0/\sqrt{-a}.$$

At the future (past) time, compute

$$n = k\sqrt{\mu}/(-a)^{3/2} \qquad (2A.61)$$

$$M - M_0 = n(t - t_0), \qquad (2A.62)$$

and solve Kepler's equation for $g$ by the Newton procedure in the form

$$g_{n+1} = g_n - \frac{S_h \sinh^2 g_n + C_h \sinh g_n \cosh g_n - g_n - \frac{1}{2}(M - M_0)}{2S_h \sinh g_n \cosh g_n + C_h(1 + 2\sinh^2 g_n) - 1}, \qquad (2A.63)$$

for $n = 1, 2, 3 \ldots q$ until $|g_{n+1} - g_n| < \epsilon$.  Continue calculating with

$$F - F_0 = 2g \qquad (2A.64)$$

$$S = \sqrt{-a} \sinh (F - F_0) \qquad (2A.65)$$

$$C = -a[\cosh (F - F_0) - 1] \qquad (2A.66)$$

$$f = 1 - \frac{C}{r_0} \qquad (2A.67)$$

$$g = \frac{1}{\sqrt{\mu}} (r_0 S + D_0 C) \qquad (2A.68)$$

$$r = r_0 + \left(1 - \frac{r_0}{a}\right) C + D_0 S \qquad (2A.69)$$

$$\dot{f} = \frac{-\sqrt{\mu}}{rr_0} S \qquad (2A.70)$$

$$\dot{g} = 1 - \frac{C}{r} \qquad (2A.71)$$

$$\mathbf{r} = f\mathbf{r}_0 + g\dot{\mathbf{r}}_0 \qquad (2A.72)$$

$$\dot{\mathbf{r}} = \dot{f}\mathbf{r}_0 + \dot{g}\dot{\mathbf{r}}_0. \qquad (2A.73)$$

This is the end of the hyperbolic calculations.  Proceed to subheading (i).

## h.  A parabolic orbit

If $e = 1 \pm \epsilon$ and $p \neq 0 \pm \epsilon$, but $1/a = 0 \pm \epsilon$ where $\epsilon$ is a specified tolerance, the orbit is nearly a parabola and can be forced to a true parabola by

$$S_0 = \dot{r}_0/V_0, \qquad (2A.74)$$

where $V_0$ is obtained from the common calculations. The following quantities are now recalculated:

$$\frac{V_0^2}{\mu} = \frac{2}{r_0} \tag{2A.75}$$

$$\left[\frac{\dot{\mathbf{r}}_0}{\sqrt{\mu}}\right] = \frac{2}{r_0} S_0 \tag{2A.76}$$

$$D_0 = \mathbf{r}_0 \cdot \left[\frac{\dot{\mathbf{r}}_0}{\sqrt{\mu}}\right] \tag{2A.77}$$

$$2q = 2r_0 - D_0^2. \tag{2A.78}$$

At the future (past) time, compute

$$n = k\sqrt{\mu} \tag{2A.79}$$

$$M - M_0 = n(t - t_0), \tag{2A.80}$$

and solve for $D - D_0$ from the cubic

$$M - M_0 = r_0(D - D_0) + \tfrac{1}{2}D_0(D - D_0)^2 + \tfrac{1}{6}(D - D_0)^3. \tag{2A.81}$$

Then,

$$S = D - D_0 \tag{2A.82}$$

$$C = \tfrac{1}{2}(D - D_0)^2 \tag{2A.83}$$

$$f = 1 - \frac{C}{r_0} \tag{2A.84}$$

$$g = \frac{1}{\sqrt{\mu}} (r_0 S + D_0 C) \tag{2A.85}$$

$$r = r_0 + D_0 S + C \tag{2A.86}$$

$$\dot{f} = -\frac{\sqrt{\mu}}{rr_0} S \tag{2A.87}$$

$$\dot{g} = 1 - \frac{C}{r} \tag{2A.88}$$

$$\mathbf{r} = f\mathbf{r}_0 + g\dot{\mathbf{r}}_0 \tag{2A.89}$$

$$\dot{\mathbf{r}} = \dot{f}\mathbf{r}_0 + \dot{g}\dot{\mathbf{r}}_0. \tag{2A.90}$$

This is the end of the parabolic calculations.   Proceed to subheading (i).

## i.   End of calculations

The analysis is terminated; exit with the desired vectors $(\mathbf{r}, \dot{\mathbf{r}})$ at time $t$.

# APPENDIX III

## A closed-form solution to quadratic, cubic, and quartic equations

The calculation of the real roots of the polynomials

$$p_1 \equiv Ax^2 + Bx + C$$
$$p_2 \equiv Ax^3 + Bx^2 + Cx + D$$
$$p_3 \equiv Ax^4 + Bx^3 + Cx^2 + Dx + E$$

with real coefficients is of frequent interest in the field of astrodynamics. Parabolic motion, for example, is ultimately associated with the solution of a cubic equation. The two-body solution of the entrance and exit true anomalies of a satellite into and out of the shadow of the Earth (Chapter 5) is accomplished through the solution of a quartic equation. There are a myriad of applications to classical mechanics of such forms.

Usually the engineer prefers to solve such equations by trial and error. However, in the long run it is much more expedient to solve such equations by the formulas to be presented. Certainly a machine subroutine for the closed form solution of the equations

$$p_1 = 0$$
$$p_2 = 0$$
$$p_3 = 0$$

forms a neat concise package which will find valuable application.

In order to simplify the presentation, three separate subcases will be analyzed, $m = 4$, $m = 3$, and $m = 2$.

### A. (m = 4)—Quartic solution

The fourth-degree equation is solved according to the Descartes technique [1] as follows. Given

$$Ax^4 + Bx^3 + Cx^2 + Dx + E = 0, \tag{3A.1}$$

**430**

divide through by $A(A \neq 0)^1$ and obtain

$$x^4 + B'x^3 + C'x^2 + D'x + E' = 0. \tag{3A.2}$$

Translate the equation such that the cubic term is lacking.  Hence

$$y^4 + Py^2 + Qy + R = 0 \text{ (see footnote}^2), \tag{3A.3}$$

where

$$
\begin{aligned}
P &= 6h^2 + 3B'h + C' \\
Q &= 4h^3 + 3B'h^2 + 2C'h + D' \\
R &= h^4 + B'h^3 + C'h^2 + D'h + E',
\end{aligned} \tag{3A.4}
$$

with

$$x = y + h, \tag{3A.5}$$

and

$$h = -\frac{B'}{4}.$$

Obtain the cubic resolvent,

$$t^3 + 2Pt^2 + (P^2 - 4R)t - Q^2 = 0 \tag{3A.6}$$

or

$$Z^3 + aZ + b = 0,$$

where

$$
\begin{aligned}
a &= \tfrac{1}{3}[3(P^2 - 4R) - 4P^2] \\
b &= \tfrac{1}{27}[16P^3 - 18P(P^2 - 4R) - 27Q^2],
\end{aligned} \tag{3A.7}
$$

with

$$
\begin{aligned}
Z &= t - s \\
s &= -\tfrac{2}{3}P.
\end{aligned} \tag{3A.8}
$$

Compute the quantity

$$\Delta = \frac{a^3}{27} + \frac{b^2}{4}. \tag{3A.9}$$

---

[1] If $A = 0$, proceed to subheading $B$.
[2] A test is made on the coefficient $Q$ in order to assure that it is not equal to zero. If $Q = 0$, then in effect Eq. 3A.3 is reduced by the substitution $z = y^2$, and solution is effected with the help of the quadratic formula for $m = 2$.

If $\Delta > 0$, solve the resolvent by the Cardan formula so that the roots are

$$Z_1 = \sqrt[3]{-\frac{b}{2} + \sqrt{\Delta}} + \sqrt[3]{-\frac{b}{2} - \sqrt{\Delta}}$$

$$Z_2 = \text{complex} \tag{3A.10}$$

$$Z_3 = \text{complex.}$$

If $\Delta = 0$, the roots of the resolvent are given by

$$Z_1 = 2\sqrt[3]{-\frac{b}{2}}$$

$$Z_2 = \sqrt[3]{\frac{b}{2}} \tag{3A.11}$$

$$Z_3 = \sqrt[3]{\frac{b}{2}}.$$

If $\Delta < 0$, solve the resolvent by the trigonometric technique. Hence

$$\begin{aligned}
Z_1 &= E_0 \cos (\phi/3) \\
Z_2 &= E_0 \cos (\phi/3 + 120°) \\
Z_3 &= E_0 \cos (\phi/3 + 240°),
\end{aligned} \tag{3A.12}$$

where

$$E_0 \equiv 2\sqrt{-\frac{a}{3}},$$

and the angle $\phi$ is defined by

$$\cos \phi = -\frac{b}{2\sqrt{-\frac{a^3}{27}}} \tag{3A.13}$$

$$\sin \phi = +\sqrt{1 - \cos^2 \phi}, \quad 0 \le \phi \le \pi.$$

Now, in accordance with the sign of $\Delta$, take the critical root of Eq. 3A.6 as

$$R' \equiv \max[\text{real roots } (Z_1 + s, Z_2 + s, Z_3 + s)]. \tag{3A.14}$$

A positive real root can always be found.

Having obtained $R'$, the parameters $\xi$ and $\beta$ can be obtained from

$$\xi = \frac{1}{2}\left(P + R' - \frac{Q}{\sqrt{R'}}\right)$$

$$\beta = \frac{1}{2}\left(P + R' + \frac{Q}{\sqrt{R'}}\right). \tag{3A.15}$$

Knowing $\xi$ and $\beta$, the factorization of Eq. 3A.3 is

$$(y^2 + \sqrt{R'}\, y + \xi)(y^2 - \sqrt{R'}\, y + \beta) = 0. \tag{3A.16}$$

The solution of the two quadratics[3] yields the $y_i(i = 1, 4)$ of Eq. 3A.3. Hence, the roots of Eq. 3A.1 are

$$x_i = y_i + h, \quad i = 1, \ldots, 4. \tag{3A.17}$$

## B.   (m = 3)—Cubic solution

The solution of the cubic equation

$$Ax^3 + Bx^2 + Cx + D = 0, \tag{3A.18}$$

proceeds as follows.   Divide through by $A$ $(A \neq 0)$,[4] so that

$$x^3 + Px^2 + Qx + R = 0. \tag{3A.19}$$

Translate the equation so that the quadratic term is lacking, that is,

$$Z^3 + aZ + b = 0, \tag{3A.20}$$

where

$$a = \tfrac{1}{3}(3Q - P^2)$$
$$b = \tfrac{1}{27}(2P^3 - 9PQ + 27R). \tag{3A.21}$$

Utilize Eqs. 3A.9 and (3A.10 or 3A.11 or 3A.12) to obtain

$$Z_1, Z_2, Z_3 \tag{3A.22}$$

Then,

$$x_i = Z_i - P/3, \quad i = 1, 2, 3. \tag{3A.23}$$

## C.   (m = 2)—Quadratic solution

The equation

$$Ax^2 + Bx + C = 0, \tag{3A.24}$$

---

[3] See ($m = 2$), the quadratic section.
[4] If $A = 0$, proceed to subheading $C$.

possesses two roots given by

$$x_i = \frac{-B \pm \sqrt{B^2 - 4AC}}{2A}.$$
(3A.25)

**REFERENCES**

1. Arthur Schultze, *Advanced Algebra*, The Macmillan Company, New York, 1922.
2. J. V. Uspensky, *Theory of Equations*, McGraw-Hill Book Company, New York, 1948.

# Nomenclature of methods of orbit determination

Though a definite and repetitive effort has been made to define symbols in the text as they appear, the nomenclature of this field is so extensive that a tabulation of symbols is deemed necessary.

## Superscripts

|   |   |
|---|---|
| · | Relating to modified time differentiation.  Also (··). |
| ′ | Relating to general differentiation. |
|   | Relating to geocentric latitude. |
| * | Particular parameter or special form of an analytical expression. |
| ~ | Particular parameter or special form of an analytical expression. |
| ‾ | Used to denote average or special form of an analytical expression or parameter. |
| ° | Degrees. |
| hr | Hours. |
| min | Minutes. |
| sec | Seconds. |
| ′ | Minutes of arc. |
| ″ | Seconds of arc. |

## Special symbols

|   |   |
|---|---|
| ≡ | Identically equal to. |
|   | Equal to by definition. |
| ≐ | Replace left side of equation with right side of equation. |
| ≅ | Approximately equal to. |
| ♈ | Vernal equinox (sign of the Ram's Horns). |
| ∞ | Infinity. |
| ∠x, y | Angle between $x$ and $y$. |
| → | Yields. |
| \|x\| | Absolute value of $x$. |
| ℄ | Centerline. |

**435**

## Subscripts

$A$   Denoting primary body.
$B$   Barycenter of a system.
     Denoting secondary body.
$c$   Indicating a computed quantity.
     Indicating a reference quantity.
$D$   Relating to drag.
     Determinant of a system of equations.
$E$   East.
$e$   Relating to planet Earth.
     Relating to elliptic orbits.
$g$   Relating to Greenwich or prime meridian.
$h$   Relating to the azimuth-elevation coordinate system (Chapter 4).
     Relating to hyperbolic orbits.
$i$   General index.
$j$   General index.
$ij$   With $ij$ any integer values relate to the distance between body $i$ and body $j$.
$k$   General index.
$L$   Relating to lift.
$m$   Relating to Moon.
$O$   Relating to observations.
     Relating to reference.
$o$   Relating to some epoch time.
     Relating to oblate spheroidal coordinate system (Chapter 4).
$p$   Relating to perifocus.
     Relating to planet.
$R$   Relating to radial.
$r$   Relating to relative.
$S$   South
$s$   Relating to Sun.
     Relating to sub-vehicle point.
     Relating to satellite.
$t$   Relating to topocentric conditions.
$v$   Relating to vehicle-centered coordinate system.
     Relating to orbital axes in the orbit plane coordinate system.
$x, y, z$   Relating to components along $x$, $y$, $z$ orthogonal axes.
$\delta$   Relating to hour-angle declination coordinate system (Chapter 4).
$\epsilon$   Relating to celestial latitude-longitude coordinate system (Chapter 4).
     Relating to ecliptic.
$\Omega$   Relating to the ascending node.
$\mho$   Relating to the descending node.
$\omega$   Relating to orbit plane coordinate system (Chapter 4).

⊙   Sun.
☿   Mercury.
♀   Venus.
⊕   Earth.
☽   Moon.
♂   Mars.
♃   Jupiter.

## English symbols

$A$   Azimuth angle.
Miscellaneous constants.
Area.

$A_h$   Apofocus.

**A**   Auxiliary vector used in the method of Gauss.
Unit vector pointing due east.

$a$   Semimajor axis of a conic section.
Matrix coefficient.

$a_e$   Equational radius of Earth.

$B$   Miscellaneous constants.

**B**   Auxiliary vector used in the method of Gauss.
Semiminor axis of a conic section.

$b$   Drag parameter.

$C$   Coefficients of the linear relation between two position vectors and a third position vector.
Miscellaneous constants.

$C_D$   Drag coefficient.

$C_\psi$   The dot product of $(-\mathbf{R} \cdot \mathbf{L})$.

$C_e$   Element $(= e \cos E_0)$.

$C_h$   Element $(= e \cosh F_0)$.

$C_v$   Element $(= e \cos v_0)$.

$c$   Ratio of sector to triangle in the method of Gauss.

$D$   Drag force magnitude.

Dynamical parameter $\left( = \dfrac{r\dot{r}}{\sqrt{\mu}} \right)$, Chapter 3.

Dynamical parameter $\left( = \dfrac{r\dot{r}}{\sqrt{\mu a}} \right)$, Chapter 9.

Angular deviation (see Chapter 4, System 8).
Value of determinant in the method of Gauss.

**D**   Unit vector directed north along a specified meridian.

$E$   Eccentric anomaly.
Miscellaneous constants.

$e$   Orbital eccentricity.
Mathematical constant.

$F$   Hyperbolic anomaly (in correspondence with $E$).
     Miscellaneous constants.
$f$   Geometrical flattening of reference spheroid adopted for central planet.
     Functional notation.
     Coefficient of $f$ and $g$ series (Chapter 3).
$G$   Station location and shape coefficients.
     Universal gravitational constant.
     Miscellaneous constants.
$g$   Coefficient of $f$ and $g$ series (Chapter 3).
     Gravitational acceleration.
$H_s$  Altitude of satellite measured normal to adopted ellipsoid.
$h$   Elevation angle (Chapter 4, System 1).
**h**   Angular momentum vector.
**I**   Unit vector along the principal axis of a given coordinate system.
$i$   Orbital inclination.
     The imaginary $(= \sqrt{-1})$.
$J$   Harmonic coefficients of the Earth's potential function.
**J**   Unit vector advanced to $I$ by a right angle in the fundamental plane.
$K$   A constant.
**K**   Unit vector defined by $I \times J = K$.
$k$   Gravitational constant (Chapter 1).
$L$   Lift force magnitude.
**L**   Unit vector from observational station to satellite.
$M$   Mean anomaly $[= n(t - T)]$.
$N$   Number of revolutions.
$m$   General symbol for mass.
     Meters.
$n$   Mean motion $(= k\sqrt{\mu}/a^{3/2})$.
     Number of revolutions.
$P$   Orbital period (time from perigee crossing to perigee crossing).
$P_h$  Perifocus.
**P**   Unit vector pointing towards perifocus.
$p$   Orbital semiparameter $[= a(1 - e^2)]$.
**Q**   Unit vector advanced to **P** by a right angle in the direction and plane of motion.
$q$   Generalized element.
     Perifocal distance $[= a(1 - e)]$.
     Parameter of $f$ and $g$ series expansions.
$R$   Perturbative function $(= \Phi - V)$.
     Magnitude of station coordinate vector.
**R**   Station coordinate vector (Chapter 3).
     Alternate notation for **U**.

$r$    Magnitude of satellite radius vector.

**r**    Satellite radius vector.

$S$    Satellite symbol.

$S_e$    Element ($= e \sin E_0$).

$S_h$    Element ($= e \sinh F_0$).

$S_v$    Element ($= e \sin v_0$).

$s$    A parameter taking the value 1 or $-1$.

$T$    Time of perifocal passage.

   Thrust force magnitude.

**T**    Thrust vector.

$t$    Universal or ephemeris time (Chapter 1).

**U**    Unit vector pointing towards given satellite.

$u$    Argument of latitude (Chapter 3).

   Parameter of $f$ and $g$ series expansions.

$V$    General symbol for velocity vector magnitude.

   Spherical potential of planet.

**V**    Unit vector advanced to **U** by a right angle in the direction and plane of motion.

$v$    True anomaly (Chapter 3).

**W**    Unit vector perpendicular to orbit plane.

$X, Y, Z$    Rectangular coordinates of station coordinate vector (Chapter 3).

$x, y, z$    Rectangular coordinates of an object.

**Z**    Unit vector in the zenith direction (Chapter 5).

# Greek symbols

$\alpha$    Right ascension.

$\bar{\alpha}$    angle of attack.

$\beta$    Celestial latitude.

   Vehicle bank angle.

$\Gamma$    Mean longitude.

$\gamma$    Flight path angle.

$\Delta$    Increment or difference.

$\nabla$    gradient operator

$$\left( \nabla(\cdot) = \frac{\partial(\cdot)}{\partial x} \mathbf{I} + \frac{\partial(\cdot)}{\partial y} \mathbf{J} + \frac{\partial(\cdot)}{\partial z} \mathbf{K} \right).$$

$\delta$    Declination.

   Variation.

$\epsilon$    Obliquity of the ecliptic.

   Specified tolerance.

$\zeta$    Coefficient.

$\theta$    Sidereal time.

$\lambda$    Longitude.

$\mu$    Sum of masses or mass.

$\rho$   Atmospheric density.
   Libration in inclination.

$\mathsf{p}$   Slant range vector.

$\sigma$   Libration in node.

$\tau$   Modified time [$= k(t - t_0)$].
   Libration in longitude.

$\Phi$   Gravitational potential.

$\phi$   Geodetic latitude.

$\phi'$   Geocentric latitude.

$\phi_a$   Astronomical latitude.

$\psi$   Elongation angle.

$\Omega$   Longitude of ascending node.

$\mho$   Longitude of descending node.

$\omega$   Argument of perigee.

$\omega_s$   Angular rotational rate of planet.

## Abbreviations

|         |                                                                                           |
|---------|-------------------------------------------------------------------------------------------|
| a.u.    | Astronomical units.                                                                       |
| cm      | Centimeters.                                                                              |
| c.m.    | Central masses.                                                                           |
| c.u.    | Characteristic units.                                                                     |
| c.s.u.  | Circular satellite units (also g.c.s.u.; geocentric circular satellite units).            |
| deg     | Degrees.                                                                                  |
| e.m.    | Earth masses.                                                                             |
| e.r.    | Earth radii.                                                                              |
| ft      | Feet.                                                                                     |
| gm      | Grams.                                                                                    |
| hr      | Hours.                                                                                    |
| h.c.s.u.| Heliocentric circular satellite units.                                                    |
| km      | Kilometers.                                                                               |
| m       | Meters.                                                                                   |
| sec     | Seconds.                                                                                  |
| s.m.    | Solar masses.                                                                             |

# Answers and Hints to Exercises

## CHAPTER 1

*Problem*

1. Yes.
2. Yes.
3. The equations of motion will be much simpler.
4. $a_{\tau^2} = \dfrac{\tau_3(X_2 - X_1) + \tau_1(X_3 - X_2)}{\tau_3\tau_1(\tau_3 - \tau_1)}$

   $b_\tau = -\dfrac{\tau_1{}^2(X_3 - X_2) + \tau_3{}^2(X_2 - X_1)}{\tau_3\tau_1(\tau_3 - \tau_1)}, \quad c = X_2.$

5. 1.979231 g.c.s.u., 0.525651 h.c.s.u.
6. $\mu = 1$, $\tau = k_\delta(t - t_0)$, distance measured in $a_\delta$.
7. 5.
8. 1984 January $15^{\text{day}}$, $9^{\text{hr}}$, $20^{\text{min}}$, $0^{\text{sec}}$.
9. 2442769.5, 2443744.72942476.
10. 2437860.92361111.
11. $335°7442$.
12. 1958 June $1^{\text{day}}$, $0^{\text{hr}}$, $2^{\text{min}}$, $2.80^{\text{sec}}$.
13. Differentiate $u \equiv \tan(\phi - \phi') = \dfrac{(2f - f^2)\sin\phi\cos\phi}{1 - (2f - f^2)\sin^2\phi}$ and reduce the problem to a quadratic equation in $\cos 2\phi$. Obtain $\phi$ and calculate $u$ so that $(\phi - \phi')_{\max} = \tan^{-1} u$.
14. $x_c = 0.76728894$ e.r., $z_c = 0.63952347$ e.r.
15. $x_c = 0.86759434$ m.r., $z_c = 0.49425032$ m.r.

## CHAPTER 2

*Problem*

1. Because $r_{ij} = 0$, that is, attraction of body 1 upon itself is of no physical significance.
2. By segregating the two-body term, the added perturbative effects to a two-body reference orbit are diminished.
3. *Mercury* ($\mathaccent{}{\text{☿}}$)

$$\frac{d^2\mathbf{r}_{\text{☿}}}{dt^2} = -k^2{}_\odot(m_\odot + m_{\text{☿}})\frac{\mathbf{r}_{\text{☿}}}{r_{\text{☿}}{}^3} + k_\odot{}^2 \sum_{j=3}^{8} m_j\left(\frac{\mathbf{r}_{\text{☿}j}}{r_{\text{☿}j}{}^3} - \frac{\mathbf{r}_{\odot j}}{r_{\odot j}{}^3}\right)$$

with $j = 1 = $ Sun, $j = 2 = $ Mercury, $j = 3 = $ Venus, $j = 4 = $ Earth, $j = 5 = $ Jupiter, etc.

*Venus* ($♀$)

$$\frac{d^2\mathbf{r}_♀}{dt^2} = -k_\odot{}^2(m_\odot + m_♀)\frac{\mathbf{r}_♀}{r_♀{}^3} + k_\odot{}^2 \sum_{\substack{j=2 \\ j \neq 3}}^{8} m_j\left(\frac{\mathbf{r}_{♀j}}{r_{♀j}{}^3} - \frac{\mathbf{r}_{\odot j}}{r_{\odot j}{}^3}\right).$$

Another seven equations define the motion of the remaining planets. Masses are obtained from Table 1.2 (in Sun masses). Note also that in the above equation, for example, for Mercury, $\mathbf{r}_{\varphi j} = \mathbf{r}_{\varphi} - \mathbf{r}_{\varphi}$ for $j = 3$, $\mathbf{r}_{\varphi j} = \mathbf{r}_{\oplus} - \mathbf{r}_{\varphi}$ for $j = 4$, $\mathbf{r}_{\varphi j} = \mathbf{r}_{\sigma} - \mathbf{r}_{\varphi}$ for $j = 5$, etc. This will express all distances in terms of central coordinates. The above system of nine differential equations must be integrated simultaneously in order to locate the positions of all the planets.

4. See equations in text.

5. $\dfrac{d^2\mathbf{r}_2}{dt^2} = \nabla\Phi_m + k_m{}^2 m_{\oplus}\left(\dfrac{\mathbf{r}_{2\oplus}}{r_{2\oplus}{}^3} - \dfrac{\mathbf{r}_{m\oplus}}{r_{m\oplus}{}^3}\right)$, where $m_{\oplus}$ is in Moon masses, and $\mathbf{r}_{2\oplus} = \mathbf{r}_{\oplus} - \mathbf{r}_2$, $\mathbf{r}_{m\oplus} = \mathbf{r}_{\oplus} - \mathbf{r}_m$, with the subscript 2 denoting the spaceship.

6. $k^2 = Gm_{\oplus} = (6.673 \times 10^{-11}$ newtons-m$^2$/kg$^2$) $(5.977 \times 10^{24}$ kg) $\times$ $(9.80665$ m/sec$^2$) $(3600$ sec$^2$/m$^2$)/$(6378175)^3$ m$^3$/e.r.$^3 = 0.00544$ (e.r.)$^3$/min$^2$.

7. The total weight of the rocket as a function of time is given by

$$W = 50,000 - \frac{30,000}{150}\, t,$$

where $t$ is the number of seconds after ignition. Instantaneous thrust $T$ is given by

$$T = \frac{dm}{dt}\, v = \frac{200}{g} \times 8000 = \frac{1,600,000}{g}\ \text{lb.}$$

A summation of forces vertically yields

$$\frac{dV}{dt} = g\left(\frac{T}{W} - 1\right) \text{ so that } V = \int_0^{150}\left(\frac{1,600,000}{50,000 - 200\,t} - g\right)dt.$$

8. Consider resolution of the velocity vector $\dot{\mathbf{r}}$ up along the meridian, $\mathbf{D}$ direction; due east, $\mathbf{A}$ direction; and at right angles to $\mathbf{A}$ and $\mathbf{D}$, $\mathbf{L}$ direction, that is,

$$\dot{\mathbf{r}} = V_N\mathbf{D} + V_E\mathbf{A} + V_R\mathbf{L}.$$

Notice that

$$D_x = -\sin\delta\cos\alpha = -\frac{z}{r}\frac{x}{\sqrt{x^2 + y^2}}$$

$$D_y = -\sin\delta\sin\alpha = -\frac{z}{r}\frac{y}{\sqrt{x^2 + y^2}}$$

$$D_z = \cos\delta = \frac{\sqrt{x^2 + y^2}}{r}.$$

$\mathbf{A}$ and $\mathbf{L}$ may be similarly derived. Then, $V_N = \dot{\mathbf{r}} \cdot \mathbf{D}$, $V_E = \dot{\mathbf{r}} \cdot \mathbf{A}$ and $A$, the azimuth is obtained from

$$A = \tan^{-1}\frac{V_E}{V_N}.$$

9. Consider the dot product of $\mathbf{r}$ and $\dot{\mathbf{r}}$.

**CHAPTER 3**

*Problem*

1. a. $\sqrt{5}$ e.r.

   b. 3 e.r., $\frac{1}{3}\sqrt{5}$.

   c. $\frac{4}{3}$ e.r.

   d. $r = (\frac{4}{3})/(1 + \frac{1}{3}\sqrt{5}\cos v)$, No.

   e. $[(14 + 3\sqrt{5})/12]^{1/2}$ g.c.s.u.

   f. 439.02458 min.

2. $U_x = -0.17677669$
   $U_y = +0.88388347$
   $U_z = +0.43301270$
   $x_\omega = +0.91764774$
   $y_\omega = +0.49190485$.

3. Appıy the Newton formula
   $$x_{n+1} = x_n - \frac{f(x_n)}{f'(x_n)}.$$

4. $a = +1.51515151$ e.r.
   $S_e = +0.73116346$
   $C_e = -0.65000000$
   $U_x = +0.60000000$
   $U_y = +0.80000000$
   $U_z = +0.00000000$
   $V_x = -0.15689293$
   $V_y = +0.11766969$
   $V_z = +0.98058081$.

5. $E - E_0 = 1893.1984$ rads.
   $x = 1.191894$ e.r.      $\dot{x} = -0.308247$ e.r.
   $y = 1.746794$ e.r.      $\dot{y} = -0.409805$ e.r.
   $z = 0.472805$ e.r.      $\dot{z} = +0.003573$ e.r.

6. $e = 0$, $a = \left(\dfrac{120\,k}{\pi}\right)^{3/2}$

7. $v = 35°\ 6'\ 14''$ or 0.6126784 rad.

8. $D = 11.0342$, $v = 159°\ 27'\ 10''$.

9. $f = 0.9908$, $g = 0.5559$; about four figures.

10. $x = 0.444104$ e.r.,
    $y = 0.280629$ e.r.,
    $z = 1.062396$ e.r.

11. Note that $\cos v = \dfrac{x_\omega}{r}$, etc.

12. Note that $x_\omega = x_\omega(E)$, $y_\omega = y_\omega(E)$ and differentiate. Eliminate $\dot{E}$ and notice that $\mathbf{r} = \mathbf{P}x_\omega + \mathbf{Q}y_\omega$, $\dot{\mathbf{r}} = \mathbf{P}\dot{x}_\omega + \mathbf{Q}\dot{y}_\omega$.

13. Consider the three equations
    $$r_1 = \frac{a(1 - e^2)}{1 + e\cos v}$$
    $$r_1 + r_2 = 2a$$
    $$r_1^2 + r_2^2 - 2r_1r_2\cos(2\gamma) = 4a^2e^2$$

    and eliminate $r_1$ and $r_2$ from the last equation.

14. Evaluate the determinant. Compare the expressions with the components of **P, Q, W**.
15. $T = 1984$ January 15, $10^{hr}$, $8^{min}$, $56.54^{sec}$.

## CHAPTER 4

*Problem*

1. Systems 2, 5, 7, 8, 9, 10.
2. Use Transformation 7. It will only be possible, with the given data, to obtain topocentric right ascensions and declinations.
3. Use Transformation 16 to obtain $x_\varepsilon$, $y_\varepsilon$, $z_\varepsilon$ and then apply Transformation 18.
6. Use Transformation 5. To precess use Transformation 32 with $T_0 = 0.6$ and corresponding J.D. in Equation 1A.233. Finally use Transformation 16.
7. Differentiate the transformation matrix of the system. Be careful of units.

## CHAPTER 5

*Problem*

1. Consider the mappings

$$\cos E = \frac{\cos v + e}{1 + e \cos v}, \qquad \sin E = \frac{\sqrt{1 - e^2}\, \sin v}{1 + e \cos v} \quad \text{and let} \quad v = -\omega.$$

$T_\Omega = 1962$ January 2, $3228.5265^{min}$, $E = 337°7526$
$T_\Upsilon = 1962$ January 2, $3085.5025^{min}$, $E = 139°8803$.
2. $v_{exit} = 295°\,18'$, $v_{entrance} = 47°\,45'$.
3. $\phi' = \pm 6°\,18'$.
4. $E_{rise} = 73°40$, $E_{set} = 124°80$,
Revolution 2.
5. $E_{rise} = 67°2352$, $E_{set} = 121°6788$,
Revolution 2.
6. $a = 1.08045$ e.r., $e = 0.05$, $i = 25°8083$, $\Omega = 204°378$, $\omega = 0$, $T_{J.D.} = 2407040.3168649$.
7. $v_{entrance} = 35°\,13'$, $v_{exit} = 83°\,8'$, $t_{entrance} = 1962$ January 3, $23.38^{min}$, $t_{exit} = 1962$ January 3, $55.19^{min}$.
8. Use Equations 5.108.
9. Define an equatorial unit vector pointing towards any meridian for sidereal time $\theta$; that is, $\mathbf{M} = \cos\theta\mathbf{I} + \sin\theta\mathbf{J}$, and dot this into the satellite radius vector in the equator; $\mathbf{r} = x\mathbf{I} + y\mathbf{J}$. Notice that $\mathbf{M} \cdot \mathbf{r} = r$ at meridian crossing.
10. Obtain the zero of the expression for $\dot\rho$.

## CHAPTER 6

*Problem*

1. Notice that

$$\mathbf{r}_1 \times \mathbf{r}_2 = |\mathbf{r}_1 \times \mathbf{r}_2| \sin(v_2 - v_1)\mathbf{W}.$$

The $z$ component of the cross product yields $x_1 y_2 - x_2 y_1 = |x_1 y_2 - x_2 y_1| \sin(v_2 - v_1)W_z$, and, for a direct orbit, $W_z \geq 0$ so that sin

$(v_2 - v_1)$ has the sign of $x_1 y_2 - x_2 y_1$. Likewise, for a retrograde orbit, $W_z < 0$ and $\sin (v_2 - v_1)$ has the sign of $-(x_1 y_2 - x_2 y_1)$. Also, with $\mathbf{U}_1 = \mathbf{r}_1/r_1$, $\mathbf{U}_2 = \mathbf{r}_2/r_2$, $\cos (v_2 - v_1) = \mathbf{U}_1 \cdot \mathbf{U}_2$.

2. Starting with

$$x = \frac{m}{y^2} - l,$$ substitute for $y$ from $y = 1 + X(l + x)$ and eliminate $X$ as a function of $x$.

3. Let the limit of such an equation, such as $x' = F(x')$, with the recurrence relation $x_{n+1} = F(x_n)$, where $x_1, x_2, \ldots, x_n$ are a sequence of successive approximations, be denoted by $\hat{x}$. Hence, $F(\hat{x}) = \hat{x}$, that is, $x = \hat{x}$ is the desired real root. The last equation, however, implies that $\hat{x} - x_{n+1} = F(x) - F(x_n) = (x - x_n)F'(\xi_n)$, where $\xi_n$ lies between $x_n$ and $\hat{x}$. Notice that a continuous derivative of $F(x)$ is implied. Assuming the iteration converges and $x_n \to \hat{x}$ as $n \to \infty$, then, for large enough $n$, $F'(\xi_n) \cong F'(\hat{x})$, and $\hat{x} - x_n \cong a[F'(\hat{x})]^n$ or $\hat{x} = x_n + ab^n$, where $a$ and $b$ are constants which are, as can be seen, independent of $n$. Furthermore, one can write

$$\hat{x} = x_{n+1} + ab^{n+1}$$
$$\hat{x} = x_{n+2} + ab^{n+2}$$

and eliminate $a$ and $b$ to arrive at the improved estimator for $\hat{x}$.

4. Yes. $\dot{x} = -0.4064129$, $\dot{y} = -0.0697294$, $\dot{z} = +0.2380712$.

5. $e = \frac{2}{5}$, $a = \frac{60}{21}$, No.

6. $a = 1.5$, $e = 0.2$, $i = 45°$, $\Omega = 45°$, $\omega = 45°$.

7. After Eq. (6.240), insert the following: If $e \leq 1$, return to Eq. (6.238) and increment $v_1$ by $\Delta v_1$, say 10 degrees. If $e > 1$, proceed with Eq. (6.241), that is,

$$a = \frac{r_1(1 + e \cos v_1)}{(1 - e^2)}. \tag{6.241}$$

If $e > 1$ but $a > 0$, return to Eq. (6.238) and increment $v_1$, by say 10 degrees; if $a < 0$, proceed with Eq. (6.241a).

After $e > 1$, $a < 0$ has been satisfied, calculate the double value of limiting true anomalies in second and third quadrants, that is,

$$\cos v_l = -\frac{1}{e}.$$

Find these angles as

$$\cos v_{\text{III}} = -\frac{1}{e} \tag{6.241a}$$

$$\sin v_{\text{III}} = +\left(1 - \frac{1}{e^2}\right)^{1/2}$$

$$\cos v_{\text{IIII}} = -\frac{1}{e}$$

$$\sin v_{\text{IIII}} = -\left(1 - \frac{1}{e^2}\right)^{1/2} \tag{6.241b}$$

Note that at this point, the $v_1$ and $v_2$ used to calculate $e$ from Eq. (6.240) *cannot* be in the region $v_{III} < v_1$, $v_2 < v_{IIII}$, since it does not exist for a hyperbola. Therefore, taking the tolerances $\Delta_1 = 0.001$ radian and $\Delta_2 = 0.02$ radian,

if $|v_2 - v_1| > v_{IIII} - v_{III}$ and $|1 + e \cos v_1| < \Delta_1$, set $v_1 = v_{IIII} + \Delta_2$ and return to Eq. (6.238).
If $|v_2 - v_1| > v_{IIII} - v_{III}$ and $|1 + e \cos v_2| > \Delta_1$, continue with Eq. (6.242c).
If $|v_2 - v_1| < v_{IIII} - v_{III}$ and $|1 + e \cos v_2| < \Delta_1$, set $v_1 = v_{IIII} + \Delta_2$ and return to Eq. (6.238).
If $|v_2 - v_1| < v_{IIII} - v_{III}$ and $|1 + e \cos v_2| > \Delta_1$, continue with Eq. (6.242c).

$$\sinh F_1 = \frac{\sqrt{e^2 - 1} \sin v_1}{1 + e \cos v_1} \tag{6.242c}$$

$$\cosh F_1 = \frac{\cos v_1 + e}{1 + e \cos v_1} \tag{6.242d}$$

$$\sinh F_2 = \frac{\sqrt{e^2 - 1} \sin v_2}{1 + e \cos v_2} \tag{6.242e}$$

$$\cosh F_2 = \frac{\cos v_2 + e}{1 + e \cos v_2} \tag{6.242f}$$

$$M_2 - M_1 = e(\sinh F_2 - \sinh F_1) + F_1 - F_2 \tag{6.242g}$$

$$n = k\sqrt{\frac{\mu}{-a^3}}. \tag{6.242h}$$

Proceed as in the elliptical algorithm from Eq. (6.248) through Eq. (6.253).
Replace Eqs. (6.254) and (6.255) by the following:

$$f = 1 - \frac{a}{r_1} [1 - \cosh (F_2 - F_1)] \tag{6.242i}$$

$$g = \tau + \sqrt{\frac{-a^3}{\mu}} [F_2 - F_1 - \sinh (F_2 - F_1)] \tag{6.242j}$$

$$\dot{r}_1 = \frac{r_2 - f r_1}{g}. \tag{6.242k}$$

9. $a = 1.143129$ e.r., $e = 0.0376494$, $i = 55°25643$, $\Omega = 41°95624$, $\omega = 29°85541$, $T = 1059.079$ min.
10. Since,

$$X = \frac{2g - \sin 2g}{\sin^3 g}$$

with $g = (E_2 - E_1)/2$. Then, by differentiation, $\sin g(dX/dg) = 4 - 3X \cos g$. Also, since $x = \sin^2 g/2$, by differentiation

$$\frac{dx}{dg} = \sin (g/2) \cos (g/2) = \tfrac{1}{2} \sin g.$$

Evaluating $dX/dx$ as

$$dX/dx = \frac{8 - 6X \cos g}{\sin^2 g} = \frac{4 - 3X(1 - 2x)}{2x(1 - x)},$$

and assuming a solution of the form $X = a_0 + a_1 x + a_2 x^2 + \cdots$, upon direct substitution into $dX/dx$ and equating coefficients, yields

$$X = \frac{4}{3}\left(1 + \frac{6}{5}x + \frac{6 \cdot 8}{5 \cdot 7}x^2 + \frac{6 \cdot 8 \cdot 10}{5 \cdot 7 \cdot 9}x^3 + \cdots\right).$$

Finally, from Eq. (6.46), that is,

$$y = 1 + X(l + x),$$
$$y = 1 + \tfrac{4}{3}l.$$

## CHAPTER 7

*Problem*

1. $a = 1.3391$, $e = 0.17907$, $T = -62.507$ min, $i = 32°882$, $\Omega = 224°87$, $\omega = 255°20$.
   The time of perifocal passage is referenced to the middle observation.

2. $\alpha = \dfrac{\tau(\tau - \tau_3)}{\tau_1(\tau_1 - \tau_3)}\alpha_1 + \dfrac{(\tau - \tau_1)(\tau - \tau_3)}{\tau_1 \tau_3}\alpha_2 + \dfrac{\tau(\tau - \tau_1)}{\tau_3(\tau_3 - \tau_1)}\alpha_3,$

   with $\alpha$ replaced by $\delta$ and $\alpha_1, \alpha_2, \alpha_3$ replaced by $\delta_1, \delta_2, \delta_3$ for the declination equation.

3. Yes, the iterative variance of $r$ is less than $\rho$. Furthermore, it is easier to estimate $r$ than $\rho$.

4. For any time $t$, compute $M = n(t - T)$ and solve Kepler's equation for the eccentric anomaly, that is, $M = E - e \sin E$.
   Obtain $x_\omega = a(\cos E - e)$, $y_\omega = a\sqrt{1 - e^2} \sin E$ and compute $\mathbf{P}$ and $\mathbf{Q}$ from the standard expressions of Section 3.4. Then compute

   $$\mathbf{r} = x_\omega \mathbf{P} + y_\omega \mathbf{Q}, \qquad \boldsymbol{\rho} = \mathbf{r} + \mathbf{R},$$

   where $\mathbf{R}$ is obtained from Section 3.11. Form the $\mathbf{L}$ unit vector from

   $$\rho = (\boldsymbol{\rho} \cdot \boldsymbol{\rho})^{1/2}$$
   $$\mathbf{L} = \frac{\boldsymbol{\rho}}{\rho}$$

   and obtain

   $$\sin \delta_t = L_z$$
   $$\cos \delta_t = \sqrt{1 - L_z^2} \qquad \to \delta_t$$
   $$\sin \alpha_t = \frac{L_y}{\cos \delta_t}$$
   $$\cos \delta_t = \frac{L_x}{\cos \delta_t}. \qquad \to \alpha_t$$

5. Evaluate the $d_i$ explicitly as a function of $\tau$.

6. $a = 1.4400$, $e = 0.23167$, $T = 1959$ September $26^{day}$ $21^{hr}$ $43^{min}$ $6.7^{sec}$, $i = 33°281$, $\Omega = 205°110$, $\omega = 161°790$.

7. Since the observations will probably be over a short arc, the method of Gauss with Omicron 3's radius vector replacing **R**, the usual station coordinate vector, will probably yield the orbit with the least difficulty.
8. Notice that

$$c_1 = \frac{r_2 \sin (v_3 - v_2)}{r_1 \sin (v_3 - v_1)}, \qquad c_3 = \frac{r_2 \sin (v_2 - v_1)}{r_3 \sin (v_3 - v_1)}$$

and, from Section 6.2.2,

$$y_{23} = \frac{+ \sqrt{\mu p}\ \tau_{23}}{r_3 r_2 \sin (v_3 - v_2)} \qquad y_{13} = \frac{+ \sqrt{\mu p}\ \tau_{13}}{r_3 r_1 \sin (v_3 - v_1)}$$

$$y_{12} = \frac{- \sqrt{\mu p}\ \tau_{21}}{r_2 r_1 \sin (v_2 - v_1)}.$$

The ratios will yield the appropriate results. Notice that $\tau_{23} = \tau_3$ and $\tau_{21} = \tau_1$, if the central date is assumed as an epoch.
9. $r_2 = 1.269$.
10. Assume $E_j - E_0$ and solve $F_j$ by a Newtonian procedure. Notice that $F_j$ is obtained by eliminating $y_{kl}$ from Eqs. 7.96 and 7.97.

## CHAPTER 8

*Problem*

1. $\dot{\rho} = \dfrac{\dot{\boldsymbol{\rho}} \cdot \boldsymbol{\rho}}{\rho}$

2. A unit vector cannot change in length, therefore $\dot{\mathbf{L}}$ must be at right angles to **L**.
3. Form the mean anomaly for any time $t$ from $M = n(t - T)$, and solve Kepler's equation for $E$, that is, $M = E - e \sin E \rightarrow E$. Compute the standard orientation vectors **P**, **Q**, from Section 3.4, so that

$$x_\omega = a(\cos E - e)$$
$$y_\omega = a\sqrt{1 - e^2} \sin E$$
$$\mathbf{r} = x_\omega \mathbf{P} + y_\omega \mathbf{Q}.$$

Compute the station coordinate vector **R** from Section 3.11, so that

$$\boldsymbol{\rho} = \mathbf{r} + \mathbf{R} \qquad \rho = (\boldsymbol{\rho} \cdot \boldsymbol{\rho})^{1/2} \qquad \dot{\rho} = \dot{\boldsymbol{\rho}} \cdot \boldsymbol{\rho}/\rho.$$

5. See answers to Exercise 9, Chapter 6.
6. See answers to Exercise 9, Chapter 6.
8. Eliminate $\rho^2$ and $\rho$ from $\rho^2 + \rho C_\psi + R^2 - r^2 = 0$ by means of

$$\rho = \frac{A + B/r^3}{C + D/r^3}.$$

9. In the last term of the $E$ coefficient.
10. By using Eq. 7.241.
11. Consider the dot product of **Z** and $-\mathbf{R}$ (Section 5.4.2, and Section 3.11) to yield $\zeta$. Then, consider Figure 1.

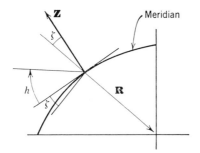

FIGURE 1

## CHAPTER 9

*Problem*

1. At the central date, the two linear equations of the $M_D{}^*$ matrix are

$$a_{21} \Delta x_0 + a_{22} \Delta y_0 = c_{21}$$
$$a_{51} \Delta x_0 + a_{52} \Delta y_0 = c_{51} - a_{53} \Delta z_0.$$

The determinant of this system is $D = a_{21}a_{52} - a_{51}a_{22}$, so that

$$\Delta x_0 = \frac{a_{52}c_{21} - a_{22}c_{51}}{D} + \frac{a_{22}a_{53}}{D} \Delta z_0 \equiv A + B \Delta z_0,$$

$$\Delta y_0 = \frac{a_{21}c_{51} - a_{51}c_{21}}{D} - \frac{a_{21}a_{53}}{D} \Delta z_0 \equiv A' + B' \Delta z_0.$$

Certainly, then, substitution of the linear expressions for $\Delta x_0$ and $\Delta y_0$ into the first, third, fourth, and sixth equations of the $M_D{}^*$ matrix, yields a linear system of four equations in four unknowns, that is, $\Delta z_0$, $\Delta \dot{x}_0$, $\Delta \dot{y}_0$, $\Delta \dot{z}_0$.

2.
$$M_L = \begin{bmatrix} \omega_1 & a_{14} & a_{15} & a_{16} \\ \omega_2 & a_{34} & a_{35} & a_{36} \\ \omega_3 & a_{44} & a_{45} & a_{46} \\ \omega_4 & a_{64} & a_{65} & a_{66} \end{bmatrix}$$

with

$$\omega_1 \equiv a_{11}B + a_{12}B' + a_{13}$$
$$\omega_2 \equiv a_{31}B + a_{32}B' + a_{33}$$
$$\omega_3 \equiv a_{41}B + a_{42}B' + a_{43}$$
$$\omega_4 \equiv a_{61}B + a_{62}B' + a_{63}$$

where, as in the discussion of Exercise 1,

$$B \equiv a_{22}a_{53}/(a_{21}a_{52} - a_{51}a_{22}), \qquad B' \equiv -a_{21}a_{53}/(a_{21}a_{52} - a_{51}a_{22}).$$

Notice that

$$
M_L \begin{bmatrix} \Delta z_0 \\ \Delta \dot{x}_0 \\ \Delta \dot{y}_0 \\ \Delta \dot{z}_0 \end{bmatrix} = \begin{bmatrix} \mathcal{N}_1 \\ \mathcal{N}_2 \\ \mathcal{N}_3 \\ \mathcal{N}_4 \end{bmatrix}
$$

so that

$$
\begin{bmatrix} \Delta z_0 \\ \Delta \dot{x}_0 \\ \Delta \dot{y}_0 \\ \Delta \dot{z}_0 \end{bmatrix} = M_L^{-1} \begin{bmatrix} \mathcal{N}_1 \\ \mathcal{N}_2 \\ \mathcal{N}_3 \\ \mathcal{N}_4 \end{bmatrix},
$$

where

$$
\begin{aligned}
\mathcal{N}_1 &\equiv c_{11} - a_{11}A - a_{12}A' \\
\mathcal{N}_2 &\equiv c_{31} - a_{31}A - a_{32}A' \\
\mathcal{N}_3 &\equiv c_{41} - a_{41}A - a_{42}A' \\
\mathcal{N}_4 &\equiv c_{61} - a_{61}A - a_{62}A'.
\end{aligned}
$$

The $A$ and $A'$ coefficients are defined in Exercise 1, as

$$
\begin{aligned}
A &= (a_{52}c_{21} - a_{22}c_{51})/(a_{21}a_{52} - a_{51}a_{22}) \\
A' &= (a_{21}c_{51} - a_{51}c_{21})/(a_{21}a_{52} - a_{51}a_{22}),
\end{aligned}
$$

with the $c_{ij}$ column matrix defined by

$$
\begin{bmatrix} \Delta \mathbf{L}_i \cdot \mathbf{A}_i \\ \Delta \mathbf{L}_i \cdot \mathbf{D}_i \end{bmatrix}, \quad \text{for } i = 1, 0, 2.
$$

3. At the end of the differential correction process, only a two-body orbit has been found. When perturbations are included in the prediction process, a non two-body orbit has been found, whose elements at the central date (or correction date) are instantaneously exact.

4. $x_0 = 0.482867$     $\dot{x}_0 = 0.633941$
   $y_0 = -1.269360$     $\dot{y}_0 = 0.313504$
   $z_0 = 0.801753$     $\dot{z}_0 = 0.145559$

5. Take the partial derivatives of Eqs. 9.14.

6. Notice that at time $t_0$, the position of the intercepting craft cannot be instantaneously varied, hence,

$$
\mathbf{r} = \mathbf{r}(\dot{x}_0\dot{y}_0\dot{z}_0)
$$

$$
\Delta \mathbf{r} = \frac{\partial \mathbf{r}}{\partial \dot{x}_0} \Delta \dot{x}_0 + \frac{\partial \mathbf{r}}{\partial \dot{y}_0} \Delta \dot{y}_0 + \frac{\partial \mathbf{r}}{\partial \dot{z}_0} \Delta \dot{z}_0
$$

or, using the $N$ matrix,

$$
\begin{bmatrix} \Delta x \\ \Delta y \\ \Delta z \end{bmatrix} = [N] \begin{bmatrix} \Delta \dot{x}_0 \\ \Delta \dot{y}_0 \\ \Delta \dot{z}_0 \end{bmatrix},
$$

so that the required velocity impulse and direction is given by

$$
\begin{bmatrix} \Delta \dot{x}_0 \\ \Delta \dot{y}_0 \\ \Delta \dot{z}_0 \end{bmatrix} = [N]^{-1} \begin{bmatrix} \Delta x \\ \Delta y \\ \Delta z \end{bmatrix}.
$$

# CHAPTER 10

*Problem*

1. Bounded oscillations are not included in the analysis, and thus only an average departure of a given element from an adopted mean epoch value is carried forward in the analysis. The so-called secular term is always correct within a set bound and therefore never drifts increasingly far from its true value.

2. Differentiate Kepler's equation, that is,

$$M = E - e \sin E,$$

so that

$$\frac{dM}{dE} = \frac{r}{a}.$$

Note that

$$\cos E = \frac{\cos v + e}{1 + e \cos v},$$

and therefore

$$\sqrt{1 - e^2}\, \frac{dE}{dv} = \frac{r}{a}.$$

Finally,

$$\frac{dM}{dv} = \frac{dM}{dE}\frac{dE}{dv} = \left(\frac{r}{a}\right)^2 \frac{1}{\sqrt{1 - e^2}}.$$

3. 1.

4. For $\Omega$  maximum rate of change corresponds to $i = 0$
   minimum rate of change corresponds to $i = \pi/2$.
   For $\omega$  maximum rate of change corresponds to $i = 0$
   minimum rate of change corresponds to $i = \pi/2$.

5. $\sin i = + \sqrt{\tfrac{2}{3}}$.

6. $a = 1.5$ e.r.,    $e = 0.2$,    $M_0 = 172°538$
   $i = 30°$,    $\Omega = 160°915$,    $\omega = 87°535$.

7. $i = \sigma \pm \cos^{-1} \dfrac{4}{\sqrt{29}},$

   where

   $$\cos \sigma = \frac{-2}{\sqrt{29}} \qquad \sin \sigma = \frac{5}{\sqrt{29}}.$$

# Index